CATALYST the pearson custom library for chemistry

CHEMISTRY for Changing Times
Fourth Custom Edition for De Anza College
Chem 10

PEARSON

Cover Art: Courtesy of Photodisc, Age Fotostock America, Inc., and Photo Researchers, and Getty Images.

Pyrex, pHydrion, Chem3D Plus, Apple, Macintosh, Chemdraw, Hypercard, graphTool, Corning, Teflon, Mel-Temp, Rotaflow, Tygon, Spec20, and LambdaII UV/Vis are registered trademarks.

Chem3D Plus is a registered trademark of the Cambridge Soft Corp.

The information, illustrations, and/or software contained in this book, and regarding the above mentioned programs, are provided "as is," without warranty of any kind, express or implied, including without limitation any warranty concerning the accuracy, adequacy, or completeness of such information. Neither the publisher, the authors, nor the copyright holders shall be responsible for any claims attributable to errors, omissions, or other inaccuracies contained in this book. Nor shall they be liable for direct, indirect, special, incidental, or consequential damages arising out of the use of such information or material.

The authors and publisher believe that the lab experiments described in this publication, when conducted in conformity with the safety precautions described herein and according to the school's laboratory safety procedures, are reasonably safe for the students for whom this manual is directed. Nonetheless, many of the described experiments are accompanied by some degree of risk, including human error, the failure or misuse of laboratory or electrical equipment, mismeasurement, spills of chemicals, and exposure to sharp objects, heat, body fluids, blood or other biologics. The authors and publisher disclaim any liability arising from such risks in connections with any of the experiments contained in this manual. If students have questions or problems with materials, procedures, or instructions on any experiment, they should always ask their instructor for help before proceeding.

This special edition published in cooperation with Pearson Learning Solutions.

Printed in the United States of America.

V092

Please visit our website at *www.pearsonlearningsolutions.com.*

Attention bookstores: For permission to return unused stock, contact us at *pe-uscustomreturns@pearson.com.*

Pearson Learning Solutions, 501 Boylston Street, Suite 900, Boston, MA 02116
A Pearson Education Company
www.pearsoned.com

ISBN 10: 1-256-61558-7
ISBN 13: 978-1-256-61558-3

Table of Contents

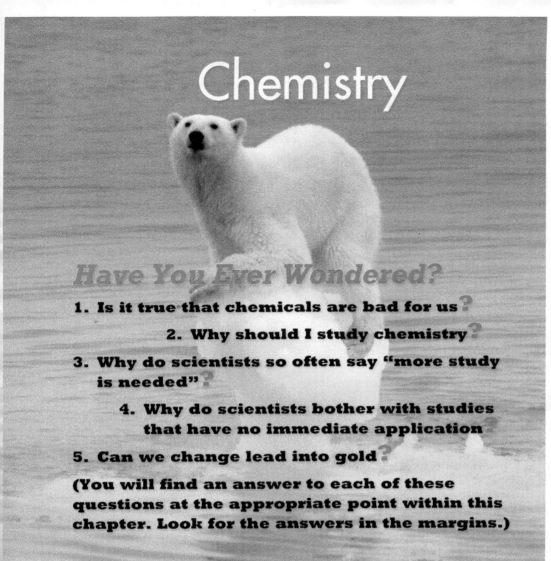

Chemistry

Have You Ever Wondered?

1. **Is it true that chemicals are bad for us?**

2. **Why should I study chemistry?**

3. **Why do scientists so often say "more study is needed"?**

4. **Why do scientists bother with studies that have no immediate application?**

5. **Can we change lead into gold?**

(You will find an answer to each of these questions at the appropriate point within this chapter. Look for the answers in the margins.)

Arne Naevra

Tomukas/Shutterstock

Learning Objectives

> Distinguish science from technology. (1)

> Define *alchemy* and *natural philosophy*. (1)

> Briefly describe the contributions of Bacon, Galileo, and Carson to the perceptions of science. (2)

> Define *hypothesis*, *scientific law*, *scientific theory*, and *scientific model*, and explain their relationships in science. (3)

> Define *risk* and *benefit*, and give an example of each. (4)

> Estimate a desirability quotient from benefit and risk data. (4)

> Give an example of a use of chemistry in your daily life and in society at large. (5)

> Distinguish basic research from applied research. (6)

> Differentiate: mass and weight; physical and chemical change; physical and chemical properties. (7)

> Classify matter according to state and as mixture, substance, compound, and/or element. (8)

> Assign proper units of measurement to observations, and manipulate units in conversions. (9)

> Calculate the density, mass, or volume of an object given the other two quantities. (10)

> Distinguish between heat and temperature. (11)

> Explain how the temperature scales are related. (11)

> Use critical thinking to evaluate claims and statements. (12)

> Define green chemistry.

> Describe how *green chemistry* reduces risk and prevents environmental problems.

A Science for All Seasons

Chemistry pervades every aspect of our lives. Look around you. Everything you see is made of chemicals: the food we eat, the air we breathe, the clothes we wear, the medicines we take, the vehicles we ride in, and the buildings we live and work in.

Everything we *do* also involves chemistry. Whenever we eat a sandwich, bathe, drive a car, listen to music, or ride a bicycle, we use chemistry. Even when we are asleep, chemical reactions go on constantly throughout our bodies.

Chemistry also affects society as a whole. Developments in health and

Chemistry is everywhere, not just in laboratories. Chemistry occurs in soil and rocks, in waters, in clouds, and in us. Knowledge of chemistry enhances our understanding of climate change, helps to provide food for Earth's increasing population, and is crucial to the development and production of sustainable fuels.

Armin Rose/Shutterstock

From Chapter 1 of *Chemistry for Changing Times*, Thirteenth Edition. John W. Hill, Terry W. McCreary, Doris K. Kolb.

▲ Organic foods are not chemical-free. In fact, they are made entirely of chemicals!

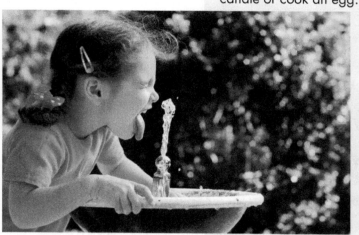

Stephen Denness/Shutterstock

▲ A century ago, contaminated drinking water was often the cause of outbreaks of cholera. Modern water treatment uses chemicals to remove solid matter and kill disease-causing bacteria, making water safe to drink.

1. Is it true that chemicals are bad for us? Everything you can see, smell, taste, or touch is either a chemical or is made of chemicals. Chemicals are neither good nor bad in themselves. They can be put to good use, bad use, or anything in between.

2. Why should I study chemistry? Chemistry is a part of many areas of study and affects everything you do. Knowledge of chemistry helps you to understand many facets of modern life.

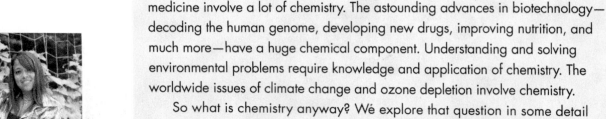

medicine involve a lot of chemistry. The astounding advances in biotechnology—decoding the human genome, developing new drugs, improving nutrition, and much more—have a huge chemical component. Understanding and solving environmental problems require knowledge and application of chemistry. The worldwide issues of climate change and ozone depletion involve chemistry.

So what is chemistry anyway? We explore that question in some detail in Section 7. And just what is a chemical? The word *chemical* may sound ominous, but it is simply a name for any material. Gold, water, salt, sugar, air, coffee, ice cream, a computer, a pencil—all are chemicals or are made entirely of chemicals.

Material things undergo changes. Sometimes these changes occur naturally—maple leaves turn yellow and red in autumn. Often, we change material things intentionally, to make them more useful, as when we light a candle or cook an egg. Most of these changes are accompanied by changes in energy. For example, when we burn gasoline, the process releases energy that we can use to propel an automobile.

Your own body is a marvelous chemical factory. It takes the food you eat and turns it into skin, bones, blood, and muscle, while also generating energy for all your activities. This amazing chemical factory operates continuously 24 hours a day for as long as you live. Chemistry affects your own life every moment, and it also transforms society as a whole. Chemistry shapes our civilization.

1 Science and Technology: The Roots of Knowledge

Learning Objectives ❯ Distinguish science from technology ❯ Define *alchemy* and *natural philosophy*.

Chemistry is a *science*, but what is science? **Science** is an accumulation of knowledge about nature and our physical world and of theories that we use to explain that knowledge. Let's examine the roots of science. Our study of the material universe has two interrelated facets: the *technological* (or *factual*) and the *philosophical* (or *theoretical*).

Technology is the application of knowledge for practical purposes. It arose long before science, originating in prehistoric times. Early people used fire to bring about chemical changes. They cooked food, baked pottery, and smelted ores to produce metals such as copper. They made beer and wine by fermentation and obtained dyes and drugs from plants. These tasks—and many others—were accomplished without an understanding of the scientific principles involved.

About 2500 years ago, Greek philosophers were among the first to formulate *theories* of chemistry—rational explanations of the behavior of matter. Those philosophers generally did not test their theories by experimentation. Nevertheless, their view of nature—attributed mainly to Aristotle—dominated Western thinking about the workings of the material world for the next 20 centuries.

The experimental roots of chemistry are in **alchemy**, a mixture of chemistry and magic that flourished in Europe during the Middle Ages, from about C.E. 500 to 1500. Alchemists searched for a "philosophers' stone" that would turn cheaper metals into gold and for an elixir that would bring eternal life. Although alchemists never achieved these goals, they discovered many new chemical substances and perfected techniques such as distillation and extraction that are still used today. Modern chemists inherited from the alchemists an abiding interest in human health and the quality of life.

Technology also developed rapidly during the late Middle Ages in Europe, though its progress was hampered by the Aristotelian philosophy that still prevailed. The beginnings of modern science are more recent, however, and coincide with the emergence of the experimental method. What we now call science grew out of **natural philosophy**—philosophical speculation about nature. Science had its true beginnings in the seventeenth century, when astronomers, physicists, and physiologists began to rely on experimentation.

▲ Aristotle (384–322 B.C.E.), Greek philosopher and tutor of Alexander the Great, believed that we could understand nature through logic. The idea of experimental science did not triumph over Aristotelian logic until about C.E. 1500.

Beyond the Alchemists' Wildest Dreams

Modern chemists can transform matter in ways that would astound the alchemists. They can change ordinary salt into lye and laundry bleach. They can convert sand into transistors and computer chips. And they can turn crude oil into plastics, fibers, pesticides, drugs, detergents, and a host of other products. Many products of modern chemistry are much more valuable than the glittering metal that the alchemists vainly sought. For example, a form of carbon called *nanotubes* has thousands of potential uses but is extremely expensive to make. A kilogram of purified nanotubes costs more than $2,500,000, while a kilogram of gold will set you back only about $50,000.

Self-Assessment Questions

Match each term in the left column with the best definition or explanation of it in the right column.

1. alchemy
2. natural philosophy
3. science
4. technology

a. application of knowledge for practical purposes
b. grew out of Greek philosophy, alchemy, and natural philosophy
c. a mixture of chemistry and magic
d. philosophical speculation about nature

Answers: 1, c; 2, d; 3, b; 4, a

▲ Alchemists made many positive contributions to chemistry. This illustration from the 1512 edition of Hieronymus Brunschwig's *Liber de arte distillandi* (On the art of distilling) shows a distillation apparatus. *(Source: Donald and Mildred Othmer Collection)*

2 Changing Perceptions and Changing Practices

Learning Objectives ❯ Briefly describe the contributions of Bacon, Galileo, and Carson to the perceptions of science.

Science is ever-changing. Francis Bacon, a philosopher who practiced law and served as a judge, was among the first to argue that science should be experimental. His dream was that science could solve the world's problems and enrich human life with new inventions, thereby increasing happiness and prosperity. Bacon was not a scientist, and it was left to others to bring about the birth of modern science. Notable

▲ Francis Bacon (1561–1626), English philosopher and Lord Chancellor to King James I.

▲ Rachel Carson's *Silent Spring* was one of the first publications to point out a number of serious environmental issues.

among these was the Italian Galileo Galilei (1564–1642). Galileo developed a vastly improved telescope and advanced the science of astronomy through observations such as sunspots, the moons of Jupiter, and the phases of Venus. He also did experiments and made many other observations that led many to call him the father of modern science.

The science of chemistry also has changed over the years. Early people used plant, animal, and mineral materials much as they occurred in nature. They later learned to modify materials to better meet their needs—for example, baking clay to make ceramic materials, cooking food to make it more digestible, and obtaining metals from ores. For most of human history, people exploited resources such as metals and petroleum and gave little thought to ever running out of such resources. An environmental movement arose in the 1970s as people became increasingly aware that reckless use of resources not only caused appalling pollution but would lead in the end to severe shortages. Rachel Carson, a biologist, was an early proponent of environmental awareness. The main theme of her book *Silent Spring* (1962) was that our use of chemicals to control insects was threatening to destroy all life, including ourselves. People in the pesticide industry and their allies roundly denounced Carson as a "propagandist," while some scientists rallied to support her. By the late 1960s, however, the threatened extinction of several species of birds and the disappearance of fish from many rivers, lakes, and areas of the ocean caused many scientists to move into Carson's camp. Popular support for Carson's views became overwhelming.

In response to growing public concern, chemists developed the concept of **green chemistry**, which uses materials and processes that are intended to prevent or reduce pollution at its source. This approach was further extended in the first decade of the twenty-first century to include the idea of sustainability. **Sustainable chemistry** is designed to meet the needs of the present generation without compromising the needs of future generations. Sustainability preserves resources and aspires to produce environmentally friendly products from renewable resources.

Some chemicals can indeed cause problems, especially when misused, but many others have extremely helpful uses. Chemicals are used to kill bacteria that cause dreadful diseases, to relieve pain and suffering, to increase food production, to provide fuel for heating, cooling, lighting, and transportation, and to provide materials for building our machines, making our clothing, and constructing our houses. Chemistry has provided ordinary people with luxuries that were not available even to the mightiest rulers in ages past. Chemicals are essential to our lives—life itself would be impossible without chemicals.

Self-Assessment Questions

Select the best answer or response.

1. Francis Bacon thought that science would
   a. destroy life on Earth
   b. increase human happiness and prosperity
   c. find a way to turn lead to gold
   d. produce toxic chemicals

2. The main theme of Rachel Carson's *Silent Spring* was that life on Earth would be destroyed by
   a. botulism
   b. nuclear war
   c. overpopulation
   d. pesticides

3. Galileo has been called the father of modern science because he
   a. anticipated environmental problems
   b. made observations and did experiments
   c. thought that science would destroy life on Earth
   d. tried to use science to get rich

4. A goal of green chemistry is to
   a. produce cheap green dyes
   b. provide great wealth for corporations
   c. reduce pollution
   d. turn deserts into forests and grasslands

5. Which best exemplifies sustainable chemistry?
   a. Toluene, extracted from coal, is used to make TNT, an explosive.
   b. Paper is made from hardwood trees.
   c. Minerals mined in South America are used in China to make LCD screens.
   d. Plastic bottles are made from both petroleum and recycled plastic.

Answers: 1, b; 2, d; 3, b; 4, c; 5, b

3 Science: Reproducible, Testable, Tentative, Predictive, and Explanatory

Learning Objectives ❯ Define *hypothesis, scientific law, scientific theory,* and *scientific model,* and explain their relationships in science.

We have defined science, but science has *characteristics* that distinguish it from other studies.

Scientists often disagree about what is and what will be, but does that make science merely a guessing game in which one guess is as good as another? Not at all. Science is based on observations and experimental tests of our assumptions. However, it is not a collection of unalterable facts; we cannot force nature to fit our preconceived ideas. Science is good at correcting errors, but it is not especially good at establishing truths. Science is an unfinished work. The things we have learned from science fill millions of books and scholarly journals, but what we know pales in comparison to what we do not yet know.

Scientific Data Must Be Reproducible

Scientists collect data by making careful observations. Data reported by a scientist must also be observable by other scientists. The data must be *reproducible*. Careful measurements are required, conditions are thoroughly controlled and described, and scientific work is not fully accepted until it has been verified by other scientists.

Observations, though, are just the beginning of the intellectual processes of science. There are many different paths to scientific discovery, and there is no general set of rules. Science is not a straightforward process for cranking out discoveries.

Scientific Hypotheses Are Testable

Scientists do not merely state what they feel may be true. They develop *testable* **hypotheses** (educated guesses) as tentative explanations of observed data. They test these hypotheses by designing and performing experiments. Experimentation distinguishes science from the arts and humanities. In the humanities, people still argue about some of the same questions that were being debated thousands of years ago: What is truth? What is beauty? These arguments persist because the proposed answers cannot be tested and confirmed objectively.

Like artists and poets, scientists are often imaginative and creative. The tenets of science, however, are *testable*. Experiments can be devised to answer most scientific questions. Ideas can be tested and thereby either verified or rejected. For example, it was long thought that exercise caused muscles to tire and become sore from a buildup of lactic acid. Recent findings suggest instead that lactic acid *delays* muscle tiredness and that the cause of tired, sore muscles may be related to other factors, including leakage of calcium ions inside muscle cells, which weakens contractions. Through many experiments, scientists have established a firm foundation of knowledge, allowing each new generation to build on the past.

Scientific Laws Summarize Observations

Large amounts of scientific data can sometimes be summarized in brief statements called **scientific laws**. For example, Robert Boyle (1627–1691), an Irishman, conducted

3. Why do scientists so often say "more study is needed"?
More data help scientists refine a hypothesis so that it is better defined, clearer, or more applicable.

5

A Possible Scientific Process

Observation reported
↓
Observation confirmed by others
↓
Hypothesis suggested
↓
Experiments designed to
test hypothesis
↓
Experiments do not
support hypothesis
↓
Hypothesis rejected
↓
New hypothesis offered
↓
New experiments tried
↓
Experiments support
(new) hypothesis
↓
Experiments repeated and
results confirmed
↓
Theory formulated
↓
Many further experiments
↓
and so on

▲ A molecular model of diamond shows the tightly linked, rigid structure that explains why diamonds are so hard.

▶ **Figure 1** The evaporation of water. (a) When a container of water is left standing open to the air, the water slowly disappears. (b) Scientists explain evaporation in terms of the motion of molecules.

many experiments on gases. In each experiment, he found that the volume of the gas decreased when the pressure applied to the gas was increased.

Many scientific laws can be stated mathematically. For example, Boyle's law can be written as $PV = k$, where P is the pressure on a gas, V is its volume, and k is a constant number. If P is doubled, V will be cut in half. Scientific laws are *universal*. Under the specified conditions, they hold everywhere in the observable universe.

Scientific Theories Are Tentative and Predictive

Scientists organize the knowledge they accumulate on a framework of detailed explanations called theories. A **theory** represents the best current explanation for a phenomenon, but it is always *tentative*. In the future, a theory may have to be modified or even discarded as a result of new observations, for the body of knowledge that is science is rapidly growing and always changing.

Theories provide organization for scientific knowledge, but they are also useful for their *predictive* value. Predictions based on theories are tested by further experiments. Theories that make successful predictions are usually widely accepted by the scientific community. A theory developed in one area is often found to apply in others.

Scientific Models Are Explanatory

Scientists often use models to help *explain* complicated phenomena. A *scientific model* uses tangible items or pictures to represent invisible processes. For example, the invisible particles of a gas can be visualized as billiard balls, as marbles, or as dots or circles on paper. We know that when a glass of water is left standing for a period of time, the water disappears through the process of evaporation (Figure 1). Scientists explain evaporation with a theory, the kinetic–molecular theory, which proposes that a liquid is composed of tiny particles called *molecules* that are in constant motion. In the bulk of the liquid, these molecules are held together by forces of attraction. The molecules collide with one another like billiard balls on a playing table. Sometimes, a "hard break" of billiard balls causes one ball to fly off the table. Likewise, some of the molecules of a liquid gain enough energy through collisions to break the attraction to their neighbors, escape from the liquid, and disperse among the widely spaced molecules in air. The water in the glass gradually disappears. This model gives us more than a name for evaporation; it gives us an understanding of the phenomenon.

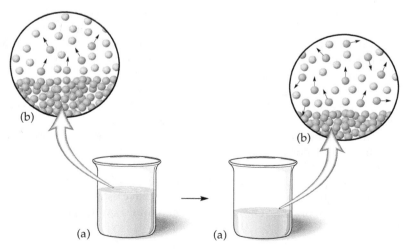

(b)

(b)

(a)

(a)

◯ = Water molecule

◯ = Air (nitrogen or oxygen) molecule

What Science Is Not

Responsible news media generally try to be fair, presenting both sides of an issue regardless of where the prevailing evidence lies. In science, the evidence often indicates that one side is simply wrong. Scientists strive for accuracy, not balance. The idea of a flat Earth is not given equal credence to a (roughly) spherical Earth. Only ideas that have survived experimental testing or that can be tested by experiment are considered valid. Ideas that are beautiful, elegant, or even sacrosanct can be invalidated by experimental data.

Science is not a democratic process. Majority rule does not determine what constitutes sound science. Science does not accept notions that are proven false or remain untested by experiment.

When doing experiments, developing theories, and constructing models, it is important to note that a *correlation* between two items is not necessarily evidence that one *causes* the other. For example, many people suffer from allergies in the fall when goldenrod is in bloom. However, research has shown that the main cause of these allergies is ragweed pollen. There is a correlation between the blooming of goldenrod and autumnal allergies, but goldenrod pollen is not the cause. Ragweed happens to bloom at the same time.

The Limitations of Science

Some people say that we could solve many of our problems if we would only attack them using the methods of science. Why can't the procedures of the scientist be applied to social, political, ethical, and economic problems? And why do scientists disagree over environmental, social, and political issues?

Disagreement often results from the inability to control *variables*. A **variable** is something that can change over the course of an experiment. If, for example, we wanted to study in the laboratory how the volume of a gas varies with changes in pressure, we could hold constant such factors as temperature and the amount and kind of gas. If, on the other hand, we wanted to determine the effect of low levels of a particular pollutant on the health of a human population, we would find it almost impossible to control such variables as individuals' diets, habits, and exposure to other substances, all of which affect health. Although we could make observations, formulate hypotheses, and conduct experiments on the health effect of the pollutant, interpretation of the results would be difficult and subject to disagreement.

Self-Assessment Questions

Select the best answer or response.

1. To gather information to support or discredit a hypothesis, a scientist
   a. conducts experiments
   b. consults an authority
   c. establishes a scientific law
   d. formulates a scientific theory

2. The statement that mass is always conserved when chemical changes occur is an example of a scientific
   a. experiment
   b. hypothesis
   c. law
   d. theory

3. A successful theory
   a. can be used to make predictions
   b. eventually becomes a scientific law
   c. is not subject to further testing
   d. is permanently accepted as true

4. Which of the following is *not* a hypothesis?
   a. All solutions of seaborgium (element 106) are blue.
   b. Copernicum (element 112) will have properties similar to those of mercury.
   c. Extrasensory perception works only when no negative forces are present.
   d. Water reacts with seaborgium to form hydrogen gas.

5. A possible explanation for a collection of observations is called a(n)
   a. experiment
   b. law
   c. myth
   d. theory

6. Social problems are difficult to solve because it is difficult to
   a. control variables
   b. discount paranormal events
   c. form hypotheses
   d. formulate theories

4 Science and Technology: Risks and Benefits

Learning Objectives › Define *risk* and *benefit*, and give an example of each.
› Estimate a desirability quotient from benefit and risk data.

Most people recognize that society has benefited from science and technology, but many seem not to realize that there are risks associated with every technological advance. How can we determine when the benefits outweigh the risks? One approach, called **risk–benefit analysis**, involves the estimation of a desirability quotient (DQ).

$$DQ = \frac{Benefits}{Risks}$$

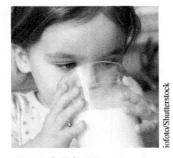

▲ It DOES Matter!
For most people of northern European ancestry, milk is a wholesome food; its benefits far outweigh its risks. Other ethnic groups have high rates of lactose intolerance among adults, and the desirability quotient for milk is much smaller.

A *benefit* is anything that promotes well-being or has a positive effect. Benefits may be economic, social, or psychological. A *risk* is any hazard that leads to loss or injury. Some of the risks associated with modern technology have led to disease, death, economic loss, and environmental deterioration. Risks and benefits may involve one individual, a group, or society as a whole.

Every technological advance has both benefits and risks. Most people recognize the benefits of the automobile. But driving a car involves risk—individual risks of injury or death in a traffic accident and societal risks such as pollution and climate change. Most people consider the benefits of driving a car to outweigh the risks.

Weighing the benefits and risks connected with a product is more difficult when considering a group of people. For example, pasteurized low-fat milk is a safe, nutritious beverage for many people of northern European descent. However, a few people in this group can't tolerate lactose, the sugar in milk. And some are allergic to milk proteins. For these individuals, drinking milk can be harmful. But milk allergies and lactose intolerance are relatively uncommon among people of northern European descent, so the benefits of milk are large and the risks are small, resulting in a large DQ. However, adults of other ethnic backgrounds often are lactose-intolerant, and for them, milk has a small DQ. Thus, milk is not always suitable for use in programs to relieve malnutrition.

The artificial sweetener aspartame is the most highly studied of all food additives. There is little evidence that use of an artificial sweetener helps with efforts to lose weight. (Aspartame may provide some benefit to diabetics, however, because sugar consumption presents a large risk to them.) There are anecdotal reports of problems due to use of the sweetener, but these have not been confirmed in controlled studies. To most people, the risk involved in using aspartame is small. This leads to an uncertain DQ—and, it seems, to endless debate over the product's safety.

Other technologies provide large benefits and present large risks. For these technologies, too, the DQ is uncertain. An example is the conversion of coal to liquid fuels. Most people find liquid fuels to be very beneficial in transportation, home heating, and industry. There are great risks associated with coal conversion, however, including risks to coal mine workers, air and water pollution, and the exposure of conversion plant workers to toxic chemicals. The result, again, is an uncertain DQ and political controversy.

There are yet other problems in risk–benefit analysis. Some technologies benefit one group of people while presenting a risk to another. For example, gold plating and gold wires in computers and other consumer electronics benefit the consumer, providing greater reliability and longer life. But when the devices are scrapped, small-scale attempts to recover the gold often produce serious pollution in the area of recovery. Difficult political decisions are needed in such cases.

Other technologies provide current benefits but present future risks. For example, although nuclear power now provides useful electricity, improperly stored wastes from nuclear power plants might present hazards for centuries. Thus, the use of nuclear power is controversial.

Science and technology obviously involve *both* risks and benefits. The determination of benefits is almost entirely a social judgment. Although risk assessment also involves social and personal decisions, it can often be greatly aided by scientific investigation.

CONCEPTUAL Example 1   Risk–Benefit Analysis

Heroin is thought by some to be more effective than other drugs for the relief of severe pain. For example, heroin is a legal prescription drug in the United Kingdom. People can become addicted to heroin with continued use in as little as three days, and recreational use often renders addicts unable to function in society. Do a risk–benefit analysis of the use of heroin in treating the pain of **(a)** a young athlete with a broken leg and **(b)** a terminally ill cancer patient.

Solution
a. The heroin would provide the benefit of pain relief, but its use for such purposes has been judged to be too risky by the U.S. Food and Drug Administration. The DQ is low.
b. The heroin would provide the benefit of pain relief. The risk of addiction in a dying person is irrelevant. Heroin is banned for any purpose in the United States. The DQ is uncertain. (Both answers involve judgments that are not clearly scientific; people can differ in their assessments of each.)

■ EXERCISE 1A
Chloramphenicol is a powerful antibacterial drug that often destroys bacteria unaffected by other drugs. It is highly dangerous to some individuals, however, causing fatal aplastic anemia in about 1 in 30,000 people. Do a risk–benefit analysis of administering chloramphenicol to **(a)** sick farm animals, whose milk or meat might contain residues of the drug, and **(b)** a person with Rocky Mountain spotted fever facing a high probability of death or permanent disability.

■ EXERCISE 1B
The drug thalidomide was introduced in the 1950s as a sleeping aid. It was found to be a *teratogen*, a substance that causes birth defects, and was removed from the market after children in Europe whose mothers took it during pregnancy were born with deformed limbs. Recently, thalidomide has been investigated as an effective treatment for the lesions caused by leprosy and for Kaposi's sarcoma (a form of cancer often suffered by AIDS patients). Do a risk-benefit analysis of prescribing thalidomide to **(a)** all women and **(b)** women with AIDS.

Self-Assessment Questions

Select the best answer or response.

1. Our perception of risk is
   a. always based on sound science
   b. always higher than actual risk
   c. always lower than actual risk
   d. often different from actual risk
2. Among the following, the highest risk of death (see Table 1) is associated with
   a. airplane accident
   b. car accident
   c. cigarettes
   d. radon

Risks of Death

Our perception of risk often differs from the actual risk we face. Some people fear flying but readily assume the risk of an automobile trip. The odds of dying from various causes are listed in Table 1.

Table 1 Approximate Lifetime Risks of Death in the United States

Action	Lifetime Risk[a]	Approximate Lifetime Odds	Details/Assumptions
All causes	1	1 in 1	We all die of something.
Cigarettes	0.25	1 in 4	Cigarette smoking, 1 pack/day
Heart disease	0.20	1 in 5	Heart attacks, congestive heart failure
All cancers	0.14	1 in 7	All cancers
Motor vehicles	0.011	1 in 88	Death in motor vehicle accident
Home accidents	0.010	1 in 100	Home accident death
Radon	0.0030	1 in 300	Radon in homes, cancer deaths
Background radiation	0.0010	1 in 1000	Sea level background radiation, cancers
Peanut butter (aflatoxin)	0.00060	1 in 1700	4 tablespoons peanut butter per day
Airplane accidents	0.0002	1 in 5000	Death in aircraft crashes
Terrorist attack[b]	0.00077	1 in 1300	One 9/11-level attack per year
Terrorist attack[c]	0.000077	1 in 13,000	One 9/11-level attack every 10 years

[a]The odds of dying of a particular cause in a given year are calculated by dividing the population by the number of deaths by that cause in that year. Lifetime odds of dying of a specific cause are calculated by dividing the one-year odds by the life expectancy of a person born in that year.

[b]Unlikely scenario

[c]More reasonable scenario

5 Chemistry: Its Central Role

Learning Objective ❯ Give an example of a use of chemistry in your daily life and in society at large.

Science is a unified whole. Common scientific laws apply everywhere and on all levels of organization. The various areas of science interact and support one another. Accordingly, chemistry is not only useful in itself but also fundamental to other scientific disciplines. The application of chemical principles has revolutionized biology and medicine, has provided materials for powerful computers used in mathematics, and has profoundly influenced other fields such as psychology. The social goals of better health, nutrition, and housing are dependent to a large extent on the knowledge and techniques of chemists. Many modern materials have been developed by chemists, and even more amazing materials are in the works. Recycling of basic materials—paper, glass, and metals—involves chemical processes. Chemistry is indeed a central science (Figure 2). There is no area of our daily lives that is not affected by chemistry.

Chemistry is also important to the *economy* of industrial nations. In the United States, the chemical industry makes thousands of consumer products, including personal-care products, agricultural products, plastics, coatings, soaps, and detergents. It produces 80% of the materials used to make medicines. The U.S. chemical industry is one of the country's largest industries, with sales of more than $675 billion per year, and it accounts for 10% of all U.S. exports. It employs 800,000 workers, including scientists, engineers, and technicians, and it generates nearly 11% of all U.S. patents. And despite widespread fear of chemicals, workers in the chemical industry are five times safer than the average worker in the U.S. manufacturing sector.

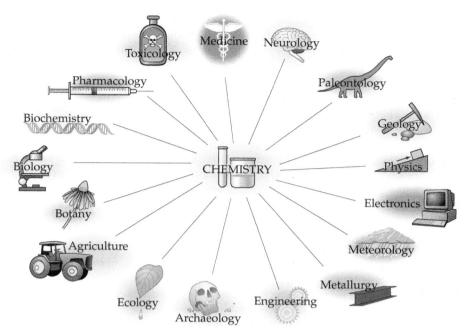

◀ **Figure 2** Chemistry has a central role among the sciences.

Self-Assessment Question

Select the best answer or response.

1. Chemistry is called the central science because
   a. the chemical industry is based mainly in the U.S. Midwest
   b. it is the core course in all college curricula
   c. it is fundamental to other scientific disciplines
   d. the source of many environmental problems

2. The U.S. chemical industry is
   a. patently unsafe
   b. the source of nearly all pollution
   c. the source of many consumer products
   d. unimportant to the U.S. economy

Answers: 1, c; 2, c

6 Solving Society's Problems: Scientific Research

Learning Objective ❯ Distinguish basic research from applied research.

Chemistry is a powerful force in shaping society today. Chemical research not only plays a pivotal role in other sciences but it also has a profound influence on society as a whole. Chemists, like other scientists, do one of two categories of research: *applied research* or *basic research*. The two often overlap, and it isn't always possible to label a particular project as one or the other.

Applied Research

Some chemists test polluted soil, air, and water. Others analyze foods, fuels, cosmetics, detergents, and drugs. Still others synthesize new substances for use as drugs or pesticides or formulate plastics for new applications. These activities are examples of **applied research**—work oriented toward the solution of a particular problem in an industry or the environment.

Among the most monumental accomplishments in applied research were those of George Washington Carver. Born in slavery, Carver attended Simpson College and later graduated from Iowa State University. A botanist and agricultural chemist, Carver taught and did research at Tuskegee Institute. He developed over 300 products from peanuts, from peanut butter to hand cleaner to insulating board. He created other new

▲ George Washington Carver (1864–1943), research scientist, in his laboratory at Tuskegee Institute.

11

products from sweet potatoes, pecans, and clay. Carver also taught southern farmers to rotate crops and to use legumes to replenish the nitrogen removed from the soil by cotton crops. Carver's work helped to revitalize the economy of the South.

Basic Research: The Search for Knowledge

Many chemists are involved in **basic research**, the search for knowledge for its own sake. Some chemists work out the fine points of atomic and molecular structure. Others measure the intricate energy changes that accompany complex chemical reactions. Some synthesize new compounds and determine their properties. Done for the sheer joy of unraveling the secrets of nature and discovering order in our universe, basic research is characterized by the absence of any predictable, marketable product.

Lack of a product doesn't mean that basic research is useless. Far from it! Findings from basic research often *are* applied at a later time. This may be the hope, but it is not the main goal of the researcher. In fact, most of our modern technology is based on results obtained in basic research. Without this base of factual information, technological innovation would be haphazard and slow.

Applied research is carried out mainly by industries seeking to gain a competitive edge by developing a novel, better, or more salable product. The ultimate aim of such research is usually profit for the stockholders. Basic research is conducted mainly at universities and research institutes. Most support for this research comes from federal and state governments and foundations, although some larger industries also support it.

An example of basic research that was later applied to improving human welfare is the work of Gertrude Elion (1918–1999) and George Hitchings (1905–1998), who studied compounds called *purines* in an attempt to understand their role in the chemistry of the cell. Their basic research at Burroughs Wellcome Research Laboratories in North Carolina led to the discovery of a number of valuable new drugs that facilitate organ transplants and treat various diseases such as gout, malaria, herpes, and cancer. Elion and Hitchings shared the 1988 Nobel Prize in Physiology or Medicine, and in 1991 Elion became the first woman to be inducted into the National Inventors Hall of Fame.

Another example involves the work of two physicists. In 1930, Otto Stern (1888–1969) and Walther Gerlach (1889–1979) determined that certain atomic nuclei have a property called *spin*, which causes these nuclei to act as tiny magnets. Isidor Isaac Rabi (1898–1988) later developed a method for recording the magnetic properties of atomic nuclei. For their basic research in studying and measuring these minuscule magnetic fields, Stern and Rabi won the Nobel Prize in Physics in 1943 and 1944, respectively. In the 1940s, teams led by Edward M. Purcell and Felix Bloch used nuclear spins to work out the structure of complicated molecules. Their technique, called *nuclear magnetic resonance* (NMR), has become a major tool of chemists for determining molecular structure. Purcell and Bloch shared the Nobel Prize in Physics in 1952 for their research. Still later, in the 1960s, Paul Lauterbur, Peter Mansfield, and other scientists applied the principles of NMR to performing scans of the human body. This noninvasive diagnostic technique, called *magnetic resonance imaging* (MRI), has replaced many exploratory surgical operations and made other surgical procedures much more precise. Lauterbur and Mansfield won the 2003 Nobel Prize in Physiology or Medicine for their work.

4. Why do scientists bother with studies that have no immediate application? The results of basic research may not have an immediate practical use; however, basic research extends our understanding of the world and can be considered an investment in the future.

▲ **It DOES Matter!**
Gertrude Elion won a Nobel Prize for her basic research on purines. Her work has led to many applications in pharmaceuticals and medicine. Many important modern applications started out with basic research.

Importance of Basic Research

"There are two compelling reasons why society must support basic science. One is substantial: The theoretical physics of yesterday is the nuclear defense of today; the obscure synthetic chemistry of yesterday is curing disease today. The other reason is cultural. The essence of our civilization is to explore and analyze the nature of man and his surroundings. As proclaimed in the Bible in the Book of Proverbs: 'Where there is no vision, the people perish.'"

Arthur Kornberg (1918–2007), American biochemist and recipient of Nobel Prize in Physiology or Medicine, 1959

Classify each of the following as (a) basic research or (b) applied research.

1. A chemist tries to develop a new antibiotic similar to ampicillin.
2. A team of scientists tries to genetically engineer a variety of rice that contains vitamin A.
3. A scientist seeks to extract biologically active compounds from sea sponges.
4. Scientists identify adrenal hormones and determine their structure and biological effects.

Answers: 1, b; 2, b; 3, a; 4, a

7 Chemistry: A Study of Matter and Its Changes

Learning Objective ❯ Differentiate: mass and weight; physical and chemical change; and physical and chemical properties.

Chemistry is often defined as the study of matter and the changes it undergoes. Because the entire physical universe is made up of matter and energy, the field of chemistry extends from atoms to stars, from rocks to living organisms. Now let's look at matter a little more closely.

Matter is the stuff that makes up all material things. It is anything that occupies space and has mass. Matter has *mass*; you can weigh it. Wood, sand, water, air, and people have mass and are therefore matter. **Mass** is a measure of the quantity of matter that an object contains. The greater the mass of an object, the more difficult it is to change its velocity. You can easily deflect a tennis ball coming toward you at 30 meters per second (m/s), but you would have difficulty stopping a cannonball of the same size moving at the same speed. A cannonball has more mass than a tennis ball of equal size.

The mass of an object does not vary with location. An astronaut has the same mass on the moon as on Earth. In contrast, **weight** measures a force. On Earth, it measures the force of attraction between our planet and the mass in question. On the moon, where gravity is one-sixth that on Earth, an astronaut weighs only one-sixth as much as on Earth (Figure 3). Weight varies with gravity; mass does not.

NASA

▲ **Figure 3** Astronaut John W. Young leaps from the lunar surface, where gravity pulls at him with only one-sixth as much force as on Earth.

Q: *If an astronaut has a mass of 72 kg, what would be his mass on the moon? If an astronaut weighs 180 lb on Earth, what would he weigh on the moon?*

CONCEPTUAL Example 2   Mass and Weight

Gravity on the planet Mercury is 0.376 times that on Earth. **(a)** What would be the mass on Mercury of a person who has a mass of 62.5 kilograms (kg) on Earth? **(b)** What would be the weight on Mercury of a person who weighs 124 pounds (lb) on Earth?

Solution

a. The person's mass would be the same as on Earth (62.5 kg). The quantity of matter has not changed.
b. The person would weigh only 0.376×124 lb $= 46.6$ lb; the force of attraction between Mercury and the person would be only 0.376 times that between Earth and the person.

■ EXERCISE 2

At the surface of Venus, the force of gravity is 0.903 times that at Earth's surface. **(a)** What would be the mass of a 1.00-kg object on Venus? **(b)** How much would a man who weighs 198 lb on Earth weigh on the surface of Venus?

► **Figure 4** A comparison of the physical properties of two elements. Copper (left), obtained as pellets, can be hammered into thin foil or drawn into wire. Iodine (right) consists of brittle gray crystals that crumble into a powder when struck.

Q: *What additional physical properties of copper and iodine are apparent from the photographs?*

Physical and Chemical Properties

We can use our knowledge of chemistry to change matter to make it more useful. Chemists can change crude oil into gasoline, plastics, pesticides, drugs, detergents, and thousands of other products. Changes in matter are accompanied by changes in energy. Often, we change matter to extract part of its energy. For example, we burn gasoline to get energy to propel our automobiles.

To distinguish between samples of matter, we can compare their properties (Figure 4). A **physical property** of a substance is a characteristic or behavior that can be observed or measured without generating new types of matter. Color, odor, and hardness are physical properties (Table 2). A **chemical property** describes how a substance reacts with other types of matter—how its basic building blocks can change (Table 3).

A **physical change** involves an alteration in the physical appearance of matter without changing its chemical identity or composition. An ice cube can melt to form a liquid, but it is still water. Melting is a physical change, and the temperature at which it occurs—the melting point—is a physical property.

A **chemical change** involves a change in the chemical identity of matter into other substances that are chemically different. In exhibiting a chemical property, matter undergoes a chemical change. At least one substance in the original matter is replaced by one or more new substances. Iron metal reacts with oxygen from the air to form rust (iron oxide). When sulfur burns in air, sulfur, which is made up of

Table 2	Some Examples of Physical Properties
Property	**Examples**
Temperature	0 °C for ice water, 100 °C for boiling water.
Mass	A nickel weighs 5 g. A penny weighs 2.5 g.
Color	Sulfur is yellow. Bromine is reddish-brown.
Taste	Acids are sour. Bases are bitter.
Odor	Benzyl acetate smells like jasmine. Hydrogen sulfide smells like rotten eggs.
Boiling point	Water boils at 100 °C. Ethyl alcohol boils at 78.5 °C.
Hardness	Diamond is exceptionally hard. Sodium metal is soft.
Density	1.00 g/mL for water, 19.3 g/cm³ for gold.

Table 3	Some Examples of Chemical Properties
Substance	**Typical Chemical Property**
Iron	rusts (combines with oxygen to form iron oxide).
Carbon	burns (combines with oxygen to form carbon dioxide).
Silver	tarnishes (combines with sulfur to form silver sulfide).
Nitroglycerin	explodes (decomposes to produce a mixture of gases).
Carbon monoxide	is toxic (combines with hemoglobin, causing anoxia).
Neon	is inert (does not react with anything).

one type of atom, and oxygen (from air), which is made up of another type of atom, combine to form sulfur dioxide, which is made up of molecules that have sulfur and oxygen atoms in the ratio 1:2. (A *molecule* is a group of atoms bound together as a single unit. You'll learn more about atoms and molecules later.)

It is difficult at times to determine whether a change is physical or chemical, but we can decide on the basis of what happens to the composition or structure of the matter involved. *Composition* refers to the types of atoms that are present and their relative proportions, and *structure* to the arrangement of those atoms with respect to one another or in space. A chemical change results in a change in composition or structure, whereas a physical change does not.

CONCEPTUAL Example 3   Chemical Change and Physical Change

Which of the following events involve chemical changes and which involve physical changes?
- **a.** You trim your fingernails.
- **b.** Lemon juice converts milk to curds and whey.
- **c.** Molten aluminum is poured into a mold, where it solidifies.
- **d.** Sodium chloride (table salt) is broken down into sodium metal and chlorine gas.

Solution
We examine each change and determine whether there has been a change in composition or structure. In other words, we ask, "Have any substances that are chemically different been created?" If so, the change is chemical; if not, it is physical.
- **a.** Physical change: The composition of a fingernail is not changed by cutting.
- **b.** Chemical change: The compositions of curds and whey are different from the composition of milk.
- **c.** Physical change: Whether it is solid or liquid, aluminum is the same substance with the same composition.
- **d.** Chemical change: New substances, sodium and chlorine, are formed.

■ EXERCISE 3A
Which of the following events involve chemical changes and which involve physical changes?
- **a.** Gasoline vaporizes from an open container.
- **b.** Magnesium metal burns in air to form a white powder called *magnesium oxide*.
- **c.** A dull knife is sharpened with a whetstone.

■ EXERCISE 3B
Which of the following events involve chemical changes and which involve physical changes?
- **a.** A steel wrench left out in the rain becomes rusty.
- **b.** A stick of butter melts.
- **c.** Charcoal briquettes are burned.
- **d.** Peppercorns are ground into flakes.

Self-Assessment Questions

Select the best answer or response.

1. Which of the following is *not* an example of matter?
   a. gasoline fumes   b. ether fumes   c. gold   d. a sentiment

2. Which of the following is an example of matter?
   a. air   b. a prayer   c. a thought   d. yellow light

3. Two identical items are taken from Earth to Mars, where they have
   a. both the same mass and the same weight as on Earth
   b. neither the same mass nor the same weight as on Earth
   c. the same mass but not the same weight as on Earth
   d. the same weight but not the same mass as on Earth

4. What kind of change does not alter the identity of a material?
   a. chemical   b. physical   c. physical state   d. temperature

5. Bending glass tubing in a hot flame involves
   a. applied research   b. a chemical change
   c. an experiment   d. a physical change

6. Transforming liquid water into steam involves
   a. removing energy from the water   b. a change in chemical makeup
   c. a chemical change   d. a physical change

7. Which of the following is a chemical property?
   a. iodine vapor is purple   b. copper tarnishes
   c. salt dissolves in water   d. balsa wood is easily carved

8. Which of the following is an example of a physical change?
   a. A cake is baked from flour, baking powder, sugar, eggs, shortening, and milk.
   b. Milk left outside a refrigerator overnight turns sour.
   c. Sheep are sheared, and the wool is spun into yarn.
   d. Spiders eat flies and make silk.

9. Which of the following is an example of a chemical change?
   a. An egg is broken and poured into an eggnog mix.
   b. A tree is pruned, shortening some branches.
   c. A tree is watered and fertilized, and it grows larger.
   d. Frost forms on a cold windowpane.

Answers: 1, d; 2, a; 3, c; 4, b; 5, d; 6, d; 7, b; 8, c; 9, c

8 Classification of Matter

Learning Objective ❯ Classify matter according to state and as mixture, substance, compound, and/or element.

In this section, we examine three of the many ways of classifying matter. First, we look at the physical forms or *states of matter*.

The States of Matter

There are three familiar states of matter: solid, liquid, and gas (Figure 5). They can be classified by bulk properties (a *macro* view) or by arrangement of the particles that comprise them (a *molecular*, or *micro*, view). A **solid** object maintains its shape and volume regardless of its location. A **liquid** occupies a definite volume but assumes the shape of the portion of a container that it occupies. If you have 355 milliliters (mL) of a soft drink, you have 355 mL whether the soft drink is in a can, in a bottle, or, through a mishap, on the floor—which demonstrates another property of liquids. Unlike solids, liquids flow readily. A **gas** maintains neither shape nor volume. It expands to fill completely whatever container it occupies. Gases flow and are easily compressed. For example, enough air for many minutes of breathing can be compressed into a steel tank for SCUBA diving.

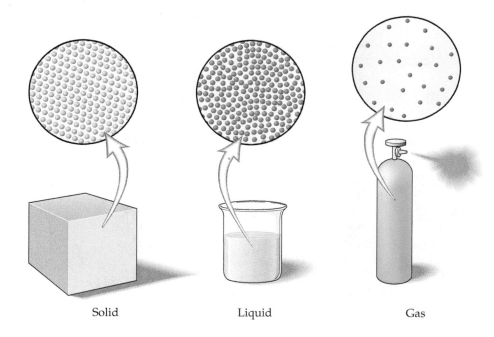

Solid   Liquid   Gas

◄ Figure 5 The kinetic–molecular theory can be used to interpret (or explain) the bulk properties of *solids*, *liquids*, and *gases*. In solids, the particles are close together and in fixed positions. In liquids, the particles are close together, but they are free to move about. In gases, the particles are far apart and are in rapid random motion.

Q: *Based on this figure, why does a quart of water vapor weigh so much less than a quart of liquid water?*

Bulk properties of *solids*, *liquids*, and *gases* are explained using the kinetic–molecular theory. In solids, the particles are close together and in fixed positions. In liquids, the particles are close together, but they are free to move about. In gases, the particles are far apart and are in rapid random motion.

Substances and Mixtures

Matter can be either pure or mixed (Figure 6). Pure matter is considered to be a **substance**, defined as having a definite, or fixed, composition that does not vary from one sample to another. Pure gold (24-karat gold) consists entirely of gold atoms; it is a substance. All samples of pure water are comprised of molecules consisting of two hydrogen atoms and one oxygen atom; water is a substance.

The composition of a **mixture** of two or more substances is variable. The substances retain their identities. They do not change chemically; they simply mix. Mixtures can be separated by physical means. Mixtures can be either *homogeneous* or *heterogeneous*. All parts of a homogeneous mixture have the same composition (Section 6.4) and the same appearance. A saline solution—a solution of salt in water—is a homogeneous mixture. The proportions of salt and water can vary from one solution to another, but the water is still water and the salt remains salt. The two substances can be separated by physical means. For example, the water can be boiled away, leaving the salt behind.

Sand and water form a heterogeneous mixture. The appearance is not the same throughout. The grains of sand are different from the liquid water. Most things we deal with each day are heterogeneous mixtures. All you have to do is look at a computer, a book, a pen, or a person to see that different parts of those mixtures have different compositions (your hair is quite different from your skin, for example).

Elements and Compounds

A *substance* is either an element or a compound. An **element** is one of the fundamental substances from which all material things are constructed. Elements cannot be broken down into simpler substances by any chemical process. There are more than 100 known elements, of which this text deals with only about a third, which are listed on the inside front cover. Oxygen, carbon, sulfur, aluminum, and iron are familiar elements.

A **compound** is a substance made up of two or more elements chemically combined in a fixed ratio. For example, water is a compound because it has fixed

Chemistry

▲ Figure 6 A scheme for classifying matter. The "molecular-level" views are of gold, an *element*; water, a *compound*; 12-karat gold, a *homogeneous mixture* of silver and gold; and the contents of a prospector's pan, a *heterogeneous mixture* of gold flakes in water.

5. Can we change lead into gold? One element cannot be changed into another element by chemical reactions. An element cannot be created or destroyed, although an element can be extracted from a mixture or compound containing the element.

A chemical symbol in a formula stands for one atom of the element. If more than one atom is included in a formula, a subscript number is used after the symbol. For example, the formula H_2 represents two atoms of hydrogen, and the formula CH_4 stands for one atom of carbon and four atoms of hydrogen. Mixtures do not have such formulas because a mixture does not have a fixed composition.

proportions of hydrogen (H) and oxygen (O). Aluminum oxide (the "sand" on sandpaper), carbon dioxide, and iron disulfide (FeS_2, "fool's gold") are other compounds.

Because elements are so fundamental to our study of chemistry, we find it useful to refer to them in a shorthand form. Each element can be represented by a **chemical symbol** made up of one or two letters derived from the name of the element. Symbols for the elements are listed in the Table of Atomic Masses (inside front cover). The first letter of a symbol is always capitalized. The second (if there are two) is always lowercase. (It makes a difference. For example, Co is the symbol for cobalt, a metallic element, but CO is the formula for carbon monoxide, a poisonous compound.)

The elements' symbols are the alphabet of chemistry. Most are based on the English names of the elements, but a few are based on Latin names (Table 4).

CONCEPTUAL Example 4   Elements and Compounds

Which of the following represent elements and which represent compounds?

C Cu HI BN In HBr

Solution

The periodic table shows that C, Cu, and In represent elements (each is a single symbol). HI, BN, and HBr are each composed of two symbols and represent compounds.

■ EXERCISE 4A

Which of the following represent elements and which represent compounds?

He CuO No NO KF Os

■ EXERCISE 4B

How many *different* elements are represented in the list in Exercise 4A?

18

Table 4 Some Elements with Symbols Derived from Latin Names

Usual English Name	Latin Name	Symbol	Spanish Name[b]	French Name[b]
Copper	cuprum	Cu	cobre	cuivre
Gold	aurum	Au	oro	or
Iron	ferrum	Fe	hierro	fer
Lead	plumbum	Pb	plomo	plomb
Mercury	hydrargyrum	Hg	mercurio	mercure
Potassium	kalium[a]	K	potasio	potassium
Silver	argentum	Ag	plata	argent
Sodium	natrium[a]	Na	sodio	sodium
Tin	stannum	Sn	estaño	étain

[a]The elements potassium and sodium were unknown in ancient times. The names *kalium* and *natrium* are the names that were used then for the compounds potassium carbonate and sodium carbonate.

[b]Note that element names in Spanish and French are often close to the Latin names.

Atoms and Molecules

An **atom** is the smallest characteristic part of an element. Each element is composed of atoms of a particular kind. For example, the element copper is made up of copper atoms, and gold is made up of gold atoms. All copper atoms are alike in a fundamental way and are different from gold atoms.

The smallest characteristic part of most compounds is a molecule. A **molecule** is a group of atoms bound together as a unit. All the molecules of a given compound have the same atoms in the same proportions. For example, all water molecules have two hydrogen (H) atoms and one oxygen (O) atom, as indicated by the formula (H_2O).

Self-Assessment Questions

1. Which state of matter has neither a definite volume nor a definite shape?
   a. gas
   c. liquid
   b. homogeneous
   d. solid

2. Which of the following is a mixture?
   a. carbon
   c. silver
   b. copper
   d. soda water

3. Which of the following is *not* an element?
   a. aluminum
   c. lead
   b. brass
   d. sulfur

4. A compound can be separated into its elements
   a. by chemical means
   c. by physical means
   b. by mechanical means
   d. using a magnet

5. The smallest part of an element is a(n)
   a. atom
   c. mass
   b. corpuscle
   d. molecule

6. The symbol for potassium is
   a. K
   c. Pm
   b. P
   d. Po

7. Br is the symbol for
   a. beryllium
   c. brass
   b. boron
   d. bromine

Answers: 1, a; 2, d; 3, b; 4, a; 5, a; 6, a; 7, d

Figure 7 Comparisons of metric and customary units of measure. The meter stick is 100 centimeters long and is slightly longer than the yardstick below it (1 m = 1.0936 yd).

Q: *From this figure, approximately how many pounds are in a kilogram? Which two units are closer in size, the inch and centimeter or the quart and the liter?*

9 The Measurement of Matter

Learning Objective ❯ Assign proper units of measurement to observations, and manipulate units in conversions.

Accurate measurements of such properties as mass, volume, time, and temperature are essential to the compilation of dependable scientific data. Such data are of critical importance in all science-related fields. Measurements of temperature and blood pressure are routinely made in medicine, and modern medical diagnosis depends on a whole battery of other measurements, including careful chemical analyses of blood and urine.

The measurement system agreed on by scientists since 1960 is the *International System of Units*, or **SI units** (from the French *Système Internationale*), a modernized version of the metric system established in France in 1791. Most countries use metric measures in everyday life. In the United States these units are used mainly in science laboratories, although they are increasingly being used in commerce, especially in businesses with an international component. The contents of most bottled beverages are given in metric units, and metric measurements are also common in sporting events. Figure 7 compares some metric and customary units.

Because SI units are based on the decimal system, it is easy to convert from one unit to another. All measured quantities can be expressed in terms of the seven base units listed in Table 5. We use the first six in this text.

Table 5	The Seven SI Base Units	
Physical Quantity	**Name of Unit**	**Symbol of Unit**
Length	meter[a]	m
Mass	kilogram	kg
Time	second	s
Temperature	kelvin	K
Amount of substance	mole	mol
Electric current	ampere	A
Luminous intensity	candela	cd

[a]Spelled *metre* in most countries.

Exponential Numbers: Powers of Ten

Scientists deal with objects smaller than atoms and as large as the universe. We usually use exponential notation to describe the sizes of such objects. A number is in *exponential notation* when it is written as the product of a coefficient and a power of 10, such as 1.6×10^{-19} or 35×10^6. A number is said to be expressed in *scientific notation* when the coefficient has a value between 1 and 10.

An electron has a diameter of about 10^{-15} meter (m) and a mass of about 10^{-30} kilogram (kg). At the other extreme, a galaxy typically measures about 10^{23} m across and has a mass of about 10^{41} kg. It is difficult even to imagine numbers so small and so large. The accompanying figure offers some perspectives on size.

Because measurements using the basic SI units can be of awkward magnitude, we often use exponential numbers. However, it is sometimes more convenient to use prefixes (Table 6) to indicate units larger and smaller than the base unit. The following examples show how prefixes and powers of ten are interconverted.

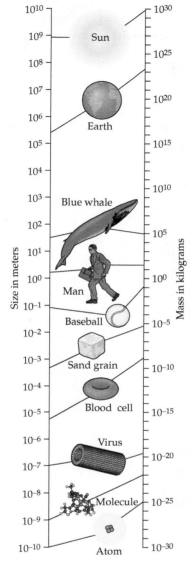

▲ Comparison of very large and very small objects is much easier with exponential notation.

Example 5 Prefixes and Powers of Ten

Convert each of the following measurements to a unit that replaces the power of ten by a prefix.

a. 2.89×10^{-6} g   b. 4.30×10^3 m

Solution

Our goal is to replace each power of ten with the appropriate prefix from Table 6. For example, $10^{-3} = 0.0001$ corresponds to milli(unit). (It doesn't matter what the unit is; here we are dealing only with the prefixes.)

a. 10^{-6} corresponds to the prefix *micro-*, that is, $10^{-6} \times$ (unit) = micro (unit); so we have $2.89\ \mu$g

b. 10^3 corresponds to the prefix *kilo-*, that is, $10^3 \times$ (unit) = kilo (unit); so we have 4.30 km

■ EXERCISE 5

Convert each of the following measurements to a unit that replaces the power of ten by a prefix.

a. 7.24×10^3 g   b. 4.29×10^{-6} m   c. 7.91×10^{-3} s

d. 2.29×10^{-2} g   e. 7.90×10^6 m

Example 6 Prefixes and Powers of Ten

Use scientific notation to express each of the following measurements in terms of an SI base unit.

a. 4.12 cm   b. 947 ms   c. 3.17 nm

Solution

a. Our goal is to find the power of ten that relates the given unit to the SI base unit. That is, centi (base unit) = $10^{-2} \times$ (base unit)

$$4.12 \text{ cm} = 4.12 \text{ centimeter} = 4.12 \times 10^{-2} \text{ m}$$

b. To change millisecond (ms) to the base unit second, we replace the prefix *milli-* by 10^{-3}. To obtain an answer in conventional scientific notation, we also need to replace the coefficient 947 by 9.47×10^2. The result of these two changes is

$$9.47 \text{ ms} = 9.47 \times 10^{-3}\text{s} = 9.47 \times 10^2 \times 10^{-3}\text{s} = 9.47 \times 10^{-1}\text{s}$$

c. To change nanometer (nm) to the base unit meter, we replace the prefix *nano-* by 10^{-9}. The answer in exponential form is 3.17×10^{-9} m.

Table 6 Approved Numerical Prefixes[a]

Exponential Expression	Decimal Equivalent	Prefix	Pronounced	Symbol
10^{12}	1,000,000,000,000	tera-	TER-uh	T
10^{9}	1,000,000,000	giga-	GIG-uh	G
10^{6}	1,000,000	mega-	MEG-uh	M
10^{3}	1,000	kilo-	KIL-oh	k
10^{2}	100	hecto-	HEK-toe	h
10^{1}	10	deka-	DEK-uh	da
10^{-1}	0.1	deci-	DES-ee	d
10^{-2}	0.01	centi-	SEN-tee	c
10^{-3}	0.001	milli-	MIL-ee	m
10^{-6}	0.000001	micro-	MY-kro	μ
10^{-9}	0.000000001	nano-	NAN-oh	n
10^{-12}	0.000000000001	pico-	PEE-koh	p
10^{-15}	0.000000000000001	femto-	FEM-toe	f

[a]The most commonly used prefixes are shown in color.

■ EXERCISE 6

Use scientific notation to express each of the following measurements in terms of an SI base unit.

a. 7.45 nm   **b.** 5.25 μs   **c.** 1.415 km

d. 2.06 mm   **e.** 6.19×10^{6} mm

Mass

The SI base unit for mass is the **kilogram (kg)**, about 2.2 pounds (lb). This base unit is unusual in that it already has a prefix. A more convenient mass unit for most laboratory work is the gram (g).

$$1 \text{ kg} = 10^{3} \text{ g} = 1000 \text{ g} \quad \text{or} \quad 1 \text{ g} = 0.001 \text{ kg} = 10^{-3} \text{ kg}$$

The milligram (mg) is a suitable unit for small quantities of materials, such as some drug dosages.

$$1 \text{ mg} = 10^{-3} \text{ g} = 0.001 \text{ g}$$

Chemists can now detect masses in the microgram (μg), nanogram (ng), picogram (pg), and even smaller ranges.

Length, Area, and Volume

The SI base unit of length is the **meter (m)**, a unit about 10% longer than 1 yard (yd). The kilometer (km) is used to measure distances along highways.

$$1 \text{ km} = 1000 \text{ m}$$

In the laboratory, we usually find lengths smaller than the meter to be more convenient. For example, we use the centimeter (cm), which is about the width of a typical calculator button, or the millimeter (mm), which is about the thickness of the cardboard backing in a notepad.

$$1 \text{ cm} = 0.01 \text{ m} \quad 1 \text{ mm} = 0.001 \text{ m}$$

For measurements at the atomic and molecular level, we use the micrometer (μm), the nanometer (nm), and the picometer (pm). For example, a hemoglobin molecule, which is nearly spherical, has a diameter of 5.5 nm or 5500 pm, and the diameter of a sodium atom is 372 pm.

The units for area and volume are derived from the base unit of length. The SI unit of area is the square meter (m^2), but we often find square centimeters (cm^2) or square millimeters (mm^2) to be more convenient for laboratory work.

$$1\ cm^2 = (10^{-2}\ m)^2 = 10^{-4}\ m^2 \qquad 1\ mm^2 = (10^{-3}\ m)^2 = 10^{-6}\ m^2$$

Similarly, the SI unit of volume is the cubic meter (m^3), but two units more likely to be used in the laboratory are the cubic centimeter (cm^3 or cc) and the cubic decimeter (dm^3). A cubic centimeter is about the volume of a sugar cube, and a cubic decimeter is slightly larger than 1 quart (qt).

$$1\ cm^3 = (10^{-2}\ m)^3 = 10^{-6}\ m^3 \qquad 1\ dm^3 = (10^{-1}\ m)^3 = 10^{-3}\ m^3$$

The cubic decimeter is commonly called a liter. A **liter (L)** is 1 cubic decimeter or 1000 cubic centimeters.

$$1\ L = 1\ dm^3 = 1000\ cm^3$$

The milliliter (mL) or cubic centimeter is frequently used in laboratories. A milliliter is about one "squirt" from a medicine dropper.

$$1\ mL = 1\ cm^3$$

Time

The SI base unit for measuring intervals of time is the second (s). Extremely short time periods are expressed using SI prefixes: millisecond (ms), microsecond (μs), nanosecond (ns), and picosecond (ps).

$$1\ ms = 10^{-3}\ s \qquad 1\ \mu s = 10^{-6}\ s \qquad 1\ ns = 10^{-9}\ s \qquad 1\ ps = 10^{-12}\ s$$

Long time intervals, in contrast, are usually expressed in traditional, non-SI units: minute (min), hour (h), day (d), and year (y).

$$1\ min = 60\ s \qquad 1\ h = 60\ min \qquad 1\ d = 24\ h \qquad 1\ y = 365\ d$$

Problem Solving: Estimation

Many chemistry problems require calculations that yield numerical answers. When you use a calculator, it will always give you an answer—but the answer may not be correct. You may have punched a wrong number or used the wrong function. You can learn to estimate answers so you can tell whether your calculated answers are reasonable. At times an estimated answer is good enough, as the following Example and Exercises illustrate. This ability to estimate answers can be important in everyday life as well as in a chemistry course. Note that estimation does *not* require a detailed calculation. Only a rough calculation—or none at all—is required.

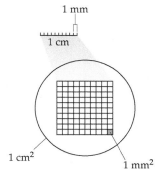

▲ Units of area such as mm^2 and cm^2 are derived from units of length.

Q: *How many mm are in 1 cm? How many mm^2 are in 1 cm^2?*

Example 7   Mass, Length, Area, Volume

Without doing detailed calculations, determine which of the following is a reasonable **(a)** mass (weight) and **(b)** height for a typical two-year-old child.

Mass: 10 mg   10 g   10 kg   100 g
Height: 85 mm   85 cm   850 cm   8.5 m

Solution

a. In customary units, a two-year-old child should weigh about 20–25 lb. Since 1 kg is a little more than 2 lb, the only reasonable answer is 10 kg.

b. In customary units, a two-year-old child should be about 30–36 in. tall. Since 1 cm is a little less than 0.5 in., the answer must be a little more than twice that range, or a bit over 60–72 cm. Thus the only reasonable answer is 85 cm.

■ EXERCISE 7A

Without doing a detailed calculation, determine which of the following is a reasonable area for the front cover of your textbook.

$$500 \text{ mm}^2 \qquad 50 \text{ cm}^2 \qquad 500 \text{ cm}^2 \qquad 50 \text{ m}^2$$

■ EXERCISE 7B

Without doing a detailed calculation, determine which of the following is a reasonable volume for your textbook.

$$1600 \text{ mm}^3 \qquad 16 \text{ cm}^3 \qquad 1600 \text{ cm}^3 \qquad 1.6 \text{ m}^3$$

Problem Solving: Unit Conversions

It is easy to convert from one metric unit to another using the *unit conversion* method of problem solving. In the following problems and throughout the text, we will simply carry three digits in most calculations.

Example 8 Unit Conversions

Convert **(a)** 1.83 kg to grams and **(b)** 729 μL to milliliters.

Solution

a. We start with the given quantity, 1.83 kg, and use the equivalence 1 kg = 1000 g to form a conversion factor (see Appendix A.3) that allows us to cancel the unit kg and end with the unit g.

$$1.83 \text{ kg} \times \frac{1000 \text{ g}}{1 \text{ kg}} = 1830 \text{ g}$$

b. Here we start with the given quantity, 729 μL, and use the equivalences 10^6 μL = 1 L and 10^3 mL = 1 L to form conversion factors that allow us to cancel the unit μL and end with the unit mL.

$$729 \text{ μL} \times \frac{1 \text{ L}}{10^6 \text{ μL}} \times \frac{1000 \text{ mL}}{1 \text{ L}} = 0.729 \text{ mL}$$

■ EXERCISE 8

Convert **(a)** 0.755 m to millimeters, **(b)** 205.6 mL to liters, **(c)** 0.206 g to micrograms, and **(d)** 7.38 cm to millimeters.

Self-Assessment Questions

1. The SI unit of length is the
   a. foot **b.** kilometer **c.** pascal **d.** meter

2. The SI unit of mass is the
   a. dram **b.** gram **c.** grain **d.** kilogram

3. The prefix that means 10^{-6} is
   a. centi- **b.** deci- **c.** micro- **d.** milli-

4. A meter is about 10% longer than a(n)
   a. foot **b.** inch **c.** mile **d.** yard

5. One cubic centimeter is equal to one
   a. deciliter **b.** dram **c.** liter **d.** milliliter

6. One quart is slightly less than one
   a. deciliter **b.** kiloliter **c.** liter **d.** milliliter

Nanoworld

For over two centuries, chemists have been able to re-arrange atoms to make molecules, which have dimensions in the *picometer* (10^{-12} m) range. This ability has led to revolutions in the design of drugs, plastics, and many other materials. Over the last several decades, scientists have made vast strides in handling materials with dimensions in the *micrometer* (10^{-6} m) range. The revolution in electronic devices—computers, cell phones, and so on—was spurred by the ability of scientists to produce computer chips by photolithography on a micrometer scale.

Now many scientists focus on *nanotechnology*. The prefix *nano-* means one-billionth (10^{-9}). Nanotechnology bridges the gap between picometer-sized molecules and micrometer-sized electronics. A nanometer-sized object contains just a few hundred to a few thousand atoms or molecules, and such objects often have different properties than large objects of the same substance. For example, bulk gold is yellow, but a ring made up of nanometer-sized gold particles appears red. Carbon in the form of graphite (pencil lead) is quite weak and soft, but carbon nanotubes can be 100 times stronger than steel. Nanotubes, so called because of their size (only one 10,000th the thickness of a human hair) and their shape (hollow tube), have thousands of potential uses but are extremely expensive to make. Scientists can now manipulate matter on every scale, from nanometers to meters, greatly increasing the scope of materials design. We will examine some of the many practical applications of nanotechnology.

7. A rope is 5.775 cm long. What is its length in millimeters?
   a. 0.05775 mm   **b.** 0.5775 mm
   c. 5.775 mm   **d.** 57.75 mm

8. Which of the following has a mass of roughly 1 g?
   a. an ant   **b.** an orange
   c. a peanut   **d.** a watermelon

9. Which of the following has a thickness of roughly 1 cm?
   a. a brick   **b.** a cell phone
   c. a knife blade   **d.** this textbook

10. Which of the following has a volume of roughly 250 mL (0.250 L)?
    a. 1 cup   **b.** 1 gallon
    c. 1 pint   **d.** 1 tablespoon

Answers: 1, d; 2, d; 3, c; 4, d; 5, d; 6, c; 7, d; 8, c; 9, b; 10, a

▲ Molecular view of a carbon nanotube—stronger than steel and more expensive than gold.

10 Density

Learning Objective ⟩ Calculate the density, mass, or volume of an object given the other two quantities.

In everyday life, we might speak of lead as "heavy" or aluminum as "light," but such descriptions are imprecise at best. Scientists use the term *density* to describe this important property. The **density**, *d*, of a substance is the quantity of mass, *m*, per unit of volume, *V*.

$$d = \frac{m}{V}$$

For substances that don't mix, such as oil and water, the concept of density allows us to predict which will float on the other. It isn't just the mass of each material, but the *mass per unit volume*—the density—that determines the result. Density is the property that explains why oil (lower density) floats on water (higher density) in a bottle of Italian salad dressing. Figure 8 shows other examples.

We can rearrange the equation for density to give

$$m = d \times V \qquad \text{and} \qquad V = \frac{m}{d}$$

▲ One cubic centimeter of copper weighs 8.94 g, so the density of copper is 8.94 g/cm^3.

Q: *What is the mass of 2 cm^3 of copper? What is the density of 2 cm^3 of copper?*

25

Table 7	Densities of Some Common Substances at Specified Temperatures	
Substance*	Density	Temperature
Solids		
Copper (Cu)	8.94 g/cm³	25 °C
Gold (Au)	19.3 g/cm³	25 °C
Magnesium (Mg)	1.738 g/cm³	20 °C
Water (ice) (H_2O)	0.917 g/cm³	0 °C
Liquids		
Ethanol (CH_3CH_2OH)	0.789 g/mL	20 °C
Hexane ($CH_3CH_2CH_2CH_2CH_2CH_3$)	0.660 g/mL	20 °C
Mercury (Hg)	13.534 g/mL	25 °C
Urine (a mixture)	1.003–1.030 g/mL	25 °C
Water (H_2O)	0.998 g/mL	0 °C
	1.000 g/mL	4 °C
	0.998 g/mL	20 °C

*Formulas are provided for possible future reference.

▲**Figure 8** At room temperature, the density of water is 1.00 g/mL. A coin sinks in water, but a cork floats on water.

Q: *Is the density of these coins less than, equal to, or greater than 1.00 g/mL? Is the density of the corks less than, equal to, or greater than 1.00 g/mL?*

You can do your own demonstration of a density difference. Make a classic French vinaigrette salad dressing by adding 10 mL of red wine vinegar to 30–40 mL of extra virgin olive oil. Add seasonings such as salt, pepper, oregano, thyme, Dijon mustard, and garlic. Which material, oil or vinegar, forms the top layer? Enjoy!

These equations are useful for calculations. Densities of some common substances are listed in Table 7. They are customarily reported in grams per milliliter (g/mL) for liquids and grams per cubic centimeter (g/cm³) for solids. Values listed in the table are used in some of the following Examples and Exercises and in some of the end-of-chapter problems.

As with problems involving mass, length, area, and volume, it is often sufficient to estimate answers to problems involving densities, for example, in determining relative volumes of materials or whether or not a material will float or sink in water. Such estimation is illustrated in the following Example and Exercises. Note again that estimation does *not* require a detailed calculation.

Example 9   Mass, Volume, and Density

Answer the following without doing detailed calculations. **(a)** Which has the greater volume, a 50.0-g block of copper or a 50.0-g block of gold? **(b)** Which has the greater mass, 225 mL of ethanol or 225 mL of hexane?

Solution

a. From Table 7, we see that the density of gold (19.3 g/cm³) is greater than that of copper (8.94 g/cm³). A block of copper thus has to be larger in volume than a block of gold of the same mass. A 50.0-g block of copper has a greater volume than a 50.0-g block of gold.

b. From Table 7, we see that the density of ethanol (0.789 g/mL) is greater than that of hexane (0.660 g/mL). Because ethanol is more dense (that is, it has more mass in each unit of volume), 225 mL of it has a greater mass than does 225 mL of hexane.

■ EXERCISE 9A
Without doing a detailed calculation, determine which has the greater volume, a 500.0-g block of ice or a 500.0-g block of magnesium.

■ EXERCISE 9B
Wood does not dissolve in water and will float on water if its density is less than that of water. Padauk ($d = 0.86$ g/cm³) and ebony ($d = 1.2$ g/cm³) are tropical woods. Which will float on water and which will sink in water? What will padauk and ebony do in ethyl alcohol?

When we need a numerical answer, we can use the relationship of mass and volume to density to form conversion factors. Then we use the unit conversion method of problem solving.

Example 10   Density from Mass and Volume

What is the density of iron if 156 g of iron occupies a volume of 20.0 cm³?

Solution

The given quantities are

$$m = 156 \text{ g} \quad \text{and} \quad V = 20.0 \text{ cm}^3$$

We use the equation that defines density.

$$d = \frac{m}{V} = \frac{156 \text{ g}}{20.0 \text{ cm}^3} = 7.80 \text{ g/cm}^3$$

■ EXERCISE 10A

What is the density, in grams per milliliter, of a salt solution if 210 mL has a mass of 234 g?

■ EXERCISE 10B

What is the density, in grams per cubic centimeter, of a metal alloy if a cube of it that measures 2.00 cm on an edge has a mass of 94.3 g?

Example 11   Mass from Density and Volume

What is the mass in grams of 1.00 L of gasoline if its density is 0.703 g/mL?

Solution

We can express the given density as a ratio, 0.703 g/1.00 mL, and use it as a conversion factor. We also need the factor 1000 mL/1 L to convert liters to milliliters.

$$m = d \times V = \frac{0.703 \text{ g}}{1 \text{ mL}} \times 1 \text{ L} \times \frac{1000 \text{ mL}}{1 \text{ L}} = 703 \text{ g}$$

■ EXERCISE 11A

What is the mass in grams of 250.0 mL of glycerol, which has a density of 1.264 g/mL at 20 °C?

■ EXERCISE 11B

What is the mass in kilograms of the ethanol that fills a 16-gallon "gas tank"? (1 gallon = 3.78 L; also see Table 7)

Example 12   Volume from Mass and Density

What volume in milliliters is occupied by 461 g of mercury? (See Table 7.)

Solution

Here we can express the inverse of the density as a ratio, 1 mL/13.534 g, and use it as a conversion factor.

$$V = 461 \text{ g} \times \frac{1 \text{ mL}}{13.534 \text{ g}} = 34.1 \text{ mL}$$

■ EXERCISE 12A
What volume in cubic centimeters is occupied by a 25.8-g piece of magnesium? (See Table 7.)

■ EXERCISE 12B
You need 875 g of hexane. Will it fit in a 1.00-L container? (See Table 7.)

Self-Assessment Questions

The density of a wood plank floating on a lake is
a. less than that of air
b. less than that of water
c. more than that of water
d. the same as that of water

2. A pebble and a lead sinker both sink when dropped into a pond. This shows that the two objects
a. are both less dense than water
b. are both more dense than water
c. have different densities
d. have the same density

3. Ice floats on liquid water. A reasonable value for the density of ice is
a. 0.92 g/cm^3
b. 1.08 g/cm^3
c. 1.98 g/cm^3
d. 4.90 g/cm^3

4. A prospector panning for gold swirls a mixture of mud, gravel, and water in a pan. He looks for gold at the bottom because gold
a. dissolves in water and sinks
b. has a high density and sinks
c. is less dense than rocks
d. is repelled by the other minerals

5. Which of the following metals will sink in a pool of mercury (d = 13.534 g/cm^3)?
a. aluminum (d = 2.6 g/cm^3)
b. iron (d = 7.9 g/cm^3)
c. lead (d = 11.34 g/cm^3)
d. uranium (d = 19.5 g/cm^3)

6. If the volume of a rock is 80.0 cm^3 and its mass is 160.0 g, its density is
a. 0.03 g/cm^3
b. 0.50 g/cm^3
c. 2.0 g/cm^3
d. 128 g/cm^3

Answers: 1, b; 2, b; 3, a; 4, b; 5, d; 6, c

11 Energy: Heat and Temperature

Learning Objectives ❯ Distinguish between heat and temperature. ❯ Explain how the temperature scales are related.

The physical and chemical changes that matter undergoes are almost always accompanied by changes in energy. **Energy** is required to make something happen that wouldn't happen by itself. Energy is the ability to change matter, either physically or chemically.

Two important concepts in science that are related, and sometimes confused, are *temperature* and *heat*. When two objects at different temperatures are brought together, heat flows from the warmer to the cooler object until both are at the same temperature. **Heat** is energy on the move, the energy that flows from a warmer object to a cooler one. **Temperature** is a measure of how hot or cold an object is. Temperature tells us the direction in which heat will flow. Heat flows from more energetic (higher-temperature) to less energetic (lower-temperature) atoms or molecules. For example, if you touch a hot test tube, heat will flow from the tube to your hand. If the tube is hot enough, your hand will be burned.

The SI base unit of temperature is the **kelvin (K)**. For laboratory work, we often use the more familiar **Celsius scale**. On this temperature scale, the freezing point of water is 0 degrees Celsius (°C) and the boiling point is 100 °C. The interval between these two reference points is divided into 100 equal parts, each a *degree Celsius*. The Kelvin scale is called an *absolute scale* because its zero point is the coldest temperature possible, or absolute zero. (This fact was determined by theoretical considerations and has been confirmed by experiment.) The zero point on the Kelvin scale, 0 K, is equal to −273.15 °C, which we often round to −273 °C. A kelvin is the same size as a degree Celsius, so the freezing point of water on the Kelvin scale is 273 K. The Kelvin scale has no negative temperatures, and we don't use a degree sign with the K. To convert from degrees Celsius to kelvins, simply add 273.15 to the Celsius temperature.

$$K = °C + 273.15$$

Example 13   Temperature Conversions

Diethyl ether boils at 36 °C. What is the boiling point of this liquid on the Kelvin scale?

Solution

$$K = °C + 273.15$$
$$K = 36 + 273.15 = 309 \text{ K}$$

■ EXERCISE 13A
What is the boiling point of ethanol (78 °C) expressed in kelvins?

■ EXERCISE 13B
At atmospheric pressure, liquid nitrogen boils at −196 °C. Express that temperature in kelvins.

The Fahrenheit temperature scale is widely used in the United States. Figure 9 compares the three temperature scales. Note that on the Fahrenheit scale, there are 180 Fahrenheit degrees between the freezing point and the boiling point of water. On the Celsius scale there are 100 Celsius degrees between these two points. Thus, one Celsius degree equals 1.8 Fahrenheit degrees. Conversions between Fahrenheit and Celsius temperatures use this relationship.

The SI-derived unit of energy is the **joule (J)**, but the **calorie (cal)** is the more familiar unit in everyday life.

$$1 \text{ cal} = 4.184 \text{ J}$$

A calorie is the amount of heat required to raise the temperature of 1 g of water by 1 °C.

The "calorie" used for expressing the energy content of foods is actually a **kilocalorie (kcal)**.

$$1000 \text{ cal} = 1 \text{ kcal} = 4184 \text{ J}$$

A dieter might be aware that a banana split contains 1500 "calories." If the dieter realized that this was really 1500 *kilo*calories, or 1,500,000 calories, giving up the banana split might be easier!

◀ **Figure 9** A comparison of the Fahrenheit, Celsius, and Kelvin temperature scales.

29

▶ **Figure 10** Temperature and heat are different phenomena. Both the tub and the pool are at roughly the same temperature—about 40 °C—but it took much more heat to warm the pool to that temperature than it did the tub of water.

Example 14   Energy Conversions

When 1.00 g of gasoline burns, it yields about 10.3 kcal of energy. What is this quantity of energy in kilojoules (kJ)?

Solution

$$10.3 \ \text{kcal} \times \frac{1000 \ \text{cal}}{1 \ \text{kcal}} \times \frac{4.184 \ \text{J}}{1 \ \text{cal}} \times \frac{1 \ \text{kJ}}{1000 \ \text{J}} = 43.1 \ \text{kJ}$$

■ **EXERCISE 14A**

Each day the average European woman consumes food with an energy content of 7525 kJ. What is this daily intake in kilocalories (food calories)?

■ **EXERCISE 14B**

It takes about 12 kJ of energy to melt a single ice cube. How much energy in kilocalories does it take to melt a tray of 12 ice cubes?

Self-Assessment Questions

1. Heat is
   a. an element
   b. the energy flow from a hot object to a cold one
   c. a measure of energy intensity
   d. a temperature above room temperature

2. The SI scale for temperature is known as the
   a. Celsius scale   **b.** Fahrenheit scale   **c.** Kelvin scale   **d.** Richter scale

3. Water freezes at
   a. 0 °C   **b.** 0 °F   **c.** 273 °C   **d.** 373 K

4. To convert a temperature on the Kelvin scale to degrees Celsius, we
   a. add 100   **b.** add 273   **c.** subtract 100   **d.** subtract 273

5. The SI unit of energy is the
   a. ampere   **b.** joule   **c.** newton   **d.** watt

Answers: 1, b; 2, c; 3, a; 4, d; 5, b

Normal Body Temperature

Carl Wunderlich (1815–1877), a German physician, first recognized that fever is a symptom of disease. He recorded thousands of temperature measurements from healthy people and reported the average value as 37 °C. When this value was converted to the Fahrenheit scale, it somehow (improperly) acquired an extra significant figure, and 98.6 °F became widely (and incorrectly) known as the *normal body temperature*. In recent years, millions of measurements have revealed that *average* normal body temperature is actually 98.2 °F and that body temperatures in healthy people range from 97.7 °F to 99.5 °F.

GREEN CHEMISTRY

Jennifer L. Young and Robert Peoples, *ACS Green Chemistry Institute®*

Green chemistry is the design of chemical products and processes that reduce or eliminate the generation and use of hazardous substances. To put this definition into practice, chemists follow the twelve principles of green chemistry, which are listed in the inside front cover. Overall, green chemistry is about preventing waste, using nonhazardous chemicals, conserving energy, using renewable resources, and making products that degrade after use. The goal of green chemistry is to minimize the harmful impacts of substances on human health and the environment by using safer alternatives. As you will learn in this chapter, green chemistry applies to all chemistry areas and concepts, and pervades all types of chemistry.

Green chemistry was developed about 20 years ago as a new, holistic way of thinking about chemicals and chemistry—considering the sources of chemicals, where they will end up, and what impact they will have on human beings and the planet. The proven twelve principles are in commercial practice around the world, and a growing number of products on store shelves have been made by green chemistry.

Green chemistry is as rigorous as traditional chemistry. The scientific method involving hypotheses, laws, theories, and models (Section 3) still applies in green chemistry. Because some concepts of green chemistry are still relatively new, especially compared to other chemistry ideas that have been around for centuries, many students and even professional chemists are learning about green chemistry for the first time. Green chemistry is a hard science and a new science that will be critical for developing future technologies that are safe for people and the planet.

This chapter discusses the risk associated with science (Section 5). Risk includes both hazard and exposure; reducing either one reduces risk. Protective equipment and other safety measures can prevent exposure of workers, the public, and the environment to hazardous chemicals. However, there is always a possibility that the protection will fail (because of human error or acts of nature), causing exposure to the materials. Green chemistry, on the other hand, aims to dramatically reduce risk by using chemicals that are inherently safer and less hazardous. When selecting chemicals to use in a product or process, chemists consider the physical and chemical properties (Section 7). Green chemists also evaluate other properties, including toxicity toward human beings and degradability in the environment.

The world faces a growing number of environmental problems, some of which have been caused by chemicals. However, green chemistry can provide solutions and minimize future problems by avoiding hazardous materials and preventing pollution. You will read about many green chemistry technologies and solutions throughout this text. This chapter contains a green chemistry essay that presents some of the latest technologies in areas such as biofuels, plastics, medicine, and food.

Many companies are using green chemistry to design new products and processes. Companies that make or use chemicals are choosing to use less energy, create less waste, and select chemicals and solvents that are less hazardous. They are making these decisions based on green chemistry, not only because it's the right thing to do but also because these actions save money and make good business sense. Between 1996 and 2011, 82 professors, small businesses, and large companies were presented with the Presidential Green Chemistry Challenge Award (PGCCA). These awards have recognized advances in pest control, plastics, medicines, fuel, paints, electronics, textiles, cosmetics, cleaning products, and a wide range of other areas that depend on chemistry. Several of the award-winning technologies are featured throughout this text.

The future of this planet and its growing number of inhabitants will all depend on clean energy, water, air, food, medicine, and technology. You can contribute to sustainability through the products you purchase, recycling, conserving energy, and even through your career choices. Green chemistry is essential to a sustainable future!

Dmitrijs Bindemanis/Shutterstock

▲ Natular™ is a greener mosquito larvicide, developed by Clarke, for which the company won a 2010 PGCCA. Mosquitoes are much more than a summer annoyance; they spread malaria, yellow fever, and other diseases, and their control is a huge issue worldwide. Natular™ is a new, environmentally more responsible weapon in this control.

12 Critical Thinking

Learning Objective   ⟩ Use critical thinking to evaluate claims and statements.

One of the hallmarks of science is the ability to think critically—to evaluate statements and claims in a rational, objective fashion. For example, a diet-plan advertisement shows people who have lost a lot of weight. Somewhere in the ad, in tiny print, you may find a statement such as "results may vary" or "results not typical." Such ads also often advise combining the plan with diet and exercise. Does an ad like this prove that a diet plan works? You can use critical thinking to evaluate the ad's claim. Critical thinking involves gathering facts, assessing them, using logic to reach a conclusion, and then evaluating the conclusion. The ability to think critically can be learned, and it will serve you well in everyday life as well as in science courses. Critical thinking is important for workers in all types of professions and employees in all kinds of industries. We will use an approach adapted from one developed by James Lett.[1] This approach is outlined below and followed by several examples.

You can use the acronym **FLaReS** (ignore the vowels) to remember four principles used to test a claim: *f*alsifiability, *l*ogic, *r*eplicability, and *s*ufficiency.

- **Falsifiability:** Can any conceivable evidence show the claim to be false? It must be possible to think of evidence that would prove the claim false. A hypothesis that cannot be falsified is of no value. Science cannot prove anything true in an absolute sense, although it can provide overwhelming evidence. Science *can* prove something false.

- **Logic:** Any argument offered as evidence in support of a claim must be sound. An argument is sound if its conclusion follows inevitably from its premises and if its premises are true. It is unsound if a premise is false, and it is unsound if there is a single exception in which the conclusion does not necessarily follow from the premises.

- **Replicability:** If the evidence for a claim is based on an experimental result, it is necessary that the evidence be replicable in subsequent experiments or trials. Scientific research is almost always reviewed by other qualified scientists. The peer-reviewed research is then published in a form that enables others to repeat the experiment. Sometimes bad science slips through the peer-review process, but such results eventually fail the test of replicability. For example, in May 2005 the journal *Science* published research by Korean biomedical scientist Hwang Woo-suk in which he claimed to have tailored embryonic stem cells so that every patient could receive custom treatment. Others were unable to reproduce Hwang's findings, and evidence emerged that he had intentionally fabricated results. *Science* retracted the article in January 2006. Research results published in media that are not peer reviewed have little or no standing in the scientific community—nor should you rely on them.

- **Sufficiency:** The evidence offered in support of a claim must be adequate to establish the truth of that claim, with these stipulations: (1) The burden of evidence for any claim rests on the claimant, (2) extraordinary claims demand extraordinary evidence, and (3) evidence based on an authority figure or on testimony is never adequate.

If a claim passes all four FLaReS tests, then it *might* be true. On the other hand, it could still be proven false. However, if a claim fails even one of the FLaReS tests, it is likely to be false. The FLaReS method is a good starting point for evaluating the myriad claims that you will find on the Internet and elsewhere. We apply one or more of the FLaReS principles to evaluate a claim in each of the following examples.

[1] Lett used the acronym FiLCHeRS (ignore the vowels) as a mnemonic for six rules: *f*alsifiability, *l*ogic, *c*omprehensiveness, *h*onesty, *r*eplicability, and *s*ufficiency. See Lett, James, "A Field Guide to Critical Thinking," *The Skeptical Inquirer*, Winter 1990, pp. 153–160.

Lett, James, "A Field Guide to Critical Thinking" from THE SKEPTICAL INQUIRER, Winter 1990.

CRITICAL THINKING EXAMPLES

1 A practitioner claims outstanding success in curing cancer with a vaccine made from a patient's own urine. However, the vaccine works only if the patient's immune system is still sufficiently strong. Is the claim falsifiable?

Solution

No. The practitioner can always say that the patient's immune system was no longer sufficiently strong.

2 A website claims, "The medical-industrial complex suppresses natural treatments because they cure the patient. A cured patient no longer needs a doctor, and the doctor loses income." Is the claim logical?

Solution

No. Doctors do not cure all patients. Many remain ill and some die.

3 Many "psychics" claim to be able to predict the future. These predictions are often made near the end of one year and concern the next year. Apply all the FLaReS tests to evaluate this claim.

Solution

1. Is the claim falsifiable? Yes. You could write down a prediction and then check it yourself at the end of the year.

2. Is the claim logical? No. If psychics could really predict the future, they could readily win lotteries, ward off all kinds of calamities by providing advance warning, and so on.

3. Is the claim reproducible? No. Psychics often make broad, general predictions, such as "tornadoes will hit Oklahoma in April and May." (It would be a rare year when there were no tornadoes in Oklahoma in those months.) The psychics later make claim-specific references to "hits" while ignoring "misses." Here are some past predictions of Sylvia Browne, a self-proclaimed world-famous psychic: Bill Bradley would be elected U.S. president in 2000; Michael Jackson would be found guilty in his 2005 child molestation trial (he was acquitted); a cure for breast cancer would be found by the end of 1999. None of the well-known psychics, including Browne, James Van Praagh, John Edward, and the Jamison sisters (Terry and Linda), predicted the terrorist attacks on the United States on September 11, 2001.

4. Is the claim sufficient? No. Any such claim is extraordinary; it would require extraordinary evidence. The burden of proof for the claim rests on the claimant.

CRITICAL THINKING EXERCISES

Apply knowledge that you have gained in this chapter and one or more of the FLaReS principles to evaluate the following statements or claims.

1 An alternative health practitioner claims that a nuclear power plant releases radiation at a level so low that it cannot be measured, but that this radiation is harmful to the thyroid gland. He sells a thyroid extract that he claims can prevent the problem.

2 A doctor claims that she can cure a patient of arthritis by simply massaging the affected joints. If she has the patient's complete trust, she can cure the arthritis within a year. Several of her patients have testified that the doctor has cured their arthritis.

3 German physicist Jan Hendrik Schön of Bell Labs claimed in 2001 that he had produced a molecular scale transistor. Other scientists noted that his data contained irregularities. Attempts to perform experiments similar to Schön's did not give similar results.

4 A mercury-containing preservative called thiomersal was used to prevent bacterial and fungal contamination in vaccines from the 1930s until its use was phased out starting in 1999. In the United States, a widespread concern arose that these vaccines caused autism. There was no such concern in the United Kingdom, although the vaccine with the same preservative was used there. Is the concern valid?

5 A woman claims that she has memorized the New Testament. She offers to quote any chapter of any book entirely from memory.

6 The label on a bag of Morton solar salt crystals has the statement "No chemicals or additives."

SUMMARY

Section 1—Technology is the practical application of knowledge, while science is an accumulation of knowledge about nature and our physical world along with our explanations of that knowledge. The roots of chemistry lie in natural philosophy, philosophical speculation about nature, and in alchemy, a mixture of chemistry and magic practiced in Europe in the Middle Ages.

Section 2—Green chemistry uses materials and processes that are intended to prevent or reduce pollution at its source. Sustainable chemistry is designed to meet the needs of the present generation without compromising the needs of future generations.

Section 3—Science is *reproducible, testable, predictive, explanatory,* and *tentative.* In one common scientific method, a set of confirmed observations about nature may lead to a hypothesis—a tentative explanation of the observations. A scientific law is a brief statement that summarizes large amounts of data. If a hypothesis stands up to testing and further experimentation, it may become a theory—the best current explanation for a phenomenon. A theory is always tentative and can be rejected if it does not continue to stand up to further testing. A valid theory can be used to predict new scientific facts. Scientists disagree over social and political issues partly because of the inability to control variables, factors that can change during an experiment.

Section 4—Science and technology have provided many benefits for our world, but they have also introduced new risks. A risk–benefit analysis can help us decide which outweighs the other.

Section 5—Chemistry is fundamental to other scientific disciplines and plays a central role in society and daily life.

Section 6—Most chemists are involved in some kind of research. The purpose of applied research is to make useful products or to solve a particular problem, while basic research is carried out simply to obtain new knowledge or to answer a fundamental question. Basic research often also leads to a useful product or process.

Section 7—Chemistry is the study of matter and the changes it undergoes. Matter is anything that has mass and takes up space. Mass is a measure of the amount of matter in an object, while weight represents the gravitational force of attraction for an object. Physical properties of matter can be observed without making new substances. When chemical properties are observed, new substances are formed. A physical change does not entail a change in chemical composition. A chemical change does involve such a change.

Section 8—Matter can be classified according to physical state. A solid has definite shape and volume. A liquid has defi-nite volume but takes the shape of its container. A gas takes both the shape and the volume of its container. Matter also can be classified according to composition. A substance always has the same composition, no matter how it is made or where it is found. A mixture can have different compositions depending on how it is prepared. Substances are either elements or compounds. An element is composed of atoms of one type, an atom being the smallest characteristic particle of an element. There are over a hundred elements, each of which is represented by a chemical symbol consisting of one or two letters derived from the element's name. A compound is made up of two or more elements, chemically combined in a fixed ratio. Most compounds exist as molecules, groups of atoms bound together as a unit.

Section 9—Scientific measurements are expressed with SI units, which comprise an agreed-on standard version of the metric system. Base units include the kilogram (kg) for mass and the meter (m) for length. Although it is not the SI standard unit of volume, the liter (L) is widely used. Prefixes make basic units larger or smaller by factors of ten.

Section 10—Density can be thought of as "how heavy something is for its size." It is the amount of mass per unit volume.

$$d = \frac{m}{V}$$

Density can be used as a conversion factor. The density of water is almost exactly 1 g/mL.

Section 11—When matter undergoes a physical or chemical change, a change in energy is involved. Energy is the *ability* to cause these changes. Heat is energy flow from a warmer object to a cooler one. Temperature is a measure of how hot or cold an object is. The kelvin (K) is the SI base unit of temperature, but the Celsius scale (°C) is more commonly used. On the Celsius scale, water boils at 100 °C and freezes at 0 °C. The SI unit of heat is the joule (J). A more familiar unit, the calorie (cal), is the amount of heat needed to raise the temperature of 1 g of water by 1 °C. The food "calorie" is actually a kilocalorie (kcal), or 1000 calories.

Section 12—Claims may be tested by applying critical thinking. The acronym FLaReS represents four principles used to test a claim: *f*alsifiability, *l*ogic, *r*eplicability, and *s*ufficiency.

Green chemistry Green chemistry means preventing waste, using nonhazardous chemicals and renewable resources, conserving energy, and making products that degrade after use. Developed about 20 years ago, green chemistry takes into account the sources and ultimate destinations of chemicals, and the impact they will have on humans and the planet.

Learning Objectives

> Distinguish science from technology. (1)	Problem 1
> Define *alchemy* and *natural philosophy.* (1)	Problems 43, 44
> Briefly describe the contributions of Bacon, Galileo, and Carson to the perceptions of science. (2)	Problem 2
> Define *hypothesis, scientific law, theory,* and *scientific model,* and explain their relationships in science. (3)	Problems 3, 71, 72, 74, 75

REVIEW QUESTIONS

1. State five distinguishing characteristics of science. Which characteristic best serves to distinguish science from other disciplines?

2. Why is Galileo regarded by some as the father of modern science?

3. Why can't scientific methods always be used to solve social, political, ethical, and economic problems?

4. How does technology differ from science?

5. What is risk–benefit analysis?

6. What sorts of judgments go into (a) the evaluation of benefits and (b) the evaluation of risks?

7. What is a DQ? What does a large DQ mean? Why is it often difficult to estimate a DQ?

8. What derived units of (a) mass and (b) length are commonly used in the laboratory?

9. What is the SI-derived unit for volume? What volume units are more often used in the laboratory?

10. Following is an incomplete table of SI prefixes, their symbols, and their meanings. Fill in the blank cells. The first row is completed as an example.

11. Identify the following research projects as either applied or basic.
    a. A Virginia Tech chemist tests a method for analyzing coal powder in less than a minute, before the powder goes into a coal-fired energy plant.
    b. A Purdue engineer develops a method for causing aluminum to react with water to generate hydrogen for automobiles.
    c. A worker at University of Illinois Urbana-Champaign examines the behavior of atoms at high temperatures and low pressures.

12. Identify the following work as either applied research or basic research.
    a. An engineer determines the strength of a titanium alloy that will be used to construct notebook-computer cases.
    b. A biochemist runs experiments to determine how oxygen binds to the blood cells of lobsters.
    c. A biologist determines the number of eagles that nest annually in Kentucky's Land Between the Lakes area over a six-year period.

Prefix	Symbol	Definition
tera-	T	10^{12}
_____	M	_____
centi-	_____	_____
_____	μ	_____
milli-	_____	_____
_____	_____	10^{-1}
_____	K	_____
nano-	_____	_____

PROBLEMS

A Word of Advice You cannot learn to work problems by reading them or by watching your instructor work them, just as you cannot become a piano player solely by reading about piano-playing skills or by attending performances. Working problems will help you improve your understanding of the ideas presented in the chapter and your ability to synthesize concepts as well as allow you to practice your estimation skills. Plan to work through the great majority of these problems.

Risk–Benefit Analysis

13. Penicillin kills bacteria, thus saving the lives of thousands of people who otherwise might die of infectious diseases. Penicillin causes allergic reactions in some people, which can lead to death if the resulting condition is not treated. Do a risk–benefit analysis of the use of penicillin by society as a whole.

14. Do a risk–benefit analysis of the use of penicillin by a person who is allergic to it. (See Problem 13.)

15. Paints used on today's automobiles are often composed of two components and harden several hours after mixing. One component is an *isocyanate* that can sensitize a person, causing an allergic reaction, if it is breathed (even in small amounts) over a long time period. Do a risk-benefit analysis of the use of these paints by **(a)** an automotive factory worker and **(b)** a hobbyist who is restoring a 1965 Mustang. How might the DQ for both of these people be increased?

16. X-rays are widely used in medicine and dentistry. Do a risk-benefit analysis for **(a)** a dental patient who has one set of x-rays done per year and **(b)** a dentist who stays in the room with a patient while x-rays are taken, three times each day.

17. Synthetic food colorings make food more attractive and increase sales. A few such dyes are suspected *carcinogens* (cancer inducers). Who derives most of the benefits from the use of food colorings? Who assumes most of the risk associated with use of these dyes?

18. The virus called HIV causes AIDS, a devastating and often deadly disease. Several drugs are available to treat HIV infection, but all are expensive. Used separately and in combination, these drugs have resulted in a huge drop in AIDS deaths. An expensive new drug shows promise for treating HIV/AIDS patients, especially in preventing passage of the HIV virus from a pregnant woman to her fetus. What is the DQ for administering this drug to **(a)** a man who thinks he may be infected with HIV, **(b)** a pregnant woman who is HIV positive, and **(c)** an unborn child whose mother has AIDS?

Mass and Weight

19. Which are realistic masses for a cellular telephone and a laptop computer, respectively?

    100 mg, 100 g   100 g, 100 mg   100 g, 2 kg   1 kg, 2 kg

20. In Europe, A2 sized paper measures 594 mm × 420 mm. Is this larger or smaller than the standard 8½ in. × 11 in. paper used in the United States?

21. Two samples are weighed under identical conditions in a laboratory. Sample A weighs 1.00 lb and Sample B weighs 2.00 lb. Does Sample B have twice the mass of Sample A?

22. Sample X on the moon has exactly the same mass as Sample Y on Earth. Do the two samples weigh the same? Explain.

Length, Area, and Volume

23. Which of the following is a reasonable volume for a teacup?

    25 mL   250 mL   2.5 L   25 L

24. Which of the following is a reasonable approximation for the area of a credit card?

    $4 \, cm^2$ $40 \, cm^2$ $400 \, cm^2$ $4 \, m^2$

25. Earth's oceans contain $3.50 \times 10^8 \, mi^3$ of water and cover an area of $1.40 \times 10^8 \, mi^2$. What is the volume of ocean water in cubic kilometers?

26. What is the area of Earth's oceans in square kilometers? See Problem 25.

27. Consider the two tubes shown below. The aluminum tube has an outside diameter of 0.998 in. and an inside diameter of 0.782 in. Without doing a detailed calculation, determine whether the aluminum tube will fit inside another aluminum tube with an inside diameter of 26.3 mm.

Terry McCreary

28. Which one(s) of the following could be the inside diameter of the paper tube shown above (with Problem 27): 19.9 mm; 24.9 mm, 18.7 mm?

Physical and Chemical Properties and Changes

29. Identify the following as physical or chemical properties.
    a. Zinc metal can be shaped into many different forms by hammering.
    b. Silver metal tarnishes, forming black silver sulfide.
    c. Sodium metal is soft enough to cut with a butter knife.
    d. Gold melts at 1064 °C.

30. Identify the following as physical or chemical properties.
    a. Milk chocolate melts in the mouth.
    b. A laser printer prints faster than an inkjet printer.
    c. Titanium chips burn with a brilliant white light.
    d. Yogurt is made by allowing a bacterial culture to ferment in warm milk.

31. Identify the following changes as physical or chemical.
    a. Bits of yellow plastic are melted and forced into a mold to make a yellow toy.
    b. Waste oil from restaurants is converted to biodiesel fuel that burns differently from cooking oil.
    c. Orange juice is prepared by adding three cans of water to one can of orange-juice concentrate.

32. Identify the following changes as physical or chemical.
    a. Bacteria are killed by chlorine added to a swimming pool.
    b. Brown print is created in an inkjet printer by mixing cyan, magenta, and yellow inks.
    c. Sugar is dissolved in water to make syrup.

Substances and Mixtures

33. Identify each of the following as a substance or a mixture.
    a. helium gas used to fill a balloon
    b. the juice squeezed from an orange
    c. distilled water
    d. carbon dioxide gas

34. Identify each of the following as a substance or a mixture.
    a. hydrogen peroxide, H_2O_2
    b. oxygen
    c. smog
    d. a carrot
    e. blueberry pancakes
    f. cellophane tape

35. Which of the following mixtures are homogeneous and which are heterogeneous?
    a. copper water pipe   b. distilled water
    c. liquid oxygen   d. chicken noodle soup

36. Which of the following mixtures are homogeneous and which are heterogeneous?
    a. gasoline
    b. Italian salad dressing
    c. rice pudding
    d. an intravenous glucose solution

37. Every sample of the sugar glucose (no matter where on Earth it comes from) consists of 8 parts (by mass) oxygen, 6 parts carbon, and 1 part hydrogen. Is glucose a substance or a mixture? Explain.

38. An advertisement for shampoo says, "Pure shampoo, with nothing artificial added." Is this shampoo a substance or a mixture? Explain.

Elements and Compounds

39. Which of the following represent elements and which represent compounds?
    a. H   b. He   c. HF   d. Hf

40. Which of the following represent elements and which represent compounds?
    a. Li   b. CO   c. Cf   d. CF_4

41. Without consulting tables, name each of the following.
    a. Al   b. Ca   c. Cl   d. Ag

42. Without consulting tables, write a symbol for each of the following.
    a. oxygen   b. phosphorus
    c. sodium   d. helium

43. In his 1789 textbook, *Traité élémentaire de Chimie*, Antoine Lavoisier listed 33 known elements, one of which was baryte. Which of the following observations best shows that baryte cannot be an element?
    a. Baryte is insoluble in water.
    b. Baryte melts at 1580 °C.
    c. Baryte has a density of 4.48 g/cm³.
    d. Baryte is formed in hydrothermal veins and around hot springs.
    e. Baryte is formed as a solid when sulfuric acid and barium hydroxide are mixed.
    f. Baryte is formed as a sole product when a particular metal is burned in oxygen.

44. In 1774 Joseph Priestley isolated a gas that he called "dephlogisticated air." Which of the following observations best shows that dephlogisticated air is an element?
    a. Dephlogisticated air combines with charcoal to form "fixed air."
    b. Dephlogisticated air combines with "inflammable air" to form water.
    c. Dephlogisticated air combines with a metal to form a solid called a "calx."
    d. Dephlogisticated air has never been separated into simpler substances.
    e. Dephlogisticated air and "mephitic air" are the main components of the atmosphere.

The Metric System: Measurement and Unit Conversion

45. Change the unit for each of the following measurements by replacing the power of ten with an appropriate SI prefix.
    a. 8.01×10^{-6} g   b. 7.9×10^{-3} L
    c. 1.05×10^3 m

46. Use exponential notation to express each of the following measurements in terms of an SI base unit.
    a. 45 mg   b. 125 ns   c. 10.7 μL

47. Carry out the following conversions.
    a. 37.4 mL to L   b. 1.55×10^2 km to m
    c. 0.198 g to mg   d. 1.19 m² to cm²
    e. 78 μs to ms

48. Carry out the following conversions.
    a. 546 mm to m
    b. 65 ns to μs
    c. 87.6 mg to kg
    d. 46.3 dm³ to L
    e. 181 pm to μm

49. Indicate which is the larger unit in each pair.
    a. mm or cm   b. kg or g   c. dL or μL

50. Indicate which is the larger unit in each pair.
    a. L or cm³   b. dm³ or mL   c. μs or ps

51. How many millimeters are there in 1.00 cm? In 1.83 m?

52. How many milliliters are there in 1.00 cm^3? In 15.3 cm^3?

Density

(You may need data from Table 7 for some of these problems.)

53. What is the density, in grams per milliliter, of **(a)** a salt solution if 37.5 mL has a mass of 43.75 g and **(b)** 2.75 L of the liquid glycerol, which has a mass of 3465 g?

54. What is the density, in grams per milliliter, of **(a)** a sulfuric acid solution if 10.00 mL has a mass of 15.04 g and **(b)** a 10.0-cm^3 block of plastic with a mass of 9.23 g?

55. What is the mass, in grams, of **(a)** 125 mL of castor oil, a laxative, which has a density of 0.962 g/mL and **(b)** 477 mL of blood plasma, with $d = 1.027$ g/mL?

56. What is the mass, in grams, of **(a)** 30.0 mL of the liquid propylene glycol, a moisturizing agent for foods, which has a density of 1.036 g/mL at 25 °C and **(b)** 1.000 L of mercury at 25 °C?

57. What is the volume of **(a)** 227 g of hexane (in milliliters) and **(b)** a 454-g block of ice (in cubic centimeters)?

58. What is the volume of **(a)** a 475-g piece of copper (in cubic centimeters) and **(b)** a 253-g sample of mercury (in milliliters)?

59. Suppose you put 40 mL of mercury, 40 mL of hexane, and 80 mL of water in the 250-mL beaker shown here. The three liquids do not mix with one another. Provide a sketch that shows the relative locations and depths of the three liquids in the container.

David Anderson/iStockphoto

60. A piece of red maple wood ($d = 0.49$ g/cm^3), a piece of balsa wood ($d = 0.11$ g/cm^3), a copper coin, a gold coin, and a piece of ice are dropped into the mixture of Problem 59. Where will each solid end up in the beaker?

61. A metal stand specifies a maximum load of 450 lb. Will it support an aquarium that weighs 59.5 lb and is filled with 37.9 L of seawater ($d = 1.03$ g/mL)?

62. E85 fuel is a mixture of 85% ethanol and 15% gasoline by volume. What mass in kilograms of E85 ($d = 0.758$ g/mL) can be contained in a 14.0-gal tank?

63. An artist wants to produce a pot with a mass of 2.45 kg. She starts with wet clay that loses 10.9% of its mass after firing. The wet clay has a density of 1.60 g/cm^3. What should be the diameter of a sphere of wet clay that she starts with? (*Hint:* The volume of a sphere is $4\pi r^3/3$ where r is the radius.)

64. Air has an average density of about 1.29 g/L. What is the mass in grams of the air inside a car that has a volume of about 2550 L?

Energy: Heat and Temperature

65. Convert 195 K to degrees Celsius.

66. Normal body temperature is about 37 °C. What is this temperature in kelvins?

67. The label on a 100-mL container of orange juice packaged in New Zealand reads in part, "energy . . . 161 kJ." What is that value in kilocalories (food "calories")?

68. To vaporize 1.00 g of sweat (water) from your skin, the water must absorb 584 calories. What is that value in kilojoules?

ADDITIONAL PROBLEMS

69. A certain chemistry class is 1.00 microcentury (μcen) long. What is its length in minutes?

70. A unit of beauty, a *helen*, thought to have been invented by British mathematician W.A.H. Rushton, is based on Helen of Troy (from Christopher Marlowe's translation of Homer's *Iliad*), who is widely known as having "the face that launched a thousand ships." How many ships could be launched by a face with 1.00 millihelen of beauty?

71. English chemist William Henry studied the amounts of gases absorbed by water at different temperatures and under different pressures. In 1803, he stated a formula, $p = k_H c$, which related the concentration of the dissolved gas at a constant temperature to the partial pressure of that gas in equilibrium with that liquid. This relationship describes a scientific
    a. hypothesis
    b. law
    c. observation
    d. theory

72. Which of the following activities involve chemistry?
    a. cooking breakfast
    b. eating breakfast
    c. riding a bicycle to classes
    d. working on a laptop computer
    e. sleeping

73. American writer Cullen Murphy coined a unit of fame, the warhol, based on artist Andy Warhol's claim that "everyone will be famous for fifteen minutes."

$$1 \text{ warhol} = 15 \text{ min of fame}$$

Entertainer Herbert Khaury (stage name Tiny Tim) was famous, starting in 1962, for about 200 kilowarhols. How long was that in years?

For Problems 74 and 75, classify each of the numbered statements as (a) an experiment, (b) a hypothesis, (c) a scientific law, (d) an observation, or (e) a theory. (It is not necessary to understand the science involved to do these problems.)

74. Many scientific advances of the nineteenth century came from the study of gases. (1) For example, Joseph Gay-Lussac reacted hydrogen and oxygen to produce water vapor and he reacted nitrogen and oxygen to form either dinitrogen oxide (N_2O) or nitrogen monoxide (NO). Gay-Lussac found that hydrogen and oxygen react in a 2:1 volume ratio and that nitrogen and oxygen can react in 2:1 or 1:1 volume ratios, depending on the product. (2) In 1808 Gay-Lussac published a paper in which he stated that the relative volumes of gases in a chemical reaction are present in the ratio of small integers provided that all gases are measured at the same temperature and pressure. (3) In 1811 Amedeo Avogadro proposed that equal volumes of all gases measured at the same temperature and pressure contain the same number of molecules. (4) By the middle of the century, Rudolf Clausius, James Clerk Maxwell, and others had developed a detailed rationalization of the behavior of gases in terms of molecular motions.

75. Potassium bromate acts as a conditioner in flour dough. Flour contains a protein called *gluten*. Proteins consist of amino-acid units linked in long chains. (1) Dough to which potassium bromate has been added rises better, producing a lighter, larger volume loaf. (2) Potassium bromate acts by oxidizing the gluten and cross-linking tyrosine (an amino acid) units of the protein molecules, enabling the dough to retain gas better. (3) A scientist wonders if sodium bromate might cross-link separate tyrosine molecules, forming a dimer (a molecule consisting of two subunits). (4) She adds sodium bromate to a solution of tyrosine. (5) She notes that a precipitate (solid falling out of solution) is formed.

76. A glass container weighs 48.462 g. A sample of 8.00 mL of antifreeze solution is added, and the container and the antifreeze together weigh 60.562 g. Calculate the density of the antifreeze solution.

77. A rectangular block of balsa wood ($d = 0.11 \text{ g/cm}^3$) measures 7.6 cm × 7.6 cm × 94 cm. What is the mass of the block in grams?

78. Arrange the following in order of increasing length (shortest first): (1) a 1.21-m chain, (2) a 75-in. board, (3) a 3-ft 5-in. rattlesnake, (4) a yardstick.

79. Arrange the following in order of increasing mass (lightest first): (1) a 5-lb bag of potatoes, (2) a 1.65-kg cabbage, (3) 2500 g of sugar.

80. One of the people in the photo has a mass of 47.2 kg and a height of 1.53 m. Which one is it likely to be?

Yana Petruseva/Shutterstock

81. Some metal chips having a volume of 3.29 cm³ are placed on a piece of paper and weighed. The combined mass is found to be 18.43 g. The paper itself weighs 1.21 g. Calculate the density of the metal.

82. A 10.5-inch (26.7-cm) iron skillet has a mass of 7.00 lb (3180 g). How many cubic centimeters of iron does it contain? (See Table 7.)

83. A 5.79-mg piece of gold is hammered into gold leaf of uniform thickness with an area of 44.6 cm². What is the thickness of the gold leaf? (See Table 7.)

84. Suppose that you were assigned to determine the effect of saturated fat intake in mice. List three specific variables that would exist in such an experiment, and suggest a way to minimize each variable.

85. What is the mass, in metric tons, of a cube of gold that is 36.1 cm on each side? (1 metric ton = 1000 kg) (See Table 7.)

86. A collection of gold-colored metal beads has a mass of 425 g. The volume of the beads is found to be 48.0 cm³. Using the given densities and those in Table 7, identify the metal: bronze ($d = 9.87 \text{ g/cm}^3$), copper, gold, or nickel silver ($d = 8.86 \text{ g/cm}^3$).

87. The density of a planet can be approximated from its radius and estimated mass. Calculate the approximate average density, in grams per cubic centimeter, of **(a)** Jupiter, which has a radius of about 7.0×10^4 km and a mass of 1.9×10^{27} kg; **(b)** Earth, radius of 6.4×10^3 km and mass of 5.98×10^{24} kg; and **(c)** Saturn, radius 5.82×10^4 km and mass 5.68×10^{26} kg. The volume of a sphere is $4\pi r^3/3$ where r = radius. How does the density of each planet compare to that of water?

88. The extrasolar planet HAT-P-1 orbits a star 450 light-years from Earth. The planet has about half the mass of Jupiter, and its radius is about 1.38 times that of Jupiter (see Problem 87). Calculate the approximate average density, in grams per cubic centimeter, of HAT-P-1. How does this density compare to that of water?

David A. Aguilar/Harvard-Smithsonian
Center for Astrophysics

89. Define green chemistry.
90. List six of the Twelve Principles of Green Chemistry.
91. How does green chemistry reduce risk? (choose one)
    a. by reducing hazard and exposure
    b. by avoiding the use of chemicals
    c. by increasing exposures to higher levels
    d. by reducing human errors

92. For companies implementing green chemistry, how does green chemistry save money?
    a. by lowering costs
    b. by using less energy
    c. by creating less waste
    d. all of the above

COLLABORATIVE GROUP PROJECTS

Prepare a PowerPoint, poster, or other presentation (as directed by your instructor) to share with the class.

1. The Global University Leadership Forum has developed a Sustainable Campus Charter by which a school's core mission is aligned with sustainable development, facilities, research, and education. Is your school committed to sustainability? If so, in what way is it working toward sustainability? If not, consult with administrative, faculty, and student groups on how to get such a program started.

2. Prepare a brief biographical report on one of the following.
    a. Francis Bacon
    b. Rachel Carson
    c. Galileo
    d. George Washington Carver

(The following problem is best done in a group of four students.)

3. Make copies of the following form. Student 1 should write a word from the list in the first column of the form and its definition in the second column. Then, she or he should fold the first column under to hide the word and pass the sheet to Student 2, who uses the definition to determine what word was defined and place that word in the third column. Student 2 then folds the second column under to hide it and passes the sheet to Student 3, who writes a definition for the word in the third column and then folds the third column under and passes the form to Student 4. Finally, Student 4 writes the word corresponding to the definition given by Student 3.

Compare the word in the last column with that in the first column. Discuss any differences in the two definitions. If the word in the last column differs from that in the first column, determine what went wrong in the process.
    a. hypothesis   b. theory
    c. mixture   d. substance

Text Entry	Student 1	Student 2	Student 3	Student 4
Word	Definition	Word	Definition	Word

BRIEF ANSWERS TO SELECTED PROBLEMS

Answers are provided for *all in-chapter exercises*. Brief answers are given for *odd-numbered Review Questions*; more complete answers can be obtained by reviewing the text. Answers are provided for *all odd-numbered Problems and Additional Problems*.

NOTE: For numerical problems, your answer may differ slightly from ours because of rounding and the use of significant figures.

1 **A. a.** DQ would probably be small.
    b. DQ would probably be large.
   B. a. DQ would be uncertain.
    b. DQ would probably be large.
2 **A. a.** 1.00 kg
    b. 179 lb
3 **A.** physical: a, c; chemical: b
   B. physical: b, d; chemical: a, c
4 **A.** elements: He, No, Os; compounds: CuO, NO, KF
   B. 8
5 **a.** 7.24 kg
   b. 4.29 μm
   c. 7.91 ms
   d. 2.29 cg
   e. 7.90 Mm
6 **a.** 7.45×10^{-9} m
   b. 5.25×10^{-6} s
   c. 1.415×10^{3} m

   d. 2.06×10^{-3} m
   e. 6.19×10^{3} m
7 **A.** 500 cm^2
   B. 1600 cm^3
8 **a.** 7.55×10^{2} mm
   b. 0.2056 L
   c. 2.06×10^{5} μg
   d. 73.8 mm
9 **A.** Ice
   B. Padauk floats, and ebony sinks. Both sink in ethyl alcohol.
10 **A.** 1.11 g/mL
   B. 11.8 g/cm^3
11 **A.** 316 g
   B. 47.7 kg
12 **A.** 14.8 cm^3
   B. No (1.33 L)
13 **A.** 351 K
   B. 77 K
14 **A.** 1799 kcal
   B. 34 kcal
1. Science is testable, reproducible, explanatory, predictive, and tentative. Testability best distinguishes science.
3. These problems usually involve too many variables to be treated by scientific methods.
5. Risk–benefit analysis compares benefits of an action with risks of that action.

7. A desirability quotient (DQ) is benefits divided by risks. A large DQ means that risks are minimal compared with benefits.
9. liter; milliliter
11. **(a)** applied; **(b)** applied; **(c)** basic.
13. Penicillin has saved thousands of lives, causing harm to a very few. The DQ for penicillin is large.
15. **(a)** high; **(b)** high, but lower than (a).
17. Food producers benefit through increased profits. The consumer assumes the greatest risk.
19. 100 g, 2 kg
21. Yes
23. 250 mL
25. 1.46×10^9 km^3
27. Yes; the 26.3-mm i.d. tube is larger than 25.4 mm (1 inch).
29. physical property: a, c, d; chemical property: b.
31. physical change: a, c; chemical change: b
33. substance: a, c, d; mixture: b
35. homogeneous: a, b, c; heterogeneous: d
37. a substance
39. elements: a, b, d; compound: c
41. **a.** aluminum; **b.** calcium; **c.** chlorine; **d.** silver
43. f
45. **a.** 8.01 μg **b.** 7.9 mL **c.** 1.05 km
47. **a.** 0.0374 L **b.** 1.55×10^5 m **c.** 198 mg **d.** 1.19×10^4 cm^2 **e.** 0.078 ms
49. **a.** cm **b.** kg **c.** dL
51. 10.0 mm; 1830 mm
53. **a.** 1.17 g/mL **b.** 1.26 g/mL
55. **a.** 120 g **b.** 490 g
57. **a.** 344 mL **b.** 495 cm^3
59.

Hexane
Water
Mercury

61. Yes
63. 14.8 cm
65. −78 °C
67. 38.5 kcal
69. 52.6 min
71. b.
73. 5.7 y
75. 1, d; 2, e; 3, b; 4, a; 5, d
77. 600 g
79. Cabbage (lightest) < potatoes < sugar (heaviest)
81. 5.23 g/cm^3
83. 6.73×10^{-6} cm
85. 0.908 metric ton
87. **a.** 1.3 g/cm^3; **b.** 5.4 g/cm^3; **c.** 0.688 g/cm^3; Jupiter and Earth are more dense than water; Saturn is less dense and would float (in a large enough ocean!).
89. Green chemistry is an approach that uses materials and processes that are intended to prevent or reduce pollution at its source.
91. a

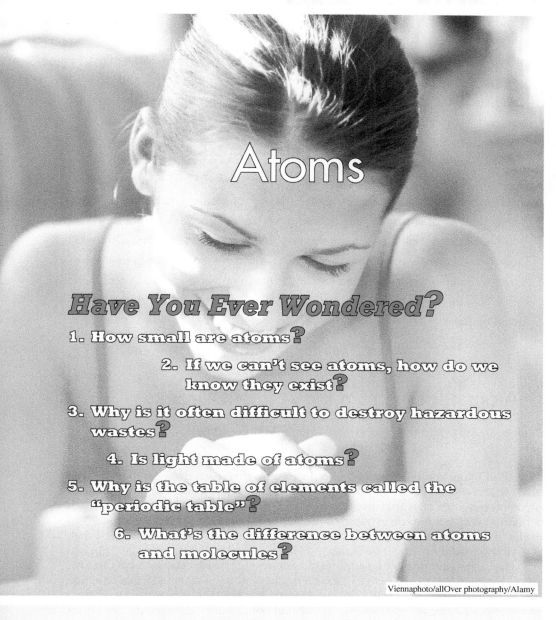

Atoms

Have You Ever Wondered?

1. **How small are atoms?**

2. **If we can't see atoms, how do we know they exist?**

3. **Why is it often difficult to destroy hazardous wastes?**

4. **Is light made of atoms?**

5. **Why is the table of elements called the "periodic table"?**

6. **What's the difference between atoms and molecules?**

Viennaphoto/allOver photography/Alamy

Stockbyte/Getty Images, Inc

Learning Objectives

> Explain the ancient Greeks' ideas about the characteristics of matter. (1)

> Describe the significance of the laws of conservation of mass and definite proportions. (2)

> Calculate the amounts of elements from the composition of a compound. (2)

> Explain why the idea that matter is made of atoms is a theory. (3)

> Understand how atomic theory explains the law of conservation of mass. (3)

> Describe how the elements are arranged in the periodic table and why the arrangement is important. (4)

> Distinguish atoms from molecules. (5)

> Identify elements that could be classified as hazardous or rare.

> Explain how green chemistry can change technologies that rely on hazardous or rare elements.

Are They for Real?

We hear something about atoms almost every day. The twentieth century saw the start of the so-called Atomic Age. The terms *atomic power*, *atomic energy*, and *atomic bomb* are a part of our ordinary vocabulary. But just what are atoms?

Every material thing in the world is made up of atoms, tiny particles that are much, much too small to see even with the finest optical microscope. The smallest speck of matter that can be detected by the human eye is made up of many billions of atoms. There are more than 10^{22} (10,000,000,000,000,000,000,000) atoms in a penny. Imagine that the

At the heart of every tablet computer (above), printer, telephone, television, MP3 player, and virtually every other electronic device lies a wafer of silicon (above right) in one or more integrated circuits (ICs or "chips"). The silicon used for electronics must be so pure that these devices were not possible until zone-refining purification was developed, about sixty years ago. Silicon is an *element*, made of a single type of atom. For making ICs, only about one atom of impurity can be present for every billion atoms of silicon. But how do we even know that atoms exist? The false-color image at the right shows individual silicon atoms in a hexagonal arrangement, using a recently developed technique called *scanning tunneling microscopy*. However, the behavior of matter led scientists to the atomic nature of matter over two hundred years ago. In this chapter, we will see some of that history, and we will explore the properties of atoms.

Wilson Ho

Atoms are so small that the smallest particle of matter visible to your eye contains more atoms than you could count in a lifetime!

atoms in a penny were enlarged until they were barely visible, like tiny grains of sand. The atoms in a single penny would then make enough "sand" to cover the entire state of Texas several feet deep. Comparing an atom to a penny is like comparing a grain of sand to a Texas-size sandbox.

Why should we care about something as tiny as an atom? Because our world is made up of atoms, and atoms are a part of all we do. *Everything* is made of atoms, including you and me. And because chemistry is the study of the behavior of matter, it observes the behavior of atoms. The behavior and interactions of atoms determine the behavior and interactions of matter.

Atoms are not all alike. Each element has its own kind of atom. On Earth, about 90 elements occur in nature. About two dozen more have been synthesized by scientists. As far as we know, the entire universe is made up of these same few elements. An **atom** is the smallest particle that is characteristic of a given element.

Haydn Hansell/Alamy

▲ A marble statue of Democritus, who first formulated the atomic nature of matter.

1 Atoms: Ideas from the Ancient Greeks

Learning Objective ❯ Explain the ancient Greeks' ideas about the characteristics of matter.

A pool of water can be separated into drops, and then each drop can be split into smaller and smaller drops. Suppose that you could keep splitting the drops into still smaller ones even after they became much too small to see. Would you ever reach a point at which a tiny drop could no longer be separated into smaller droplets of water? Is water infinitely divisible, or would you eventually come to a particle that, if divided, would no longer be water?

The Greek philosopher Leucippus, who lived in the fifth century B.C.E., and his pupil Democritus (ca. 460–ca. 370 B.C.E.) might well have discussed this question as they strolled along the beach by the Aegean Sea. Leucippus reasoned that there must ultimately be tiny particles of water that could not be divided further. After all, from a distance the sand on the beach looked continuous, but closer inspection showed it to be made up of tiny grains (Figure 1).

Democritus expanded on Leucippus's idea. He called the particles *atomos* (meaning "cannot be cut"), from which we derive the modern name *atom* for the tiny, discrete particle of an element. Democritus thought that each kind of atom was distinct in shape and size (Figure 2). He thought that real substances were mix-

▶ **Figure 1** A sandy beach.

Q: *Sand looks continuous— infinitely divisible—when you look at a beach from a distance. Is it really continuous? Water looks continuous, even when viewed up close. Is it really continuous? Is a cloud continuous? Is air?*

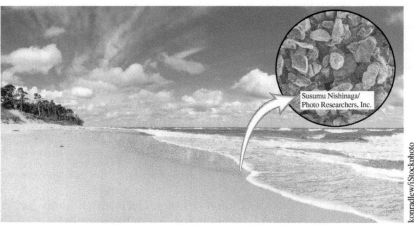

Susumu Nishinaga/ Photo Researchers, Inc.

konradlew/iStockphoto

tures of various kinds of atoms. The Greeks at that time believed that there were four basic elements: earth, air, fire, and water. These "elements" were related by four "principles"—hot, moist, dry, and cold—as shown in Figure 3. These ideas seem strange to us today, but they persisted for two millennia.

Four centuries after Democritus, the Roman poet Lucretius (ca. 95–ca. 55 B.C.E.) wrote a long didactic poem (a poem meant to teach), *On the Nature of Things*, in which he presented strong arguments for the atomic nature of matter. Unfortunately, a few centuries earlier, the famous Greek philosopher Aristotle (ca. 384–ca. 322 B.C.E.) had declared that matter was continuous (infinitely divisible) rather than discrete (consisting of tiny indivisible particles). The people of that time had no way to determine which view was correct. To most of them, Aristotle's continuous view of matter seemed more logical and reasonable, and so it prevailed for 2000 years, even though it was wrong.

▲ **Figure 2** Democritus imagined that "atoms" of water might be smooth, round balls and that atoms of fire might have sharp edges.

Self-Assessment Questions

1. Consider how the qualities *discrete* and *continuous* apply to materials at the macroscopic (visible to the unaided eye) level. Which of the following is continuous?
   a. apple juice
   b. a ream of paper
   c. a bowl of cherries
   d. chocolate chips

2. The view that matter is continuous rather than atomic prevailed for centuries because it was
   a. actually correct
   b. not considered important
   c. not tested by experiment
   d. tested and found to be true

Answers: 1, a; 2, c

2 Scientific Laws: Conservation of Mass and Definite Proportions

Learning Objectives ❯ Describe the significance of the laws of conservation of mass and definite proportions. ❯ Calculate the amounts of elements from the composition of a compound.

The eighteenth century saw the triumph of careful observation and measurement in chemistry. Antoine Lavoisier (1743–1794) perhaps did more than anyone to establish chemistry as a quantitative science. He found that when a chemical reaction was carried out in a closed container, the total mass of the system was not changed. Perhaps the most important chemical reaction that Lavoisier performed was decomposition of a red compound containing mercury to form metallic mercury and a gas he named *oxygen*. Both Carl Wilhelm Scheele (1742–1786), a Swedish apothecary, and Joseph Priestley (1733–1804), a Unitarian minister who later fled England and settled in America in 1794, had carried out the same reaction earlier, but Lavoisier was the first to weigh all the substances present before and after the reaction. He was also the first to interpret the reaction correctly.

The Law of Conservation of Mass

Lavoisier carried out many quantitative experiments. He found that when coal was burned, it united with oxygen to form carbon dioxide. He experimented with animals, observing that when a guinea pig breathed, oxygen was consumed and carbon dioxide was formed. Lavoisier therefore concluded that respiration was related

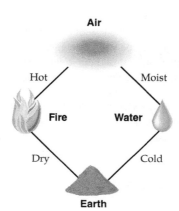

▲ **Figure 3** The Greek view of matter was that there were only four elements (in bold) connected by four "principles."

▲ The work of Antoine Lavoisier marked the beginning of chemistry as a quantitative science. Here, Lavoisier is shown with his wife, Marie, in a painting by Jacques Louis David in 1788.

100.00 grams of mercuric oxide

92.61 grams of mercury

7.39 grams of oxygen

| 100.00 | = | 92.61 | + | 7.39 |

▲ **Figure 4** Although mercuric oxide (a red solid) has none of the properties of mercury (a silver liquid) or oxygen (a colorless gas), when 100.00 g of mercuric oxide is decomposed by heating, the products are 92.61 g of mercury and 7.39 g of oxygen. Properties are completely changed in this reaction, but there is no change in mass.

Q: *When 10.00 g of mercuric oxide decomposes, 0.739 g of oxygen forms. What mass of mercury forms?*

to combustion. In each of these reactions, he found that matter was *conserved*—the amount remained constant.

Lavoisier summarized his findings as the **law of conservation of mass**, which states that matter is neither created nor destroyed during a chemical change (Figure 4). The total mass of the reaction products is always equal to the total mass of the reactants (starting materials). For now, some simple examples and discussion will illustrate the conservation of mass.

Scientists by this time had abandoned the Greek idea of the four elements and were almost universally using Robert Boyle's working definition of an element presented in his book *The Sceptical Chymist* (published in 1661). Boyle said that a supposed *element* must be tested. If a substance could be broken down into simpler substances, it was not an element. The simpler substances might be elements and should be regarded as such until the time (if it ever came) when they in turn could be broken down into still simpler substances. On the other hand, two or more elements might combine to form a more complex substance called a *compound*.

Using Boyle's definition, Lavoisier included a table of elements in his book *Elementary Treatise on Chemistry*. (The table included some substances that we now know to be compounds, as well as light and heat, which are actually forms of energy.) Lavoisier was the first to use systematic names for chemical elements. He is often called the "father of modern chemistry," and his book is usually regarded as the first chemistry textbook.

The law of conservation of mass is the basis for many chemical calculations. This law states that we cannot create materials from nothing. We can make new materials only by changing the way atoms are combined. For example, we can obtain iron metal from iron ore only because the ore contains iron atoms. Furthermore, we cannot get rid of wastes by the destruction of matter. We must put wastes somewhere. However, through chemical reactions, we can change some kinds of potentially hazardous wastes to less harmful forms. Such transformations of matter from one form to another are what chemistry is all about.

2. If we can't see atoms, how do we know they exist?

If matter had no "smallest particles," the law of conservation of mass, the law of definite proportions, and the law of multiple proportions would be almost impossible to explain. Atomic theory provides a simple explanation for these laws and for many others.

The Law of Definite Proportions

By the end of the eighteenth century, Lavoisier and other scientists noted that many substances were compounds, composed of two or more elements. Each compound had the same elements in the same proportions, regardless of where

(a)   (b)   (c)

▲ **Figure 5** The compound known as *basic copper carbonate* has the formula $Cu_2(OH)_2CO_3$ and occurs in nature as the mineral *malachite* **(a)**. It is formed as a patina on copper roofs **(b)**. It can also be synthesized in the laboratory **(c)**. Regardless of its source, basic copper carbonate always has the same composition. Analysis of this compound led Proust to formulate the law of definite proportions.

it came from or who prepared it. The painstaking work of Joseph Louis Proust (1754–1826) convinced most chemists of the general validity of these observations. In one set of experiments, for example, Proust found that basic copper carbonate, whether prepared in the laboratory or obtained from natural sources, was always composed of 57.48% by mass copper, 5.43% carbon, 0.91% hydrogen, and 36.18% oxygen (Figure 5).

To summarize these and many other experiments, Proust formulated a new scientific law in 1799. The **law of definite proportions** states that a compound always contains the same elements in certain definite proportions and in no others. (This generalization is also sometimes called the *law of constant composition*.)

An early illustration of the law of definite proportions is found in the work of the noted Swedish chemist J. J. Berzelius, illustrated in Figure 6. Berzelius heated a quantity (say, 10.00 g) of lead with various amounts of sulfur to form lead sulfide. Lead is a soft, grayish metal, and sulfur is a yellow solid. Lead sulfide is a shiny, black solid. Therefore, it was easy to tell when all the lead had reacted. Excess sulfur was washed away with carbon disulfide, a solvent that dissolves sulfur but not lead sulfide. As long as he used at least 1.55 g of sulfur with 10.00 g of lead, Berzelius got exactly 11.55 g of lead sulfide. Any sulfur in excess of 1.55 g was left over; it did not react. If Berzelius used more than 10.00 g of lead with 1.55 g of sulfur, he got 11.55 g of lead sulfide, with some lead left over.

▲ Jöns Jacob Berzelius (1779–1848) was the first person to prepare an extensive list of atomic weights. Published in 1828, it agrees remarkably well with most of today's accepted values.

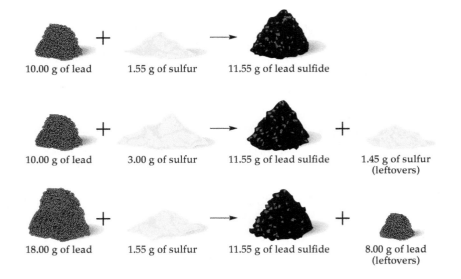

10.00 g of lead   1.55 g of sulfur   11.55 g of lead sulfide

10.00 g of lead   3.00 g of sulfur   11.55 g of lead sulfide   1.45 g of sulfur (leftovers)

18.00 g of lead   1.55 g of sulfur   11.55 g of lead sulfide   8.00 g of lead (leftovers)

◀ **Figure 6** An example showing how Berzelius's experiments illustrate the law of definite proportions.

Q: *What mass of sulfur can react completely with 20.00 g of lead? What mass of lead sulfide forms?*

▲ **Figure 7** Electrolysis of water. Hydrogen and oxygen are always produced in a volume ratio of 2:1.

Q: *If 24 cubic feet of hydrogen gas is produced by electrolysis, how much oxygen gas will be produced?*

The law of definite proportions is further illustrated by the electrolysis of water. In 1783, Henry Cavendish (1731–1810), a wealthy, eccentric English nobleman, found that water forms when hydrogen burns in oxygen. (It was Lavoisier, however, who correctly interpreted the experiment and who first used the names *hydrogen* and *oxygen*.) Later, in 1800, the English chemists William Nicholson and Anthony Carlisle decomposed water into hydrogen and oxygen gases by passing an electric current through the water (Figure 7). (The Italian scientist Alessandro Volta had invented the chemical battery only six weeks earlier.) The two gases are always produced in a 2:1 volume ratio. Although this is a volume ratio and Berzelius's experiment gave a mass ratio, both substantiate the law of definite proportions. This scientific law led to rapid developments in chemistry and dealt a death blow to the ancient Greek idea of water as an element.

The law of definite proportions is the basis for chemical formulas, such as H_2O for water. Constant composition also means that substances have constant properties. Pure water always dissolves salt or sugar, and at normal pressure it always freezes at 0 °C and boils at 100 °C.

Self-Assessment Questions

1. In any chemical change, compared to the mass of the reactants, the mass of the products is
   a. always equal
   b. always greater
   c. always less
   d. often different

2. In an experiment in which 36.04 g of liquid water is decomposed into hydrogen gas and oxygen gas, the total mass of the products is
   a. 0 g
   b. 18.02 g
   c. 36.04 g
   d. uncertain

3. The ancient Greeks thought that water was an element. In 1800, Nicholson and Carlisle decomposed water into hydrogen and oxygen. Their experiment proved that
   a. electricity causes decomposition
   b. the Greeks were correct
   c. hydrogen and oxygen are elements
   d. water is not an element

4. The fact that salt (sodium chloride) from any place on Earth is always 39.34% sodium and 60.66% chlorine by mass illustrates
   a. Dalton's atomic theory
   b. Democritus's atomic theory
   c. the law of definite proportions
   d. the law of conservation of mass

5. Ammonia produced in an industrial plant contains 3.0 kg of hydrogen for every 14.0 kg of nitrogen. The ammonia dissolved in a window-cleaning preparation contains 30.0 g of hydrogen for every 140.0 g of nitrogen. What law does this illustrate?
   a. Dalton's atomic theory
   b. Democritus's atomic theory
   c. the law of definite proportions
   d. the law of conservation of mass

6 When 60.0 g of carbon is burned in 160.0 g of oxygen, 220.0 g of carbon dioxide is formed. What mass of carbon dioxide is formed when 60.0 g of carbon is burned in 750.0 g of oxygen?
   a. 60.0 g
   b. 160.0 g
   c. 220.0 g
   d. 810.0 g

Answers: 1, a; 2, c; 3, d; 4, c; 5, c; 6, c

3 John Dalton and the Atomic Theory of Matter

Learning Objectives ❭ Explain why the idea that matter is made of atoms is a theory. ❭ Understand how atomic theory explains the law of conservation of mass.

Lavoisier's law of conservation of mass and Proust's law of definite proportions were repeatedly verified by experiment. This work led to attempts to develop theories to explain these laws.

In 1803, John Dalton, an English schoolteacher, proposed a model to explain the accumulating experimental data. By this time, the composition of a number of substances was known with a fair degree of accuracy. (To avoid confusion, we will use modern values, terms, and examples rather than those actually used by Dalton.) For example, all samples of water have an oxygen-to-hydrogen mass ratio of 7.94:1.00. Similarly, all samples of ammonia have a nitrogen-to-hydrogen mass ratio of 4.63:1.00 (14:3). Dalton explained these unvarying ratios by assuming that matter is made of atoms.

As Dalton continued his work, he discovered another law that his theory would have to explain. Proust had stated that a compound contains elements in certain proportions and only those proportions. Dalton's new law, called the **law of multiple proportions**, stated that elements might combine in *more* than one set of proportions, with each set corresponding to a different compound. For example, carbon combines with oxygen in a mass ratio of 1.00:2.66 (or 3.00:8.00) to form carbon dioxide, a gas that is a product of respiration and of the burning of coal or wood. But Dalton found that carbon also combines with oxygen in a mass ratio of 1.00:1.33 (or 3.00:4.00) to form carbon monoxide, a poisonous gas produced when a fuel is burned in the presence of a limited air supply.

Dalton then used his **atomic theory** to explain the various laws. Following are the important points of Dalton's atomic theory, with some modern modifications that we will consider later.

▲ John Dalton (1766–1844), who, in addition to developing the atomic theory, carried out important investigations of the behavior of gases. All of his contributions to science were made in spite of the fact that he was color-blind.

Dalton's Atomic Theory	Modern Modifications
1. All matter is composed of extremely small particles called atoms.	1. Dalton assumed atoms to be indivisible. This isn't quite true.
2. All atoms of a given element are alike, but atoms of a given element differ from the atoms of any other element.	2. Dalton assumed that all the atoms of a given element were identical in all respects, including mass. We now know this to be incorrect.
3. Compounds are formed when atoms of different elements combine in fixed proportions.	3. Unmodified. The numbers of each kind of atom in simple compounds usually form a simple ratio. For example, the ratio of carbon atoms to oxygen atoms is 1:1 in carbon monoxide and 1:2 in carbon dioxide.
4. A chemical reaction involves a *rearrangement* of atoms. No atoms are created, destroyed, or broken apart in a chemical reaction.	4. Unmodified for *chemical* reactions. Atoms are broken apart in *nuclear* reactions.

3. Why is it often difficult to destroy hazardous wastes?
Hazardous wastes that are compounds or mixtures can be converted to other compounds or mixtures—but the elements from those compounds or mixtures are still present and may be hazardous as well. For example, insecticide containing arsenic oxide can be broken down into the elements arsenic and oxygen—but the element arsenic is poisonous and can't be broken down into something else.

Explanations Using Atomic Theory

Dalton's theory clearly explains the difference between elements and compounds. *Elements* are composed of only one kind of atom. For example, a sample of the element phosphorus contains only phosphorus atoms. *Compounds* are made up of two or more kinds of atoms chemically combined in definite proportions.

▶ Figure 8 The law of definite proportions and the law of conservation of mass interpreted in terms of Dalton's atomic theory.

Q: *If 20 molecules of fluorine and 28 molecules of hydrogen react, how many molecules of HF can form? Which element is left over? How many molecules of the leftover element are there?*

Dalton set up a table of relative atomic masses based on hydrogen having a mass of 1. Many of Dalton's atomic masses were inaccurate, as we might expect because of the equipment available at that time. The masses we use today are relative atomic masses, usually called simply *atomic masses*. Historically, these relative masses were determined by comparison with a standard mass, a technique called *weighing*. For this historical reason, these relative masses are often called *atomic weights*. You will find a table of atomic masses on the inside front cover of this text. We will use these modern values in some examples showing how Dalton's atomic theory explains the various laws.

To explain the law of definite proportions, Dalton's reasoning went something like this: Why should 1.0 g of hydrogen always combine with 19 g of fluorine? Why shouldn't 1.0 g of hydrogen also combine with 18 g, or 20 g, or any other mass of fluorine? If an atom of fluorine has a mass 19 times that of a hydrogen atom, the compound formed by the union of one atom of each element would have to consist of 1 part by mass of hydrogen and 19 parts by mass of fluorine. Matter must be atomic for the law of definite proportions to be valid (Figure 8).

Atomic theory also explains the law of conservation of mass. When fluorine atoms combine with hydrogen atoms to form hydrogen fluoride, the atoms are merely rearranged. Matter is neither lost nor gained; the mass does not change.

Finally, atomic theory explains the law of multiple proportions. For example, 1.00 g of carbon combines with 1.33 g of oxygen to form carbon monoxide or with 2.66 g of oxygen to form carbon dioxide. Carbon dioxide has twice the mass of oxygen per gram of carbon as carbon monoxide does. This is because one atom of carbon combines with *one* atom of oxygen to form carbon monoxide, whereas one atom of carbon combines with *two* atoms of oxygen to form carbon dioxide.

Using modern values, we assign an oxygen atom a relative mass of 16.0 and a carbon atom a relative mass of 12.0. One atom of carbon combined with one atom of oxygen (in carbon monoxide) means a mass ratio of 12.0 parts carbon to 16.0 parts oxygen, or 3.00 : 4.00. One atom of carbon combined with two atoms of oxygen (in carbon dioxide) gives a mass ratio of 12.0 parts carbon to 2 × 16.0 = 32.0 parts oxygen, or 3.00 : 8.00. Because all oxygen atoms have the same average mass, and all carbon atoms have the same average mass, the ratio of oxygen in carbon dioxide to oxygen in carbon monoxide is 8.00 to 4.00 or 2 : 1. The same law holds true for other compounds formed from the same two elements. Table 1 shows another example of the law of multiple proportions, involving nitrogen and oxygen.

Dalton also invented a set of symbols (Figure 9) to represent the different kinds of atoms. These symbols have since been replaced by modern symbols of one or two letters (inside front cover).

▲ It DOES Matter!

A molecule with one carbon (C) atom and two oxygen (O) atoms is carbon dioxide (CO_2), a gas that you exhale and that provides the "fizz" in soft drinks. Cooled to about −80 °C, it becomes dry ice (shown above), used to keep items frozen during shipping. But a molecule with one less O atom is deadly carbon monoxide, CO. Just 0.2% CO in the air is enough to kill. Unfortunately, most fuels produce a little CO when they burn, which is why a car engine should never be left running in a closed garage.

Isotopes: Atoms of an Element with Different Masses

As we have noted, Dalton's second assumption, that all atoms of an element are alike, has been modified. Atoms of an element can have different masses, and such atoms are called *isotopes*. For example, most carbon atoms have a relative atomic

Mat Meadows/Peter Arnold/Alamy

Table 1   The Law of Multiple Proportions

Compound	Representation[a]	Mass of N per 1.000 g of O	Ratio of the Masses of N[b]
Nitrous oxide	●●●	1.750 g	$(1.750 \div 0.4375) = 4.000$
Nitric oxide	●●	0.8750 g	$(0.8750 \div 0.4375) = 2.000$
Nitrogen dioxide	●●●	0.4375 g	$(0.4375 \div 0.4375) = 1.000$

[a] ● = nitrogen atom and ● = oxygen atom

[b] We obtain the ratio of the masses of N that combine with a given mass of O by dividing each quantity in the third column by the smallest (0.4375 g).

mass of 12 (carbon-12), but 1.1% of carbon atoms have a relative atomic mass of 13 (carbon-13).

Problem Solving: Mass and Atom Ratios

We can use proportions, such as those determined by Dalton, to calculate the amount of a substance needed to combine with (or form) a given quantity of another substance. To learn how to do this, let's look at some examples.

CONCEPTUAL Example 1   Mass Ratios

Hydrogen gas for fuel cells can be made by decomposing *methane* (CH_4), the main component of natural gas. The decomposition gives carbon (C) and hydrogen (H) in a ratio of 3.00 parts by mass of carbon to 1.00 part by mass of hydrogen. How much hydrogen can be made from 90.0 g of methane?

Solution

We can express the ratio of parts by mass in any units we choose—pounds, grams, kilograms—as long as it is the same for both elements. Using grams as the units, we see that 3.00 g of C and 1.00 g of H would be produced if 4.00 g of CH_4 were decomposed. To convert g CH_4 to g H, we need a conversion factor that includes 1.00 g H and 4.00 g CH_4.

We start with the given quantity.

We multiply by the conversion factor, expressed in grams.

$$90.0 \text{ g CH}_4 \times \frac{1.00 \text{ g H}}{4.00 \text{ g CH}_4} = 22.5 \text{ g H}$$

the number   the unit

■ EXERCISE 1A

The gas ammonia can be decomposed to give 3.00 parts by mass of hydrogen and 14.0 parts by mass of nitrogen. What mass of nitrogen is obtained if 10.2 g of ammonia is decomposed?

■ EXERCISE 1B

Nitrous oxide, sometimes called "laughing gas," can be decomposed to give 7.00 parts by mass of nitrogen and 4.00 parts by mass of oxygen. What mass of nitrogen is obtained if enough nitrous oxide is decomposed to yield 36.0 g of oxygen?

▲ **Figure 9** Some of Dalton's symbols for the elements.

Q: *Using Dalton's symbols, draw diagrams for sulfur dioxide and sulfur trioxide. (Place the sulfur atom in the center and arrange the oxygen atoms around it.) What law do these two compounds illustrate?*

4. Is light made of atoms? Light is not matter and is not made of atoms. Light is a form of *energy*. Energy—including chemical energy, electrical energy, and nuclear energy—is defined as the ability to do work.

CONCEPTUAL **Example 2**   Atom Ratios

Hydrogen sulfide gas can be decomposed to give sulfur and hydrogen in a mass ratio of 16.0:1.00. If the relative mass of sulfur is 32.0 when the mass of hydrogen is taken to be 1.00, how many hydrogen atoms are combined with each sulfur atom in the gas?

Solution

We start with the relative mass of a sulfur atom · We multiply by the given mass factor · Then we multiply by the relative mass of a hydrogen atom · The answer: a ratio of 2 atoms H to 1 atom S

$$\frac{32.0 \text{ units S}}{1 \text{ atom S}} \times \frac{1.00 \text{ unit H}}{16.0 \text{ units S}} \times \frac{1 \text{ atom H}}{1 \text{ unit H}} = \frac{2 \text{ atoms H}}{1 \text{ atom S}}$$

■ EXERCISE 2

Phosphine gas can be decomposed to give phosphorus and hydrogen in a mass ratio of 10.3:1.00. If the relative mass of phosphorus is 31.0 when the mass of hydrogen is taken to be 1.00, how many hydrogen atoms are combined with each phosphorus atom in the gas?

Despite some inaccuracies, Dalton's atomic theory was a great success. Why? Because it served—and still serves—to explain a large amount of experimental data. It also successfully predicted how matter would behave under a wide variety of circumstances. Dalton arrived at his atomic theory by basing his reasoning on experimental findings, and with modest modification, the theory has stood the test of time and of modern, highly sophisticated instrumentation. Formulation of so successful a theory was quite a triumph for a Quaker schoolteacher in 1803.

Self-Assessment Questions

1. Two compounds, ethylene and acetylene, both contain only carbon and hydrogen. A sample of acetylene contains 92.26 g of C and 7.74 g H. An ethylene sample contains 46.13 g of C and 7.74 g H. If the formula for acetylene is C_2H_2, the formula for ethylene is
   a. CH   **b.** C_2H
   c. CH_3 **d.** C_2H_4

2. According to Dalton, elements are distinguished from each other by
   a. density in the solid state   **b.** nuclear charge
   c. shapes of their atoms   **d.** weights of their atoms

3. Dalton postulated that atoms were indestructible to explain why
   a. the same two elements can form more than one compound
   b. no two elements have the same atomic mass
   c. mass is conserved in chemical reactions
   d. nuclear fission (splitting) is impossible

4. Dalton viewed chemical change as
   a. a change of atoms from one type into another
   b. creation and destruction of atoms
   c. a rearrangement of atoms
   d. a transfer of electrons

5. How many types of atoms are present in a given compound?
   a. at least two   **b.** hundreds
   c. three or more   **d.** depends on the mass of the compound

6. Hydrogen and carbon combine in a 4.0:12.0 mass ratio to form methane. If every molecule of methane contains 4 H atoms and 1 C atom, an atom of carbon must have a mass that is
   a. $\frac{4}{12}$ times the mass of a hydrogen atom   **b.** 4 times the mass of a hydrogen atom
   c. $\frac{12}{3}$ times the mass of a hydrogen atom   **d.** 12 times the mass of a hydrogen atom

Questions 7–9 refer to the following figures:

(a)   (b)   (c)

7. Which figure represents an element?
8. Which figure represents a compound?
9. Which figure represents a mixture?

Answers: 1, d; 2, d; 3, c; 4, c; 5, a; 6, d; 7, b; 8, a; 9, c

4 Mendeleev and the Periodic Table

Learning Objective > Describe how the elements are arranged in the periodic table and why the arrangement is important.

During the eighteenth and nineteenth centuries, new elements were discovered with surprising frequency. By 1830 there were 55 known elements, all with different properties that demonstrated no apparent order. Dalton had set up a table of relative atomic masses in his 1808 book *A New System of Chemical Philosophy*. Dalton's rough values were improved in subsequent years, notably by Berzelius, who, in 1828, published a table of atomic weights containing 54 elements. Most of Berzelius's values agree well with modern values.

Relative Atomic Masses

Although it was impossible to determine actual masses of atoms in the nineteenth century, chemists were able to determine relative atomic masses by measuring the amounts of various elements that combined with a given mass of another element. Dalton's atomic masses were based on an atomic mass of 1 for hydrogen. As more accurate atomic masses were determined, this standard was replaced by one in which the atomic mass of naturally occurring oxygen was assigned a value of 16.0000. Because the isotopic composition of oxygen varies a bit depending on its source, the oxygen standard was replaced in 1961 by a more logical one based on a single isotope of carbon, carbon-12. Adoption of this new standard caused little change in atomic masses. These relative atomic masses are usually expressed in **atomic mass units (amu)**, commonly referred to today simply as *units* (*u*).

In December 2010, the atomic masses for eleven elements were adjusted slightly. Although their atomic masses had not actually changed, the isotopic composition of these elements varies slightly from location to location. For example, boron's atomic mass is now listed in some sources as 10.806–10.821 u. Most periodic tables still list a single value, however, which is accurate enough for most purposes.

Mendeleev's Periodic Table

Various attempts were made to arrange the elements in some sort of systematic fashion. The most successful arrangement—one that soon became widely accepted by chemists—was published in 1869 by Dmitri Ivanovich Mendeleev (1834–1907), a Russian chemist. Mendeleev's **periodic table** arranged the 63 elements known at the time primarily in order of increasing atomic mass. However, his first consideration in this table was an element's *properties*. He placed silver, gold, and several other

▲ Dmitri Mendeleev, the Russian chemist who arranged the 63 known elements into a periodic table similar to the one we use today, was considered one of the great teachers of his time. Unable to find a suitable chemistry textbook, he wrote his own, *The Principles of Chemistry*. Mendeleev also studied the nature and origin of petroleum and made many other contributions to science. Element 101 is named mendelevium (Md) in his honor.

Library of Congress

Tabelle II.

Reihen	Gruppe I. — R²O	Gruppe II. — RO	Gruppe III. — R²O³	Gruppe IV. RH⁴ RO²	Gruppe V. RH³ R²O⁵	Gruppe VI. RH² RO³	Gruppe VII. RH R²O⁷	Gruppe VIII. — RO⁴
1	H = 1							
2	Li = 7	Be = 9,4	B = 11	C = 12	N = 14	O = 16	F = 19	
3	Na = 23	Mg = 24	Al = 27,3	Si = 28	P = 31	S = 32	Cl = 35,5	
4	K = 39	Ca = 40	— = 44	Ti = 48	V = 51	Cr = 52	Mn = 55	Fe = 56, Co = 59, Ni = 59, Cu = 63.
5	(Cu = 63)	Zn = 65	— = 68	— = 72	As = 75	Se = 78	Br = 80	
6	Rb = 85	Sr = 87	?Yt = 88	Zr = 90	Nb = 94	Mo = 96	— = 100	Ru = 104, Rh = 104, Pd = 106, Ag = 108.
7	(Ag = 108)	Cd = 112	In = 113	Sn = 118	Sb = 122	Te = 125	J = 127	
8	Cs = 133	Ba = 137	?Di = 138	?Ce = 140	—	—	—	— — —
9	(—)	—	—	—	—	—	—	
10	—		?Er = 178	?La = 180	Ta = 182	W = 184	—	Os = 195, Ir = 197, Pt = 198, Au = 199.
11	(Au = 199)	Hg = 200	Ti = 204	Pb = 207	Bi = 208	—	—	— — —
12	—	—	—	Th = 231	—	U = 240	—	

der chemischen Elemente.

▲ **Figure 10** Mendeleev's periodic table. In this 1898 version, he wrongly "corrected" the atomic weight of tellurium to be less than that of iodine.

5. Why is the table of elements called the "periodic table"?

Periodic indicates that something occurs regularly. The physical and chemical properties of the elements are periodic. That is, many of those properties are similar for elements in a given column of the table.

metals slightly out of order. This allowed sulfur, selenium, and tellurium, which have similar chemical properties, to appear in the same column. This rearrangement also put iodine in the same column as chlorine and bromine, which it resembles chemically.

To place elements in groups with similar properties, Mendeleev also had to leave gaps in his table. Instead of considering these blank spaces as defects, he boldly predicted the existence of elements yet undiscovered. Further, he even predicted the properties of some of the missing elements. For example, three of the missing elements were soon discovered and named scandium, gallium, and germanium. As can be seen in Table 2, Mendeleev's predictions for germanium were amazingly successful. This remarkable predictive value led to wide acceptance of Mendeleev's table.

The modern periodic table (inside front cover) contains 118 elements, some of which have reportedly been observed or synthesized but have not yet been verified or named. Each element is represented by a box in the periodic table, as shown in Figure 11.

26 ← atomic number, Z
Fe ← chemical symbol
55.847 ← atomic mass (weighted average)

▲ **Figure 11** Representation of an element on the modern periodic table.

Table 2 Properties of Germanium: Predicted and Observed

Property	Predicted by Mendeleev for Eka-Silikon (1871)	Observed by Winkler for Germanium (1886)
Atomic mass	72	72.6
Density (g/cm³)	5.5	5.47
Color	Dirty gray	Grayish white
Density of oxide (g/cm³)	EsO₂: 4.7	GeO₂: 4.703
Boiling point of chloride	EsCl₄: below 100 °C	GeCl₄: 86 °C

CONCEPTUAL Example 3 — Predicting Periodic Properties

In 1829, Johann Dobereiner, a German chemist, published his observations that there were several groups of three elements that were quite similar. In each case, the middle element seemed to be halfway between the other two in atomic mass, reactivity, and other properties. One such group, which he called *alkali formers,* was lithium, sodium, and potassium. Show that the relative atomic mass of the middle element in this triad is close to the average of the relative atomic masses of the other two elements.

Solution

The atomic mass of lithium (Li) is 6.941 u and that of potassium (K) is 39.098 u. The average of the two is (6.941 u + 39.098 u) ÷ 2 = 22.795 u, quite close to the modern value for sodium (Na) of 22.989 u.

■ EXERCISE 3

Another of Dobereiner's triads was the *salt formers* chlorine, bromine, and iodine. Show that the relative atomic mass of the middle element in this triad is close to the average of the relative atomic masses of the other two elements.

Self-Assessment Questions

1. Which of the following is *not* true of Mendeleev's periodic table?
   a. It includes new elements that he had just discovered.
   b. The elements are arranged generally in order of increasing atomic mass.
   c. He left gaps for predicted new elements.
   d. He placed some heavier elements before lighter ones.

2. Relative masses in the modern periodic table are based on the value for
   a. the carbon-12 isotope   b. the hydrogen atom
   c. naturally occurring oxygen   d. the oxygen-16 isotope

3. The number of elements known today is approximately
   a. 12   b. 100
   c. 1000   d. 30 million

Answers: 1, a; 2, a; 3, b

Drs. Ali Yazdani & Daniel J. Hornbaker/Photo Researchers, Inc.

▲ An image of atoms of manganese obtained using STM.

5 Atoms and Molecules: Real and Relevant

Learning Objective > Distinguish atoms from molecules.

Are atoms real? Certainly they are real as a concept, a highly useful concept. And scientists today can observe computer-enhanced images of individual atoms. These portraits provide powerful (though still indirect) evidence that atoms exist.

Are atoms relevant? Much of modern science and technology—including the production of new materials and the technology of pollution control—is based on the concept of atoms. We have seen that atoms are conserved in chemical reactions. Thus, material things—things made of atoms—can be recycled, for the atoms are not destroyed no matter how we use them. The one way we might "lose" a material from a practical standpoint is to spread its atoms so thinly that it would take too much time and energy to put them back together again. The essay on recycling describes a real-world example of such loss.

Now back to Leucippus and Democritus and their musings on that Greek beach. We now know that if we keep dividing drops of water, we will ultimately obtain a small particle—called a *molecule*—that is still water. A **molecule** is a group of atoms chemically bonded, or connected, to one another. Molecules are represented by chemical formulas. The symbol H represents an *atom* of hydrogen. The formula

6. What's the difference between atoms and molecules? A molecule is made of atoms that are combined in fixed proportions. A carbon atom is the smallest particle of the element carbon, and a carbon dioxide molecule is the smallest particle of the compound carbon dioxide. As you have probably figured out, molecules can be broken down into their atoms.

Recycling

Because it is an element, iron cannot be created or destroyed, but that does not mean it always exists in its elemental state. Let's consider two different pathways for the recycling of iron.

1. Hematite, an iron ore, is obtained from a mine and converted into pig iron, which is used to make steel cans. Once discarded, the cans rust. Iron ions slowly leach from the rust into groundwater and eventually wind up in the ocean. These dissolved ions can be

absorbed by and incorporated into marine plants. Marine creatures that eat the plants will in turn absorb and incorporate iron ions. The original iron atoms are now widely separated in space. Some of them might even become part of the hemoglobin in your blood. The iron has been recycled, but it will never again resemble the original pig iron.

(a) Harry Taylor/Dorling Kindersley
(b) Mark Wragg/iStockphoto
(c) Sieto/iStockphoto
(d) Tammy Peluso/iStockphoto

2. Iron ore is taken from a mine and converted to pig iron and then into steel. The steel is used in making an automobile, which is driven for a decade and then sent to the junkyard. There it is compacted and sent to a recycling plant, where the steel is recov-

ered and ultimately used again in a new automobile. Once the iron was removed from its ore, it was conserved in its elemental metallic form. In this form of recycling, the iron continues to be useful for a long time.

(a) Harry Taylor/Dorling Kindersley
(b) Michael Shake/Shutterstock
(c) Joe Potato Photo/iStockphoto
(d) Lya Cattel/iStockphoto

H_2 represents a *molecule* of hydrogen, which is composed of two hydrogen atoms. The formula H_2O represents a molecule of water, which is composed of two hydrogen atoms and one oxygen atom. If we divide a water molecule, we will obtain *two atoms* of hydrogen and *one atom* of oxygen.

And if we divide those atoms ... but that is a story for another time.

Dalton regarded the atom as indivisible, as did his successors up until the discovery of radioactivity in 1895.

Self-Assessment Questions

1. We can recycle materials because atoms
   a. always combine in the same way
   b. are conserved
   c. are indivisible
   d. combine in multiple portions

2. A molecule is
   a. a collection of like atoms
   b. conserved in chemical reactions
   c. a group of atoms chemically bonded to one another
   d. indivisible

Answers: 1, b; 2, c

Lallie C. McKenzie, *Chem11 LLC*

It's Elemental

In this chapter, you learned that everything is made up of atoms and that atoms are the smallest particles of an element. Although the universe is composed of an uncountable number of compounds and mixtures, the basic building blocks of these are elements. The periodic table (inside front cover) organizes the elements by relative mass and, more importantly, by their predictable chemical properties.

What do elements have to do with green chemistry? When chemists design products and processes, they take advantage of the entire periodic table, including elements used rarely or not at all in nature or in our bodies. It is important to think about possible impacts of the chosen elements on human health and on the environment. Two important factors to evaluate are inherent hazard and natural abundance. Hazard can be different for the element itself or when it is in a compound, so the element's form can determine whether it causes harm. For example, sodium is very reactive with water, but sodium chloride is a compound that we eat. Also, as you learned from the law of conservation of mass (Section 2), elements cannot be created or destroyed. Therefore, the amounts of these materials on the planet are limited and may be scarce.

Green Chemistry Principles 3, 7, and 10 apply to products and processes that involve hazardous and rare elements. Understanding the impacts of toxic elements and compounds on human health and the environment lets us reduce or eliminate their use by developing safer alternatives. Also, designing new technologies that rely on abundant elements can prevent depletion of resources. Finally, reclaiming materials after use is critical if they can cause harm or are scarce.

The use of lead and mercury, two particularly hazardous elements, has been reduced through green chemistry. These elements are known to harm many of the systems of the human body and can impact children's development. Although lead and mercury are important in many products, the urgent need to limit exposure to them has led to their replacement with safer alternatives. For example, lead in paints has been replaced with titanium dioxide, compounds with lower toxicity now substitute for lead stabilizers in plastics, and new lead-free chemicals are being used instead of traditional solder in electronics. In addition, recent developments have reduced the liquid mercury required in fluorescent lighting, and mercury-based thermometers and switches have been replaced with electronic or non-hazardous versions. Because coal-fired power plants emit mercury, advances in alternative energy sources also reduce our exposure to this element.

Many current technologies may be limited by their need for scarce elements. For example, the permanent magnets in computer hard drives, wind turbines, and hybrid cars are mainly made of neodymium and dysprosium. Green chemistry can promote new opportunities. Although almost all of the elements are found in the Earth's crust, eight account for more than 98% of the total. In fact, almost three-fourths of the crust is comprised of two elements, silicon and oxygen. Besides being scarce, some elements, such as rare earth metals like cerium, yttrium, neodymium, and lanthanum, are drawn from a single source and can be difficult to separate from other materials. Current supplies are much lower than needed to support projected growth.

Approaches based on earth-abundant elements (such as silicon, iron, and aluminum) would support technology and protect resources. As discussed in the essay on page 54, atoms of a material can be reclaimed directly through recycling processes or spread through the environment. If released, hazardous materials can impact health and the environment, so recycling of these elements should be a priority. Reclaimed raw materials reduce the demand for natural resources—notably, scarce elements. Green chemistry supports the design of materials where the individual elemental components can be recycled easily.

Green chemistry approaches are especially important when products and processes present health or environmental risks. Identifying and replacing hazardous and rare elements can lead to greener technologies and a sustainable future for everyone.

© Libby Welch/Alamy.

◄ New technologies have led to mercury-free efficient lightbulbs like this one. These products save energy and do not contain toxic elements used in traditional fluorescent lighting.

CRITICAL THINKING EXERCISES

Apply knowledge that you have gained in this chapter and one or more of the FLaReS principles to evaluate the following statements or claims.

1 In a science fiction movie, a woman proceeds through nine months of pregnancy in minutes. She takes in no nutrients during this time. She dies during labor and an emergency C-section is performed to save the child. The child lives for only a matter of hours, rapidly aging, and dies a withered old man. A classmate claims that the movie is based on a documented, secret alien encounter.

2 A health-food store has a large display of bracelets made of copper metal. Some people claim that wearing such a bracelet will protect the wearer from arthritis or rheumatoid diseases.

3 An old cookbook claims that cooking acidic food, such as spaghetti sauce, in an iron pot provides more nutrients than cooking the same food in an aluminum pot.

4 A company markets a device it calls a "water energizer." It claims the device can supply so much energy to drinking water that the mass of oxygen in the water is increased, thereby providing more oxygen to the body.

SUMMARY

Section 1—The concept of atoms was first suggested in ancient Greece by Leucippus and Democritus. However, this idea was rejected for almost 2000 years in favor of Aristotle's view that matter was continuous in nature.

Section 2—The law of conservation of mass resulted from careful experiments by Lavoisier and others, who weighed all the reactants and products for a number of chemical reactions and found that no change in mass occurred. Boyle said that a proposed element must be tested. If it could be broken down into simpler substances, it was not an element. The law of definite proportions (law of constant composition) was formulated by Proust, based on his experiments and on those of Berzelius. It states that a given compound always contains the same elements in exactly the same proportions by mass.

Section 3—In 1803, Dalton explained the laws of definite proportions and conservation of mass with his atomic theory, which had four main points: (1) Matter is made up of tiny particles called atoms; (2) atoms of the same element are alike; (3) compounds are formed when atoms of different elements combine in certain proportions; and (4) during chemical reactions, atoms are rearranged, not destroyed. Dalton also discovered the law of multiple proportions, which states that different elements might combine in two or more different sets of proportions, each set corresponding to a different compound. His atomic theory also explained this new law.

These laws can be used to perform calculations to find the amounts of elements that combine or are present in a compound or reaction. In more than two centuries atomic theory has undergone only minor modification.

Section 4—Berzelius published a table of atomic weights in 1828, and his values agree well with modern ones. In 1869, Mendeleev published his version of the periodic table, a systematic arrangement of the elements that allowed him to predict the existence and properties of undiscovered elements. In the modern periodic table, each element is listed, along with its symbol and the average mass of an atom of that element in atomic mass units, which are very tiny units of mass.

Section 5—Because atoms are conserved in chemical reactions, matter (which is made of atoms) can always be recycled. Atoms can be lost, in effect, if they are scattered in the environment. A molecule is a group of atoms chemically bonded together. Just as an atom is the smallest particle of an element, a modecule is the smallest particle of most compounds.

Green chemistry When chemists design products and processes, potential impacts on human health and the environment of the incorporated elements should be considered. Identifying and replacing toxic and rare elements can lead to greener technologies and enhance sustainability.

Learning Objectives

> Explain the ancient Greeks' ideas about the characteristics of matter. (1)

Problems 1–3

> Describe the significance of the laws of conservation of mass and definite proportions. (2)

Problems 6, 10, 15–28, 45, 48

> Calculate the amounts of elements from the composition of a compound. (2)

Problems 41–43, 46, 49–51

> Explain why the idea that matter is made of atoms is a theory. (3)

Problem 8

> Understand how atomic theory explains the law of conservation of mass. (3)

Problem 11, 35–40, 44, 47

> Describe how the elements are arranged in the periodic table and why the arrangement is important. (4)

Problem 50

> Distinguish atoms from molecules. (5)

Problem 12

> Identify elements that can be classified as hazardous or rare.

Problem 52

> Explain how green chemistry can change technologies that rely on hazardous or rare elements.

Problems 53, 54

 REVIEW QUESTIONS

1. Distinguish between **(a)** the atomic view and the continuous view of matter and **(b)** the ancient Greek definition of an element and the modern one.

2. What was Democritus's contribution to atomic theory? Why did the idea that matter was continuous (rather than atomic) prevail for so long? What discoveries finally refuted the idea?

3. Consider the following *macroscopic* (visible to the unaided eye) objects. Which are best classified as *discrete* (like Democritus's description of matter) and which are *continuous* (like Aristotle's description)?
   a. people
   b. cloth
   c. calculators
   d. milk chocolate
   e. M&M's candies

4. Describe Lavoisier's contribution to the development of modern chemistry.

5. How did Boyle define an element?

6. State the law of definite proportions, and illustrate it using the compound zinc sulfide, ZnS.

7. State the law of multiple proportions. For a fixed mass of the first element in each of the following compounds, what is the relationship between (ratio of) the
   a. masses of oxygen in ClO_2 and in ClO?
   b. masses of fluorine in ClF_3 and ClF?
   c. masses of oxygen in P_4O_6 and P_4O_{10}?

8. Outline the main points of Dalton's atomic theory.

9. In the figure, the blue spheres represent phosphorus atoms, and the red ones represent oxygen atoms. The box

labeled "Initial" represents a mixture. Which one of the other three boxes (A, B, or C) could *not* represent that mixture after a chemical reaction occurred? Explain briefly.

10. Fructose (fruit sugar) is always composed of 40.0% carbon, 53.3% oxygen, and 6.7% hydrogen regardless of the fruit that it comes from. What law does this illustrate?

11. Use Dalton's atomic theory to explain each of the following laws and give an example that illustrates each law.
    a. conservation of mass
    b. definite proportions
    c. multiple proportions

12. Lavoisier considered *alumina* an element. In 1825, the Danish chemist Hans Christian Oersted isolated aluminum metal by reacting aluminum chloride with potassium. Later experiments showed that alumina is formed by reacting aluminum metal with oxygen. What did these experiments prove?

13. What law does the following list of compounds illustrate? N_2O, NO, NO_2, N_2O_4

14. What did each of the following contribute to the development of modern chemistry?
    a. J. J. Berzelius
    b. Henry Cavendish
    c. Joseph Proust
    d. Dmitri Mendeleev

PROBLEMS

Conservation of Mass

15. If 45.0 g of vinegar is added to 5.0 g of baking soda in an open beaker, the total mass after reaction is less than 50.0 g. The vinegar bubbles and fizzes during the reaction. Has the law of conservation of mass been violated? Explain.

16. An iron nail dissolves in a solution of hydrochloric acid. The nail disappears. Have the iron atoms been destroyed? If so, how? If not, where are they?

17. Water is about 11.2% hydrogen and 88.8% oxygen by weight. If you fill a container with 11.2 g of hydrogen and 88.8 g of oxygen, does that vessel contain water? Explain.

18. Many reactions seem to violate the law of conservation of mass. For example, **(a)** when an iron object rusts, the rusty object has a greater mass than before, and **(b)** when a piece of charcoal burns, the remaining material (ash) has less mass than the charcoal. Explain these observations, and suggest an experiment that would demonstrate that mass is conserved in each case.

19. Acetylene, used for welding, contains 24.02 g of carbon for every 2.02 g of hydrogen. If you have 78.5 g of carbon that can be converted to acetylene, what mass of hydrogen will be needed for the conversion?

20. Nitrous oxide (N_2O, "laughing gas") contains 28.01 g of nitrogen in every 44.01 g of nitrous oxide. What mass of nitrous oxide can be formed from 48.7 g of nitrogen?

21. A student in a chemistry class calculates the mass of titanium(IV) oxide (which contains only titanium and oxygen) that can be formed from 37.7 g of titanium and 20.1 g of oxygen. Her calculated answer is 59.8 g of titanium(IV) oxide. Explain to the student why her answer is impossible.

22. A student heats 2.796 g of zinc powder with 2.414 g of sulfur. He reports that he obtains 4.169 g of zinc sulfide and recovers 1.041 g of unreacted sulfur. Show by calculation whether or not his results obey the law of conservation of mass.

23. When 1.00 g zinc and 0.80 g sulfur are allowed to react, all the zinc is used up, 1.50 g of zinc sulfide is formed, and some unreacted sulfur remains. What is the mass of *unreacted* sulfur (choose one)?
    a. 0.20 g
    b. 0.30 g
    c. 0.50 g
    d. impossible to determine from this information alone

24. A city has to come up with a plan to dispose of its solid wastes. The solid wastes consist of many different kinds of materials, and the materials are comprised of many different kinds of atoms. The options for disposal include burying the wastes in a landfill, incinerating them, and dumping them at sea. Which method, if any, will get rid of the atoms that make up the wastes? Which method, if any, will immediately change the chemical form of the wastes?

Definite Proportions

25. When 18.02 g of water is decomposed by electrolysis, 16.00 g of oxygen and 2.02 g of hydrogen are formed. According to the law of definite proportions, what masses, in grams, of **(a)** hydrogen and **(b)** oxygen will be formed by the electrolysis of 775 g of water?

26. Hydrogen from the decomposition of water has been promoted as the fuel of the future. What mass of water, in kilograms, would have to be electrolyzed to produce 125 kg of hydrogen? (See Problem 25.)

27. Given a plentiful supply of air, 3.0 parts carbon will react with 8.0 parts oxygen by mass to produce carbon dioxide. Use this mass ratio to calculate the mass of carbon required to produce 14 kg of carbon dioxide.

28. When 31 g of phosphorus reacts with oxygen, 71 g of an oxide of phosphorus is the product. What mass of phosphorus is needed to produce 39 g of this product?

Multiple Proportions

29. Carbon combines with oxygen in a mass ratio of 1.000:2.664 to form carbon dioxide (CO_2) and in a mass ratio of 1.000:1.332 to form carbon monoxide (CO). A third carbon-oxygen compound, called carbon suboxide, is 52.96% C by mass and 47.04% O by mass. Show that these compounds follow the law of multiple proportions.

30. A compound containing only oxygen and rubidium has 0.187 g of O per 1.00 g of Rb. The relative atomic masses are 16.0 for O and 85.5 for Rb. What is a possible O-to-Rb mass ratio for a different oxide of rubidium (choose one)?
    a. 8.0:85.5
    b. 16.0:85.5
    c. 32.0:85.5
    d. 16.0:171

31. A sample of an oxide of tin with the formula SnO consists of 0.742 g of tin and 0.100 g of oxygen. A sample of another oxide of tin consists of 0.555 g of tin and 0.150 g of oxygen. What is the formula of the second oxide?

32. Consider three oxides of nitrogen, X, Y, and Z. Oxide X has an oxygen-to-nitrogen mass ratio of 2.28:1.00, oxide Y has an oxygen-to-nitrogen mass ratio of 1.14:1.00, and oxide Z has an oxygen-to-nitrogen mass ratio of 0.57:1.00. What is the whole-number ratio of masses of oxygen in these compounds given a fixed mass of nitrogen?

33. Sulfur forms two compounds with fluorine, T and U. Compound T has 0.447 g of sulfur combined with 1.06 g of fluorine; compound U has 0.438 g of sulfur combined with 1.56 g of fluorine. Show that these data support the law of multiple proportions.

34. Two compounds, V and W, are composed only of hydrogen and carbon. Compound V is 80.0% carbon by mass and 20.0% hydrogen by mass. Compound W is 83.3% carbon by mass and 16.7% hydrogen by mass. What is the ratio of masses of hydrogen in these compounds given a fixed mass of carbon?

Dalton's Atomic Theory

35. Are the following findings, expressed to the nearest atomic mass unit, in agreement with Dalton's atomic theory? Explain your answers.
    a. An atom of calcium has a mass of 40 u; an atom of vanadium, 50 u.
    b. An atom of calcium has a mass of 40 u; an atom of potassium, 40 u.

36. To the nearest atomic mass unit, one calcium atom has a mass of 40 u and another calcium atom has a mass of

44 u. Do these findings support or contradict Dalton's atomic theory? Explain.

37. An atom of uranium splits into two smaller atoms when struck by a particle called a *neutron*. Do these findings support or contradict Dalton's atomic theory? Explain.

38. According to Dalton's atomic theory, when elements react, their atoms combine in (choose one)
    a. a simple whole-number ratio that is unique for each set of elements
    b. exactly a 1:1 ratio
    c. one or more simple whole-number ratios
    d. pairs
    e. random proportions

39. Hydrogen and oxygen combine in a mass ratio of about 1:8 to form water. If every water molecule consists of two atoms of hydrogen and one atom of oxygen, what fraction or multiple of the mass of a hydrogen atom is the mass of an oxygen atom?
    a. $\frac{1}{16}$ b. $\frac{1}{8}$ c. 8 times   d. 16 times

40. The elements fluorine and nitrogen combine in a mass ratio of 57:14 to form a compound. If every molecule of the compound consists of three atoms of fluorine and one atom of nitrogen, what fraction or multiple of the mass of a fluorine atom is the mass of a nitrogen atom?
    a. $\frac{19}{14}$ b. 3 times   c. $\frac{14}{19}$ d. 14 times

Chemical Compounds

41. A blue solid called *azulene* is thought to be a pure compound. Analyses of three samples of the material yield the following results.

	Mass of Sample	Mass of Carbon	Mass of Hydrogen
Sample 1	1.000 g	0.937 g	0.0629 g
Sample 2	0.244 g	0.229 g	0.0153 g
Sample 3	0.100 g	0.094 g	0.0063 g

Could the material be a pure compound?

42. A colorless liquid is thought to be a pure compound. Analyses of three samples of the material yield the following results.

	Mass of Sample	Mass of Carbon	Mass of Hydrogen
Sample 1	1.000 g	0.862 g	0.138 g
Sample 2	1.549 g	1.295 g	0.254 g
Sample 3	0.988 g	0.826 g	0.162 g

Could the material be a pure compound? Explain.

ADDITIONAL PROBLEMS

43. When 0.2250 g of magnesium is heated with 0.5331 g of nitrogen in a closed container, the magnesium is completely converted to 0.3114 g of magnesium nitride. What mass of unreacted nitrogen must remain?

44. Gasoline can be approximated by the formula C_8H_8. An environmental advocate points out that burning one gallon (about 7 lb) of gasoline produces about 19 lb of carbon dioxide, a greenhouse gas that raises the temperature of the atmosphere. Explain this seeming contradiction of the law of conservation of mass.

45. A compound of uranium and fluorine is used to generate uranium for nuclear power plants. The gas can be decomposed to yield 2.09 parts by mass of uranium for every 1 part by mass of fluorine. If the relative mass of a uranium atom is 238 and the relative mass of a fluorine atom is 19, calculate the number of fluorine atoms that are combined with one uranium atom.

46. Two experiments were performed in which sulfur was burned completely in pure oxygen gas, producing sulfur dioxide and leaving some unreacted oxygen. In the first experiment, burning 0.312 g of sulfur produced 0.623 g of sulfur dioxide. In the second experiment, 1.305 g of sulfur was burned. What mass of sulfur dioxide was produced?

47. In an experiment illustrated at right, about 15 mL of hydrochloric acid solution was placed in a flask and approximately 3 g of sodium carbonate was put into a balloon. The opening of the balloon was then carefully stretched over the top of the flask, taking care not to allow the sodium carbonate to fall into the acid in the flask. The flask was placed on an electronic balance, and the mass of the flask and its contents was found to be 38.61 g. The sodium carbonate was then slowly shaken into the acid. The balloon began to fill with gas. When the reaction was complete, the mass of the flask and its contents, including the gas in the balloon, was found to be 38.61 g. What law does this experiment illustrate? Explain.

Richard Megna/Fundamental Photographs

48. In one experiment, 3.06 g hydrogen was allowed to react with an excess of oxygen to form 27.35 g water. In a second experiment, electric current broke down a sample of water into 1.45 g hydrogen and 11.51 g oxygen. Are these results consistent with the law of definite proportions? Show why or why not.

49. Use Figure 4 to calculate the mass of mercuric oxide that would be needed to produce 100.0 g of mercury metal.

50. Gold chloride, $AuCl_3$, is formed when gold metal is dissolved in *aqua regia*, a highly corrosive mixture of acids. Determine the mass ratio of gold to chlorine in gold chloride:
   a. based on Mendeleev's values from his periodic table (Figure 10)
   b. based on values in the modern periodic table in the inside front cover of this text

51. See Table 1. Another compound of nitrogen and oxygen contains 0.5836 g of nitrogen per 1.000 g of oxygen. Calculate the ratio of mass of N in this compound to mass of N in nitrogen dioxide. What *whole-number* ratio does this value represent?

52. Identify whether the following elements are hazardous, rare, or neither.
   a. silicon
   b. neodymium
   c. mercury
   d. oxygen
   e. lead

53. Give two examples of how green chemistry has helped to reduce the use of lead in consumer products.

54. Why is it important to recycle mercury-based fluorescent lightbulbs instead of putting them in landfills?

 COLLABORATIVE GROUP PROJECTS

Prepare a PowerPoint, poster, or other presentation (as directed by your instructor) to share with the class.

1. Prepare a brief biographical report on one of the following.
   a. Henry Cavendish   **b.** Joseph Proust
   c. John Newlands   **d.** Lothar Meyer
   e. Dmitri Mendeleev   **f.** John Dalton
   g. Antoine Lavoisier   **h.** Marie-Anne Pierrette Paulze

2. Prepare a brief report on early Greek contributions to and ideas in the field of science, focusing on the work of one of the following: Aristotle, Leucippus, Democritus, Thales, Anaximander, Anaximenes of Miletus, Heraclitus, Empedocles, or another Greek philosopher of the time before 300 B.C.E.

3. Prepare a brief report on the *phlogiston theory*. Describe what the theory was, how it explained changes in mass when something is burned, and why it was finally abandoned.

4. Write a brief essay on recycling of one of the following: metals, paper, plastics, glass, food wastes, or grass clippings. Contrast a recycling method that maintains the properties of an element with one that changes them.   1
   A. 2.19 g nitrogen   **B.** 63.0 g nitrogen   .

BRIEF ANSWERS TO SELECTED PROBLEMS

Answers are provided for *all in-chapter exercises.* Brief answers are given for *odd-numbered Review Questions*; more complete answers can be obtained by reviewing the text. Answers are provided for *all odd-numbered Problems and Additional Problems.*

NOTE: For numerical problems, your answer may differ slightly from ours because of rounding and the use of significant figures.

1 **A.** 2.19 g nitrogen   **B.** 63.0 g nitrogen
2 3 atoms hydrogen/1 atom phosphorus
3 average Cl + I is 81.2; actual Br is 79.9.
1. a. atomic: matter is made of discrete particles; continuous: matter is infinitely divisible.
   b. Greek: four elements, no atoms; modern: each element has its own kind of atom.
3. discrete: a, c, e; continuous: b, d
5. An element is a substance that could not be broken down into simpler substances.
7. Different elements can combine in two or more different sets of proportions, each set corresponding to a different compound.
   a. 2:1   **b.** 3:1   **c.** 3:5
9. C has 15 oxygen atoms; the initial mixture has only 14.
11. a. conservation of mass: no atoms are created or destroyed.
   b. definite proportions: only whole atoms combine.
   c. multiple proportions; 1 C atom can combine with 1 O atom to make CO, or 1 C atom can combine with 2 O atoms to make CO_2.
13. Law of multiple proportions
15. No. In the open vessel, a gas has escaped and is not part of the weight after reaction.
17. No. The elements have only been mixed; they have not reacted chemically.
19. 6.60 g

21. The mass of titanium(IV) oxide formed cannot be greater than the masses of titanium and oxygen together.
23. (b)
25. a. 86.9 g hydrogen.   **b.** 688 g oxygen
27. 3.8 kg carbon
29. C:O ratio for carbon suboxide is 1.000:0.888. Ratio of 1.332:0.888 = 3:2; 2.664:0.888 = 3:1.
31. SnO_2
33. The S:F ratios are (T) 1.00:2.37 and (U) 1.00:3.56. 3.56:2.37 = 1.50:1 or 3:2.
35. a. Yes; Dalton assumed that atoms of different elements had different masses.
   b. No; Dalton assumed that atoms of one element differ (in mass) from atoms of any other element.
37. Contradict. Dalton regarded atoms as indivisible.
39. (d)
41. Yes; the ratio of carbon to hydrogen is the same for the different samples.
43. 0.4467 g nitrogen
45. Six fluorine atoms
47. Conservation of mass
49. 108.0 g of mercury oxide
51. 1.334:1.000 or 4:3
53. (1) Lead compounds, once used in paints, have been replaced with titanium dioxide, a much safer material. (2) Metal salts with lower toxicity now substitute for the lead stabilizers in plastics.

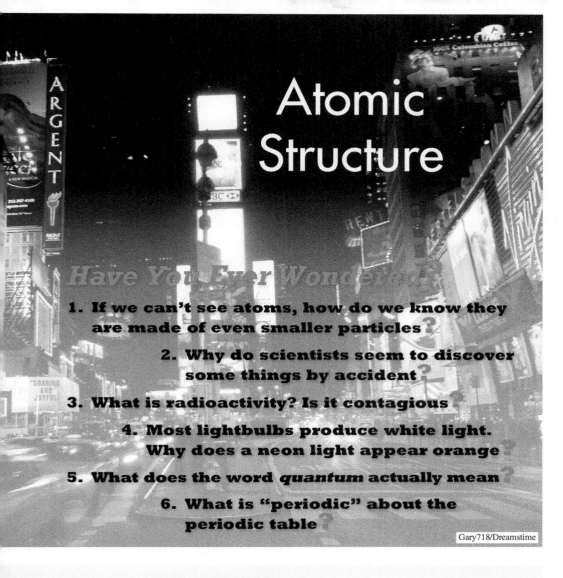

Atomic Structure

Have You Ever Wondered?

1. **If we can't see atoms, how do we know they are made of even smaller particles?**

2. **Why do scientists seem to discover some things by accident?**

3. **What is radioactivity? Is it contagious?**

4. **Most lightbulbs produce white light. Why does a neon light appear orange?**

5. **What does the word *quantum* actually mean?**

6. **What is "periodic" about the periodic table?**

Gary718/Dreamstime

Learning Objectives

> Explain the electrical properties of an atom. (1)

> Describe how the properties of electricity explain the structure of atoms. (1)

> Describe the experiments that led to the discovery of X-rays and an explanation of radioactivity. (2)

> Distinguish the three main kinds of radioactivity: alpha, beta, and gamma. (3)

> Sketch the nuclear model of the atom, and identify its parts. (4)

> List the particles that make up the nucleus of an atom, and give their relative masses and electric charges. (5)

> Identify elements and isotopes from their nuclear particles. (5)

> Define *quantum*. (6)

> Arrange the electrons in a given atom in energy levels (shells). (6)

> Relate the idea of a quantum of energy to an orbital. (7)

> Write an electron configuration (in subshell notation) for a given atom. (7)

> Describe how an element's electron configuration relates to its location in the periodic table. (8)

> Distinguish the conversion of solar energy into electrical energy in a solar cell from the conversion of solar energy into the chemical-bond energy of a solar fuel.

> Explain why splitting water into the elements hydrogen and oxygen requires an energy input and producing water by the reaction of hydrogen and oxygen releases energy.

Images of the Invisible

Atoms are exceedingly tiny particles, much too small to see even with an optical microscope. It is true that scientists can obtain images of individual atoms, but they use special instruments such as the scanning tunneling microscope (STM). Even so, we can see only outlines of atoms and their arrangements in a substance. If atoms are so small, how can we possibly know anything about their inner structures?

Although scientists have never examined the interior of an atom directly, they have been able to obtain a great deal of *indirect* information. By designing clever experiments and exercising their powers of deduction, scientists have constructed an amazingly detailed model of what an atom's interior must be like.

Neon lights—the signature of entertainment, restaurants, bars, and the big city. Interestingly enough, most of the flickering illumination seen at the Radio City Music Hall, on Times Square, and in Las Vegas is not from the element neon. The liquid fire of real neon lights is a characteristic orange-red color, and neon cannot be made to glow in any other color. Other colors are created by coating the inside of the tubing with a *phosphor* that glows in a specific color when current is applied to the tube. But why will neon only give off orange-red light? The answer lies in the structure of its atoms—the subject of this chapter.

Angelo Cavalli/SuperStock

Why do we care about the structure of particles as tiny as atoms? The reason is that the arrangement of various parts of atoms determines the properties of different kinds of matter. Only by understanding atomic structure can we learn how atoms combine to make millions of different substances. With such knowledge, we can modify and synthesize materials to meet our needs more precisely. Knowledge of atomic structure is even essential to good health care. Many medical diagnoses are based on chemical analyses that have been developed from our understanding of atomic structure.

Perhaps of greater interest to you is the fact that your understanding of chemistry (as well as much of biology and other sciences) depends, at least in part, on your knowledge of atomic structure. Let's begin by going back to the time of John Dalton.

▲ In addition to Michael Faraday's work in electrochemistry, he also devised methods for liquefying gases such as chlorine and invented the electrical transformer.

1 Electricity and the Atom

Learning Objectives ❯ Explain the electrical properties of an atom. ❯ Describe how the properties of electricity explain the structure of atoms.

Dalton, who set forth his atomic theory in 1803, regarded the atom as hard and indivisible. However, it wasn't long before evidence accumulated to show that matter has electrical properties. Indeed, the electrolytic decomposition of water by Nicholson and Carlisle in 1800 had already indicated this. Electricity played an important role in unraveling the structure of the atom.

Static electricity has been known since ancient times, but continuous electric current was born with the nineteenth century. In 1800, Alessandro Volta invented an electrochemical cell much like a modern battery. If the poles of such a cell are connected by a wire, current flows through the wire. The current is sustained by chemical reactions inside the cell. Volta's invention soon was applied in many areas of science and everyday life.

Electrolysis

▲ **Figure 1** An electrolysis apparatus. The electricity source (for example, a battery) directs electrons through wires from the anode to the cathode. Cations (+) are attracted to the cathode (−), and anions (−) are attracted to the anode (+). This migration of ions is the flow of electricity through the solution.

Soon after Volta's invention, Humphry Davy (1778–1829), a British chemist, built a powerful battery that he used to pass electricity through molten (melted) salts. Davy quickly discovered several new elements. In 1807, he liberated highly reactive potassium metal from molten potassium hydroxide. Shortly thereafter, he produced sodium metal by passing electricity through molten sodium hydroxide. Within a year, Davy had also produced magnesium, strontium, barium, and calcium metals for the first time. The science of electrochemistry was born.

Davy's protégé, Michael Faraday (1791–1867), greatly extended this new science. Lacking in formal education, Faraday consulted others to define many of the terms we still use today. His physician, Whitlock Nicholl (1786–1838), helped coin the term **electrolysis** for chemical reactions caused by electricity (Figure 1) and the name **electrolyte** for a compound that conducts electricity when melted or dissolved in water. English classical scholar William Whewell (1794–1866) suggested the names for the parts of the electrolytic apparatus. The carbon rods or metal strips inserted into a molten compound or a solution to carry the electric current are called **electrodes**. The electrode that bears a positive charge is the **anode**, and the negatively charged electrode is the **cathode**. The entities that carry the electric current through a melted compound or a solution are called *ions*. An **ion** is an atom or a group of atoms bonded together that has an electric charge. An ion with a negative charge is an **anion**; it travels toward the anode. A positively charged ion is a **cation**; it moves toward the cathode.

(a)   (b)

▲ **Figure 2** Thomson's apparatus, showing deflection of the cathode rays (a beam of electrons). Cathode rays are invisible but can be observed because they produce a green fluorescence when they strike a zinc sulfide–coated screen. The diagram (a) shows deflection of the beam in an electric field. The photograph (b) shows the deflection in a magnetic field. Cathode rays travel in straight lines unless some kind of external field is applied.

Faraday's work established that atoms have electrical properties, but further details of atomic structure had to wait several decades for more powerful sources of electricity and better vacuum pumps.

Cathode-Ray Tubes

In 1875, William Crookes (1832–1919), an English chemist, was able to construct a low-pressure gas-discharge tube that would allow electricity to pass through it. His experiment is shown in Figure 2. Crookes's tube is the antecedent of neon tubes used for signs and of cathode-ray tubes used in old television sets and computer monitors. Metal electrodes are sealed in the tube, which is connected to a vacuum pump so that most of the air can be removed from it. A beam of current produces a green fluorescence when it strikes a screen coated with zinc sulfide. This beam, which seems to leave the cathode and travel to the anode, was called a **cathode ray**.

Thomson's Experiment: Mass-to-Charge Ratio

Considerable speculation arose about the nature of cathode rays, and many experiments were undertaken. Were these rays beams of particles, or did they consist of a wavelike form of energy much like visible light? The answer came (as scientific answers should) from an experiment performed by the English physicist Joseph John Thomson in 1897. Thomson showed that cathode rays were deflected in an electric field (look again at Figure 2a). The beam was attracted to the positive plate and repelled by the negative plate. Thomson concluded that cathode rays consisted of negatively charged particles. His experiments also showed that the particles were the same regardless of the materials from which the electrodes were made or the type of gas in the tube. He concluded that these negative particles are part of all kinds of atoms. Thomson named these negatively charged units **electrons**. Cathode rays, then, are beams of electrons emanating from the cathode of a gas-discharge tube.

Cathode rays are deflected in magnetic fields as well as in electric fields. The greater the charge on a particle, the more it is deflected in an electric (or magnetic) field. The heavier the particle, the less it is deflected by a force. By measuring the amount of deflection in fields of known strength, Thomson was able to calculate the *ratio* of the mass of the electron to its charge. (He could not measure either the mass or the charge separately.) Thomson was awarded the Nobel Prize in Physics in 1906.

1. If we can't see atoms, how do we know they are made of even smaller particles? The existence of electrons and other subatomic particles was deduced from the behavior of electricity. The existence and behavior of the subatomic particles make atoms behave the way they do.

Atomic Structure

Goldstein's Experiment: Positive Particles

In 1886, German scientist Eugen Goldstein performed experiments with gas-discharge tubes that had perforated cathodes (Figure 3). He found that although electrons were formed and sped off toward the anode as usual, positive particles were also formed and shot in the opposite direction, toward the cathode. Some of these positive particles went through the holes in the cathode. In 1907, a study of the deflection of these particles in a magnetic field indicated that they were of varying mass. The lightest particles, formed when there was a little hydrogen gas in the tube, were later shown to have a mass 1837 times that of an electron.

Millikan's Oil-Drop Experiment: Electron Charge

The charge on the electron was determined in 1909 by Robert A. Millikan (1868–1953), a physicist at the University of Chicago. Millikan observed electrically charged oil drops in an electric field. A diagram of his apparatus is shown in Figure 4. A spray bottle is used to form tiny droplets of oil. Some acquire negative charges, either from irradiation with X-rays or from the friction generated as the particles rub against the opening of the spray nozzle and against each other. (The charge is static electricity, just like the charge you get from walking across a nylon carpet.) Either way, the droplets acquire one or more extra electrons.

Some of the oil droplets pass into a chamber where they can be viewed through a microscope. The negative plate at the bottom of the chamber repels the negatively charged droplets, and the positive plate attracts them. By manipulating the charge on each plate and observing the behavior of the droplets, the charge on each droplet can be determined. Millikan took the smallest possible difference in charge between two droplets to be the charge of an individual electron. For his research, he received the Nobel Prize in Physics in 1923.

From Millikan's value for the charge and Thomson's value for the mass-to-charge ratio, the mass of the electron was readily calculated. That mass was found to be only 9.1×10^{-28} g. To have a mass of 1 g would require more than 1×10^{27} electrons—that's a 1 followed by 27 zeros, or a billion billion billion electrons. More important, the electron's mass is much *smaller* than that of the lightest atom. This means that electrons are much smaller than atoms.

▲ **Figure 3** Goldstein's apparatus for the study of positive particles. This apparatus, with holes in the cathode, is a modification of the cathode-ray tube in Figure 2. Some positive ions, attracted toward the cathode, pass through the holes in the cathode. The deflection of these particles (not shown) in a magnetic field can be studied in the region to the left of the cathode.

You can find out more about numbers like 9.1×10^{-28} and 1×10^{27} in the Appendix. However, in practice, we seldom use the actual mass and charge of the electron. For many purposes, the electron is considered the unit of electrical charge. The charge is shown as a superscript minus sign (meaning $^{1-}$). In indicating charges on ions, we use $^{-}$ to indicate a net charge due to one "extra" electron, $^{2-}$ to indicate a charge due to two "extra" electrons, and so on.

▲ **Figure 4** The Millikan oil-drop experiment. Oil drops irradiated with X-rays pick up electrons and become negatively charged. Their fall due to gravity can be balanced by adjusting the voltage of the electric field. The charge on the oil drop can be determined from the applied voltage and the mass of the oil drop. The charge on each drop is that of some whole number of electrons.

Self-Assessment Questions

1. The use of electricity to cause a chemical reaction is called
   a. anodizing   **b.** corrosion   **c.** electrolysis   **d.** hydrolysis

2. During electrolysis of molten sodium hydroxide, chloride anions move to the
   a. anode, which is negatively charged
   b. anode, which is positively charged
   c. cathode, which is negatively charged
   d. cathode, which is positively charged

3. Cathode rays are *not*
   a. composed of negatively charged particles
   b. composed of particles with a mass of 1 u
   c. deflected by electric fields
   d. the same from element to element

4. Thomson used a cathode-ray tube to discover that cathode rays
   a. are deflected by an electric field
   b. are radiation similar to X-rays
   c. could ionize air inside the tube
   d. could ionize the air outside the far end of the tube

5. When J. J. Thomson discovered the electron, he measured its
   a. atomic number   **b.** charge   **c.** mass   **d.** mass-to-charge ratio

6. In his oil-drop experiment, Millikan determined the charge of an electron by
   a. measuring the diameters of the tiniest drops
   b. noting that the drops had either a certain minimum charge or multiples of that charge
   c. using an atomizer that could spray out individual electrons
   d. viewing the smallest charged drops microscopically and noting that they had one extra electron

Answers: 1, c; 2, b; 3, b; 4, a; 5, d; 6, b

2 Serendipity in Science: X-Rays and Radioactivity

Learning Objective ❯ Describe the experiments that led to the discovery of X-rays and an explanation of radioactivity.

Let's take a look at two serendipitous discoveries of the last years of the nineteenth century that profoundly changed the world and are related to atomic structure.

Roentgen: The Discovery of X-Rays

In 1895, German scientist Wilhelm Conrad Roentgen (1845–1923) was working in a dark room, studying the glow produced in certain substances by cathode rays. To his surprise, he noted this glow on a chemically treated piece of paper some distance from the cathode-ray tube. The paper even glowed when a wall separated the tube from the paper; this type of ray could travel through walls. When he waved his hand between the radiation source and the glowing paper, he was able to see an image of the bones of his hand in darker shades on the paper. He called these mysterious rays **X-rays**. He found in general that X-rays were absorbed more by bone or other hard and fairly dense materials than by soft, less dense tissues.

X-rays are a form of electromagnetic radiation—energy with electric and magnetic components. Among other types, electromagnetic radiation also includes visible light, radio waves, microwaves, infrared radiation, ultraviolet light, and gamma rays (Section 3). These forms differ in energy, with radio waves lowest in energy, followed by microwaves, infrared radiation, visible light, ultraviolet light, X-rays, and gamma rays.

Today, X-rays are one of the most widely used tools in the world for medical diagnosis. Not only are they employed for examining decayed teeth, broken bones,

2. Why do scientists seem to discover some things by accident? *Serendipity*—a "happy accident" like drilling for water and striking oil—happens to everyone at times. Scientists, however, are trained observers. When something unexpected happens, they often wonder why and investigate. The same accident might happen to an untrained person and go unnoticed (though often even scientists miss important finds at first). Or, if noticed, its significance might not be grasped.

Otto Glasser/Images from the History of Medicine/National Library of Medicine

▲ X-rays were used in medicine shortly after they were discovered by Wilhelm Roentgen in 1895. In fact, the first known X-ray photograph is the one seen here—of Mrs. Roentgen's hand!

▲ Marie Sklodowska Curie in her laboratory.

3. What is radioactivity? Is it contagious? Radioactivity is the spontaneous decay (occurring without a cause) of an atom into one or more other atoms. The radiation—alpha, beta, or gamma rays—given off by radioactive material is hazardous but you cannot "catch" radiation sickness from a person exposed to radiation any more than you can "catch" a sunburn from a sunburned friend.

and diseased lungs, but they are also the basis for such procedures as mammography and computerized tomography. In the United States alone, payments for various radiological procedures total more than $20 billion each year. How ironic that Roentgen himself made no profit at all from his discovery. He considered X-rays a "gift to humanity" and refused to patent any part of the discovery. However, he did receive much popular acclaim and in 1901 was awarded the first Nobel Prize in Physics.

The Discovery of Radioactivity

Certain chemicals exhibit *fluorescence* after exposure to strong sunlight. They continue to glow even when taken into a dark room. In 1895, Antoine Henri Becquerel (1852–1908), a French physicist, was studying fluorescence by wrapping photographic film in black paper, placing a few crystals of the fluorescing chemical on top of the paper, and then placing the package in strong sunlight. If the glow was like ordinary light, it would not pass through the paper. On the other hand, if it was similar to X-rays, it would pass through the black paper and fog the film.

While working with a uranium compound, Becquerel made an important accidental discovery. When placed in sunlight, the compound fluoresced and fogged the film. On several cloudy days when exposure to sunlight was not possible, he prepared samples and placed them in a drawer. To his great surprise, the photographic film was fogged even though the uranium compound had not been exposed to sunlight. Further experiments showed that the radiation coming from the uranium compound was unrelated to fluorescence but was a characteristic of the element uranium.

Other scientists immediately began to study this new radiation. Becquerel's graduate student from Poland, Marie Sklodowska, gave the phenomenon a name: radioactivity. **Radioactivity** is the spontaneous emission of radiation from certain unstable elements. Marie later married Pierre Curie, a French physicist. Together they discovered the radioactive elements polonium and radium, and with Becquerel they shared the 1903 Nobel Prize in Physics.

After her husband's death in 1906, Marie Curie continued to work with radioactive substances, winning the Nobel Prize in Chemistry in 1911. For more than 50 years, she was the only person ever to have received two Nobel Prizes.

Self-Assessment Questions

1. When Roentgen saw an X-ray image of his hand, the bones were darker than the glowing paper because the X-rays were
   a. absorbed more by bone than by flesh
   b. radiation that is less energetic than visible light
   c. made up of fast-moving atoms
   d. a type of radioactivity

2. Radioactivity arises from elements that
   a. absorb radio waves and release stronger radiation
   b. are unstable and emit radiation
   c. give off X-rays
   d. undergo fission (splitting) of their atoms when they absorb energy

Answers: 1, a; 2, b

3 Three Types of Radioactivity

Learning Objective ❯ Distinguish the three main kinds of radioactivity: alpha, beta, and gamma.

Scientists soon showed that three types of radiation emanated from various radioactive elements. Ernest Rutherford (1871–1937), a New Zealander who pursued his career in Canada and Great Britain, chose the names *alpha*, *beta*, and *gamma* for

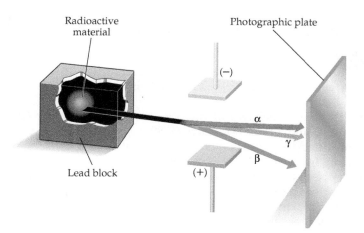

◀ **Figure 5** Behavior of a beam of radioactivity in an electric field.

Q: *Why are alpha rays deflected upward in this figure? Why are beta rays deflected downward?*

the three types of radioactivity. When passed through a strong magnetic or electric field, the alpha type was deflected in a manner indicating that it consisted of a beam of positive particles (Figure 5). Later experiments showed that an **alpha particle** has a mass four times that of a hydrogen atom and a charge twice the magnitude of, but opposite in sign to, that of an electron. An alpha particle is in fact identical to the nucleus (Section 4) of a helium atom and is often symbolized by He^{2+}.

The beta radiation was shown to be made up of negatively charged particles identical to those of cathode rays. Therefore, a **beta particle** is an electron, although it has much more energy than an electron in an atom. **Gamma rays** are not deflected by a magnetic field. They are a form of electromagnetic radiation, much like the X-rays used in medical work but even more energetic and more penetrating. The three types of radioactivity are summarized in Table 1.

The discoveries of the late nineteenth century paved the way for an entirely new picture of the atom, which developed rapidly during the early years of the twentieth century.

STR/AFP/Getty Images/Newscom

▲ **It DOES Matter!**

It is important to distinguish between the *rays* given off by a radioactive element and the radioactive element itself. Like light, alpha, beta, and gamma rays can be absorbed by materials and do not generally cause problems thereafter. A potato that has absorbed gamma rays is not harmful to eat. The serious problem from nuclear disasters, such as the Fukushima disaster of March 2011, arises because radioactive atoms escape from the reactor. Those atoms can lodge on or be absorbed by materials and give off damaging alpha, beta, or gamma rays when those materials are used. These workers from the Fukushima plant are being checked for radioactive particles on their clothing.

Table 1	Types of Radioactivity		
Name	**Greek Letter**	**Mass (u)**	**Charge**
Alpha	α	4	2+
Beta	β	$\dfrac{1}{1837}$	1−
Gamma	γ	0	0

Self-Assessment Questions

1. The mass of an alpha particle is about
   a. four times that of a hydrogen atom
   b. the same as that of an electron
   c. the same as that of a hydrogen atom
   d. the same as that of a beta particle

2. Compared to the charge on an electron (designated 1−), the charge on an alpha particle is about
   a. 4−   b. 1−   c. 1+   d. 2+   e. 4+

3. A beta particle is a(n)
   a. boron atom   b. electron   c. helium nucleus   d. proton

4. The mass of a gamma ray is
   a. −1 u   b. 0 u   c. 1 u   d. 4 u

Answers: 1, a; 2, d; 3, b; 4, b

4 Rutherford's Experiment: The Nuclear Model of the Atom

Learning Objectives ➤ Sketch the nuclear model of the atom, and identify its parts.

At Rutherford's suggestion, two of his coworkers—Hans Geiger (1882–1945), a German physicist, and Ernest Marsden (1889–1970), an English undergraduate student—bombarded very thin metal foils with alpha particles from a radioactive source (Figure 6). In an experiment with gold foil, most of the particles behaved as Rutherford expected, going right through the foil with little or no scattering. However, a few particles were deflected sharply. Occasionally, one was sent right back in the direction from which it had come!

Rutherford had assumed that positive charge was spread evenly over all the space occupied by the atom, but obviously it was not. To explain the results, Rutherford concluded that all the positive charge and nearly all the mass of an atom are concentrated at the center of the atom in a tiny core called the **nucleus**.

When an alpha particle, which is positively charged, directly approached the positively charged nucleus, it was strongly repelled and therefore sharply deflected (Figure 7). Because only a few alpha particles were deflected, Rutherford concluded that the nucleus must occupy only a tiny fraction of the volume of an atom. Most of the alpha particles passed right through because most of an atom is empty space. The space outside the nucleus isn't completely empty, however. It contains the

▶ **Figure 6** Rutherford's gold-foil experiment. Most alpha particles passed right through the gold foil, but now and then a particle was deflected.

Alpha source

Zinc sulfide screen for detecting radiation

Alpha radiation

Gold foil

▶ **Figure 7** Model explaining the results of Rutherford's gold-foil experiment. Most of the alpha particles pass right through the foil because the gold atoms are mainly empty space. But some alpha particles are deflected as they pass close to a dense, positively charged atomic nucleus. Once in a while, an alpha particle encounters an atomic nucleus head-on and is knocked back in the direction from which it came.

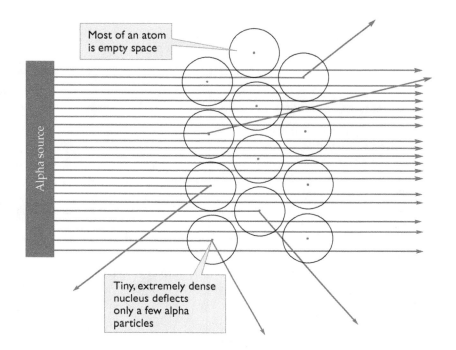

Most of an atom is empty space

Alpha source

Tiny, extremely dense nucleus deflects only a few alpha particles negatively charged electrons. Rutherford concluded that the electrons had so little mass that they were no match for the alpha particle "bullets." It would be analogous to a mouse trying to stop a charging hippopotamus.

Rutherford's nuclear theory of the atom, set forth in 1911, was revolutionary. He postulated that all the positive charge and nearly all the mass of an atom are concentrated in a tiny, tiny nucleus. The negatively charged electrons have almost no mass, yet they occupy nearly all the volume of an atom. To picture Rutherford's model, visualize a sphere as big as the largest covered football stadium. The nucleus at the middle of the sphere is as small as a pea but weighs several million tons. A few flies flitting here and there throughout the sphere represent the electrons.

Self-Assessment Questions

1. The most persuasive evidence from Rutherford's gold-foil experiment was that
   a. all the alpha particles were deflected a bit
   b. most of the alpha particles went right through the foil, but a tiny fraction were reflected right back toward the source
   c. some gold atoms were converted to lead atoms
   d. some gold atoms were split

2. Rutherford's gold-foil experiment showed that
   a. gold atoms consisted of protons in a "pudding" of electrons
   b. the nucleus was huge and positively charged
   c. the nucleus was tiny and positively charged
   d. some gold atoms were shattered by alpha particles

3. From his gold-foil experiment, Rutherford concluded that atoms consist mainly of
   a. electrons
   b. empty space
   c. neutrons
   d. protons

4. The positively charged part of the atom is its
   a. cation
   b. nucleus
   c. outer electrons
   d. widespread cloud of electrons

Answers: 1, b; 2, c; 3, b; 4, b

5 The Atomic Nucleus

Learning Objectives ❭ List the particles that make up the nucleus of an atom, and give their relative masses and electric charges. ❭ Identify elements and isotopes from their nuclear particles.

In 1914, Rutherford suggested that the smallest positive particle (the one formed when there is hydrogen gas in Goldstein's apparatus—see Section 1) is the unit of positive charge in the nucleus. This particle, called a **proton**, has a charge equal in magnitude to that of the electron and has nearly the same mass as a hydrogen atom. Rutherford's suggestion was that protons constitute the positively charged matter in all atoms. The nucleus of a hydrogen atom consists of one proton, and the nuclei of larger atoms contain greater numbers of protons.

But most atomic nuclei are heavier than is indicated by the number of positive charges (number of protons). For example, the helium nucleus has a charge of 2+ (and therefore two protons, according to Rutherford's theory), but its mass is *four* times that of hydrogen. This excess mass puzzled scientists at first. Then, in 1932, English physicist James Chadwick (1891–1974) discovered a particle with about the same mass as a proton but with no electrical charge. It was called a **neutron**, and its existence explains the unexpectedly high mass of the helium nucleus. Whereas the

Table 2	Subatomic Particles			
Particle	**Symbol**	**Mass (u)**	**Charge**	**Location in Atom**
Proton	p^+	1	1+	Nucleus
Neutron	n	1	0	Nucleus
Electron	e^-	$\dfrac{1}{1837}$	1−	Outside nucleus

hydrogen nucleus contains only one proton of mass 1 u, the helium nucleus contains not only two protons (2 u) but also two neutrons (2 u), giving it a total mass of 4 u.

With the discovery of the neutron, the list of "building blocks" we will need for "constructing" atoms is complete. The properties of these particles are summarized in Table 2. (There are dozens of other subatomic particles, but most exist only momentarily and are not important to our discussion.)

Atomic Number

The number of protons in the nucleus of an atom of any element is the **atomic number (Z)** of that element. This number determines the kind of atom—that is, the identity of the element—and it is found on any periodic table or list of the elements. Dalton thought that the mass of an atom determines the element. We now know it is not the mass but the number of protons that determines the identity of an element. For example, every atom with 26 protons is an atom of iron (Fe), whose atomic number $Z = 26$. Any atom with 50 protons is an atom of tin (Sn), which has $Z = 50$. In a neutral atom (one with no electrical charge), the positive charge of the protons is exactly neutralized by the negative charge of the electrons. The attractive forces between the unlike charges help hold the atom together.

A proton and a neutron have almost the same mass, 1.0073 u and 1.0087 u, respectively. This difference is so small that it usually can be ignored. Thus, for many purposes, we can assume that the masses of the proton and the neutron are the same, 1 u. The proton has a charge equal in magnitude but opposite in sign to that of an electron. This charge on a proton is written as 1+. The electron has a charge of 1− and a mass of 0.00055 u. The electrons in an atom contribute so little to its total mass that their mass is usually disregarded (treated as if it were 0).

Isotopes

We can now more precisely define *isotopes*, a term we mentioned. Atoms of a given element can have different numbers of neutrons in their nuclei. For example, most hydrogen atoms have a nucleus consisting of a single proton and no neutrons. However, about 1 hydrogen atom in 6700 has a neutron as well as a proton in its nucleus. This heavier hydrogen atom is called *deuterium*. A third, rare isotope of hydrogen is *tritium*, which has two neutrons and one proton in the nucleus. Whether it has one neutron, two neutrons, or none, any atom with $Z = 1$—that is, with one proton—is a hydrogen atom. Atoms that have this sort of relationship—having the same number of protons but different numbers of neutrons—are called **isotopes** (Figure 8).

▶ **Figure 8** The three isotopes of hydrogen. Each has one proton and one electron, but they differ in the number of neutrons in the nucleus.

Q: *What is the atomic number and mass number of each of the isotopes? What is the mass of each, in atomic mass units, to the nearest whole number?*

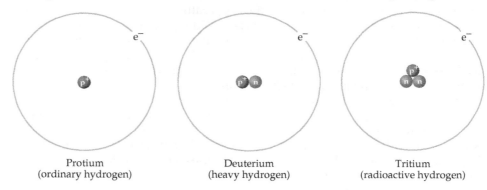

Protium	Deuterium	Tritium
(ordinary hydrogen)	(heavy hydrogen)	(radioactive hydrogen)

Most, but not all, elements exist in nature in isotopic forms. For example, tin is present in nature in 10 different isotopic forms. It also has 15 radioactive isotopes that do not occur in nature. Aluminum, on the other hand, has only one naturally occurring isotope.

Isotopes usually have little or no effect on ordinary chemical reactions. For example, all three hydrogen isotopes react with oxygen to form water. Because these isotopes differ in mass, compounds formed with them have different physical properties, but such differences are usually slight. For example, water in which both hydrogen atoms are deuterium is called *heavy water*, often represented as D_2O. Heavy water boils at 101.4 °C (instead of 100 °C) and freezes at 3.8 °C (instead of 0 °C). In nuclear reactions, however, isotopes are of the utmost importance.

Symbols for Isotopes

Collectively, the two main nuclear particles, protons and neutrons, are called **nucleons**. Isotopes are represented by symbols with subscripts and superscripts.

$$^A_Z X$$

In this general symbol, Z is the nuclear charge (atomic number, or number of protons), and A is the **mass number**, or the **nucleon number** because it is the number of nucleons. (*Nucleon number* is the term recommended by the International Union of Pure and Applied Chemistry.) As an example, the isotope with the symbol

$$^{35}_{17} Cl$$

has 17 protons and 35 nucleons. The number of neutrons is therefore $35 - 17 = 18$.

Isotopes often are named by adding the mass number as a suffix to the name of the element. The three hydrogen isotopes are represented as

$$^1_1 H \quad ^2_1 H \quad ^3_1 H$$

and named hydrogen-1, hydrogen-2, and hydrogen-3.

Example 1   Number of Neutrons

How many neutrons are there in the $^{235}_{92} U$ nucleus?

Solution

We simply subtract the atomic number Z (number of protons) from the mass number A (number of protons plus number of neutrons).

$$A - Z = \text{number of neutrons}$$
$$235 - 92 = 143$$

There are 143 neutrons in the $^{235}_{92} U$ nucleus.

■ EXERCISE 1A
How many neutrons are there in the $^{60}_{27} Co$ nucleus?

■ EXERCISE 1B
An iodine isotope has 78 neutrons in its nucleus. What is the mass number and the name of the isotope?

CONCEPTUAL Example 2   Isotopes

Refer to the following isotope symbols, in which the letter X replaces each element symbol. **(a)** Which represent isotopes of the same element? **(b)** Which have the same mass number? **(c)** Which have the same number of neutrons?

$$^{16}_8 X \quad ^{16}_7 X \quad ^{14}_7 X \quad ^{14}_6 X \quad ^{12}_6 X$$

Solution

a. Isotopes of the same element have the same atomic number (subscript). There-fore, $^{16}_{7}X$ and $^{14}_{7}X$ are isotopes of nitrogen (N), and $^{14}_{6}X$ and $^{12}_{6}X$ are isotopes of carbon (C).

b. The mass number is the superscript, so $^{16}_{8}X$ and $^{16}_{7}X$ have the same mass number. The first is an isotope of oxygen, and the second an isotope of nitrogen. $^{14}_{7}X$ and $^{14}_{6}X$ also have the same mass number. The first is an isotope of nitrogen, and the second an isotope of carbon.

c. To determine the number of neutrons, we subtract the atomic number from the mass number. We find that $^{16}_{8}X$ and $^{14}_{6}X$ each have eight neutrons ($16 - 8 = 8$ and $14 - 6 = 8$, respectively).

■ EXERCISE 2A
Which of the following represent isotopes of the same element?

$$^{90}_{37}X \quad ^{90}_{35}X \quad ^{88}_{37}X \quad ^{88}_{38}X \quad ^{93}_{38}X$$

■ EXERCISE 2B
How many different elements are represented in Exercise 2A?

Self-Assessment Questions

1. The three basic components of an atom are
   a. protium, deuterium, and tritium
   b. protons, neutrinos, and ions
   c. protons, neutrons, and electrons
   d. protons, neutrons, and ions

2. The identity of an element is determined by its
   a. atomic mass
   b. number of atoms
   c. number of electrons
   d. number of protons

3. How many electrons are required to equal the mass of one proton?
   a. 1   b. 18   c. about 1800   d. 1×10^{27}

4. Which particles have approximately the same mass?
   a. electrons and neutrons
   b. electrons and protons
   c. electrons, neutrons, and protons
   d. neutrons and protons

5. A change in the number of protons of an atom produces a(n)
   a. compound
   b. atom of a different element
   c. ion
   d. different isotope of the same element

6. The number of protons plus neutrons in an atom is its
   a. atomic mass   b. atomic number   c. isotope number   d. nucleon number

7. How many protons (p) and how many neutrons (n) are there in a $^{15}_{7}N$ nucleus?
   a. 7 p, 7 n   b. 7 p, 8 n   c. 7 p, 15 n   d. 8 p, 8 n

8. A neutral atom has 5 electrons and 6 neutrons. Its atomic number is
   a. 1   b. 5   c. 6   d. 11

9. The symbol for the isotope potassium-40 is
   a. $^{21}_{19}K$ b. $^{39}_{19}K$ c. $^{40}_{19}K$ d. $^{19}_{40}K$

6 Electron Arrangement: The Bohr Model

Learning Objectives ❯ Define *quantum.* ❯ Arrange the electrons in a given atom in energy levels (shells).

Let's turn our attention once more to electrons. Rutherford demonstrated that atoms have a tiny, positively charged nucleus with electrons outside it. Evidence soon accumulated that the electrons were not randomly distributed but were arranged in an ordered fashion. We will examine that evidence soon. But first, let's take a side trip into some colorful chemistry and physics to provide a background for our study of the arrangement of electrons in atoms.

Fireworks and Flame Tests

Chemists of the eighteenth and nineteenth centuries developed flame tests that used the colors of flames to identify several elements (Figure 9). Sodium salts produce a persistent yellow flame, potassium salts a fleeting lavender flame, and lithium salts a brilliant red flame. It was not until the structure of atoms was better understood, however, that scientists could explain why each element emits a distinctive color of light.

Fireworks originated earlier than flame tests, in ancient China. The brilliant colors of aerial displays still mark our celebrations of patriotic holidays. The colors of fireworks are attributable to specific elements. Brilliant reds are produced by strontium compounds, whereas barium compounds are used to produce green, sodium compounds yield yellow, and copper salts produce blue or violet. However, the colors of fireworks and flame tests are not as simple as they seem to the unaided eye.

Continuous and Line Spectra

When white light from an incandescent lamp is passed through a prism, it produces a continuous spectrum, or rainbow of colors (Figure 10). A similar phenomenon occurs when sunlight passes through raindrops. The different colors of light correspond to different wavelengths. Blue light has shorter wavelengths than red light, but there is no sharp transition in moving from one color to the next. All wavelengths are present in a continuous spectrum (Figure 11, top). White light is simply a combination of all the various colors.

If the light from a colored flame test or a gas-discharge tube containing a particular element is passed through a prism, only narrow colored lines are observed (Figure 11). Each line corresponds to light of a particular wavelength. The pattern of lines emitted by an element is called its *line spectrum*. The line spectrum of an element is characteristic of that element and can be used to identify it. Not all the lines in the spectrum of an atom are visible; some are infrared or ultraviolet radiation.

▲ The brilliant colors of a fireworks display come from compounds added to the fireworks. Strontium compounds produce red, copper compounds produce blue or violet, and barium compounds produce green.

4. Most lightbulbs produce white light. Why does a neon light appear orange? When a solid is heated, it goes through a stage of red heat, then yellow, and finally white light is emitted, which consists of all wavelengths. When a gas such as neon is heated, we get a line spectrum (Figure 11), which gives a specific color to the light.

| Lithium, Li | Sodium, Na | Potassium, K | Calcium, Ca | Strontium, Sr |

▲ **Figure 9** Certain chemical elements can be identified by the characteristic colors their compounds impart to flames. Five examples are shown here.

David Parker/Science Photo Library/Photo Researchers, Inc.

▲ **Figure 10** A glass prism separates white light into a continuous spectrum, or rainbow, of colors just as sunlight passing through raindrops causes a rainbow in the sky.

Gary J. Shulfer/C. Marvin Lang

▲ Danish physicist Niels Bohr received the 1922 Nobel Prize in Physics for his planetary model of the atom with its quantized electron energy levels. Element 107 is named bohrium (Bh) in his honor.

5. What does the word *quantum* actually mean? Just as an atom is the smallest unit of an element, a quantum is the smallest unit of energy. There are different sizes of quanta, but energy is produced or consumed in discrete rather than continuous units. "Quantum leap" comes from the idea suggested by Figure 12, where an electron can "leap" from one energy level to another.

▶ **Figure 12** Possible electron shifts between energy levels in atoms to produce the lines found in spectra. Not all of the lines are in the visible portion of the spectrum. The four colored arrows correspond to the four colored lines in the hydrogen spectrum seen in Figure 11.

Q: *Which transition involves the greater change in energy, a drop from energy level 6 to energy level 2, or a drop from energy level 7 to energy level 6? What color of light is absorbed when an electron in a hydrogen atom is boosted from energy level 2 to energy level 3?*

CONTINUOUS SPECTRUM

EMISSION (BRIGHT LINE) SPECTRA

Cd

Sr

Ba

Ca

H

Na

Wabash Instrument Corp./Fundamental Photographs

▲ **Figure 11** Line spectra of selected elements. Some of the components of the light emitted by excited atoms appear as colored lines. A continuous spectrum is shown at the top for comparison. The numbers are wavelengths of light given in Angstrom units (1 Å = 10^{-10} m). Each element has its own characteristic line spectrum that differs from all others and can be used to identify the element.

The visible line spectrum of hydrogen is fairly simple, consisting of four lines in that portion of the electromagnetic spectrum. To explain the hydrogen spectrum, Danish physicist Niels Bohr (1885–1962) worked out a model for the electron arrangement of the hydrogen atom.

Bohr's Explanation of Line Spectra

Niels Bohr presented his explanation of line spectra in 1913. He suggested that electrons cannot have just any amount of energy but can have only certain specified amounts; that is, the energy of an electron is *quantized*. A **quantum** (plural: *quanta*) is a tiny unit of energy, whose value depends on the frequency of the radiation. A specified energy value for an electron is called its **energy level**.

By absorbing a quantum of energy (for example, when atoms of the element are heated), an electron is elevated to a higher energy level (Figure 12). By giving up

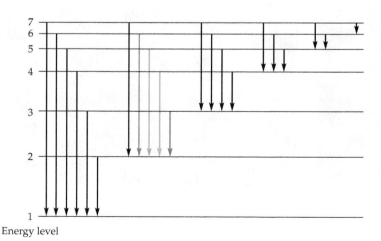

Energy level

a quantum of energy, the electron can return to a lower energy level. The energy released shows up as a line spectrum. Each line has a specific wavelength corresponding to a quantum of energy. An electron moves practically instantaneously from one energy level to another, and there are no intermediate stages.

Consider the analogy of a person on a ladder. A person can stand on the first rung, the second rung, the third rung, and so on, but is unable to stand between rungs. As the person goes from one rung to another, the potential energy (energy due to position) changes by definite amounts. As an electron moves from one energy level to another, its total energy (both potential and kinetic) also changes by definite amounts, or quanta.

Bohr based his model of the atom on the laws of planetary motion that had been set down by the German astronomer Johannes Kepler (1571–1630) three centuries before. Bohr imagined the electrons to be orbiting about the nucleus much as planets orbit the sun (Figure 13). Different energy levels were pictured as different orbits. The modern picture of the atom is different, as we will see in the next section.

▲ **Figure 13** The nuclear atom, as envisioned by Bohr. Most of its mass is in an extremely small nucleus. Bohr thought that electrons orbited about the nucleus in the same way that planets orbit the sun.

Ground States and Excited States

The electron in a hydrogen atom is usually in the first, or lowest, energy level. Electrons tend to stay in their lowest possible energy levels (those nearest the nucleus). Atoms with their electrons thus situated are said to be in their **ground state**. When a flame or other source supplies energy to an atom (of hydrogen, for example) and an electron jumps from the lowest possible level to a higher level, the atom is said to be in an **excited state**. An atom in an excited state eventually emits a quantum of energy—often a *photon*, or "particle," of light—as the electron jumps back down to one of the lower levels and ultimately reaches the ground state.

Bohr's theory was spectacularly successful in explaining the line spectrum of hydrogen. It established the important idea of energy levels in atoms. Bohr was awarded the Nobel Prize in Physics in 1922 for this work.

Atoms larger than hydrogen have more than one electron, and Bohr was also able to deduce that a given energy level of an atom could contain at most only a certain number of electrons. The maximum number of electrons that can be in a given level is indicated by the formula

$$\text{Maximum number of electrons} = 2n^2$$

where n is the energy level being considered. For the first energy level ($n = 1$), the maximum number of electrons is $2 \times 1^2 = 2 \times 1 = 2$. For the second energy level ($n = 2$), the maximum number is $2 \times 2^2 = 2 \times 4 = 8$. For the third level, the maximum number is $2 \times 3^2 = 2 \times 9 = 18$.

The various energy levels are often called **shells**. The first energy level ($n = 1$) is the first shell, the second energy level ($n = 2$) is the second shell, and so on.

Example 3   Electron-Shell Capacity

What is the maximum number of electrons in the fifth shell (fifth energy level)?

Solution

The maximum number of electrons in a given shell is given by $2n^2$. For the fifth level, $n = 5$, and so we have

$$2 \times 5^2 = 2 \times 25 = 50 \text{ electrons}$$

▪ EXERCISE 3A

What is the maximum number of electrons in the fourth shell (fourth energy level)?

▪ EXERCISE 3B

What is the lowest energy level that can hold 18 electrons?

Building Atoms: Main Shells

Imagine building up atoms by adding one electron to the proper shell as *each* proton is added to the nucleus, keeping in mind that electrons will go to the lowest energy level (shell) available. For hydrogen, with a nucleus containing only one proton ($Z = 1$), the single electron goes into the first shell. For helium, with a nucleus having two protons ($Z = 2$), both electrons go into the first shell. According to Bohr, two electrons is the maximum population of the first shell, and that level is filled in the helium atom. (We can ignore the neutrons in the nucleus; they are not involved in this process.)

With lithium ($Z = 3$), two electrons go into the first shell, and the third must go into the second shell. This process of adding electrons is continued until the second shell is filled with eight electrons, as in a neon atom ($Z = 10$), which has two of its 10 electrons in the first shell and the remaining eight in the second shell.

A sodium atom ($Z = 11$) has 11 electrons. Two are in the first shell, the second shell is filled with eight electrons, and the remaining electron is in the third shell. We can represent the **electron configuration** (or arrangement) of the first 11 elements as follows:

Element	1st shell	2nd shell	3rd shell
H	1		
He	2		
Li	2	1	
⋮	⋮	⋮	
Ne	2	8	
Na	2	8	1

Sometimes the main-shell electron configuration is abbreviated by writing the symbol for the element followed by the numbers of electrons in each shell, separated by commas, starting with the lowest energy level. Following the color scheme from the preceding table, the main-shell configuration for sodium is simply

$$\text{Na } 2, 8, 1$$

We can continue to add electrons to the third shell until we get to argon. The main-shell configuration for argon is

$$\text{Ar } 2, 8, 8$$

After argon, the notation for electron configurations is enhanced with more detail. This notation is discussed in greater detail in Section 8. Meanwhile, Example 4 shows how to determine a few main-shell configurations.

Example 4   Main-Shell Electron Configurations

What is the main-shell electron configuration for fluorine?

Solution

Fluorine has the symbol F ($Z = 9$). It has nine electrons. Two of these electrons go into the first shell, and the remaining seven go into the second shell.

$$\text{F } 2, 7$$

■ EXERCISE 4

Write the main-shell electron configurations for (a) beryllium and (b) magnesium. These elements are in the same column of the periodic table. What do you notice about the number of electrons in their outermost shells?

Self-Assessment Questions

1. When electrified in a gas-discharge tube, different elements emit light that forms narrow lines that are
   a. characteristic of each particular element
   b. the same as those of the hydrogen spectrum
   c. the same for all elements but with differing colors
   d. the same for all elements but with differing intensities

2. When an electron in an atom goes from a higher energy level to a lower one, the electron
   a. absorbs energy
   b. changes its volume
   c. changes its charge
   d. releases energy

3. An atom in an excited state is one with an electron that has
   a. moved to a higher energy level
   b. been removed
   c. bonded to another atom to make a molecule
   d. combined with a proton to make a neutron

4. The maximum number of electrons in the first shell of an atom is
   a. 2   b. 6   c. 8   d. unlimited

5. The maximum number of electrons in the third shell of an atom is
   a. 6   b. 8   c. 18   d. 32

6. The main-shell electron configuration of aluminum is
   a. 2, 8, 1   b. 2, 8, 3   c. 2, 8, 13   d. 2, 8, 8, 8, 1

7. The main-shell electron configuration of sulfur is
   a. 2, 8, 4   b. 2, 8, 6   c. 2, 8, 8, 8, 6   d. 2, 8, 18, 4

Answers: 1, a; 2, d; 3, a; 4, a; 5, c; 6, b; 7, b

7 Electron Arrangement: The Quantum Model

Learning Objectives ❯ Relate the idea of a quantum of energy to an orbital. ❯ Write an electron configuration (in subshell notation) for a given atom.

Bohr's simple planetary model of the atom has been replaced for many purposes by more sophisticated models in which electrons are treated as *both* particles and waves. The electrons have characteristic wavelengths and their locations are indicated as probabilities. The theory that the electron should have wavelike properties was first suggested in 1924 by Louis de Broglie (1892–1987), a young French physicist. Although it was hard to accept because of Thomson's evidence that electrons are particles, de Broglie's theory was experimentally verified within a few years.

Erwin Schrödinger (1887–1961), an Austrian physicist, used highly mathematical *quantum mechanics* in the 1920s to develop equations that describe the properties of electrons in atoms. Fortunately, we can make use of some of Schrödinger's results without understanding his elaborate equations. The solutions to these equations express the probability of finding an electron in a given volume of space. These variously shaped volumes of space, called **orbitals**, replace the planetary orbits of the Bohr model.

Suppose you had a camera that could photograph electrons and you left the shutter open while an electron zipped about the nucleus. The developed picture would give a record of where the electron had been. (Doing the same thing with an electric fan would give a blurred image of the rapidly moving blades, an image resembling a disk.) The electrons in the first shell would appear as a fuzzy ball (often referred to as a *charge cloud* or an *electron cloud* [Figure 14]).

An *s* orbital

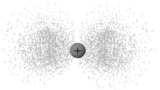

A *p* orbital

▲ **Figure 14** The modern charge-cloud representation of an atomic orbital is more accurate than the Bohr model (Figure 13). An electron cloud is the "fuzzy" region around an atomic nucleus where an electron is likely to be. The type of orbital determines the general shape of the cloud, as seen here.

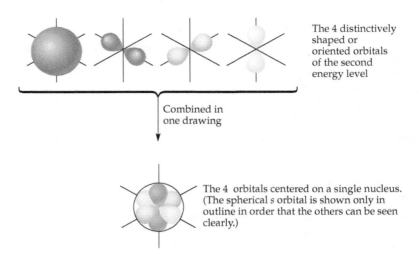

► **Figure 15** Electron orbitals of the second main shell. In these drawings, the nucleus of the atom is located at the intersection of the axes. The eight electrons that would be placed in the second shell of Bohr's model are distributed among these four orbitals in the current model of the atom, with two electrons per orbital.

The 4 distinctively shaped or oriented orbitals of the second energy level

Combined in one drawing

The 4 orbitals centered on a single nucleus. (The spherical s orbital is shown only in outline in order that the others can be seen clearly.)

Building Atoms by Orbital Filling

Schrödinger concluded that each electron orbital could contain a maximum of two electrons and that some shells could contain more than one orbital. The first shell contains a single spherical orbital called 1s. The second shell contains four orbitals: 2s is spherical, and the other three orbitals, called 2p, are dumbbell-shaped (Figure 15). Orbitals in the same shell that have the same letter designation make up a **subshell (sublevel)**. The second shell has two subshells, the 2s subshell with only one orbital and the 2p subshell with three orbitals. The third shell contains nine orbitals distributed among three subshells: a spherical 3s orbital in the 3s subshell, three dumbbell-shaped 3p orbitals in the 3p subshell, and five 3d orbitals with more complicated shapes in the 3d subshell.

In building up the electron configurations of atoms of the various elements, the lower sublevels (subshells) are filled first.

Hydrogen ($Z = 1$) has only one electron in the s orbital of the first shell. The electron configuration is

$$H \quad 1s^1$$

Helium ($Z = 2$) has two electrons and its electron configuration is

$$He \quad 1s^2$$

Lithium ($Z = 3$) has three electrons—two in the first shell and one in the s orbital of the second shell:

$$Li \quad 1s^2 2s^1$$

Skipping to nitrogen ($Z = 7$), the seven electrons are arranged as follows:

$$N \quad 1s^2 2s^2 2p^3$$

Let's review what this notation means:

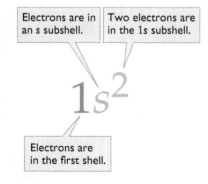

Electrons are in an s subshell. | Two electrons are in the 1s subshell.

$1s^2$

Electrons are in the first shell.

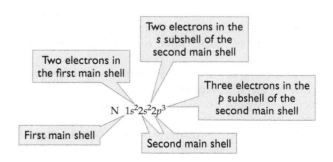

Two electrons in the first main shell

Two electrons in the s subshell of the second main shell

Three electrons in the p subshell of the second main shell

N $1s^2 2s^2 2p^3$

First main shell

Second main shell

For argon ($Z = 18$), with its 18 electrons, the configuration is

$$\text{Ar} \quad 1s^2 2s^2 2p^6 3s^2 3p^6$$

Note that the highest occupied subshell, $3p$, is filled. However, the order of subshell filling for elements with Z greater than 18 is not intuitively obvious. In potassium ($Z = 19$), for example, the $4s$ subshell fills before the $3d$ subshell. The order in which the various subshells are filled is shown in Figure 16, and Table 3 gives the electron configurations for the first 20 elements. The electrons in the outermost main shell, called *valence electrons* (Section 8), are shown in color.

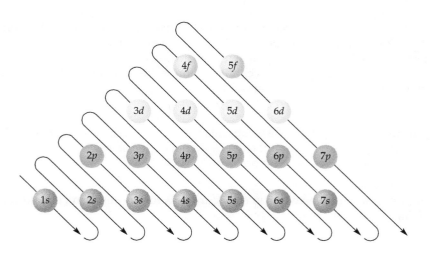

◀ **Figure 16** An order-of-filling chart for determining the electron configurations of atoms.

Table 3	Electron Configurations for Atoms of the First 20 Elements	
Name	**Atomic Number**	**Electron Configuration**
Hydrogen	1	$1s^1$
Helium	2	$1s^2$
Lithium	3	$1s^2 2s^1$
Beryllium	4	$1s^2 2s^2$
Boron	5	$1s^2 2s^2 2p^1$
Carbon	6	$1s^2 2s^2 2p^2$
Nitrogen	7	$1s^2 2s^2 2p^3$
Oxygen	8	$1s^2 2s^2 2p^4$
Fluorine	9	$1s^2 2s^2 2p^5$
Neon	10	$1s^2 2s^2 2p^6$
Sodium	11	$1s^2 2s^2 2p^6 3s^1$
Magnesium	12	$1s^2 2s^2 2p^6 3s^2$
Aluminum	13	$1s^2 2s^2 2p^6 3s^2 3p^1$
Silicon	14	$1s^2 2s^2 2p^6 3s^2 3p^2$
Phosphorus	15	$1s^2 2s^2 2p^6 3s^2 3p^3$
Sulfur	16	$1s^2 2s^2 2p^6 3s^2 3p^4$
Chlorine	17	$1s^2 2s^2 2p^6 3s^2 3p^5$
Argon	18	$1s^2 2s^2 2p^6 3s^2 3p^6$
Potassium	19	$1s^2 2s^2 2p^6 3s^2 3p^6 4s^1$
Calcium	20	$1s^2 2s^2 2p^6 3s^2 3p^6 4s^2$

Example 5   Subshell Notation

Without referring to Table 3, use subshell notation to write the electron configurations for **(a)** oxygen and **(b)** sulfur. What do the electron configurations of these two elements have in common?

Solution

a. Oxygen ($Z = 8$) has eight electrons. We place them in subshells, starting with the lowest energy level. Two go into the $1s$ orbital and two into the $2s$ orbital. That leaves four electrons to be placed in the $2p$ subshell. The electron configuration is $1s^2 2s^2 2p^4$.

b. Sulfur ($Z = 16$) atoms have 16 electrons each. The electron configuration is $1s^2 2s^2 2p^6 3s^2 3p^4$. Note that the total of the superscripts is 16 and that we have not exceeded the maximum capacity for any sublevel.

    Both O and S have electron configurations with four electrons in the highest energy sublevel (outermost subshell).

■ EXERCISE 5A

Without referring to Table 3, use subshell notation to write out the electron configurations for **(a)** fluorine and **(b)** chlorine. What do the electron configurations for these two elements have in common?

■ EXERCISE 5B

Use Figure 16 to write the electron configurations for **(a)** titanium (Ti) and **(b)** gallium (Ga).

Self-Assessment Questions

1. The shape of a $1s$ orbital is
   a. circular
   b. a dumbbell
   c. spherical
   d. variable

2. The maximum number of electrons in an atomic orbital
   a. depends on the main shell
   b. depends on the subshell
   c. is always 2
   d. is always 8

3. Which of the following subshells has the highest energy?
   a. $2p$ **b.** $2s$ **c.** $3p$ **d.** $3s$

4. What is the lowest-numbered main shell to have d orbitals?
   a. 1   **b.** 2   **c.** 3   **d.** 4

5. Which of the following atoms has a half-filled subshell in the ground state?
   a. beryllium
   b. neon
   c. nitrogen
   d. oxygen

6. Which subshell has a total of three orbitals?
   a. d **b.** f **c.** p **d.** s

7. In what main shell is a $3d$ subshell located?
   a. 1   **b.** 3   **c.** 5   **d.** none

8. The electron capacity of the $4p$ subshell is
   a. 3   **b.** 4   **c.** 6   **d.** 10

Answers: 1, c; 2, c; 3, c; 4, c; 5, c; 6, c; 7, b; 8, c

8 Electron Configurations and the Periodic Table

Learning Objective ❯ Describe how an element's electron configuration relates to its location in the periodic table.

In general, the properties of elements can be correlated with their electron configurations. Because the number of electrons equals the number of protons, the periodic table tells us about electron configuration as well as atomic number.

The modern periodic table (inside front cover) has horizontal rows and vertical columns.

- Each vertical column is a **group**, or *family*. Elements in a group have similar chemical properties.
- A horizontal row of the periodic table is called a **period**. The properties of elements change in a recurring manner across a period.

In the United States, the groups are often indicated by a numeral followed by the letter A or B.

- An element in an A group is a **main group element**.
- An element in a B group is a **transition element**.

The International Union of Pure and Applied Chemistry (IUPAC) recommends numbering the groups from 1 to 18. Both systems are indicated on the periodic table on the inside front cover, but this text uses the traditional U.S. system.

Family Features: Outer Electron Configurations

The period in which an element appears in the periodic table tells us how many main shells an atom of that element has. Phosphorus, for example, is in the third period, and so the phosphorus atom has three main shells. The U.S. group number (for main group elements) tells us how many electrons are in the outermost shell. An electron in the outermost shell of an atom is called a **valence electron**. From the fact that phosphorus is in group 5A, we can deduce that it has five valence electrons. Two of these are in an *s* orbital, and the other three are in *p* orbitals. We can indicate the outer electron configuration of the phosphorus atom as

$$P \quad 3s^2 3p^3$$

The valence electrons determine most of the chemistry of an atom. Since all the elements in the same group of the periodic table have the same number of valence electrons, they should have similar chemistry, and they do. Figure 17 relates the subshell configurations to the groups in the periodic table.

Family Groups

Elements within a group have similar properties. All the elements in group 1A have one valence electron, and all except hydrogen are very reactive metals (hydrogen is a nonmetal). All group 1A elements have the outer electron configuration ns^1, where n denotes the number of the outermost main shell.

The metals in group 1A are called **alkali metals**. They react vigorously with water, producing hydrogen gas. There are noticeable trends in properties within this family. For example, lithium is the hardest metal in the group. Sodium is softer than lithium; potassium is softer still; and so on down the group. Lithium is also the least reactive toward water. Sodium, potassium, rubidium, and cesium are progressively more reactive. Francium is highly radioactive and extremely rare. Few of its properties have been measured.

6. What is periodic about the periodic table? Figure 17 shows why there are periodic, or recurring, trends in the periodic table. Elements in the same column have similar electron configurations and often have similar chemical and physical characteristics as well.

▲ **Figure 17** Valence-shell electron configurations and the periodic table.

▲ (Above) Lithium, an alkali metal, reacts with water to form hydrogen gas. (Below) Potassium, another alkali metal, undergoes the same reaction but much more vigorously.

Hydrogen is the odd one in group 1A. It is not an alkali metal but rather a typical nonmetal. Based on its properties, hydrogen probably should be put in a group of its own.

Group 2A elements are known as **alkaline earth metals**. The metals in this group have the outer electron configuration ns^2. Most are fairly soft and moderately reactive with water. Beryllium is the odd member of the group in that it is rather hard and does not react with water. As in other families, there are trends in properties within the group. For example, magnesium, calcium, strontium, barium, and radium are progressively more reactive toward water.

Group 7A elements, often called **halogens**, also consist of reactive elements. All have seven valence electrons with the configuration ns^2np^5. Halogens react vigorously with alkali metals to form crystalline solids. There are trends in the halogen family as you move down the group. Fluorine is most reactive toward alkali metals, chlorine is the next most reactive, and so on. Fluorine and chlorine are gases at room temperature, bromine is a liquid, and iodine is a solid. (Astatine, like francium, is highly radioactive and extremely rare; few of its properties have been determined.)

Members of group 8A, to the far right on the periodic table, have a complete set of valence electrons and therefore undergo few, if any, chemical reactions. They are called **noble gases**, for their lack of chemical reactivity.

Example 6 Valence-Shell Electron Configurations

Use subshell notation to write the electron configurations for the outermost main shell of **(a)** strontium (Sr) and **(b)** arsenic (As).

Solution

a. Strontium is in group 2A and thus has two valence electrons in an s subshell. Because strontium is in the fifth period of the periodic table, its outer main shell is $n = 5$. Its outer electron configuration is therefore $5s^2$.

b. Arsenic is in group 5A and the fourth period. Its five outer (valence) electrons are in the $n = 4$ shell, and the configuration is $4s^24p^3$.

■ EXERCISE 6A

Use subshell notation to write the configurations for the outermost main shell of **(a)** rubidium (Rb), **(b)** selenium (Se), and **(c)** germanium (Ge).

■ EXERCISE 6B

The valence electrons in aluminum have the configuration $3s^2 3p^1$. In the periodic table, gallium is directly below aluminum, and indium is directly below gallium. Use only this information to write the configurations for the valence electrons in **(a)** gallium and **(b)** indium.

Metals and Nonmetals

Elements in the periodic table are divided into two classes by a heavy, stepped line (see inside front cover). Those to the left of the line are *metals*. A **metal** has a characteristic luster (shininess) and generally is a good conductor of heat and electricity. Except for mercury, which is a liquid, all metals are solids at room temperature. Metals generally are *malleable*; that is, they can be hammered into thin sheets. Most also are *ductile*, which means that they can be drawn into wires.

Elements to the right of the stepped line are *nonmetals*. A **nonmetal** lacks metallic properties. Several nonmetals are gases (oxygen, nitrogen, fluorine, and chlorine). Others are solids (e.g., carbon, sulfur, phosphorus, and iodine). Bromine is the only nonmetal that is a liquid at room temperature.

Some of the elements bordering the stepped line are called *semimetals*, or *metalloids*, and these have intermediate properties that may resemble those of both metals and nonmetals. There is a lack of agreement on just which elements fit in this category.

▲ (Top) Metals such as gold are easily shaped, and they conduct heat and electricity well. (Bottom) Nonmetals such as sulfur are usually brittle, melt at low temperatures, and often are good insulators.

Which Model to Use

For some purposes in this text, we use only main-shell configurations of atoms to picture the distribution of electrons in atoms. At other times, the electron clouds of the quantum mechanical model are more useful. Even Dalton's model sometimes proves to be the best way to describe certain phenomena (the behavior of gases, for example). The choice of model is always based on which one is most helpful in understanding a particular concept. This, after all, is the purpose of scientific models.

Self-Assessment Questions

1. Which pair of elements has the most similar chemical properties?
   a. Ca and Cd   **b.** Cl and Br   **c.** P and S   **d.** Sb and Sc

2. Elements within a period of the periodic table have the same number of
   a. electrons in the outermost shell
   b. neutrons in the nucleus
   c. occupied main shells
   d. protons in the nucleus

3. The valence-shell electron configuration of the halogens is
   a. ns^1 **b.** $ns^2 np^3$ **c.** $ns^2 np^5$ **d.** $ns^2 np^6$

4. The alkali metals are members of group
   a. 1A   **b.** 2A   **c.** 7A   **d.** 8A

5. What is the total number of valence electrons in an atom of bromine?
   a. 5   **b.** 7   **c.** 17   **d.** 35

6. Which of the following sets of elements exhibits the most similar chemical properties?
   a. Al, Sc, Si   **b.** Hg, Br, Se   **c.** Li, Na, K   **d.** N, O, F

7. In the ground state, atoms of a fourth period element must have
   a. a $3f$ sublevel
   b. electrons in the fourth shell
   c. four valence electrons
   d. properties similar to those of other elements in the fourth period

Answers: 1, b; 2, c; 3, c; 4, a; 5, b; 6, c; 7, b

Scott Cummings, *Kenyon College*

Clean Energy from Solar Fuels

Imagine a world powered by a clean fuel which is manufactured using sunlight and water, and produces no carbon dioxide emissions when used. This has been the dream of chemists around the world, who have been working for many years to develop a "solar fuel" that might someday replace some of the fossil fuels that are so important to us—oil, coal, and natural gas.

Sunlight is a free and abundant power source. More solar energy reaches Earth's surface in one hour than all of the fossil fuel energy that human beings use in one year. The goal for chemists is to develop efficient methods to capture just a tiny part of this sunlight and convert it into a useful form such as electricity. For now, this is accomplished using solar panels constructed from photovoltaic cells, devices usually made of silicon. But sunshine is intermittent; we need to convert radiant solar energy into chemical energy—a storable fuel. One idea for a solar fuel is hydrogen. Learning how to utilize sunlight to make hydrogen is one of the grand challenges of chemistry.

A full hydrogen energy cycle uses solar energy to split water (H_2O) into hydrogen (H_2) and oxygen (O_2) and then uses the hydrogen as a clean fuel to produce either heat (when burned) or electricity (using a fuel cell). Splitting water requires energy input to break the bonds that hold together the O and H atoms in water molecules. One of the simplest ways to do this is by electrolysis (Section 1), which requires electrical energy. If the electricity is produced using a solar panel, then the hydrogen formed is a solar fuel. This approach is currently quite expensive, and much research in chemistry is aimed at discovering new and inexpensive photovoltaic materials—including plastics—from which to construct solar panels. Chemists also seek electrodes and other components that can be made from abundant elements instead of the precious metal platinum (Pt) that is typically used.

For a different approach to hydrogen production, chemists are turning to green plants for inspiration. Plants use photosynthesis to take energy from the sun and store it in the chemical bonds of compounds known as *carbohydrates*. This chemical

solar energy

water (H_2O)   hydrogen (H_2) and oxygen (O_2)

heat or electricity

Clean energy cycle. Solar energy is used to produce hydrogen and oxygen from water (top). Hydrogen fuel reacts with oxygen to produce water and releases energy as either heat or electricity.

PHOTOSYNTHESIS

carbon dioxide + water ⟶ carbohydrate + oxygen

ARTIFICIAL PHOTOSYNTHESIS

water ⟶ hydrogen + oxygen

Two ways to make solar fuels. Green plants use photosynthesis to produce carbohydrate fuels. Chemists are trying to produce hydrogen fuel. Both reactions use water and solar energy.

process is essential to sustain life on the planet and depends on the ability to split water molecules with sunlight. Chemists are hoping to unlock the secrets of the leaf to develop "artificial photosynthesis" and use solar energy to produce hydrogen fuel from water.

In natural photosynthesis, plants employ many different molecules to capture and convert solar energy. Chlorophyll molecules absorb part of the solar spectrum, giving a leaf its green color. To mimic this process, chemists are designing colorful synthetic dyes to capture photons from the sun. When a dye absorbs light, one of its electrons is excited, which generates an excited-state molecule. But rather than emitting the energy back as a photon (Section 6), the energy can be harnessed to split water. Plants also employ a cluster of manganese, calcium, and oxygen atoms to crack apart water molecules and produce oxygen. Chemists have been active in trying to mimic this reaction as well, using compounds made in the laboratory.

Solar fuels such as hydrogen embody several green chemistry principles. Hydrogen fuel is only as green as the method used to make it. If produced using sunlight as the energy source and water as the chemical feedstock, though, the fuel can be clean and renewable (Principle 7). Unlike fossil fuels, hydrogen is a carbon-free fuel that, when produced from sunlight, prevents carbon dioxide emissions (Principle 1). A solar-hydrogen system relies on compounds that increase efficiency and facilitate both the water-splitting chemistry and the use of hydrogen (Principle 9). If these materials are earth-abundant and do not cause harm to the environment, this process closes the clean-fuel cycle.

CRITICAL THINKING EXERCISES

Apply knowledge that you have gained in this chapter and one or more of the FLaReS principles to evaluate the following statements or claims.

1   Suppose you read in the newspaper that a chemist in South America claims to have discovered a new element with an atomic mass of 34. Extremely rare, it was found in a sample taken from the Andes Mountains. Unfortunately, the chemist has used all of the sample in his analyses.

2   Some aboriginal tribes have rain-making ceremonies in which they toss pebbles of gypsum up into

the air. (Gypsum is the material used to make plaster of Paris by heating the rock to remove some of its water.) Sometimes it does rain several days after these rain-making ceremonies.

3   Some scientists have recently suggested that bacteria from California's Mono Lake may be able to use arsenic (As) in place of phosphorus (P) in their proteins and DNA.

◼ SUMMARY

Section 1—Davy, Faraday, and others showed that matter is electrical in nature. They were able to decompose compounds into elements by electrolysis or passing electricity through molten salts. Electrodes are carbon rods or metal strips that carry electricity into the electrolyte, the solution or compound that conducts electricity. The electrolyte contains ions—charged atoms or groups of atoms. The anode is the positive electrode, and anions (negatively charged ions) move toward it. The cathode is the negative electrode, and cations (positively charged ions) move toward it. Experiments with cathode rays in gas-discharge tubes showed that matter contained negatively charged particles, which were called electrons. Thomson determined the mass-to-charge ratio for the electron. Goldstein's experiment showed that matter also contained positively charged particles. Millikan's oil-drop experiment measured the charge on the electron, so its mass could then be calculated.

Section 2—In his studies of cathode rays, Roentgen accidentally discovered X-rays, a highly penetrating form of radiation now used in medical diagnosis. Becquerel accidentally discovered another type of radiation that comes from certain unstable elements. Marie Curie named this new discovery radioactivity and studied it extensively.

Section 3—Radioactivity was soon classified as three different types of radiation: Alpha particles have four times the mass of a hydrogen atom and a positive charge twice that of an electron. Beta particles are energetic electrons. Gamma rays are a form of energy like X-rays but more penetrating.

Section 4—Rutherford's experiments with alpha particles and gold foil showed that most of the alpha particles emitted toward the foil passed through it. A few were deflected or, occasionally, bounced back almost directly toward the source. This indicated that all the positive charge and most of the mass of an atom must be in a tiny core, which Rutherford called the nucleus.

Section 5—Rutherford called the smallest unit of positive charge the proton; it has about the mass of a hydrogen atom and a charge equal in size but opposite in sign to the electron. In 1932, Chadwick discovered the neutron, a nuclear particle as massive as a proton but with no charge. The number of

protons in an atom is the atomic number (Z). Atoms of the same element have the same number of protons but may have different numbers of neutrons; such atoms are called isotopes. Different isotopes of an element are nearly identical chemically. Protons and neutrons collectively are called nucleons, and the number of nucleons is called the mass number or nucleon number. The difference between the mass number and the atomic number is the number of neutrons. The general symbol for an isotope of element X is written $_Z^A X$, where A is the mass number and Z is the atomic number.

Section 6—Light from the sun or from an incandescent lamp produces a continuous spectrum, containing all colors. Light from a gas-discharge tube produces a line spectrum, containing only certain colors. Bohr explained line spectra by proposing that an electron in an atom resides only at certain discrete energy levels, which differ from one another by a quantum, or discrete unit of energy. An atom drops to the lowest energy state, or ground state, after being in a higher energy state, or excited state. The energy emitted when electrons move to lower energy levels manifests as a line spectrum characteristic of the particular element, with the lines corresponding to specific wavelengths (colors) of light. Bohr also deduced that the energy levels of an atom could hold at most $2n^2$ electrons, where n is the number of the energy level, or shell. A description of the shells occupied by the electrons of an atom is one way of giving the atom's electron configuration, or arrangement of electrons.

Section 7—de Broglie theorized that electrons have wave properties. Schrödinger developed equations that described each electron's location in terms of an orbital, a volume of space that the electron usually occupies. Each orbital holds at most two electrons. Orbitals in the same shell and with the same energy make up a subshell, or sublevel, each of which is designated by a letter. An s orbital is spherical and a p orbital is dumbbell-shaped. The d and f orbitals have more complex shapes. The first main shell can hold only one s orbital; the second can hold one s and three p orbitals; and the third can hold one s, three p, and five d orbitals. In writing an electron configuration using subshell notation, we give the shell number and subshell letter, followed by a superscript indicating the number of electrons in that sub-shell. The order of the shells and subshells can be remembered with a chart or by looking at the periodic table.

Section 8—Elements in the periodic table are arranged vertically in groups and horizontally in periods. Electrons in the outermost shell of an atom, called valence electrons, determine the reactivity of that atom. Elements in a group usually have the same number of valence electrons and similarities in properties. We designate groups by a number and the letter A or B. The A-group elements are main group elements. The B-group elements are transition elements. Group 1A elements are the alkali metals. Except for hydrogen, they are all soft, low-melting, highly reactive metals. Group 2A consists of the alkaline earth metals, fairly soft and reactive metals. Group 7A elements, the halogens, are reactive

nonmetals. Group 8A elements, the noble gases, react very little or not at all. A stepped line divides the periodic table into metals, which conduct electricity and heat and are shiny, malleable, and ductile, and nonmetals, which tend to lack the properties of metals. Some elements bordering the stepped line, called *metalloids*, have properties intermediate between those of metals and nonmetals.

Green chemistry Hydrogen is a promising clean fuel because it can be manufactured using sunlight and water and using it does not produce carbon dioxide as waste. Using a solar cell, energy from sunlight can be converted into electricity, which can then be used to split water into hydrogen and oxygen; this splitting of water can also be accomplished by a process that mimics photosynthesis. The hydrogen can be burned to produce heat or used in a fuel cell to produce electricity.

Learning Objectives

> Explain the electrical properties of an atom. (1) — Problems 16, 23, 24

> Describe how the properties of electricity explain the structure of atoms. (1) — Problems 13, 14, 19, 20

> Describe the experiments that led to the discovery of X-rays and an explanation of radioactivity. (2) — Problem 2

> Distinguish the three main kinds of radioactivity: alpha, beta, and gamma. (3) — Problem 3

> Sketch the nuclear model of the atom, and identify its parts. (4) — Problem 6

> List the particles that make up the nucleus of an atom, and give their relative masses and electric charges. (5) — Problems 7–9

> Identify elements and isotopes from their nuclear particles. (5) — Problems 8, 9, 15–18

> Define *quantum*. (6) — Problem 10

> Arrange the electrons in a given atom in energy levels (shells). (6) — Problems 33, 38–40

> Relate the idea of a quantum of energy to an orbital. (7) — Problem 11

> Write an electron configuration (in subshell notation) for a given atom. (7) — Problems 19–32, 37

> Describe how an element's electron configuration relates to its location in the periodic table. (8) — Problems 34 and 35

> Distinguish the conversion of solar energy into electrical energy in a solar cell from the conversion of solar energy into the chemical-bond energy of a solar fuel. — Problems 42–44

> Explain why splitting water into the elements hydrogen and oxygen requires an energy input and producing water by the reaction of hydrogen and oxygen releases energy. — Problem 43

REVIEW QUESTIONS

1. What did each of the following scientists contribute to our knowledge of the atom?
   a. William Crookes   b. Eugen Goldstein
   c. Michael Faraday   d. J. J. Thomson

2. What is radioactivity? How did the discovery of radioactivity contradict Dalton's atomic theory?

3. How are X-rays and gamma rays similar? How are they different?

4. Define or identify each of the following.
   a. deuterium   b. tritium
   c. photon

5. The following table describes four atoms.

	Atom A	Atom B	Atom C	Atom D
Number of protons	17	18	18	17
Number of neutrons	18	17	18	17
Number of electrons	17	18	18	17

Are atoms A and B isotopes? A and C? A and D? B and C?

6. Compare Dalton's model of the atom with the nuclear model of the atom.

7. Which two atoms in Question 5 have about the same mass?

8. What are the symbol, name, and atomic number of the element with $Z = 76$? You may use the periodic table and a table of atomic masses.

9. What are the symbol, name, and atomic number of the element that has 21 protons in the nuclei of its atoms?

10. Explain what is meant by the term *quantum*.

11. Which atom absorbs more energy, one in which an electron moves from the second shell to the third shell or an otherwise identical atom in which an electron moves from the first to the third shell?

12. How did Bohr refine the model of the atom?

13. Use the periodic table to determine the number of protons in an atom of each of the following elements.
   a. lithium   b. magnesium
   c. chlorine   d. fluorine
   e. aluminum   f. phosphorus

14. How many electrons are there in each neutral atom of the elements listed in Question 13?

PROBLEMS

Nuclear Symbols and Isotopes

15. Give the symbol and name for (a) an isotope with a mass number of 42 and an atomic number of 20 and (b) an isotope with 28 neutrons and 23 protons.

16. Fill in the table:

Element	Mass Number	Number of Protons	Number of Neutrons
Nickel	60		
	108	46	
		7	7
Iodine			74

17. How many different elements are listed here?
$^{23}_{11}X$ $^{22}_{10}X$ $^{11}_{5}X$ $^{24}_{11}X$ $^{25}_{12}X$

18. How many different isotopes of silver are listed here? (The X does not necessarily represent any specific element.)
$^{108}_{47}X$ $^{108}_{48}X$ $^{110}_{47}X$ $^{109}_{46}X$ $^{107}_{47}X$

Subshell Notation for Electron Configurations

19. Without referring to the periodic table, give the atomic numbers of the elements with the following electron configurations.
   a. $1s^2 2s^2 2p^3$
   b. $1s^2 2s^2 2p^6 3s^2 3p^1$
   c. $1s^2 2s^2 2p^6 3s^2 3p^6 4s^1$

20. Without referring to the periodic table, give the atomic numbers of the elements with the following electron configurations.
   a. $1s^2 2s^2 2p^6 3s^2 3p^3$
   b. $1s^2 2s^2 2p^4$
   c. $1s^2 2s^2 2p^6 3s^1$

21. Indicate whether each electron configuration represents an atom in the ground state or in a possible excited state or is incorrect. In each case, explain why.
   a. $1s^1 2s^1$ b. $1s^2 2s^2 2p^7$
   c. $1s^2 2p^2$ d. $1s^2 2s^2 2p^2$

22. Indicate whether each electron configuration represents an atom in the ground state or in a possible excited state or is incorrect. In each case, explain why.
   a. $1s^2 2s^2 3s^2$
   b. $1s^2 2s^2 2p^2 3s^1$
   c. $1s^2 2s^2 2p^6 2d^5$
   d. $1s^2 2s^4 2p^2$

23. Suppose that one electron is added to the outermost shell of a fluorine atom. What element's electron configuration would the atom then have?

24. Suppose that each of the following changes is made. Give the symbol for the element whose electron configuration matches the result.
   a. Two electrons are added to an oxygen atom.
   b. Two electrons are removed from a calcium atom.
   c. Three electrons are removed from an aluminum atom.

25. Referring only to the periodic table, tell how the electron configurations of silicon (Si) and germanium (Ge) are similar. How are they different?

26. Referring only to the periodic table, tell how the electron configurations of fluorine (F) and chlorine (Cl) are similar. How are they different? How do you expect the electron configurations of bromine (Br) and iodine (I) to be similar to those of fluorine and chlorine?

27. Refer to the periodic table to identify each element as a metal or a nonmetal.
   a. manganese
   b. strontium
   c. cesium
   d. argon

Use the following list of elements to answer Problems 28–32:
Mg, Cs, Ne, P, Kr, K, Ra, N, Fe, Ca, Mo

28. Which element(s) is (are) alkali metals?

29. Which element(s) is (are) noble gases?

30. Which element(s) is (are) transition metals?

31. How many of the elements are nonmetals?

32. All elements with more than 83 protons are *radioactive*. Are any of the elements in the list above necessarily radioactive? If so, which one(s)?

ADDITIONAL PROBLEMS

33. An atom of an element has two electrons in the first shell, eight electrons in the second shell, and five electrons in the third shell. From this information, give the element's **(a)** atomic number, **(b)** name, **(c)** total number of electrons in each of its atoms, **(d)** total number of s electrons, and **(e)** total number of d electrons.

34. Refer to Problem 24. Explain how you can answer the three parts of that problem just by looking at a periodic table, and without writing electron structures.

35. Without referring to any tables in the text, mark an appropriate location for each of the following in the blank periodic table provided: **(a)** the fourth period noble gas, **(b)** the third period alkali metal, **(c)** the fourth period halogen, and **(d)** a metal in the fourth period and in group 3B.

36. Look again at Figure 11. A patient is found to be suffering from heavy-metal poisoning. An emission spectrum is obtained from a sample of the patient's blood, by spraying a solution of the blood into a flame. The brightest emission lines are found at 5520, 5580, 5890, and 5900 Å. What two elements are likely to be present? Which one is more likely to be the culprit?

37. Refer to Figure 16 and write the electron configurations of **(a)** iron (Fe), **(b)** tin (Sn), and **(c)** lead (Pb).

38. Atoms of two adjacent elements in the third period are in the ground state. An atom of element A has only s electrons in its valence shell. An atom of element B has at least one p electron in its valence shell. Identify elements A and B.

39. Atoms of two adjacent elements in the fifth period are in the ground state. An atom of element L has only s electrons in its valence shell. An atom of element M has at least one d electron in an unfilled shell. Identify elements L and M.

40. Atoms of two elements, one above the other in the same group, are in the ground state. An atom of element Q has two s electrons in its outer shell and no d electrons. An atom of element R has d electrons in its configuration. Identify elements Q and R.

41. Which of the following is true of the water-splitting reaction?
    a. It produces energy, for example, electricity or heat.
    b. It requires an energy input, for example, electricity or sunlight.
    c. It produces twice as much oxygen as hydrogen.
    d. It occurs inside a fuel cell.

42. What is produced when solar energy is converted into chemical-bond energy in the water-splitting reaction?
    a. hydrogen and nitrogen
    b. oxygen and carbon
    c. hydrogen and oxygen
    d. oxygen and calcium

43. Which of the following is *not* a benefit of using a solar fuel such as hydrogen?
    a. A solar fuel can store the energy of sunlight, which is intermittent.
    b. A solar fuel can replace some fossil fuels.
    c. Using a solar fuel such as hydrogen produces no carbon dioxide emissions.
    d. Electrodes used in electrolysis rely on platinum metal.

44. Isotopes played an important role in one of the most important experiments investigating photosynthesis, the chemical reaction that converts water (H_2O) and carbon dioxide (CO_2) into glucose ($C_6H_{12}O_6$) and oxygen (O_2). For most of the early twentieth century, scientists thought that the oxygen produced by photosynthetic plants and algae came from carbon dioxide they absorbed. To investigate this question, in the early 1940s, chemists at Stanford University used an isotope of oxygen to study the mechanism of the photosynthetic reaction. The researchers fed photosynthesizing algae with water enriched with oxygen-18 and discovered that the oxygen produced was enriched with oxygen-18. Did this result support or refute the hypothesis that the O_2 produced by photosynthesis comes from CO_2?

COLLABORATIVE GROUP PROJECTS

Prepare a PowerPoint, poster, or other presentation (as directed by your instructor) to share with the class.

1. Prepare a brief biographical report on one of the following.
    a. Humphry Davy   **b.** William Crookes
    c. Wilhelm Roentgen   **d.** Marie Curie
    e. Robert Millikan   **f.** Niels Bohr
    g. Alessandro Volta   **h.** Ernest Rutherford
    i. Michael Faraday   **j.** J. J. Thomson

2. Draw a grid containing 16 squares, in two rows of 8, representing the 16 elements in the periodic table from lithium

to argon. For each of the elements, give **(a)** the main-shell electron configuration and **(b)** the subshell notation for the electron configuration.

3. Prepare a brief report on one of the **(a)** alkali metals, **(b)** alkaline earth metals, **(c)** halogens, or **(d)** noble gases. List sources and commercial uses.

4. Many different forms of the periodic table have been generated. Prepare a brief report showing at least three different versions of the periodic table, and comment on their utility.

BRIEF ANSWERS TO SELECTED PROBLEMS

Answers are provided for *all in-chapter exercises*. Brief answers are given for *odd-numbered Review Questions*; more complete answers can be obtained by reviewing the text. Answers are provided for *all odd-numbered Problems and Additional Problems*.

NOTE: For numerical problems, your answer may differ slightly from ours because of rounding and the use of significant figures.

1 **A.** 33 neutrons   **B.** 131; iodine-131
2 **A.** $^{90}_{37}X$ and $^{88}_{37}X$; $^{88}_{38}X$ and $^{93}_{38}X$ **B.** three
3 **A.** 32 electrons   **B.** 3
4 **a.** (Be) 2 2
   b. (Mg) 2 8 2; both have the same number of outer electrons.
5 **A. a.** $1s^2 2s^2 2p^5$
      b. $1s^2 2s^2 2p^6 3s^2 3p^5$ (Both have the valence configuration $ns^2 np^5$.)
   B. a. $1s^2 2s^2 2p^6 3s^2 3p^6 3d^2 4s^2$
      b. $1s^2 2s^2 2p^6 3s^2 3p^6 3d^{10} 4s^2 4p^1$
6 **A. a.** (Rb) $5s^1$
      b. (Se) $4s^2 4p^4$
      c. (Ge) $4s^2 4p^2$
   B. a. (Ga) $4s^2 4p^1$
      b. (In) $5s^2 5p^1$
1. **a.** Crookes invented the gas discharge tube.
    b. Goldstein discovered positive particles.
    c. Faraday developed electrolysis.
    d. Thomson determined mass-to-charge ratio of the electron.
3. Both are forms of radiation; gamma rays are more energetic.
5. A and B, no; A and C, no; A and D, yes; B and C, yes
7. A and B
9. Sc; scandium; 45.0 u
11. The atom in which the electron moves from the first to the third shell.
13. **a.** 3   **b.** 12   **c.** 17   **d.** 9   **e.** 13   **f.** 15
15. **a.** $^{42}_{20}Ca$, calcium-42
    b. $^{51}_{23}V$, vanadium-51

17. 4
19. **a.** 7   **b.** 13   **c.** 19
21. **a.** Excited state; one electron has been raised to the $2p$ subshell.
    b. Incorrect; a p subshell can only hold at most 6 electrons.
    c. Excited state; two electrons have been raised to the $2p$ subshell.
    d. Ground state; all six electrons are in the lowest possible subshell.
23. neon
25. Si has two $3p$ electrons; Ge has two $4p$ electrons; germanium is a much larger atom.
27. metal, a, b, and c; nonmetal, d
29. Ne and Kr
31. Four
33. **a.** 15   **b.** phosphorus   **c.** 15   **d.** 6   **e.** 0
35.

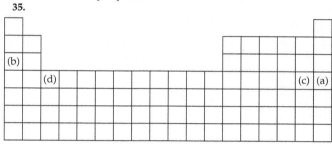

37. **a.** $1s^2 2s^2 2p^6 3s^2 3p^6 3d^6 4s^2$
    b. $1s^2 2s^2 2p^6 3s^2 3p^6 3d^{10} 4s^2 4p^6 4d^{10} 5s^2 5p^2$
    c. $1s^2 2s^2 2p^6 3s^2 3p^6 3d^{10} 4s^2 4p^6 4d^{10} 4f^{14} 5s^2 5p^6 5d^{10} 6s^2 6p^2$
39. The period 5 elements are in group 2A (only s electrons) and group 3B (d electrons). Therefore, the elements are strontium (Sr) and yttrium (Y).
41. b
43. d

Nuclear Chemistry

Have You Ever Wondered?

1. **Is radiation entirely a human-made problem?**

2. **Do cell phones and microwave ovens give off radiation?**

3. **Why can't we just burn or dissolve radioactive wastes to get rid of them?**

4. **Do irradiated foods give off radiation?**

5. **Are we exposed to dangerous radiation during X-rays and other medical procedures?**

6. **Can you get radiation sickness from someone who has been exposed to radiation?**

Scott Camazine/Alamy

Steven Needell, MD/
Custom Medical Stock Photo

Learning Objectives

> Identify the sources of the natural radiation to which we are exposed. (1)

> List the sources and dangers of ionizing radiation. (1)

> Balance nuclear equations. (2)

> Identify the products formed by various decay processes. (2)

> Solve simple half-life problems. (3)

> Use the concept of half-life to solve simple radioisotopic dating problems. (3)

> Write a nuclear equation for a transmutation, and identify the product element formed. (4)

> List some applications of radioisotopes. (5)

> Describe the nature of materials needed to block alpha, beta, and gamma radiation (6)

> Explain where nuclear energy comes from. (7)

> Describe the difference between fission and fusion. (7)

> Describe how uranium and plutonium bombs are made. (8)

> Identify the most hazardous fallout isotopes, and explain why they are particularly dangerous. (8)

> List some uses of nuclear energy. (9)

> Identify green chemistry principles that can help solve existing problems in nuclear chemistry.

> Explain how molecules used in nuclear waste processing can be designed to be safer, and give examples of such molecules.

The heart of matter

Many people associate the term *nuclear energy* with fearsome images of a mighty force: giant mushroom clouds from nuclear explosions that devastated cities, and nuclear power plant accidents at Three Mile Island, Pennsylvania, in 1979, Chernobyl, Ukraine, in 1986, and Fukushima, Japan, in 2011. But some amazing stories can also be told about life-giving applications of nuclear energy.

The discussion of atomic structure in has focused mainly on the electrons, because the electrons are the particles that determine an element's chemistry. In this chapter, we take a closer look at that tiny speck in the center of the atom—the atomic nucleus.

The photos show images from MRI (magnetic resonance imaging), PET (positron emission tomography), and x-rays for examining bones and internal organs. All of these diagnostic techniques use radiation or a radioactive isotope. With these techniques, we can examine tissues and diagnose diseases that were previously possible only by biopsy or exploratory surgery. The nuclear age has produced both serious problems and tremendous advantages, which will be examined in this chapter.

SergeyIT/Shutterstock

From Chapter 11 of *Chemistry for Changing Times*, Thirteenth Edition. John W. Hill, Terry W. McCreary, Doris K. Kolb.

An atom is incomprehensibly small, but the infinitesimal size of the atomic nucleus is almost beyond our imagination. The diameter of an atom is roughly 100,000 times greater than the diameter of its nucleus. If an atom could be magnified until it was as large as your classroom, the nucleus would be about as big as the period at the end of this sentence. Yet this tiny nucleus contains almost all the atom's mass. How dense the atomic nucleus must be! A cubic centimeter of water weighs 1 g, and a cubic centimeter of gold about 19 g. A cubic centimeter of pure atomic nuclei would weigh more than 100 million metric tons!

Even more amazing than the density of the nucleus is the enormous amount of energy contained within it. Some atomic nuclei undergo reactions that can fuel the most powerful bombs ever built or provide electricity for millions of people. Our sun is one huge nuclear power plant, supplying the energy that warms our planet and the light necessary for plant growth. The twinkling light from every star we see in the night sky is produced by powerful nuclear reactions. Radioactive isotopes are used in medicine to save lives every day, through diagnosis and treatment of diseases. Many applications of nuclear chemistry in science and industry have improved the human condition significantly. Nuclear reactions allow us to date archaeological and geological finds, to assess the quality of industrial materials, and to be alerted to deadly fires. In this chapter, you will learn about the destructive and the healing power of that infinitesimally small and wonderfully dense heart of every atom—the nucleus.

1 Natural Radioactivity

Learning Objectives > Identify the sources of the natural radiation to which we are exposed. > List the sources and dangers of ionizing radiation.

Most elements occur in nature in several isotopic forms, whose nuclei differ in their number of neutrons. Many of these nuclei are unstable and undergo **radioactive decay**. The nuclei that undergo such decay are called **radioisotopes**, and the process produces one or more types of radiation.

Background Radiation

Humans have always been exposed to radiation. Even as you read this sentence, you are being bombarded by *cosmic rays*, which originate from the sun and outer space. Other radiation reaches us from natural radioactive isotopes in air, water, soil, and rocks. We cannot escape radiation, because it is part of many natural processes, including those in our bodies. A naturally occurring radioactive isotope of potassium, ^{40}K, exists in all our cells and in many foods. The average person absorbs about 4000 particles of radiation each second from ^{40}K and another 1200 particles per second from ^{14}C. (This may sound like a lot, but recall how small atoms are and how many there are in even a tiny sample of matter.)

This ever-present natural radiation is called **background radiation**. Figure 1 shows that over three-fourths of the average radiation exposure comes from background radiation. Most of the remainder comes from medical irradiation such as X-rays. Other sources, such as fallout from testing of nuclear bombs, releases from nuclear industry power plants, and occupational exposure, account for only a minute fraction of the total average exposure.

Nuclear Chemistry

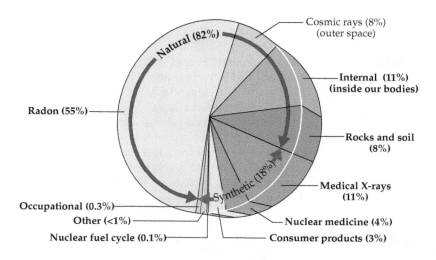

◀ **Figure 1** Most of the radiation to which we are exposed comes from natural sources (blue shades). About 18% of this radiation comes from human activities (other colors).

Q: *What natural source of ionizing radiation contributes most to our exposure? What source provides the largest proportion of our exposure due to human activities?*

Harmful effects arise from the interaction of radiation with living tissue. Radiation with enough energy to knock electrons from atoms and molecules, converting them into ions (electrically charged atoms or groups of atoms), is called **ionizing radiation**. Nuclear radiation and X-rays are examples. Because radiation is invisible and because it has such great potential for harm, we are very much concerned with our exposure to it. However, it is worth noting that the total amount of background radiation the average person is exposed to is less than 0.5% of the amount that can cause symptoms of radiation sickness.

Radiation Damage to Cells

Radiation-caused chemical changes in living cells can be highly disruptive. Ionizing radiation can devastate living cells by interfering with their normal chemical processes. Molecules can be splintered into reactive fragments called *free radicals*, which can disrupt vital cellular processes. White blood cells, the body's first line of defense against bacterial infection, are particularly vulnerable. High levels of radiation also affect bone marrow, causing a drop in the production of red blood cells, which results in anemia. Radiation has also been shown to induce leukemia, a disease of the blood-forming organs.

Ionizing radiation also can cause changes in the molecules of heredity (DNA) in reproductive cells. Such changes can show up as mutations in the offspring of exposed parents. Little is known of the effects of such exposure on humans. However, many of the mutations that occurred during the evolution of present species may have been caused by background radiation.

Because of these potentially devastating effects on living things, knowledge of radiation, radioactive decay, and nuclear chemistry in general is crucial. Next, we will see how to write balanced nuclear equations and how to identify the various types of radiation that are emitted.

1. Is radiation entirely a human-made problem?

Figure 1 shows that the majority of the ionizing radiation to which we are exposed is from natural sources.

In 1993, a Ukrainian Academy of Science study group led by Vladimir Chernousenko investigated the aftereffects of the Chernobyl nuclear accident. Chernousenko claimed that 15,000 of those who helped clean up the accident site have died and that another 250,000 have become invalids. He also said that 200,000 children have experienced radiation-induced illnesses and that half of the children in Ukraine and Belarus have symptoms.

Self-Assessment Questions

1. What percentage of background radiation comes from natural sources?
   a. 5%　**b.** 18%　**c.** 45%　**d.** 82%

2. The largest artificial source of background radiation is
   a. accidents at nuclear power plants　**b.** consumer products
   c. fallout from tests of nuclear bombs　**d.** medical X-rays

3. The largest source of natural background radiation is
   a. cosmic rays　**b.** isotopes in the body
   c. radon　**d.** isotopes in rocks and soil

Answers: 1, d; 2, d; 3, c

Cell Phones and Microwaves and Power Lines, Oh My!

There are many types of radiation. *Ionizing* radiation that comes from decaying atomic nuclei is highly energetic and can damage tissue, as discussed above. *Electromagnetic* radiation has many forms—visible light, radio waves, television broadcast waves, microwaves, ultraviolet light, military ULF (ultra-low-frequency), and others. A few types of electromagnetic radiation—X-rays and gamma rays—have enough energy to ionize tissue, and ultraviolet light has been strongly implicated in *melanoma* (skin cancer). But what about microwaves and radio waves, which don't have nearly as much energy? Although very large amounts of microwaves can cause burns (by heating), there is no conclusive evidence that low levels of microwaves pose significant threat to human health. A 2006 study involving almost half a million Danish citizens failed to show a relationship between cell phone use and cancer, though some scientists consider this study inconclusive. However, higher levels of radio frequencies over long periods of time *may* be a

different matter. In May 2011, the World Health Organization (WHO) classified heavy cell phone use—30 minutes of talking daily for ten years—as possible posing an increased risk of *glioma*, a type of brain cancer. The WHO's press release was very cautious, stating that "there could be some risk ... therefore we need to keep a close watch for a link between cell phones and cancer risk." For low levels of exposure to non-ionizing electromagnetic radiation, the hazard appears to be difficult to measure, let alone assess.

Cell phone ON   Cell phone OFF

Left   Right

Nora D. Volkow, MD/National Institute of Health

▲ A brain scan shows slight differences when a cell phone held to the ear is on (left) and off (right).

2. Do cell phones and microwave ovens give off radiation? Cell phones and microwave ovens *do* give off radiation, but it is not ionizing radiation and thus does not cause cell damage.

2 Nuclear Equations

Learning Objectives ❯ Balance nuclear equations. ❯ Identify the products formed by various decay processes.

Writing balanced equations for nuclear processes is relatively simple. Nuclear equations differ in two ways. First, while chemical equations must have the same elements on both sides of the arrow, nuclear equations rarely do. Second, while we balance atoms in ordinary chemical equations, we balance the *nucleons* (protons and neutrons) in nuclear equations. What this really means is that we must balance the atomic numbers (number of protons) and nucleon numbers (number of nucleons) of the starting materials and products. For this reason, we must always specify the *isotope* of each element appearing in a nuclear equation. We use nuclear symbols when writing nuclear equations because they make the equations easier to balance.

In one example of a nuclear reaction, radon-222 atoms break down spontaneously in a process called **alpha decay**, giving off alpha (α) particles, as shown in Figure 2(a). Because alpha particles are identical to helium nuclei, this reaction can be summarized by the equation

Mass number of starting material = 222   Mass numbers of products = 4 + 218 = 222

$$^{222}_{86}\text{Rn} \longrightarrow {}^{4}_{2}\text{He} + {}^{218}_{84}\text{Po}$$

Atomic number of starting material = 86   Atomic numbers of products = 2 + 84 = 86

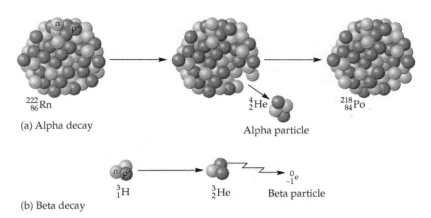

(a) Alpha decay

Alpha particle

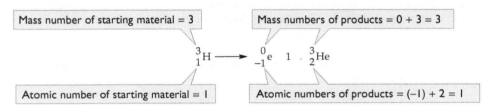

(b) Beta decay

Beta particle

◄ **Figure 2** Nuclear emission of (a) an alpha particle and (b) a beta particle.

Q: *What changes occur in a nucleus when it emits an alpha particle? A beta particle?*

We use the symbol ^4_2He (rather than α) for the alpha particle because it allows us to check the balancing of mass and atomic numbers more readily. The atomic number, $Z = 84$, identifies the element produced as polonium (Po). In nuclear chemistry, the mass number, A, equates with the number of nucleons in the starting material. The number of nucleons in the starting material must equal the total number of the nucleons in the products. The same is true for the atomic numbers.

The heaviest isotope of hydrogen, hydrogen-3, often called *tritium*, decomposes by a process called **beta decay** (Figure 2b). Because a beta (β) particle is identical to an electron, this process can be written as

Mass number of starting material = 3	Mass numbers of products = 0 + 3 = 3

$$^3_1\text{H} \longrightarrow \ ^0_{-1}\text{e} \ + \ ^3_2\text{He}$$

Atomic number of starting material = 1	Atomic numbers of products = (−1) + 2 = 1

The atomic number, $Z = 2$, identifies the product isotope as helium.

Beta decay is a little more complicated than indicated by the preceding reaction. In beta decay, a neutron within the nucleus is converted into a proton (which remains in the nucleus) and an electron (which is ejected).

$$^1_0\text{n} \longrightarrow \ ^1_1\text{p} + \ ^0_{-1}\text{e}$$

With beta decay, the atomic number increases, but the number of nucleons remains the same.

A third kind of radiation may be emitted in a nuclear reaction: gamma (γ) rays. **Gamma decay** is different from alpha and beta decay in that gamma radiation has no charge and no mass. Neither the nucleon number nor the atomic number of the emitting atom is changed; the nucleus simply become less energetic. Table 1 compares the properties of alpha, beta, and gamma radiation. Note that the penetrating power of gamma rays is extremely high. While a few millimeters of aluminum will stop most β particles, several centimeters of lead are needed to stop γ rays.

Table 1	Common Types of Radiation in Nuclear Reactions				
Radiation	**Mass (u)**	**Charge**	**Identity**	**Velocity**[a]	**Penetrating Power**
Alpha (α)	4	2+	He^{2+}	$0.1c$	Very low
Beta (β)	0.00055	1−	e$^-$	$<0.9c$	Moderate
Gamma (γ)	0	0	High-energy photon	c	Extremely high

[a]c is the speed of light.

Nuclear Chemistry

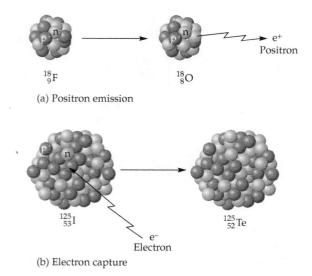

Figure 3 Nuclear change accompanying (a) positron emission and (b) electron capture.

Q: *What changes occur in a nucleus when it emits a positron? When it undergoes electron capture?*

(a) Positron emission

$^{18}_{9}F$ → $^{18}_{8}O$ e⁺ Positron

$^{125}_{53}I$ → $^{125}_{52}Te$ e⁻ Electron

(b) Electron capture

Two other types of radioactive decay are *positron emission* and *electron capture*. These two processes have the same effect on the atomic nucleus, but they occur by different pathways. Both result in a decrease of one in atomic number with no change in nucleon number (Figure 3).

The **positron** (β^+) is a particle equal in mass but opposite in charge to the electron. It is represented as $^{0}_{+1}e$. Fluorine-18 decays by positron emission.

$$^{18}_{9}F \longrightarrow {}^{0}_{+1}e + {}^{18}_{8}O$$

We can envision positron emission as the change of a proton in the nucleus into a neutron and a positron.

$$^{1}_{1}p \longrightarrow {}^{1}_{0}n + {}^{0}_{+1}e$$

After the positron is emitted, the original nucleus has one less proton and one more neutron than it had before. The nucleon number of the product nucleus is the same, but its atomic number has been reduced by one. The emitted positron quickly encounters an electron (there are many electrons in all kinds of matter), and both particles are changing into energy—in this case, two gamma rays.

$$^{0}_{+1}e + {}^{0}_{-1}e \longrightarrow 2{}^{0}_{0}\gamma$$

Electron capture (EC) is a process in which a nucleus absorbs an electron from an inner electron shell, usually the first or second. When an electron from a higher shell drops to the level vacated by the captured electron, an X-ray is released. Once inside the nucleus, the captured electron combines with a proton to form a neutron.

$$^{1}_{1}p + {}^{0}_{-1}e \longrightarrow {}^{1}_{0}n$$

Iodine-125, used in medicine to diagnose pancreatic function and intestinal fat absorption, decays by electron capture.

$$^{125}_{53}I + {}^{0}_{-1}e \longrightarrow {}^{125}_{52}Te$$

Note that, unlike alpha, beta, gamma, or positron emission, electron capture has the electron as a reactant (on the left side) and not a product. Conversion of a proton to a neutron (by the absorbed electron) yields a nucleus with the atomic number lowered by 1 but unchanged in atomic mass. Emission of a positron and absorption of an electron have the same effect on an atomic nucleus (lowering the atomic number by 1), except that positron emission is accompanied by gamma radiation and electron capture by X-radiation. Positron-emitting isotopes and those that undergo electron capture have important medical applications (Section 5).

The five types of radioactive decay are summarized in Table 2.

Table 2 — Radioactive Decay and Nuclear Change

Type of Decay	Decay Particle	Particle Mass (u)	Particle Charge	Change in Nucleon Number	Change in Atomic Number
Alpha decay	α	4	2+	Decreases by 4	Decreases by 2
Beta decay	β	0	1−	No change	Increases by 1
Gamma radiation	γ	0	0	No change	No change
Positron emission	β^+	0	1+	No change	Decreases by 1
Electron capture (EC)	e^- absorbed	0	1−	No change	Decreases by 1

Example 1 Balancing Nuclear Equations

Write balanced nuclear equations for the following processes. In each case, identify the product element formed.

a. Plutonium-239 emits an alpha particle when it decays.

b. Protactinium-234 undergoes beta decay.

c. Carbon-11 emits a positron when it decays.

d. Carbon-11 undergoes electron capture.

Solution

a. We start by writing the symbol for plutonium-239 and a partial equation showing that one of the products is an alpha particle (helium nucleus).

$$^{239}_{94}\text{Pu} \longrightarrow {}^{4}_{2}\text{He} + \, ?$$

For this equation to balance, the other product must have $A = 239 - 4 = 235$ and $Z = 94 - 2 = 92$. The atomic number 92 identifies the element as uranium (U).

$$^{239}_{94}\text{Pu} \longrightarrow {}^{4}_{2}\text{He} + {}^{235}_{92}\text{U}$$

b. We write the symbol for protactinium-234 and a partial equation showing that one of the products is a beta particle (electron).

$$^{234}_{91}\text{Pa} \longrightarrow {}^{0}_{-1}\text{e} + \, ?$$

The other product must have a nucleon number of 234 and $Z = 92$ to balance the equation. The atomic number identifies this product as another isotope of uranium.

$$^{234}_{91}\text{Pa} \longrightarrow {}^{0}_{-1}\text{e} + {}^{234}_{92}\text{U}$$

c. We write the symbol for carbon-11 and a partial equation showing that one of the products is a positron.

$$^{11}_{6}\text{C} \longrightarrow {}^{0}_{+1}\text{e} + \, ?$$

To balance the equation, a particle with $A = 11 - 0 = 11$ and $Z = 6 - 1 = 5$ (boron) is required.

$$^{11}_{6}\text{C} \longrightarrow {}^{0}_{+1}\text{e} + {}^{11}_{5}\text{B}$$

d. We write the symbol for carbon-11 and a partial equation showing it capturing an electron.

$$^{11}_{6}\text{C} + {}^{0}_{-1}\text{e} \longrightarrow \, ?$$

To balance the equation, the product must have $A = 11 + 0 = 11$ and $Z = 6 + (-1) = 5$ (boron).

$$^{11}_{6}\text{C} + {}^{0}_{-1}\text{e} \longrightarrow {}^{11}_{5}\text{B}$$

As we noted previously, positron emission and electron capture result in identical changes in atomic number and, therefore, affect a given nucleus in the same way, as parts **(c)** and **(d)** illustrate for carbon-11. Also note that carbon-11 (and certain other nuclei) can undergo more than one type of radioactive decay.

■ EXERCISE 1

Write balanced nuclear equations for the following processes. In each case, identify the product element formed.

a. Uranium-235 decays by alpha emission.

b. Lead-210 undergoes beta decay.

c. Fluorine-18 decays by positron emission.

d. Oxygen-13 undergoes electron capture.

We noted earlier that nuclear *equations* differ in two ways from ordinary chemical equations. Nuclear *reactions* also exhibit many differences from chemical reactions. Some important ones are summarized in Table 3. Some nuclear reactions also involve processes other than the five simple ones we have discussed here. Regardless, all nuclear equations must be balanced according to nucleon (mass) numbers and atomic numbers. When an unknown particle has an atomic number that does not correspond to an atom, that particle may be a subatomic particle. A list of nuclear symbols for subatomic particles is given in Table 4.

Table 3	Some Differences Between Chemical Reactions and Nuclear Reactions	
Chemical Reactions	**Nuclear Reactions**	
Atoms retain their identity.	Atoms usually change their identity—from one element to another.	
Reactions involve only electrons and usually only outermost electrons.	Reactions involve mainly protons and neutrons. It does not matter what the valence electrons do.	
Reaction rates can be increased by raising the temperature.	Reaction rates are unaffected by changes in temperature.	
The energy absorbed or given off in reactions is comparatively small.	Reactions sometimes involve enormous changes in energy.	
Mass is conserved. The mass of products equals the mass of starting materials.	Huge changes in energy are accompanied by measurable changes in mass ($E = mc^2$).	

Table 4	Symbols for Subatomic Particles	
Particle	**Symbol**	**Nuclear Symbol**
Proton	p	^1_1p or ^1_1H
Neutron	n	^1_0n
Electron	e^- or β	$^0_{-1}e$ or $^0_{-1}\beta$
Positron	e^+ or β^+	$^0_{+1}e$ or $^0_{+1}\beta$
Alpha particle	α	^4_2He or $^4_2\alpha$
Beta particle	β or β^-	$^0_{-1}e$ or $^0_{-1}\beta$
Gamma ray	γ	$^0_0\gamma$

Self-Assessment Questions

Identify items 1–4 as one of the following.

a. alpha particle   **b.** beta particle   **c.** nucleon number   **d.** radioactivity

1. an electron
2. atomic mass of 4 u
3. emission of particles and energy from a nucleus
4. number of protons and neutrons in an atom

5. What are the mass and the charge, respectively, of gamma radiation?
   a. 0, – 1   **b.** 0, 0   **c.** 0, +1   **d.** 4, +2

6. What particle is needed to complete the following nuclear equation?

$$_4^9Be + ? \longrightarrow _6^{12}C + _0^1n$$

   a. alpha particle   **b.** beta particle   **c.** neutron   **d.** proton

3 Half-Life and Radioisotopic Dating

Learning Objectives ❯ Solve simple half-life problems. ❯ Use the concept of half-life to solve simple radioisotope dating problems.

Thus far, we have discussed radioactivity as applied to single atoms. In the laboratory, we generally deal with great numbers of atoms—numbers far larger than the number of all the people on Earth. If we could see the nucleus of an individual atom, we could tell whether or not it would undergo radioactive decay by noting its composition. Certain combinations of protons and neutrons are unstable. However, we could not determine *when* the atom would undergo a change. Radioactivity is a random process, generally independent of outside influences.

Half-Life

With large numbers of atoms, the process of radioactive decay becomes more predictable. We can measure the *half-life*, a property characteristic of each radioisotope. The **half-life** of a radioactive isotope is the time it takes for one-half of the original number of atoms to undergo radioactive decay.

Suppose, for example, we had 16.00 mg of the radioactive isotope iodine-131. The half-life of iodine-131 is 8.0 days. This means that in 8.0 days, half the iodine-131, or 8.00 mg, will have decayed, and there will be 8.00 mg left. In another 8.0 days, half of the remaining 8.00 mg will have decayed. After two half-lives, or 16.0 days, then, one-quarter of the original iodine-131, or 4.00 mg, will remain. Note that two half-lives, do not make a whole. The concept of half-life is illustrated by the graph in Figure 4. Half-lives of radio isotopes can differ enormously. The half-life of tellurium-128 is 8×10^{24} y, while that of beryllium-13 is 2.7×10^{-21} s.

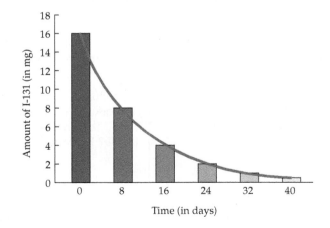

◀ **Figure 4** The radioactive decay of iodine-131, which has a half-life of 8 days.

Q: *How much of a 32-mg sample of iodine-131 remains after five half-lives have passed?*

The rate of decay is inversely related to half-life. An isotope with a long half-life decays slowly; an isotope with a short half-life decays at a high rate. We measure the rate of decay, also referred to as the isotope's **activity**, in disintegrations per second, a unit called a **becquerel (Bq)**.

We can calculate the fraction of the original isotope that remains after a given number of half-lives from the relationship

$$\text{Fraction remaining} = \frac{1}{2^n}$$

where n is the number of half-lives.

We cannot say when *all* the atoms of a radioisotope will have decayed. For most samples, we can assume that the activity is essentially gone after about ten half-lives (when the activity is $\frac{1}{2^{10}} = \frac{1}{1024}$ of the original value). That is, about a thousandth of the original activity remains.

3. Why can't we just burn or dissolve radioactive wastes to get rid of them?
The half-life of a radioisotope is a nuclear property that isn't changed by chemical reactions. For example, if we burn radioactive carbon, we get radioactive carbon dioxide as the product. Dissolving radioactive plutonium in nitric acid produces radioactive plutonium nitrate. An isotope will be radioactive for a length of time determined by its half-life—and we can't change the half-life.

Example 2   Half-Lives

A 4.00-mg sample of cobalt-60, half-life 5.271 y, is to be used for radiation treatment. How much cobalt-60 remains after 15.813 years (three half-lives)?

Solution
The fraction remaining after three half-lives is

$$\frac{1}{2^n} = \frac{1}{2^3} = \frac{1}{2 \times 2 \times 2} = \frac{1}{8}$$

The amount of cobalt-60 remaining is $\frac{1}{8} \times 4.00$ mg $= 0.50$ mg.

■ EXERCISE 2A
The half-life of phosphorus-32 is 14.3 days. What percentage of a sample of phosphorus-32 remains after four half-lives?

■ EXERCISE 2B
On April 4, 2011, a small fish caught about 50 mi south of the Fukushima nuclear complex had an activity of 4000 Bq of iodine-131 per kilogram. The half-life of iodine-131 is 8.0 d. What was the activity of the isotope **(a)** on April 28, 2011 (three half-lives later)? **(b)** On June 23, 2011 (ten half-lives later)?

CONCEPTUAL Example 3   Time and Radioactive Decay

We cannot determine how long it will take for *all* of a radioactive isotope to decay. For many isotopes, it is assumed that the activity is near zero after about ten half-lives. What mass of a 0.0260-mg sample of mercury-190, half-life 20 min, remains after ten half-lives?

Solution
The fraction remaining after ten half-lives is found in the usual manner.

$$\frac{1}{2^n} = \frac{1}{2^{10}} = \frac{1}{2 \times 2 \times 2 \times 2 \times 2 \times 2 \times 2 \times 2 \times 2 \times 2} = \frac{1}{1024}$$

The amount of mercury-190 remaining is $\frac{1}{1024} \times 0.0260$ mg $= 0.000025$ mg.

■ EXERCISE 3
The disposal of some radioactive materials is scheduled according to the rule stated in Conceptual Example 3. Would the rule work **(a)** for a 1.00-g sample of rubidium-87 with an initial decay rate of 3200 Bq? **(b)** For a 1.00-g sample of cobalt-60, which has an initial activity of 4.1×10^{13} Bq? Explain.

Radioisotopic Dating

The half-lives of certain radioisotopes can be used to estimate the ages of rocks and archaeological artifacts. Uranium-238 decays with a half-life of 4.5 billion years. The initial products of this decay are also radioactive, and they and subsequent products continue to decay until lead-206 is formed. By measuring the relative amounts of uranium-238 and lead-206, chemists can estimate the age of a rock. Some of the older rocks on Earth have been found to be 3.0–4.5 billion years old. Moon rocks

Why Are Isotopes Stable—or Unstable?

Most isotopes are radioactive, but some are stable. What factors tend to make an atomic nucleus stable? Stable isotopes tend to have:

1. *Even* numbers of either protons or neutrons or (especially) both. Of the 264 stable isotopes, 157 have *even* numbers of both protons and neutrons, and only four have odd numbers of both protons and neutrons. Elements with even Z have more stable isotopes than do those with odd Z.

2. So-called *magic numbers* of either protons or neutrons. (Magic numbers are 2, 8, 20, 50, 82, and 126.)

3. An atomic number of 83 or less. All isotopes with $Z > 83$ are radioactive.

4. Fewer, or the same number of, protons as neutrons in the nucleus, and a ratio of neutrons to protons close to 1 if the atomic number is 20 or below. As atomic number gets larger, the stable n/p ratio also increases, up to about 1.5. There is a zone of stability within which the n/p ratio should lie for an atom with a given atomic number.

and meteorites have been dated at a maximum age of about 4.5 billion years. Thus, the age of Earth (and the solar system itself) is generally estimated to be about 4.5 billion years.

The dating of artifacts derived from plants or animals usually involves radioactive carbon-14. Of the carbon on Earth, about 99% is carbon-12 and 1% is carbon-13, and both of these isotopes are stable. However, in the upper atmosphere, carbon-14 is formed by the bombardment of ordinary nitrogen by neutrons from cosmic rays.

$$^{14}_{7}N + ^{1}_{0}n \longrightarrow ^{14}_{6}C + ^{1}_{1}H$$

This process results in a tiny but steady concentration of carbon-14 in the CO_2 molecules of Earth's atmosphere. Plants use CO_2, and animals consume plants and other animals; thus, living things constantly incorporate this isotope into their cells. When organisms die, the incorporation of carbon-14 ceases, and the isotope begins to decay—with a half-life of 5730 years—back to nitrogen-14. We can measure the carbon-14 activity remaining in an artifact of plant or animal origin to determine its age, using the technique called **carbon-14 dating**. For instance, a sample that has half the carbon-14 activity of new plant material is 5730 years old; it has been dead for one half-life. Similarly, an artifact with a fourth of the carbon-14 activity of new plant material is 11,460 years old; it has been dead for two half-lives.

We have assumed that the formation of the carbon-14 isotope has been constant over the years, but this is not quite the case. For the last 7000 years or so, carbon-14 dates do correlate with those obtained from the annual growth rings of trees and with documents of known age. Calibration curves have been constructed from which accurate dates can be determined. Generally, carbon-14 is reasonably accurate for dating objects from about 100 to 50,000 years old. Newer objects may not yet have seen measurable decay of carbon-14. Objects older than 50,000 years have too little of the isotope left for accurate measurement.

Charcoal from the fires of ancient peoples, dated by determining the carbon-14 activity, is used to estimate the age of other artifacts found at the same archaeological sites. For example, carbon dating was used to confirm that ancient Hebrew writing found on a stone tablet unearthed in Israel dates from the ninth century B.C.E.

Tritium, the radioactive isotope of hydrogen, can also be used for dating materials. Its half-life of 12.26 years makes it useful for dating items up to about 100 years old. An interesting application of tritium dating is the dating of brandies. These alcoholic beverages are quite expensive when aged from 10 to 50 years. Tritium dating can be used to check the veracity of advertising claims about the ages of the most expensive kinds.

Many other isotopes are useful for estimating the ages of objects and materials. Several of the more important ones are listed in Table 5.

The Shroud of Turin

The Shroud of Turin is a very old piece of linen cloth, about 4 m long, bearing a faint human likeness. From about c.e. 1350 onward, it had been alleged to be part of the burial shroud of Jesus. However, carbon-14 dating studies in 1988 by three different laboratories indicated that the flax used to make the cloth was not grown until sometime between c.e. 1260 and 1390; therefore, the cloth could not possibly have existed at the time of Jesus. Unlike the Dead Sea Scrolls, which were shown by carbon-14 dating to be authentic records from a civilization that existed about 2000 years ago, the Shroud of Turin has been shown to be less than 800 years old. It is generally thought to be a work of art produced around that time.

Table 5	Several Isotopes Used in Radioactive Dating		
Isotope	**Half-Life (years)**	**Useful Range**	**Dating Applications**
Carbon-14	5730	100 to 50,000 years	Charcoal, organic material
Hydrogen-3 (tritium)	12.26	1 to 100 years	Aged wines and brandies
Lead-210	22	1 to 75 years	Skeletal remains
Potassium-40	1.25×10^9	10,000 years to the oldest Earth samples	Rocks, Earth's crust, the moon's crust
Rhenium-187	4.3×10^{10}	4×10^7 years to the oldest samples in the universe	Meteorites
Uranium-238	4.51×10^9	10^7 years to the oldest Earth samples	Rocks, the Earth's crust

Example 4   Radioisotopic Dating

An old wooden implement shows carbon-14 activity that is one-eighth that of new wood. How old is the artifact? The half-life of carbon-14 is 5730 y.

Solution
Using the relationship

$$\text{Fraction remaining} = \frac{1}{2^n}$$

we see that one-eighth is $\frac{1}{2^n}$, where $n = 3$; that is, the fraction $\frac{1}{8}$ is $\frac{1}{2^3}$. The carbon-14 has gone through three half-lives. The wood is therefore about $3 \times 5730 = 17{,}190$ y old.

■ EXERCISE 4
Calculate the approximate age of each of the following. (a) Human remains have been preserved for centuries in the bogs of Northern Europe. How old is a bog body that has carbon-14 activity one-fourth that of living tissue? The half-life of carbon-14 is 5730 y. (b) How old is a bottle of brandy that has a tritium activity one-sixteenth that of new brandy? The half-life of tritium (hydrogen-3) is 12.26 years.

Self-Assessment Questions

1. A patient is given a 48-mg dose of technetium-99m (half-life 6.0 h) to treat a brain cancer. How much of it will remain in his body after 36 h?
   a. 0.75 mg   **b.** 1.5 mg   **c.** 3.0 mg   **d.** 12 mg
2. What is the half-life of silver-112 if a 10.0-g sample decays to 2.5 g in 12.4 h?
   a. 1.6 h   **b.** 3.1 h   **c.** 6.2 h   **d.** 12.4 h
3. Of a 64.0-g sample of strontium-90 (half-life 28.5 y) produced by a nuclear explosion, what mass in grams would remain unchanged after 285 y?
   a. 0.000 g   **b.** 0.000625 g   **c.** 0.00625 g   **d.** 0.0625 g

4. Lead-210 (half-life 22.26 y) can be used to date skeletal remains. About how old is a bone that has an activity of 2.0 Bq if new bone has an activity of 16 Bq?

a. 7.4 y   b. 44.5 y   c. 67 y   d. 89 y

5. About how old is a piece of wood from an aboriginal burial site that has a carbon-14 (half-life 5730 y) activity of 3.9 counts/min per gram of carbon? Assume that the carbon-14 activity of the wood was 15.6 counts per minute per gram of carbon at the time of the burial.

a. 2865 y   b. 11,460 y   c. 17,190 y   d. 22,920 y

Answers: 1, a; 2, c; 3, d; 4, c; 5, b

Isotopic Signatures

For most chemical reactions, isotopes are unimportant. However, differences in isotopes can be quite important to some investigations. Isotopes' variance in mass affects their rates of reaction, with lighter isotopes generally moving a bit faster than heavier ones. This difference can lead to a measurable characteristic called an *isotopic signature* in an investigated material. For example, the ratio of carbon-13 to carbon-12 in materials formed by photosynthesis is less than that isotopic ratio in inorganic carbonates.

The ratio of oxygen-18 to oxygen-16 depends on the extent of evaporation that water has undergone because water molecules with oxygen-18 atoms are heavier and thus vaporize less readily than do water molecules with oxygen-16 atoms. This difference is less pronounced at higher temperatures. As oxygen is incorporated into the calcium carbonate shells of aquatic organisms, the isotopic ratio in the shells shifts. Fossilized shells thus provide a chronological record of the temperature of the water in which the organisms lived. The oxygen isotope ratio in the atmosphere varies with the season and with geographic location. This variation allows scientists to determine the location in which a material originated.

The ratio of nitrogen-14 to nitrogen-15 is different for herbivores and carnivores, because organisms higher in the food chain tend to concentrate the nitrogen-15 isotope in their tissues. Such variations enable scientists to determine much about the diet of people from ages past.

4 Artificial Transmutation

Learning Objective > Write a nuclear equation for a transmutation, and identify the product element formed.

During the Middle Ages, alchemists tried to turn base metals, such as lead, into gold. However, they were trying to do it chemically and were therefore doomed to failure because chemical reactions involve only atoms' outer electrons. **Transmutation** (changing one element into another) requires altering the *nucleus*.

Thus far, we have considered only natural forms of radioactivity. Nuclear reactions can also be brought about by bombardment of stable nuclei with alpha particles, neutrons, or other subatomic particles. These particles, given sufficient energy, can penetrate a stable nucleus and result in some kind of radioactive emission. Just as in natural radioactive processes, one element is changed into another. Because the change would not have occurred naturally, the process is called *artificial transmutation*.

In 1919, a few years after his famous gold-foil experiment, Ernest Rutherford reported on the bombardment of a variety of light elements with alpha particles. One such experiment, in which he bombarded nitrogen, resulted in the production of protons, as shown in this balanced nuclear equation.

$$^{14}_{7}N + ^{4}_{2}He \longrightarrow ^{17}_{8}O + ^{1}_{1}H$$

(The hydrogen nucleus is simply a proton, which can be represented by the symbol $^{1}_{1}H$.) This provided the first empirical verification of the existence of protons in atomic nuclei, which Rutherford had first postulated in 1914.

Recall that Eugen Goldstein had produced protons in his gas-discharge tube experiments in 1886. The significance of Rutherford's experiment lay in the fact that he obtained protons from the *nucleus* of an atom other than hydrogen, thus establishing that protons are constituents of nuclei. Rutherford's experiment was the first induced nuclear reaction and the first example of artificial transmutation. In producing protons, he also changed nitrogen into oxygen.

▲ Ernest Rutherford (1871–1937) carried out the first nuclear bombardment experiment. Element 104 was named rutherfordium (Rf) in his honor.

Example 5   Artificial Transmutation Equations

When potassium-39 is bombarded with neutrons, chlorine-36 is produced. What other particle is emitted?

$$^{39}_{19}\text{K} + ^{1}_{0}\text{n} \longrightarrow ^{36}_{17}\text{Cl} + ?$$

Solution

To determine the particle, we need a balanced nuclear equation. To balance the equation, the unknown particle must have $A = 4$ and $Z = 2$—it is an alpha particle.

$$^{39}_{19}\text{K} + ^{1}_{0}\text{n} \longrightarrow ^{36}_{17}\text{Cl} + ^{4}_{2}\text{He}$$

■ **EXERCISE 5A**

Technetium-97 is produced by bombarding molybdenum-96 with a deuteron (a hydrogen-2 nucleus). What other particle is emitted?

$$^{96}_{42}\text{Mo} + ^{2}_{1}\text{H} \longrightarrow ^{97}_{43}\text{Tc} + ?$$

■ **EXERCISE 5B**

A team of scientists wants to form uranium-235 by bombarding a nucleus of another element with an alpha particle. They expect a neutron to be produced along with the uranium-235 nucleus. What nucleus must be bombarded with the alpha particle?

Self-Assessment Questions

1. What isotope is formed in the following artificial transmutation?

$$^{14}_{7}\text{N} + ^{1}_{0}\text{n} \longrightarrow ^{1}_{1}\text{H} + ?$$

   a. carbon-12   **b.** carbon-14   **c.** nitrogen-15   **d.** oxygen-15

2. What isotope is formed in the following artificial transmutation?

$$^{9}_{4}\text{Be} + ^{1}_{1}\text{H} \longrightarrow ^{4}_{2}\text{He} + ?$$

   a. boron-9   **b.** boron-10   **c.** lithium-6   **d.** lithium-7

3. What isotope is formed in the following artificial transmutation?

$$^{239}_{94}\text{Pu} + ^{4}_{2}\text{He} \longrightarrow ^{1}_{0}\text{n} + ?$$

   a. americium-242   **b.** berkelium-242   **c.** curium-242   **d.** curium-243

Answers: 1, b; 2, c; 3, c

5 Uses of Radioisotopes

Learning Objective   ❯ List some applications of radioisotopes.

Most of the 3000 known radioisotopes are produced by artificial transmutation of stable isotopes. The value of both naturally occurring and artificial radioisotopes goes far beyond their contributions to our knowledge of chemistry.

Radioisotopes in Industry and Agriculture

Scientists in a wide variety of fields use radioisotopes as **tracers** in physical, chemical, and biological systems. Isotopes of a given element, whether radioactive or not, behave nearly identically in chemical and physical processes. Because radioactive isotopes are easily detected through their decay products, it is relatively easy to trace their movement, even through a complicated system. For example, tracing radioisotopes allows as to do the following:

■ **Detect leaks in underground pipes.** Suppose there is a leak in a pipe that is buried beneath a concrete floor. We could locate the leak by digging up extensive areas of the floor, or we could add a small amount of radioactive material to liquid poured into the drain and trace the flow of the liquid with a Geiger counter (an instrument that detects radioactivity). Once we located the leak, only a small area of the floor would have to be dug up to repair it. A compound containing a short-lived isotope (for example, $^{131}_{53}I$, half-life 8.04 days) is usually employed for this purpose.

- **Measure thickness of sheet metal during production.** Radiation from a beta emitter is allowed to pass through sheet metal on the production line. The amount of radiation that passes through a sheet is related to its thickness.
- **Determine frictional wear in piston rings.** The ring is subjected to neutron bombardment, which converts some of the carbon in the steel to carbon-14. Wear in the piston ring is assessed by the rate at which the carbon-14 appears in the engine oil.
- **Determine the uptake of phosphorus and its distribution in plants.** This can be done by incorporating phosphorus-32, a β^- emitter with a half-life of 14.3 d, into phosphate fertilizers fed to plants.

Radioisotopes are also used to study the effectiveness of weed killers, compare the nutritional value of various feeds, determine optimal methods for insect control, and monitor the fate and persistence of pesticides in soil and groundwater.

One of the most successful applications of radioisotopes in agriculture involves inducing heritable genetic alterations known as *mutations*. Exposing seeds or other parts of plants to neutrons or gamma rays increases the likelihood of genetic mutations. At first glance, this technique may not seem very promising. However, genetic variability is vital, not only to improve varieties but also to protect species from extinction. Some hybrid plants, such as seedless watermelons and bananas, are sterile. The lack of genetic variability among these plants may place the entire population at risk.

Radioisotopes are also used to irradiate foodstuffs as a method of preservation (Figure 5). The radiation destroys microorganisms and enzymes that cause foods to spoil. Irradiated food shows little change in taste or appearance. Some people are concerned about possible harmful effects of chemical substances produced by the radiation, but there has been no good evidence of harm to laboratory animals fed irradiated food or any known adverse effects in humans living in countries where food irradiation has been used for years. No residual radiation remains in a food after irradiation because gamma rays do not have nearly enough energy to change nuclei.

Radioisotopes in Medicine

Nuclear medicine involves two distinct uses of radioisotopes: therapeutic and diagnostic. In a therapeutic application, an attempt is made to treat or cure disease with radiation. The diagnostic use of radioisotopes is aimed at obtaining information about the state of a patient's health.

▲ Scientists can trace the uptake of phosphorus by a green plant by adding a compound containing some phosphorus-32 to the applied fertilizer. When the plant is later placed on photographic film, radiation from the phosphorus isotopes exposes the film, much as light does. This type of exposure, called a *radiograph*, shows the distribution of phosphorus in the plant.

4. Do irradiated foods give off radiation? Irradiated foods have absorbed energy in the form of gamma rays. But the foods are *not* radioactive.

◀ **Figure 5** Exposure to gamma radiation delays the decay of strawberries. Those on the right were irradiated; the ones on the left were not.

Q: *Are the strawberries on the right radioactive?*

▲ It DOES Matter!

The difference between a radioactive isotope and the alpha, beta, gamma, or positron radiation that it produces is very important and often misunderstood. A radioisotope such as iodine-131 or radon-222, when absorbed by the human body, can cause great harm because the radiation continues to be released as the isotope decays. However, matter exposed to ionizing radiation simply absorbs that energy, causing a chemical change. A patient undergoing gamma-radiation treatment does *not* become radioactive.

5. Are we exposed to dangerous radiation during X-rays and other medical procedures? A number of medical procedures do use ionizing radiation or radioisotopes, but the amount of radiation is kept to a minimum. The hazard of the ionizing radiation is ordinarily much less than the risk due to a lack of diagnosis or treatment!

Table 6 lists some radioisotopes in common use in medicine. The list is necessarily incomplete, but it should give you an idea of their importance. The claim that nuclear medicine has saved many more lives than nuclear bombs have taken is not an idle one.

Cancer is not one disease but many. Some forms are particularly susceptible to radiation therapy. The aim of **radiation therapy** is to destroy cancerous cells before too much damage is done to healthy tissue. Radiation is most lethal to rapidly reproducing cells, and rapid reproduction is the characteristic of cancer cells that allows radiation therapy to be successful. Radiation is carefully aimed at cancerous tissue while minimizing the exposure of normal cells. If the cancer cells are killed by the destructive effects of the radiation, the malignancy is halted.

Patients undergoing radiation therapy often get sick from the treatment. Nausea and vomiting are the usual early symptoms of radiation sickness. Radiation therapy can also interfere with the replenishment of white blood cells and thus increase patients' susceptibility to infection.

Radioisotopes used for diagnostic purposes provide information about the functioning of some part of the body or about the type or extent of an illness. For example, radioactive iodine-131 is used to determine the size, shape, and activity of the thyroid gland, as well as to treat cancers in this gland and to control its hyperactivity. Small doses are used for diagnostic purposes, and large doses for treatment of thyroid cancer. After the patient drinks a solution of potassium iodide incorporating iodine-131, the iodide ions become concentrated in the thyroid. A detector showing the differential uptake of the isotope is used in diagnosis. The resulting

Table 6	Some Radioisotopes and Their Medical Applications		
Isotope	**Name**	**Half-Life[a]**	**Use**
^{11}C	Carbon-11	20.39 min	Brain scans
^{51}Cr	Chromium-51	27.8 d	Blood volume determination
^{57}Co	Cobalt-57	270 d	Measuring vitamin B_{12} uptake
^{60}Co	Cobalt-60	5.271 y	Radiation cancer therapy
^{153}Gd	Gadolinium-153	242 d	Determining bone density
^{67}Ga	Gallium-67	78.1 h	Scan for lung tumors
^{131}I	Iodine-131	8.040 d	Thyroid diagnoses and therapy
^{192}Ir	Iridium-192	74 d	Breast cancer therapy
^{59}Fe	Iron-59	44.496 d	Detection of anemia
^{32}P	Phosphorus-32	14.3 d	Detection of skin cancer or eye tumors
^{238}Pu	Plutonium-238	86 y	Provision of power in pacemakers
^{226}Ra	Radium-226	1600 y	Radiation therapy for cancer
^{75}Se	Selenium-75	120 d	Pancreas scans
^{24}Na	Sodium-24	14.659 h	Locating obstructions in blood flow
^{99m}Tc	Technetium-99m	6.0 h	Imaging of brain, liver, bone marrow, kidney, lung, or heart
^{201}Tl	Thallium-201	73 h	Detecting heart problems during treadmill stress test
^{3}H	Tritium	12.26 y	Determining total body water
^{133}Xe	Xenon-133	5.27 d	Lung imaging

[a] Abbreviations: y, years; d, days; h, hours; min, minutes.

photoscan can pinpoint the location of tumors or other abnormalities in the thyroid. In cancer treatment, radiation from therapeutic (large) doses of iodine-131 kills the thyroid cells in which the radioisotope has concentrated.

The radioisotope gadolinium-153 is used to determine bone mineralization. Its widespread use is an indication of the large number of people, mostly women, who suffer from osteoporosis (reduction in the quantity of bone) as they grow older. Gadolinium-153 gives off two types of radiation: gamma rays and X-rays. A scanning device compares these types of radiation after they pass through bone. Bone density is then determined from the difference in absorption of the rays.

Technetium-99m is used in a variety of diagnostic tests (Figure 6). The *m* stands for *metastable,* which means that this isotope gives up some energy when it changes to a more stable version of technetium-99 (which has the same atomic number and same atomic mass). The energy it gives up is in the form of a gamma ray.

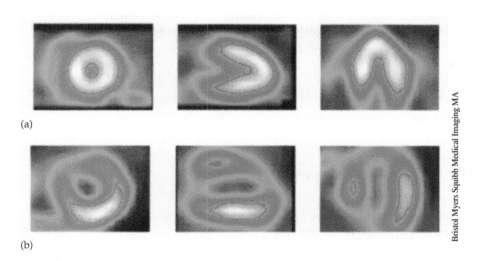

(a)

(b)

Bristol Myers Squibb Medical Imaging MA

◀ **Figure 6** Gamma-ray imaging using technetium-99m. Directional slices through (a) a healthy human heart and (b) a diseased heart. The lighter regions of the images indicate regions receiving adequate blood flow.

$$^{99m}_{43}\text{Tc} \longrightarrow {}^{99}_{43}\text{Tc} + \gamma$$

Note that the decay of technetium-99m produces no alpha or beta particles that could cause unnecessary damage to the body. Technetium-99m also has a short half-life (6.0 h), which means that the radioactivity does not linger very long in the body after the scan has been completed. With so short a half-life, use of the isotope must be carefully planned. In fact, technetium-99m is not what is purchased by medical labs. Technetium-99m is formed by the decay of molybdenum-99.

$$^{99}_{42}\text{Mo} \longrightarrow {}^{99m}_{43}\text{Tc} + {}^{0}_{-1}\text{e} + \gamma$$

A container of this molybdenum isotope is obtained, and the decay product, technetium-99m, is "milked" from the container as needed.

Using modern computer technology, *positron emission tomography (PET)* can measure dynamic processes occurring in the body, such as blood flow or the rate at which oxygen or glucose is being metabolized. For example, PET scans have shown that the brain of a schizophrenic metabolizes only about one-fifth as much glucose as a normal brain. These scans can also reveal metabolic changes that occur in the brain during tactile learning (learning by the sense of touch). PET scans can also pinpoint the area of brain damage that triggers severe epileptic seizures.

Compounds incorporating a positron-emitting isotope, such as carbon-11 or oxygen-15, are inhaled or injected before the scan. Before the emitted positron can travel very far in the body, it encounters an electron (numerous in any ordinary matter), and two gamma rays are produced, exiting from the body in exactly opposite directions.

$$^{11}_{6}\text{C} \longrightarrow {}^{11}_{5}\text{B} + {}^{0}_{+1}\text{e}$$

$$^{0}_{+1}\text{e} + {}^{0}_{-1}\text{e} \longrightarrow 2\gamma$$

(a)   (b)

Figure 7 Modern computer technology used for medical diagnosis. (a) Patient undergoing positron emission tomography (PET), a technique that uses radioisotopes to scan internal organs. (b) Images created by PET scanning, showing parts of the brain involved in different functions.

6. Can you get radiation sickness from someone who has been exposed to radiation? Alpha, beta and gamma rays, X-rays, and positrons that are absorbed by the body do cause cell damage, but by and large they are *not* energetic enough to create radioactive isotopes. One can no more "catch" radiation sickness from a person exposed to radiation than one can "catch" a sunburn.

Detectors, positioned on opposite sides of the patient, record the gamma rays. An image of an area in the body is formed using computerized calculations of the points at which annihilation of positrons and electrons occurs (Figure 7).

Example 6 Positron Emission Equations

One of the isotopes used to perform PET scans is oxygen-15, a positron emitter. What other isotope is formed when oxygen-15 decays?

Solution
First, we write the nuclear equation

$$^{15}_{8}O \longrightarrow {}^{0}_{+1}e + ?$$

The nucleon number, A, does not change, but the atomic number, Z, does: $8 - 1 = 7$. The product isotope is nitrogen-15.

$$^{15}_{8}O \longrightarrow {}^{0}_{+1}e + {}^{15}_{7}N$$

EXERCISE 6
Phosphorus-30 is a positron-emitting radioisotope suitable for doing PET scans. What other isotope is formed when phosphorus-30 decays?

Self-Assessment Questions

1. Iodine-131 is sometimes used for detecting leaks in underground pipes because
   a. it has a short half-life
   b. it is highly penetrating
   c. it is nontoxic
   d. its radiation is harmless

2. What is used to irradiate foodstuffs to extend shelf life?
   a. alpha particles   b. beta particles
   c. gamma rays   d. microwaves

For items 3–7, match each radioisotope with a major use.
3. cobalt-60   (a) bone density
4. gadolinium-153   (b) brain images
5. iodine-131   (c) heart problems
6. technetium-99m   (d) radiation therapy
7. thallium-201   (e) thyroid disorders
8. What form of radiation is detected in PET scans?
   a. beta   b. gamma   c. positron   d. X-rays

Answers: 1, a; 2, c; 3, d; 4, a; 5, e; 6, b; 7, c; 8, c

6 Penetrating Power of Radiation

Learning Objective ⟩ Describe the nature of materials needed to block alpha, beta, and gamma radiation.

The danger of radiation to living organisms comes from its potential for damaging cells and tissues. The ability to inflict injury relates to the penetrating power of the radiation. The two aspects of nuclear medicine just discussed (therapeutic and diagnostic) are also dependent on the penetrating power of various types of radiation.

All other things being equal, the more massive the particle, the less its penetrating power. *Alpha particles*, which are helium nuclei with a mass of 4 u, are the least penetrating of the three main types of radiation. *Beta particles*, which are identical to the almost massless electrons, are somewhat more penetrating. *Gamma rays*, like X-rays, have no mass; they are considerably more penetrating than the other two types.

But all other things are not always equal. The faster a particle moves or the more energetic the radiation is, the more penetrating power it has.

It may seem contrary to common sense that the biggest particles make the least headway. But keep in mind that penetrating power reflects the ability of radiation to make its way through a sample of matter. It is as if you were trying to roll some rocks through a field of boulders. The alpha particle acts as if it were a boulder itself. Because of its size, it cannot get very far before it bumps into and is stopped by other boulders. The beta particle acts as if it were a small stone. It can sneak between and perhaps ricochet off boulders until it makes its way farther into the field. The gamma ray can be compared with a grain of sand that can get through the smallest openings.

The danger of a specific type of radiation to human tissue depends on the location of the radiation's source as well as on its penetrating power. If the radioactive substance is outside the body, alpha particles are the least dangerous; they have low penetrating power and are stopped by the outer layer of skin. Beta particles are also usually stopped before they reach vital organs. Gamma rays readily pass through tissues, and so an external gamma source can be quite dangerous. People working with radioactive materials can protect themselves through one or both of the following actions:

- Move away from the source. The intensity of radiation decreases with distance from the source.
- Use shielding. A sheet of paper can stop most alpha particles, and a block of wood or a thin sheet of aluminum can stop most beta particles, but it takes a meter of concrete or several centimeters of lead to stop most gamma rays (Figure 8).

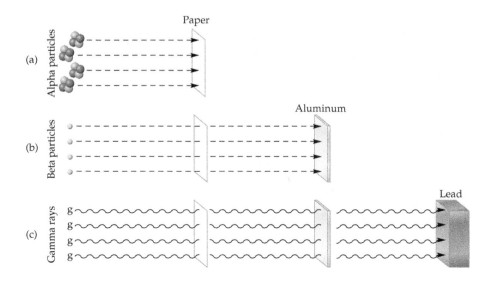

Figure 8 The relative penetrating power of alpha, beta, and gamma radiation. Alpha particles are stopped by a sheet of paper (a). Beta particles will not penetrate a sheet of aluminum (b). It takes several centimeters of lead to block gamma rays (c).

111

When the radioactive source is *inside* the body, as in the case of many medical applications, the situation is reversed. The nonpenetrating alpha particles can do great damage. All such particles are trapped within the body, which must then absorb all the energy the particles release. Alpha particles inflict all their damage in a tiny area because they do not travel far. Therefore, getting an alpha-emitting therapeutic radioisotope close to the targeted cells is vital.

Beta particles distribute their damage over a somewhat larger area because they travel farther. Tissue may recover from limited damage spread over a large area; it is less likely to survive concentrated damage.

Many diagnostic applications rely on the highly penetrating power of gamma rays. In most cases, the radiation created inside the body must be detected by instruments outside the body, so a minimum of absorption is desirable.

CONCEPTUAL Example 7 — Radiation Hazard

Most modern smoke detectors contain a tiny amount of americium-241, a solid element that is an alpha emitter. The americium is in a chamber that includes thin aluminum shielding, and the device is usually mounted on a ceiling. Rate the radiation hazard of this device in normal use as (a) high, (b) moderate, or (c) very low. Explain your choice.

Solution

Alpha particles have very little penetrating ability—they are stopped by a sheet of paper or a layer of skin. The emitted alpha particles cannot exit the detector's chamber, because even thin metal is more than sufficient to absorb them. Even if alpha particles could escape, they would likely be stopped by the air after a short distance or by the dead cells of your skin. Therefore, the radiation hazard is rated (c)—very low.

■ EXERCISE 7

Radon-222 is a gas that can diffuse from the ground into homes. Like americium-241, it is an alpha emitter. Is the radiation hazard from radon-222 likely to be higher or lower than that from a smoke detector? Explain.

Self-Assessment Questions

1. Which of the following pairs represent the *most* and *least* (most/least) penetrating types of radiation?
   a. alpha/gamma
   b. beta/gamma
   c. gamma/alpha
   d. X-rays/beta

2. Which form of radiation could not readily penetrate a sheet of paper?
   a. alpha
   b. beta
   c. gamma
   d. all of these

3. A Geiger counter registered 50 Bq of activity from an unknown type of radiation. A piece of paper inserted between the source and the counter caused the reading to drop to about 2 Bq. The radiation was mostly
   a. alpha particles
   b. beta particles
   c. gamma rays
   d. X-rays

Answers: 1, c; 2, a; 3, a

7 Energy from the Nucleus

Learning Objectives ❯ Explain where nuclear energy comes from. ❯ Describe the difference between fission and fusion.

We have seen that radioactivity—quiet and invisible—can be beneficial or dangerous. A much more dramatic—and equally paradoxical—aspect of nuclear chemistry is the release of nuclear energy by either *fission* (splitting of heavy nuclei into smaller nuclei) or *fusion* (combining of light nuclei to form heavier ones).

Einstein and the Equivalence of Mass and Energy

The potential power in the nucleus was established by Albert Einstein, a famous and most unusual scientist. Whereas most scientists work with glassware and instruments in laboratories, Einstein worked with a pencil and a notepad. By 1905, at the age of 26, he had already worked out his special theory of relativity and developed his famous **mass–energy equation**, in which mass (m) is multiplied by the square of the speed of light (c).

$$E = mc^2$$

The equation suggests that mass and energy are equivalent—just two different aspects of the same thing—and that a little bit of mass can yield enormous energy. The atomic bombs that destroyed Hiroshima and Nagasaki (Section 8) in World War II converted less than an ounce of matter into energy.

A chemical reaction that gives off heat must lose mass in the process, but the change in mass is far too small to measure. Reaction energy must be enormous—at the level of the energy given off by nuclear explosions—for the mass loss to be measurable. (If every atom in a 1-kg lump of coal became energy, it could produce 25 billion kWh of electricity—enough to keep a 100-W lightbulb going for 29 million years. Burning 1 kg of coal in a conventional power plant produces only enough energy to keep the bulb shining for 67 hours.)

Binding Energy

Nuclear fission releases the tremendous amounts of energy produced by atomic bombs and in nuclear power plants. Where does all this energy come from? It is locked inside the atomic nucleus. When protons and neutrons combine to form atomic nuclei, a small amount of mass is converted to energy. This is the **binding energy** that holds the nucleons together in the nucleus. For example, the helium nucleus contains two protons and two neutrons. The masses of these four particles add up to $2 \times 1.0073\ u + 2 \times 1.0087\ u = 4.0320\ u$ (Figure 9). However, the actual mass of the helium nucleus is only 4.0015 u, and the missing mass—called the *mass defect*—amounts to 0.0305 u. Using Einstein's equation $E = mc^2$, we can calculate (see Problem 55) a value of 28.3 million electron volts (28 MeV; 1 MeV = 1.6022×10^{-13} J) for the binding energy of the helium nucleus. This is the amount of energy it would take to separate one helium nucleus into two protons and two neutrons.

When the binding energy per nucleon is calculated for all the elements and plotted against nucleon number, a graph such as that in Figure 10 is obtained. The elements with the highest binding energies per nucleon have the most stable nuclei. They include iron and elements with nucleon members close to that of iron. When uranium atoms undergo nuclear fission, they split into atoms with higher binding energies. In other words, the fission reaction converts large atoms into smaller ones with greater nuclear stability.

We can also see from Figure 10 that even more energy can be obtained by combining small atoms, such as hydrogen or deuterium, to form larger atoms with more stable nuclei. This kind of reaction is called **nuclear fusion**. It is what happens when a hydrogen bomb explodes, and it is also the source of the sun's energy.

▲ Albert Einstein (1879–1955). Element 99 was named einsteinium (Es) in his honor.

1.0073 u

1.0073

1.0087

1.0087

4.0320 u ⟶ 4.0015 u

▲ **Figure 9** Nuclear binding energy in $^4_2$He. The mass of a helium-4 nucleus is 4.0015 u, which is 0.0305 u less than the masses of two protons and two neutrons. The missing mass is equivalent to the binding energy of the helium-4 nucleus.

Figure 10 Nuclear stability is greatest for iron and elements near iron in the periodic table. Fission of very large nuclei or fusion of very small ones results in greater nuclear stability.

Q: *Which process, fission of uranium nuclei or fusion of hydrogen nuclei, releases more energy?*

Enrico Fermi (1901–1954). Element 100 was named fermium (Fm) in his honor.

Lise Meitner (1878–1968). Element 109 was named meitnerium (Mt) in her honor.

Nuclear Fission

In 1934, the Italian scientists Enrico Fermi and Emilio Segrè (1905–1989) bombarded uranium atoms with neutrons. They were trying to make elements with higher atomic numbers than uranium, which then had the highest known atomic number. To their surprise, they found four radioactive species among the products. One was presumably element 93, formed by the initial conversion of uranium-238 to uranium-239, which then underwent beta decay.

$$^{238}_{92}\text{U} + ^{1}_{0}\text{n} \longrightarrow ^{239}_{92}\text{U}$$

$$^{239}_{92}\text{U} \longrightarrow ^{239}_{93}\text{Np} + ^{0}_{-1}\text{e}$$

They were unable to explain the remaining radioactivity.

When repeating the Fermi–Segrè experiment in 1938, German chemists Otto Hahn (1879–1968) and Fritz Strassman (1902–1980) were perplexed to find isotopes of barium among the many reaction products. Hahn wrote to Lise Meitner, his former longtime colleague, to ask what she thought about these strange results.

Lise Meitner was an Austrian physicist who had worked with Hahn in Berlin. Because she was Jewish, she fled to Sweden when the Nazis took over Austria in 1938. On hearing about Hahn's work, she noted that barium atoms were only about half the size of uranium atoms. Was it possible that the uranium nuclei might be splitting into fragments? She made some calculations that convinced her that the uranium nuclei had indeed been split apart. Her nephew, Otto Frisch (1904–1979), was visiting for the winter holidays, and they discussed this discovery with great excitement. It was Frisch who later coined the term **nuclear fission** (Figure 11).

Frisch was working with Niels Bohr at the University of Copenhagen, and when he returned to Denmark, he took the news of the fission reaction to Bohr, who happened to be going to the United States to attend a physics conference. The discussions in the corridors about this new reaction would be the most important talks to take place at that meeting.

Meanwhile, Enrico Fermi had just received the 1938 Nobel Prize in physics. Because Fermi's wife, Laura, was Jewish, and the fascist Italian dictator Mussolini was an ally of Hitler, Fermi accepted the award in Stockholm and then immediately fled with Laura and their children to the United States. Thus, by 1939, the United States had received news about the German discovery of nuclear fission and had also acquired from Italy one of the world's foremost nuclear scientists.

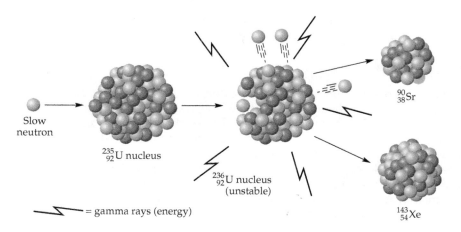

▲ **Figure 11** One possible way a uranium nucleus can undergo fission. The neutrons produced by the fission reactions can split other uranium nuclei, thus sustaining a chain reaction.

Q: *If each of the neutrons emitted by the ^{236}U nucleus caused another ^{235}U nucleus to split in the way shown here, how many more neutrons would be released?*

Nuclear Chain Reaction

Leo Szilard (1898–1964) was one of the first scientists to realize that nuclear fission could occur as a chain reaction. Szilard had been born in Hungary and educated in Germany, but he came to the United States in 1937 as one of the many Jewish refugees. He saw that neutrons released in the fission of one atom could trigger the fission of other uranium atoms, thus setting off a **chain reaction** (Figure 12). Because massive amounts of energy could be obtained from the fission of uranium, he saw that the chain reaction might be used in a bomb with tremendous explosive force.

Aware of the destructive forces that could be produced and concerned that Germany might develop such a bomb, Szilard prevailed on Einstein to sign a letter to

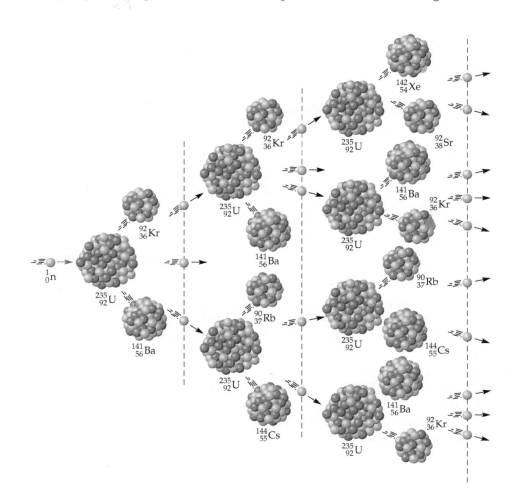

◀ **Figure 12** Schematic representation of a nuclear chain reaction. Neutrons released in the fission of one uranium-235 nucleus can strike other uranium-235 nuclei, causing them to split and release more neutrons as well as a variety of other nuclei. For simplicity, some fission fragments are not shown.

President Franklin D. Roosevelt indicating the importance of the discovery. It was critical that the U.S. government act quickly.

Thermonuclear Reactions

The chapter opening mentioned that the sun is a nuclear power plant vital to life on Earth. However, the nuclear reactions that take place in the sun are somewhat different from the ones we have discussed throughout this chapter. These **thermonuclear reactions** require enormously high temperatures (millions of degrees) to initiate them. The intense temperatures and pressures in the sun cause nuclei to fuse and release enormous amounts of energy. Instead of large nuclei being split into smaller fragments (fission), small nuclei are fused into larger ones (fusion). The main reaction in the sun is thought to be the fusion of four hydrogen nuclei to produce one helium nucleus and two positrons.

$$4{}^1_1\text{H} \longrightarrow {}^4_2\text{He} + 2\ {}^0_{+1}\text{e}$$

Fusion of 1 g of hydrogen releases an amount of energy equivalent to the burning of nearly 20 tons of coal. Every second, the sun fuses 600 tons of hydrogen, producing millions of times more energy than has been produced on Earth in the entire history of humankind. Much current research is aimed at reproducing such a reaction in the laboratory, by using ultrapowerful magnets to contain the intense heat required for ignition. To date, however, fusion reactions on Earth have been limited to the uncontrolled reactions in explosion tests of hydrogen (thermonuclear) bombs and to small amounts of energy produced by very expensive experimental fusion reactors.

Self-Assessment Questions

Look at the graph in Figure 10 to answer questions 1–3.
1. Helium has a particularly high binding energy per nucleon, which means that it
   a. is especially unstable compared to H and Li
   b. is more stable than H and Li
   c. will readily fuse into larger nuclei
   d. will readily split into hydrogen-2 atoms

2. The most stable nuclei are those of
   a. Ba   b. He   c. Fe   d. U

3. Nuclei with nuclear numbers greater than that of iron are
   a. all radioactive   b. increasingly stable
   c. less stable than iron   d. easily split into smaller nuclei

4. Which equation explains why the products of fission have less mass than the original substances?
   a. $E = h\nu/\lambda$ b. $E = h\nu$ c. $E = mc^2$ d. $PV = nRT$

5. Which subatomic particles are responsible for carrying on the chain reactions characteristic of nuclear fission?
   a. alpha particles   b. beta particles   c. neutrons   d. protons

6. When uranium-235 absorbs a neutron and undergoes fission, barium-142 and krypton-91 are two possible fission fragments. How many neutrons are released?

$${}^{235}_{92}\text{U} + {}^1_0\text{n} \longrightarrow {}^{142}_{56}\text{Ba} + {}^{91}_{36}\text{Kr} + ?\ {}^1_0\text{n}$$

   a. 0   b. 1   c. 2   d. 3

7. What process is represented by the equation ${}^2_1\text{H} + {}^3_1\text{H} \longrightarrow {}^4_2\text{He} + \text{energy}$?
   a. alpha decay   b. artificial transmutation
   c. fission   d. fusion

8. Hydrogen-2 and hydrogen-3 fuse to form helium-4. The other product is a(n)
   a. electron   b. neutron   c. positron   d. proton

Answers: 1, b; 2, c; 3, c; 4, c; 5, c; 6, c; 7, d; 8, b

8 Nuclear Bombs

Learning Objectives ❭ Describe how uranium and plutonium bombs are made.
❭ Identify the most hazardous fallout isotopes, and explain why they are particularly dangerous.

In 1939, President Roosevelt launched a highly secret research project for the study of atomic energy. Called the *Manhattan Project*, it eventually became a massive research effort involving more scientific brainpower than ever was or has been devoted to a single project. Amazingly, it was conducted under such extreme secrecy that even Vice President Harry Truman did not know of its existence until after Roosevelt's death.

The Manhattan Project included four separate research teams trying to learn how to

- sustain the nuclear-fission chain reaction,
- enrich uranium so that it contained about 90% of the fissionable isotope ^{235}U,
- make plutonium-239 (another fissionable isotope), and
- construct a bomb based on nuclear fission.

Sustainable Chain Reaction

By that time, it had been established that neutron bombardment could initiate the fission reaction, but many attributes of this reaction were unknown. Enrico Fermi and his group, working in a lab under the bleachers at Stagg Field on the campus of the University of Chicago, worked on the fission reaction itself and how to sustain it. They found that the neutrons used to trigger the reaction had to be slowed down to increase the probability that they would hit a uranium nucleus. Because graphite slows down neutrons, a large "pile" of graphite was built to house the reaction. Then the amount of uranium "fuel" was gradually increased. The major goal was to determine the **critical mass**—the amount of uranium-235 needed to sustain the fission reaction. There had to be enough fissionable nuclei in the "fuel" for the neutrons released in one fission process to have a good chance of being captured by another fissionable nucleus before escaping from the pile.

On December 2, 1942, Fermi and his group achieved the first sustained nuclear fission reaction. The critical mass of uranium (enriched to about 94% ^{235}U) for this reactor turned out to be about 16 kg.

Isotopic Enrichment

Natural uranium is 99.27% uranium-238, which does not undergo fission. Uranium-235, the fissionable isotope, makes up only 0.72% of natural uranium. Because making a bomb required *enriching* the uranium to about 90% uranium-235, it was necessary to find a way to separate the uranium isotopes. This was the job of the Manhattan Project research team in Oak Ridge, Tennessee.

Chemical separation was almost impossible; ^{235}U and ^{238}U are chemically almost identical. The separation method eventually used involved converting uranium to gaseous uranium hexafluoride, UF_6. Molecules of UF_6 containing uranium-235 are slightly lighter and therefore move slightly faster than molecules containing uranium-238. Uranium hexafluoride was allowed to pass through a series of thousands of pinholes, and the molecules containing uranium-235 gradually outdistanced the others. Enough enriched uranium-235 was finally obtained to make a small explosive device.

Synthesis of Plutonium

While the tedious work of separating uranium isotopes was underway at Oak Ridge, another research team, led by Glenn T. Seaborg, approached the problem of obtaining fissionable material by another route. Although uranium-238 would not fission when bombarded by neutrons, it was found that this more common isotope of uranium *would* decay to form a new element, named neptunium (Np). This product quickly decayed to another new element, plutonium (Pu).

$$^{238}_{92}U + ^{1}_{0}n \longrightarrow ^{239}_{92}U$$

$$^{239}_{92}U \longrightarrow ^{0}_{-1}e + ^{239}_{93}Np$$

$$^{239}_{93}Np \longrightarrow ^{239}_{94}Pu + ^{0}_{-1}e$$

Plutonium-239 was found to be fissionable and thus was suitable material for the making of a bomb. A group of large reactors was built near Hanford, Washington, to produce plutonium.

Bomb Construction

The actual building of the nuclear bombs was carried out at Los Alamos, New Mexico, under the direction of J. Robert Oppenheimer (1904–1967). In a top-secret laboratory at a remote site, a group of scientists planned and then constructed what would become known as atomic bombs. Two different models were developed, one based on ^{235}U and the other on ^{239}Pu.

The critical mass of uranium-235 could not be exceeded prematurely, so it was important that no single piece of fissionable material in the bomb be that large. The bomb was designed to contain pieces of uranium of subcritical mass, plus a neutron source to initiate the fission reaction. Then, at the chosen time, all the pieces would be forced together using an ordinary high explosive, thus triggering a runaway nuclear chain reaction.

The synthesis of plutonium turned out to be easier than the isotopic separation, and by July 1945, enough fissionable material had been made for three bombs to be assembled—two using plutonium, and one using uranium. The first atomic bomb (one of the plutonium devices) was tested in the desert near Alamogordo, New Mexico, on July 16, 1945. The heat from the explosion vaporized the 30-m steel tower on which the bomb was placed and melted the sand for several hectares around the site. The light produced was the brightest anyone had ever seen.

Some of the scientists were so awed by the force of the blast that they argued against using the bombs on Japan. A few, led by Leo Szilard, suggested a demonstration of the bombs' power at an uninhabited site. But fear of a well-publicized "dud" and the desire to avoid millions of casualties in an invasion of Japan led President Harry Truman to order the dropping of the bombs on Japanese cities. The lone uranium bomb, called "Little Boy" (Figure 13), was dropped on Hiroshima on August 6, 1945, and caused over 100,000 casualties. Three days later, the other plutonium bomb, called "Fat Man," was dropped on Nagasaki with comparable results (Figure 14). World War II ended with the surrender of Japan on August 14, 1945.

Radioactive Fallout

When a nuclear explosion occurs in the open atmosphere, radioactive materials can rain down on parts of Earth thousands of miles away, days and weeks later in what is called **radioactive fallout**. The uranium atom can split in several different ways.

▲ Glenn T. Seaborg (1912–1999). Element 106 was named seaborgium (Sg) in his honor. Seaborg is the only person to have had an element named for him while still alive. He is shown here pointing to his namesake element on the periodic table of elements.

▶ **Figure 13** An internal schematic of the atomic bomb "Little Boy" dropped on Hiroshima. Each of the cylinders of uranium-235 had less than the critical mass. The high explosive shot the cylindrical "bullet" down the gun barrel and onto the target spike. The result was about two critical masses of uranium-235, and a nuclear explosion occurred about a millisecond later.

High explosive   Hollow uranium "bullet"   Gun barrel   Uranium "target" spike

$$\ce{^{235}_{92}U} + \ce{^{1}_{0}n} \longrightarrow$$

$$\ce{^{90}_{38}Sr} + \ce{^{143}_{54}Xe} + 3\,\ce{^{1}_{0}n}$$

$$\ce{^{102}_{39}Y} + \ce{^{131}_{53}I} + 3\,\ce{^{1}_{0}n}$$

$$\ce{^{95}_{37}Rb} + \ce{^{137}_{55}Cs} + 4\,\ce{^{1}_{0}n}$$

US Air Force

▲ **Figure 14** The mushroom cloud over Nagasaki, following the detonation of "Fat Man" on August 9, 1945.

The primary (first) fission products are radioactive. These decay to daughter isotopes, many of which are also radioactive. In all, over 200 different fission products are produced, with half-lives that vary from less than a second to more than a billion years. Also, the neutrons produced in the explosion act on molecules in the atmosphere to produce carbon-14, tritium, and other radioisotopes. Fallout is therefore exceedingly complex. We consider three of the more worrisome isotopes here.

Of all the isotopes, strontium-90 (half-life 28.5 y) presents the greatest hazard to people. Strontium-90 reaches us primarily through dairy products and vegetables. Because of its similarity to calcium (both are group 2A elements), strontium-90 is incorporated into bone. There it remains an internal source of radiation for many years.

Iodine-131 may present a greater threat immediately after a nuclear explosion or reactor meltdown. Its half-life is only 8 days, but it is produced in relatively large amounts. Iodine-131 is readily transferred up the food chain. In the human body, it is concentrated in the thyroid gland, and it is precisely this characteristic that makes a trace of iodine-131 so useful for diagnostic scanning. However, for a healthy individual, larger amounts of radioactive iodine offer only damaging side effects. To minimize the absorption of radioactive iodine, many people in the areas of Chernobyl and Fukushima were given large amounts of potassium iodide, which effectively diluted the amount of radioactive iodine absorbed by their thyroid glands.

Cesium-137 (half-life 30.2 y) is, like strontium-90, capable of long-term effects. Because of its similarity to potassium (both are group 1A elements), it is taken up by living organisms as part of body fluids. It can be obtained from sources in the environment and reconcentrated in living organisms.

By the late 1950s, radioactive isotopes from atmospheric testing of nuclear weapons were detected in the environment. Concern over radiation damage from nuclear fallout led to a movement to ban atmospheric testing. Many scientists were leaders in the movement. Linus Pauling, who won the Nobel Prize in Chemistry in 1954 for his bonding theories and for his work in determining the structure of proteins, was a particularly articulate advocate of banning atmospheric tests. In 1963, a nuclear test ban treaty was signed by the major nations—with the exception of France and the People's Republic of China, which continued aboveground tests. Since the signing of the treaty, other countries have joined the nuclear club. Pauling, who had endured being called a communist and a traitor because of his outspoken position, was awarded the Nobel Peace Prize in 1962.

Self-Assessment Questions

1. The isotope used in uranium fission reactions is
   a. uranium-232
   b. uranium-234
   c. uranium-235
   d. uranium-238

2. What fraction of natural uranium is the fissionable isotope?
   a. <1%
   b. 10%
   c. 50%
   d. >99%

3. Plutonium for fission reactions is
   a. made from uranium-238
   b. made from neptunium ores
   c. obtained from the dwarf planet Pluto
   d. obtained from plutonium ores

4. Strontium-90 substitutes for calcium in bones because Sr and Ca
   a. are in the same group of the periodic table
   b. are in the same period of the periodic table
   c. have identical electron configurations
   d. have identical half-lives

5. Which of the following radioisotopes in fallout is dangerous mainly because it becomes concentrated in the thyroid gland?
   a. cesium-137   b. iodine-131   c. strontium-90   d. radon-222

Answers: 1, c; 2, a; 3, a; 4, a; 5, b

9 Uses of Nuclear Energy

Learning Objective ❯ List some uses of nuclear energy.

A significant portion of the electricity we use today is generated by nuclear power plants. In the United States, one-fifth of all the electricity produced comes from nuclear power plants. Europeans rely even more on nuclear energy. France, for example, obtains 80% of its electric power from nuclear plants, while Belgium, Spain, Switzerland, and Sweden generate about one-third of their power from nuclear reactors.

Ironically, the same nuclear chain reaction that occurred in the detonation of the bomb dropped on Hiroshima is used extensively today under the familiar concrete containment tower of a nuclear power plant. The key difference is that the power plant employs a *slow, controlled* release of energy from the nuclear chain reaction, rather than an explosion. The slowness of the process is due to the use of uranium fuel that is much less enriched (2.5–3.5% ^{235}U rather than the 90% enrichment of weapons-grade uranium).

One of the main problems with the production of nuclear power arises from the products of the nuclear reactions. As in nuclear fallout, most of the daughter nuclei produced by the fission of uranium-235 are also radioactive, some with very long half-lives. We will discuss the problems associated with nuclear waste. Perhaps a more serious problem is the potential transformation of spent nuclear fuel into weapons-grade material (see the box titled "Nuclear Proliferation and Dirty Bombs").

▶ The core of a nuclear reactor contains hollow rods filled with uranium pellets. The heat generated by the fission reaction is used to boil water, which drives turbines to generate electricity in the same way as in coal-fired or gas-fired generating plant. Because the pellets are only about 3% uranium-235, a nuclear explosion cannot occur, though loss of coolant may lead to a reactor meltdown.

JIJI PRESS/AFP/Getty Images/Newscom

Bevin W. Parks-Lee, *Industrial organic chemist*

Green Remediation of Nuclear Waste

You learned that a large amount of ^{239}Pu was manufactured in Hanford, Washington, for the Manhattan Project (Section 8). The plutonium was produced from uranium in a nuclear reactor much like the ones used to produce electricity today. After the uranium rods reacted long enough to produce usable amounts of plutonium, they were transferred from the reactor and prepared for reprocessing. The goal was to maximize the plutonium production. The waste, still highly radioactive, was stored in many million-gallon tanks. Some of these tanks have been in service for 70 years, and leaks have been detected. Green chemistry principles can guide the development of methods to handle this legacy waste responsibly.

The Manhattan Project generated more than 91 million gallons of extremely acidic radioactive waste left over from the recovery of Pu and U. The solutions, referred to as high-level liquid waste (HLLW), are radioactive because small amounts of U and Pu remain with many other radioactive *nuclides* (nuclei having specific mass numbers and atomic numbers) that were produced during the fission reactions, including Np, Am, and Nd (Sections 3 and 7). If this small amount of radioactive material (1–2% of the 91 million gallons) could be removed, the impact would be tremendous.

Spent fuel rods are made up of different metals that can be separated and reclaimed through reprocessing. The aim is to remove any remaining radioactive nuclides, but many steps are necessary to achieve this. To access the separate atoms and free them from the solid matrix, the fuel rods are dissolved in concentrated nitric acid. An oxidation-reduction reaction occurs between the acid and the metals. The protons from the acid are reduced to form hydrogen gas, and the metals are oxidized to produce cations. The radioactive metal cations remain in the acidic water. At this point, it is possible to selectively remove metals by using special organic solutions that bind specific nuclides.

Processes that reduce the amount of HLLW align with Green Chemistry Principles 1, 6, and 12. How can these principles be put into action? One way is to design remediation processes that target the radioactive parts of the waste. Specifically, isolating only the radioactive compounds that require treatment avoids the need to store millions of gallons of acidic solution. Also, since the half-lives of these nuclides are so long (Section 3), encasing the waste in glass (vitrification) has been proposed as a good storage approach. Decreasing the volume of waste, though, would minimize the use of vitrification, which is energy-intensive and expensive.

In reprocessing, specific molecules can be used to bind to the radioactive cations and to manipulate the properties (e.g., solubility) of the resulting metal compounds. The molecules react with the metals to make compounds soluble in organic solvents. This enables the radioactive materials to be removed from water and transferred into a small volume of organic solvent. If the molecules are selective for one metal over another, they will bind to and carry only that metal into the organic solvent. This reprocessing method offers the opportunity to separate and reclaim individual types of metals.

One type of organic molecule that can extract the radioactive nuclides is an *amide*. Amides are easy to synthesize, and they are stable in the highly acidic and radioactive environment. A way to further reduce the volume of radioactive waste would be to burn off the organic components—the molecules bound to the metals and the solvent carrying them—leaving only solid metal waste. Amides (composed of only C, H, N, and O) will burn completely, making them a good fit with Green Chemistry Principle 10—designing for degradation. The simple amides tested first did not bind the metal ions as well as other types of molecules, which were harder to synthesize, degraded in the waste solutions, could not be incinerated, and tended to be toxic. Further research uncovered that molecules containing two amide groups bound the metal ions very well. This example shows the application of Green Chemistry Principle 4 through the design of a safer chemical.

Overall, green chemistry principles can be used to dramatically reduce amounts of radioactive waste and to reprocess the waste in ways that are safer for human health and the environment.

▲ Construction of the storage tanks of HLLW that are buried on completion.

Nuclear Proliferation and Dirty Bombs

As power is generated in nuclear plants, important changes occur in the fuel. Neutron bombardment converts ^{235}U to radioactive daughter products. Eventually, the concentration of ^{235}U becomes too low to sustain the nuclear chain reaction. The fuel rods must be replaced about every three years. The rods then become high-level nuclear waste.

As ^{235}U undergo fission, the nonfissionable (and very concentrated) ^{238}U nuclei absorb neutrons and are converted to ^{239}Pu, a transmutation described in Section 8). In time, some ^{240}Pu is also formed. However, if the fuel rods are removed after only about three months, the fissionable plutonium-239 can be easily separated from the other fission products by chemical means. Plutonium bombs require less sophisticated technology to produce than is needed to make nuclear weapons from uranium. Plutonium is thus of greater concern with respect to weapons proliferation, because operation of a nuclear plant can produce materials suitable for use in a bomb. North Korea has nuclear power plants and a plutonium separation facility capable of producing enough ^{239}Pu for several weapons each year (Figure 15). Iran also has a facility for enriching uranium, which could lead to the production of nuclear bombs. The activities of these and other developing countries raise the fear of a dangerous proliferation of nuclear weapons.

Another security concern is a "dirty bomb," a device that uses a conventional explosive, such as dynamite, to disperse radioactive material that might be stolen from a hospital or other facility that uses radioactive isotopes. In most cases, the conventional bomb would do more immediate harm than the radioactive substances. At the levels most likely to be used, the dirty bomb would not contain enough radioactive material to kill people or cause severe illness.

GeoEye Inc.

▲ **Figure 15** Satellite photograph of the plutonium processing plant at Yongbyon, North Korea.

The Nuclear Age

The splitting of the atom made the Chinese curse "May you live in interesting times" seem quite appropriate. The goal of the alchemists, to change one element into another, has been achieved through the application of scientific principles. New elements have been formed, and the periodic table has been extended well beyond

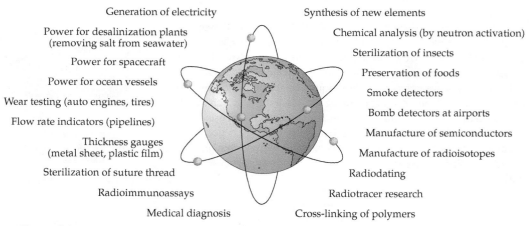

Generation of electricity
Power for desalinization plants (removing salt from seawater)
Power for spacecraft
Power for ocean vessels
Wear testing (auto engines, tires)
Flow rate indicators (pipelines)
Thickness gauges (metal sheet, plastic film)
Sterilization of suture thread
Radioimmunoassays
Medical diagnosis

Synthesis of new elements
Chemical analysis (by neutron activation)
Sterilization of insects
Preservation of foods
Smoke detectors
Bomb detectors at airports
Manufacture of semiconductors
Manufacture of radioisotopes
Radiodating
Radiotracer research
Cross-linking of polymers

▲ **Figure 16** Some constructive uses of nuclear energy.

uranium ($Z = 92$). This modern alchemy produces plutonium by the ton; neptunium ($Z = 93$), americium ($Z = 95$), and curium ($Z = 96$) by the kilogram; and berkelium ($Z = 97$) and einsteinium ($Z = 99$) by the milligram.

As we have seen, radioactive isotopes have many uses, from killing tiny but deadly cancer cells and harmful microorganisms in food to serving as tracers in a variety of biological experiments and imaging technologies and generating fearsome weapons. Figure 16 displays a number of other constructive uses of nuclear energy. We live in an age in which the extraordinary forces present in the atom have been unleashed as a true double-edged sword. The threat of nuclear war—and nuclear terrorism—has been a constant specter for the last six decades, yet it is hard to believe that the world would be a better place if we had not discovered the secrets of the atomic nucleus.

CRITICAL THINKING EXERCISES

Apply knowledge that you have gained in this chapter and one or more of the FLaReS principles to evaluate the following statements or claims.

1   Brazil nuts are known to absorb and concentrate the element barium. A nationally known laboratory announces that Brazil nuts contain tiny traces of radium.

2   For more than 600 years, it was alleged that the Shroud of Turin was the burial shroud of Jesus. In 1988, several laboratories carried out carbon-14 analyses indicating that the flax from which the shroud was made was grown between c.e. 1260 and 1390. Recently there have been claims that the 1988 analyses are unreliable because the shroud is contaminated with pollen from plants grown in the fourteenth century, and it is the age of this pollen that was actually measured in 1988. At least one of the scientists has offered to repeat the analysis on a very carefully cleaned sample of the cloth, but further access to the shroud has been refused.

3   A scientist reports that he has found an artifact that has been shown to be 80,000 years old by carbon-14 dating.

4   The americium in a smoke detector (see Conceptual Example 7) is encased in a chamber with aluminum shielding, about as thick as the wall of a soft-drink can. A woman who purchases a smoke detector mounts it at the highest point on the ceiling. She claims that this minimizes her exposure to the radiation.

5   A young girl refuses to visit her grandmother after the woman has undergone radiation therapy for breast cancer. The teenager is afraid that she will catch radiation sickness from her grandmother.

SUMMARY

Section 1—Some isotopes of elements have unstable nuclei, which undergo changes in nucleon number, atomic number, or energy; this process is called radioactive decay. The nuclei that undergo such changes are called radioisotopes. We are constantly exposed to naturally occurring radiation, called background radiation. Radiation that causes harm by dislodging electrons from living tissue and forming ions is called ionizing radiation and includes nuclear radiation and X-rays. Radiation can disrupt normal chemical processes in cells and can damage DNA, sometimes causing mutations.

Section 2—Nuclear equations are used to represent nuclear processes. These equations are balanced when the sum of nucleon numbers on each side is the same and the sum of atomic numbers on each side is the same. Four types of radioactive decay are alpha $\left(^{4}_{2}\text{He}\right)$ decay, beta $\left(^{0}_{-1}\text{e}\right)$ decay, gamma $\left(^{0}_{0}\gamma\right)$ decay, and emission of a positron $\left(^{0}_{+1}\text{e}\right)$. Electron capture (EC) is a fifth type of decay, in which a nucleus absorbs one of the atom's electrons. There are a number of important differences between nuclear reactions and chemical reactions.

Section 3—The rate of radioactive decay is measured in becquerels (Bq).

$$1 \text{ becquerel (Bq)} = 1 \text{ disintegration/s}$$

The **half-life** of a radioactive isotope is the time it takes for half of a sample to undergo radioactive decay. The fraction of a radioisotope remaining after n half-lives is given by the expression

$$\text{Fraction remaining} = \frac{1}{2^{n}}$$

Half-lives of certain isotopes can be used to estimate the ages of various objects. Carbon-14 dating is the best-known of the radioisotopic dating techniques. Relying on carbon-14's half-life of 5730 years, this technique can be used to estimate the age of once-living items up to 50,000 years old. The decay of tritium can be used to date items up to 100 years old. Other isotopes can be used to date rocks, the Earth's crust, and meteorites.

Section 4—Transmutation, the conversion of one element into another, cannot be carried out by chemical means but can be accomplished by nuclear processes. Bombarding a stable nucleus with energetic particles can cause artificial transmutation. These processes can be represented with nuclear equations.

Section 5—Radioisotopes have many uses. A radioisotope and a stable isotope of an element behave nearly the same chemically, so radioisotopes can be used as tracers in physical and biological systems. A radioactive atom in a molecule labels it so that it can be followed by a radiation detector. Radioisotopes have many uses in agriculture, including the production of useful mutations. Radiation can be used to irradiate foodstuffs as a method of preservation. Radiation therapy to destroy cancer cells depends on the fact that radiation is more damaging to those rapidly reproducing cells than to healthy cells. Radioisotopes are used in the diagnosis of various disorders. Iodine-131 is used for thyroid diagnoses, gadolinium-153 for bone mineralization examinations, and technetium-99m for a variety of diagnostic tests. Positron emission tomography (PET) involves radioisotopes that emit positrons, which are then annihilated by electrons in the body, producing gamma rays that can be used to form an image.

Section 6—Different types of radiation have different penetrating abilities. *Alpha particles* (helium nuclei) are relatively slow and have low penetrating power. *Beta particles* (electrons) are much faster and more penetrating. *Gamma rays* (high-energy photons) travel at the speed of light and have great penetrating power. How hazardous radiation is depends on the location of the source; alpha particles from a source inside the body are highly damaging. Radiation hazard can be decreased by moving away from the source or by using shielding.

Section 7—Einstein's mass–energy equation, $E = mc^2$ shows that mass and energy are different aspects of the same thing. The total mass of the nucleons in a nucleus is greater than the actual mass of the nucleus. The missing mass, or the mass defect, is equivalent to the binding energy holding the nucleons together. Binding energy can be released either by breaking down heavy nuclei into smaller ones, a process called nuclear fission, or by

joining small nuclei to form larger ones, called nuclear fusion.

Fermi and Segrè bombarded uranium atoms with neutrons and found radioactive species among the products, while Hahn and Strassman found light nuclei among the reaction products. Meitner, aided by Frisch, hypothesized that the uranium nuclei were undergoing fission. Szilard saw that neutrons released in the fission of one nucleus could trigger the fission of other nuclei, setting off a chain reaction. Thermonuclear reactions (fusion reactions) combine small nuclei to form larger ones. Nuclear fusion produces even more energy than nuclear fission. Fusion is the basis of the hydrogen bomb and the source of the sun's energy. Much research is aimed at producing controlled fusion commercially.

Section 8—The nuclear fission reaction became the center of the Manhattan Project during World War II. Its goals were (1) to achieve sustained nuclear fission and determine the critical mass, or minimum amount, of fissionable material required; (2) to enrich the amount of fissionable uranium-235 in ordinary uranium; (3) to synthesize plutonium-239, which is also fissionable; and (4) to construct a nuclear fission bomb before the Germans were able to do so. World War II ended shortly after the dropping of atomic bombs on Hiroshima and Nagasaki.

In addition to the devastation at the site of a nuclear explosion, much radioactive debris, or radioactive fallout, is, produced. Strontium-90 and iodine-131 are particularly hazardous components of fallout. Partly because of fallout, a nuclear test ban treaty was signed by most of the major nations; only underground testing is not banned.

Section 9—Nuclear power plants use the same nuclear chain reaction as in atomic bombs, but the reaction is much slower and can be controlled because of the low concentration of fissionable material. Disposal of the products of nuclear fission in power plants is an important problem facing us, as is the potential conversion of nuclear fuel into weapons. The forces within the nucleus truly constitute a double-edged sword for civilization.

Green chemistry Radioactive waste must be handled responsibly, and green chemistry principles can guide the development of new methods. A greener approach is to selectively isolate and treat the small amounts of radioactive isotopes instead of the large volumes of liquid waste. This can now be accomplished using safer chemicals, thereby reducing the amount of hazardous waste and the need for expensive and energy-intensive processing or storage methods.

Learning Objectives

› Identify the sources of the natural radiation to which we are exposed.	Problems 15, 54
› List the sources and dangers of ionizing radiation.	Problem 15
› Balance nuclear equations.	Problems 19–25, 43
› Identify the products formed by various decay processes.	Problems 26–30, 47
› Solve simple half-life problems.	Problems 31–38, 51
› Use the concept of half-life to solve simple radioisotopic dating problems.	Problems 39–42
› Write a nuclear equation for a transmutation, and identify the product element formed.	Problems 45, 46, 58

Nuclear Chemistry

REVIEW QUESTIONS

1. Match each description with the type of change.
   (i) A new compound is formed. **a.** nuclear
   (ii) A new element is formed. **b.** chemical
   (iii) Size, shape, appearance, or volume is changed without changing the composition. **c.** physical

2. Define or describe each of the following.
   a. half-life
   b. positron
   c. background radiation
   d. radioisotope

3. Write the nuclear symbols for protium, deuterium, and tritium (which are hydrogen-1, hydrogen-2, and hydrogen-3, respectively).

4. Why are isotopes important in nuclear reactions but not in most chemical reactions?

5. Write the nuclear symbols for the following isotopes. You may refer to the periodic table.
   a. cobalt-60
   b. iodine-127
   c. sodium-22
   d. calcium-42

6. Indicate the number of protons and the number of neutrons in atoms of the following isotopes.
   a. $^{65}_{30}Zn$ **b.** $^{236}_{93}Np$
   c. $^{101}_{43}Tc$ **d.** $^{81m}_{36}Kr$

7. Which of the following pairs represent isotopes? (X is a general symbol for an element.)
   a. $^{70}_{32}X$ and $^{70}_{32}X$
   b. $^{57}_{22}X$ and $^{52}_{22}X$
   c. $^{176}_{74}X$ and $^{167}_{74}X$
   d. $^{8}_{4}X$ and $^{16}_{8}X$

8. In which of the following atoms are there more protons than neutrons?
   a. ^{17}F **b.** ^{58}Ni **c.** ^{16}O **d.** ^{197}Au

9. The longest-lived isotope of einsteinium (Es) has a mass (nucleon) number of 254. How many neutrons are in the nucleus of an atom of this isotope?

10. The longest-lived isotope of polonium (Po) has 125 neutrons. What is a mass (nucleon) number of this isotope?

11. What changes occur in the nucleon number and the atomic number of a nucleus during emission of each of the following?
    a. alpha particle
    b. gamma ray
    c. proton

12. What changes occur in the nucleon number and atomic number of a nucleus during emission of each of the following?
    a. beta particle
    b. neutron
    c. positron

13. **(a)** From which type of radiation would a pair of gloves be sufficient to shield the hands: heavy alpha particles or massless gamma rays? **(b)** From which type of radiation would heavy lead shielding be necessary to protect a worker: alpha, beta, or gamma?

14. What are some of the characteristics that make technetium-99m such a useful radioisotope for diagnostic purposes?

15. Plutonium is especially hazardous when inhaled or ingested because it emits alpha particles. Why do alpha particles cause more damage to tissue than beta particles when their source is inside the body?

16. List two ways in which workers exposed to radioactive materials can protect themselves from radiation hazard.

17. Compare nuclear fission and nuclear fusion. Why is energy liberated in each case?

18. The compounds $^{235}UF_6$ and $^{238}UF_6$ are nearly chemically identical. How are they separated?

PROBLEMS

Nuclear Equations

19. Write a balanced equation for emission of **(a)** an alpha particle by californium-250, **(b)** a beta particle by bismuth-210, and **(c)** a positron by iodine-117.

20. Write a balanced equation for **(a)** alpha decay of gold-173, **(b)** beta decay of iodine-138, and **(c)** capture of an electron by cadmium-104.

21. Complete the following equations.
    a. $^{179}_{79}\text{Au} \longrightarrow ^{175}_{77}\text{Ir} + ?$
    b. $^{12}_{6}\text{C} + ^{2}_{1}\text{H} \longrightarrow ^{13}_{6}\text{C} + ?$
    c. $^{154}_{62}\text{Sm} + ^{1}_{0}\text{n} \longrightarrow ? + 2\,^{1}_{0}\text{n}$

22. Complete the following equations.
    a. $^{10}_{5}\text{B} + ^{1}_{0}\text{n} \longrightarrow ? + ^{4}_{2}\text{He}$
    b. $^{23}_{10}\text{Ne} \longrightarrow ^{23}_{11}\text{Na} + ?$
    c. $^{121}_{51}\text{Sb} + ? \longrightarrow ^{121}_{52}\text{Te} + ^{1}_{0}\text{n}$

23. Radiological laboratories often have a container of molybdenum-99, which decays to form technetium-99m. What other particle is formed? Complete the equation.
$$^{99}_{42}\text{Mo} \longrightarrow ^{99\text{m}}_{43}\text{Tc} + ?$$

24. Complete the equation for the decay of technetium-99m to technetium-99.
$$^{99\text{m}}_{43}\text{Tc} \longrightarrow ^{99}_{43}\text{Tc} + ?$$

25. When a magnesium-24 nucleus is bombarded with a neutron, a proton is ejected. What element is formed? (*Hint:* Write a balanced nuclear equation.)

26. A radioisotope decays to give an alpha particle and a protactinium-233 nucleus. What was the original nucleus?

27. A radioactive isotope decays to give an alpha particle and a bismuth-211 nucleus. What was the original nucleus?

28. When silver-107 is bombarded with a neutron, a different isotope of silver forms and then undergoes beta decay. What is the final product? (*Hint:* Write two separate nuclear equations.)

29. A nucleus of astatine-210 decays by beta emission, forming nucleus A. Nucleus A also decays by beta emission to nucleus B. Write the nuclear symbol for B.

30. A proposed method of making fissionable nuclear fuel is to bombard the relatively abundant isotope thorium-232 with a neutron. The product X of this bombardment decays quickly by beta emission to nucleus Y, and nucleus Y decays quickly to fissionable nucleus Z. Write the nuclear symbol for Z.

Half-Life

31. Gallium-67 is used in nuclear medicine (Table 6). After treatment, a patient's blood shows an activity of 20,000 counts per minute (counts/min). How long will it be before the activity decreases to about 5000 counts/min?

32. How long will it take for a 12.0-g sample of iodine-131 to decay to leave a total of 1.5 g of the isotope? The half-life of iodine-131 is 8.07 days.

33. A lab worker reports an activity of 80,000 counts/s for a sample of magnesium-21, whose half-life is 122 ms. Exactly 5.00 min later, another worker records an activity

of 10 counts/min on the same sample. What best accounts for this difference? Magnesium-21
a. gives off only neutrinos
b. has a very short half-life, so almost every radioactive atom in the sample has decayed
c. is an alpha emitter
d. is a gamma emitter

34. A patient is injected with a radiopharmaceutical labeled with technetium-99m, half-life of 6.0 h, in preparation for a gamma ray scan to evaluate kidney function. If the original activity of the sample was 48 μCi, what activity (in μCi) remains **(a)** after 24 h and **(b)** after 48 h?

35. Krypton-81m is used for lung ventilation studies. Its half-life is 13 s. How long does it take the activity of this isotope to reach one-quarter of its original value?

36. Radium-223 has a half-life of 11.4 days. Approximately how long would it take for the activity of a sample of ^{223}Ra to decrease to 1% of its initial value?

37. In an experiment with dysprosium-197, half-life of 8.1 h, an activity of 500 counts/min was recorded at 4:00 p.m. on a Friday. What was the approximate activity of this sample at 8:30 a.m. the following Monday morning, when the experiment was resumed?

38. In determining the half-life of sulfur-35, students collected the following data, with the time in days and the activity in counts/s.

Time	Activity	Time	Activity
0	1000	80	525
20	851	100	446
40	725	120	380
60	616	140	323

Without doing detailed calculations, estimate a value for the half-life.

Radioisotopic Dating

39. Living matter has a carbon-14 activity of about 16 counts/min per gram of carbon. What is the age of an artifact for which the carbon-14 activity is 8 counts/min per gram of carbon?

40. A piece of wood from an Egyptian tomb has a carbon-14 activity of 980 counts/h. A piece of new wood of the same size shows 3920 counts/h. What is the age of the wood from the tomb?

41. The ratio of carbon-14 to carbon-12 in a piece of charcoal from an archaeological excavation is found to be one-half the ratio in a sample of modern wood. Approximately how old is the charcoal? How old would it be if the isotopic ratio were 25% of that in a sample of modern wood?

42. You are offered a great price on a case of brandy supposedly bottled during the lifetime of Napoleon (1769–1821). Before buying it, you insist on testing a sample of the brandy and find that its tritium content is 12.5% of that of newly produced brandy. How long ago was the brandy bottled? Is it likely to be authentic Napoleon-era brandy?

ADDITIONAL PROBLEMS

43. Write balanced nuclear equations for **(a)** the bombardment of $^{121}_{51}Sb$ by alpha particles to produce $^{124}_{53}I$, followed by **(b)** the radioactive decay of $^{124}_{53}I$ by positron emission.

44. A typical smoke detector contains about 0.25 mg of americium-241. The activity of 1 g of ^{241}Am is 1.26×10^{11} Bq. What is the activity of the americium-241 in the smoke detector?

45. In 2010, Russian and American scientists produced a few atoms of element 117 by shooting an intense beam of ions of the rare isotope calcium-48 at a target of berkelium-247. Two isotopes of element 117 were formed, one having 176 neutrons and the other 177 neutrons. Write two separate nuclear equations for the formation of the two isotopes. How many neutrons were released in each process?

46. Meitnerium undergoes alpha decay to form element 107, which in turn also emits an alpha particle. What are the atomic number and nucleon number of the isotope formed by these two steps? Write balanced nuclear equations for the two reactions.

47. Radium-223 nuclei usually decay by alpha emission. Once in every billion decays, a radium-223 nucleus emits a carbon-14 nucleus. Write a balanced nuclear equation for each type of emission.

48. A particular uranium alloy has a density of 18.75 g/cm³. What volume is occupied by a critical mass of 49 kg of this alloy? The critical mass can be decreased to 16 kg if the alloy is surrounded by a layer of natural uranium (which acts as a neutron reflector). What is the volume of the smaller mass? Compare your answers to the approximate volumes of a baseball, a volleyball, and a basketball.

49. Plutonium has a density of 19.1 g/cm³. What volume is occupied by a mass of 16.3 kg of plutonium? If a neutron-reflecting coating (made of beryllium) is used, the critical mass can be lowered to 2.5 kg. Compare the size of this mass to the volume of a baseball, a volleyball, and a basketball.

50. There are several technological applications for the transuranium elements ($Z > 92$). An important one is in smoke detectors, which can use the decay of a tiny amount of americium-241 to neptunium-237. What subatomic particle is emitted from that decay process?

51. The radioisotopic dating problems in this chapter are deceptively easy because they involve only integral numbers of half-lives. Calculations involving other than integral half-life values require a bit more complicated math. However, carbon-14 dating calculators that make the task quite easy can be accessed on the Web. Use one of those calculators to find **(a)** the age of a scrap of paper taken from the Dead Sea Scrolls that has a $^{14}C/^{12}C$ ratio that is 79.5% of that in living plants and **(b)** the age of a piece of charcoal from a Neanderthal site that has a $^{14}C/^{12}C$ ratio that is 17.5% of that in living plants.

52. In the first step of the chain reaction of a nuclear explosion, a ^{235}U nucleus absorbs a neutron. The resulting ^{236}U nucleus is unstable and can fission into ^{92}Kr and ^{141}Ba nuclei as shown in the figure. What are the other products of this reaction? After assessing this reaction, explain how the chain reaction can continue.

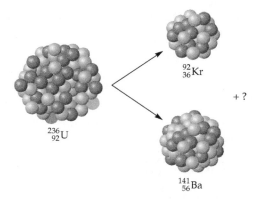

53. In 1932, James Chadwick discovered a new subatomic particle when he bombarded beryllium-9 with alpha particles. One of the products was carbon-12. What particle did Chadwick discover?

54. Several different radioisotopes can be used much like carbon-14 for determining the age of rocks and other matter. In the geosciences, the age of rocks may be determined using potassium-40, which decays to argon-40 with a half-life of 1.2 billion years. **(a)** Some rocks brought back from the moon were dated as being 3.6 billion years old. What percentage of the potassium-40 has decayed after that time? **(b)** Give a reason why uranium-238 (half-life of 4.6 billion years) is more useful for confirming this age than is carbon-14.

55. Einstein's mass–energy equation is $E = mc^2$, where mass is in kilograms and the speed of light is 3.00×10^8 m/s. The unit of energy is the joule (4.184 J = 1 cal; 1000 cal = 1 kcal).
   a. Calculate the energy released, in calories and kilocalories, when 1 g of matter is converted to energy.
   b. A bowl of cornflakes supplies 110 kcal (110 food calories). How many bowls of cornflakes would supply the same amount of energy as you calculated for 1 g of matter in part (a)?

56. Radioactive copper ($^{64}_{29}Cu$, half-life 12.7 h) is found in quantities exceeding the pollution standard in the sediments of a reservoir during a routine check on Monday, when 56 ppm/m³ was measured. The standard allows up to 14 ppm/m³. About when will the level of copper-64 return to 14 ppm/m³?

57. An unidentified corpse was discovered on April 21 at 7:00 a.m. The pathologist discovered that there were 1.24×10^{17} atoms of $^{32}_{15}P$ remaining in the victim's bones and placed the time of death sometime on March 15. The half-life of $^{32}_{15}P$ is 14.28 days. How much $^{32}_{15}P$ was present in the bones at the time of death?

58. Scientists have tried to make element 120. Three different combinations of projectile and target were used to try to produce the nucleus $^{302}_{120}X$: **(a)** nickel-64 and uranium-238, **(b)** iron-58 and plutonium-244, and **(c)** chromium-54 and curium-248. However, after 120 days, no sign of element 120 was found. Write nuclear equations for the three expected reactions.

59. True or False? Green chemistry principles can be applied only as a process is being developed.

60. List four elements of which a compound that can be completely incinerated may be composed.

61. What is the benefit of having two amide groups on one molecule that binds radioactive metal ions?

62. Vitrification is an expensive and energy-intensive method involving encasing waste in glass. What portion of HLLW is radioactive, and why is that important with respect to vitrification?

COLLABORATIVE GROUP PROJECTS

Prepare a PowerPoint, poster, or other presentation (as directed by your instructor) to share with the class.

1. Write a brief report on the impact of nuclear science on one of the following.
   a. war and peace
   b. industrial progress
   c. medicine
   d. agriculture
   e. human, animal, and plant genetics

2. Write an essay on radioisotopic dating using one or more of the isotopes in Table 5 other than carbon-14 or tritium.

3. Write a brief biography of one of the following scientists.
   a. Otto Hahn   **b.** Enrico Fermi
   c. Glenn T. Seaborg   **d.** J. Robert Oppenheimer
   e. Lise Meitner   **f.** Albert Einstein

4. The positron is a particle of antimatter. Search the Web for information about antimatter, and the positron in particular.

5. Find a Web site that is strongly in favor of nuclear power plants and one that is strongly opposed. Note the sites' sponsors, and analyze their viewpoints. Try to find a Web site with a balanced viewpoint.

6. In July 1999, researchers at Lawrence Berkeley Laboratory reported the creation of the heaviest element to date, element 118. Two years later, that report was found to be fraudulent. Report on the scientific ethical questions raised by this episode.

7. Find the location of the nuclear power plant closest to where you live. Try to determine risks and benefits of the plant. To how many houses does it provide power? What are the environmental impacts of the plant under normal operating conditions?

8. Assemble two teams of two to four people each to debate the following resolution: The dropping of the atomic bombs on Hiroshima and Nagasaki was justified. Decide beforehand which team will take the affirmative and which the negative. Each team member is to give a three- to six-minute speech followed by a cross-examination by the opposing team members. Have the rest of the class judge the debate and give written or oral comments.

BRIEF ANSWERS TO SELECTED PROBLEMS

Answers are provided for *all in-chapter exercises*. Brief answers are given for *odd-numbered Review Questions*; more complete answers can be obtained by reviewing the text. Answers are provided for *all odd-numbered Problems and Additional Problems*.

NOTE: For numerical problems, your answer may differ slightly from ours because of rounding and the use of significant figures.

1 **a.** $^{235}_{92}U \longrightarrow {}^{4}_{2}He + {}^{231}_{90}Th$ **b.** $^{210}_{82}Pb \longrightarrow {}^{0}_{-1}e + {}^{210}_{83}Bi$
   c. $^{18}_{9}F \longrightarrow {}^{0}_{+1}e + {}^{18}_{8}O$ **d.** $^{13}_{8}O + {}^{0}_{-1}e \longrightarrow {}^{13}_{7}N$

2 **A.** 6.25%   **B.** 500 Bq; 4 Bq

3 **a.** yes (3 Bq left)   **b.** no (4.0×10^{10} Bq remain)

4 **a.** 11,460 y;   **b.** 49 y

5 **a.** A neutron ($^{1}_{0}n$)   **b.** Thorium-232 ($^{232}_{90}Th$)

6 Silicon-30 ($^{30}_{14}Si$)

7 Higher; the gas can be absorbed by inhalation and decay in the body.

1. (i), (b); (ii), (a); (iii), (c)

3. $^{1}_{1}H$, $^{2}_{1}H$, $^{3}_{1}H$

5. **a.** $^{60}_{27}Co$ **b.** $^{127}_{53}I$ **c.** $^{22}_{11}Na$ **d.** $^{42}_{20}Ca$

7. Isotopes: b, c

9. 155

11. **a.** *A*, down 4; *Z*, down 2 **b.** no change in either
   c. *A*, down 1; *Z*, down 1

13. **a.** alpha   **b.** gamma

15. more massive; energy dissipated over a short distance

17. Fission is the splitting of large atoms. Fusion is the joining of small atoms. Both liberate energy because, in each case, the nuclei formed have greater nuclear stability than the reacting nuclei (Fig. 11.10).

19. **a.** $^{250}_{98}Cf \longrightarrow {}^{4}_{2}He + {}^{246}_{96}Cm$
   b. $^{210}_{83}Bi \longrightarrow {}^{210}_{84}Po + {}^{0}_{-1}e$

21. **a.** $^{179}_{79}Au \longrightarrow {}^{175}_{77}Ir + {}^{4}_{2}He$
   b. $^{12}_{6}C + {}^{2}_{1}H \longrightarrow {}^{13}_{6}C + {}^{1}_{1}H$
   c. $^{154}_{62}Sm + {}^{1}_{0}n \longrightarrow 2\,{}^{1}_{0}n + {}^{153}_{62}Sm$

23. beta particle; $^{99}_{42}Mo \longrightarrow {}^{99m}_{43}Tc + {}^{0}_{-1}e$

25. $^{24}_{12}Mg + {}^{1}_{0}n \longrightarrow {}^{1}_{1}H + {}^{24}_{11}Na$; sodium-24

27. $^{215}_{85}At \longrightarrow {}^{4}_{2}He + {}^{211}_{83}Bi$; astatine-215

29. $^{210}_{87}Fr$

31. 156 h (6.5 d)

33. b

35. 26 s

37. 2 counts/min

39. 5730 y

41. 5730 y; 11,460 y

43. **a.** $^{121}_{51}Sb + {}^{4}_{2}He \longrightarrow {}^{124}_{53}I + {}^{1}_{0}n$ **b.** $^{124}_{53}I \longrightarrow {}^{124}_{52}Te + {}^{0}_{+1}e$

45. $^{247}_{97}Bk + {}^{48}_{20}Ca \longrightarrow {}^{293}_{117}117 + 2\,{}^{1}_{0}n$; $^{247}_{97}Bk + {}^{48}_{20}Ca \longrightarrow {}^{294}_{117}117 + {}^{1}_{0}n$

47. $^{223}_{88}Ra \longrightarrow {}^{219}_{86}Rn + {}^{4}_{2}He$; $^{223}_{88}Ra \longrightarrow {}^{209}_{82}Pb + {}^{14}_{6}C$

49. 853 cm^3; 131 cm^3; smaller than a baseball (~200 cm^3)

51. **a.** 1900 y   **b.** 14,400 y

53. the neutron, $^{1}_{0}n$

55. **a.** 2.2×10^{13} cal; 2.2×10^{10} kcal
   b. 2.0×10^{8} bowls

57. 7.5×10^{17} atoms

59. false

61. The presence of two amides increases the ability to bind to metal ions without losing the benefits of using this type of molecule.

Chemical Bonds

moodboard/Alamy

Have You Ever Wondered?

1. **My air purifier uses a negative ion generator. What is a negative ion?**

2. **Why does chlorine in a swimming pool have an odor, but chlorine in salt doesn't?**

3. **My father is on a low-sodium diet. What exactly does that mean?**

4. **If there is iron in blood, why aren't we magnetic?**

Phase4Photography/Shutterstock

Learning Objectives

> Determine the number of electrons in an ion. (1)
> Write the Lewis symbol for an atom or ion. (2)
> Distinguish between an ion and an atom. (3)
> Describe the nature of the attraction that leads to formation of an ionic bond. (3)
> Write symbols for common ions, and determine their charges. (4)
> Describe the relationship between the octet rule and the charge on an ion. (4)
> Name and write formulas for binary ionic compounds. (5)
> Explain the difference between a covalent bond and an ionic bond. (6)
> Name and write formulas for covalent compounds. (6)
> Classify a covalent bond as polar or nonpolar. (7)
> Use electronegativities of elements to determine bond polarity. (7)
> Predict the number of bonds formed by common nonmetals (the HONC rules). (8)
> Recognize common polyatomic ions and be able to use them in naming and writing formulas for compounds. (9)
> Write Lewis formulas for simple molecules and polyatomic ions. (10)
> Identify free radicals. (10)
> Predict the shapes of simple molecules from their Lewis formulas. (11)
> Classify a simple molecule as polar or nonpolar from its shape and the polarity of its bonds. (12)
> Explain how shape and composition change the properties of molecules.
> Describe the concept of molecular recognition.
> Explain the green chemistry advantages of using production methods based on molecular recognition.

The Ties that Bind

The element carbon is commonly found as soft, black soot formed by incomplete combustion. By heating that soot under tremendous pressure, we can make the hardest material known—diamond. We have not changed the carbon in soot to a different element in this process ... so why is diamond so different from soot? The answer lies in the bonds that hold the carbon atoms together. We have learned a bit about the structure of the atom. Now we are ready to consider chemical bonds, the ties that bind atoms together.

Chemical bonds are the forces that hold atoms together in molecules and hold ions together in ionic crystals. The vast number and incredible

Atoms combine by forming chemical bonds. These bonds determine, to a great extent, the properties of the substance. Here we see carbon in the form of diamonds, which can form from carbon in the form of graphite (pencil lead) or soot. The only difference between the forms of carbon are the bonds between the carbon atoms. The arrangement and number of these bonds in diamond make it by far the hardest natural material in the world. In this chapter, we will look at the different kinds of bonding that can occur.

Fotocisis/Shutterstock

From Chapter 4 of *Chemistry for Changing Times*, Thirteenth Edition. John W. Hill, Terry W. McCreary, Doris K. Kolb.

variety of chemical compounds—tens of millions are known—result from the fact that atoms can form bonds with many other types of atoms. In addition, chemical bonds determine the three-dimensional shapes of molecules. Some important consequences of chemical structure and bonding include

- Whether a substance is a solid, liquid, or gas at room temperature
- The strengths of materials (as well as adhesives that hold materials together) used for building bridges, houses, and many other structures
- Whether a liquid is light and volatile (like gasoline) or heavy and viscous (like corn syrup)
- The taste, odor, and drug activity of chemical compounds
- The structural integrity of skin, muscles, bones, and teeth
- The toxicity of certain molecules to living organisms

Chemical bonding is related to the arrangement of electrons in compounds. In this chapter, we look at different types of chemical bonds and some of the unusual properties of compounds that result.

1 The Art of Deduction: Stable Electron Configurations

Learning Objective ❯ Determine the number of electrons in an ion.

In our discussion of the atom and its structure, we followed the historical development of some of the more important atomic concepts. We could continue to look at chemistry in this manner, but that would require several volumes of print—and perhaps more of your time than you care to spend. We won't abandon the historical approach entirely but will emphasize another important aspect of scientific endeavor: deduction.

The art of deduction works something like this.

- **Fact:** Noble gases, such as helium, neon, and argon, are inert; they undergo few, if any, chemical reactions.
- **Theory:** The inertness of noble gases results from their electron configurations. Each (except helium) has an octet of electrons in its outermost shell.
- **Deduction:** Other elements that can alter their electron configurations to become like those of noble gases would become less reactive by doing so.

We can use an example to illustrate this deductive argument. Sodium has 11 electrons, one of which is in the third shell. Recall that electrons in the outermost shell are called **valence electrons**, while those in all the other shells are lumped together as **core electrons**. If the sodium atom got rid of its valence electron, its remaining core electrons would have the same electron configuration as an atom of the noble gas neon. Using main-shell configurations, we can represent this as

The outermost shell is filled when it contains eight electrons, two in an s orbital and six in a p orbital. The first shell is an exception: It holds only two electrons in the 1s orbital.

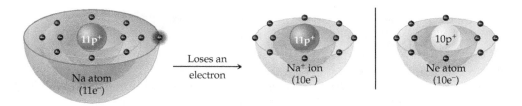

Na atom ($11e^-$) — Loses an electron → Na$^+$ ion ($10e^-$) | Ne atom ($10e^-$)

Similarly, if a chlorine atom gained an electron, it would have the same electron configuration as argon.

| Cl atom (17e⁻) | Gains an electron → | Cl⁻ ion (18e⁻) | Ar atom (18e⁻) |

The sodium atom, having lost an electron, becomes positively charged. It has 11 protons (11+) and only 10 electrons (10−). It is symbolized by Na^+ and is called a *sodium ion*. The chlorine atom, having gained an electron, becomes negatively charged. It has 17 protons (17+) and 18 electrons (18−). It is symbolized by Cl^- and is called a *chloride ion*. Note that a positive charge, as in Na^+, indicates that one electron has been lost. Similarly, a negative charge, as in Cl^-, indicates that one electron has been gained.

It is important to note that even though Cl^- and Ar are **isoelectronic** (have the same electron configuration), they are *different* chemical species. In the same way, a sodium atom does not *become* an atom of neon when it loses an electron; the sodium ion is simply isoelectronic with neon.

Self-Assessment Questions

1. Which group of elements in the periodic table is characterized by an especially stable electron arrangement?
   a. 2A   **b.** 2B   **c.** 8A   **d.** 8B

2. The structural difference between a sodium atom and a sodium ion is that the sodium ion has one
   a. less proton than the sodium atom
   b. less electron than the sodium atom
   c. more proton and one less electron than the sodium atom
   d. more proton than the sodium atom

3. Which of the following are isoelectronic?
   a. K⁺ and Ar   **b.** Mg²⁺ and Ar   **c.** Ne and Cl⁻   **d.** Xe and Kr

4. The anion Cl⁻ is isoelectronic with the cation
   a. Ca²⁺   **b.** Li⁺   **c.** Mg²⁺   **d.** Na⁺

Answers: 1, c; 2, b; 3, a; 4, a

2 Lewis (Electron-Dot) Symbols

Learning Objective ❯ Write the Lewis symbol for an atom or ion.

In forming ions, the cores of sodium atoms and chlorine atoms do not change. It is convenient therefore to let the element symbol represent the *core* of the atom (nucleus plus inner electrons). The valence electrons are then represented by dots. The equations of the preceding section then can be written as follows:

$$Na\cdot \rightarrow Na^+ + 1\,e^-$$

and

$$\cdot\ddot{\underset{\cdot\cdot}{Cl}}\colon\ +\ 1\,e^- \longrightarrow \colon\!\ddot{\underset{\cdot\cdot}{Cl}}\colon^-$$

In these representations, the element symbol represents the core, and dots stand for valence electrons. These electron-dot symbols are usually called **Lewis symbols**.

Lawrence Berkeley National Laboratory/Photo Researchers, Inc.

▲ Electron-dot symbols are called *Lewis symbols* after G. N. Lewis, the famous American chemist (1875–1946) who invented them. Lewis also made important contributions to our understanding of thermodynamics, acids and bases, and spectroscopy.

1. My air purifier uses a negative ion generator. What is a negative ion? A negative ion is an atom or a group of atoms with one or more extra electrons. In a negative ion generator, a high voltage produces negative ions.

Table 1   Lewis Symbols for Selected Main Group Elements

Group 1A	Group 2A	Group 3A	Group 4A	Group 5A	Group 6A	Group 7A	Noble Gases
H·							He:
Li·	·Be·	·Ḃ·	·Ċ·	:N̈·	:Ö·	:F̈·	:N̈e:
Na·	·Mg·	·Ȧl·	·Ṡi·	:P̈·	:S̈·	:C̈l·	:Är:
K·	·Ca·				:S̈e·	:B̈r·	:K̈r:
Rb·	·Sr·				:T̈e·	:Ï·	:Ẍe:
Cs·	·Ba·						

Lewis Symbols and the Periodic Table

It is especially easy to write Lewis symbols for most of the main group elements. The number of valence electrons for most of these elements is equal to the group number (Table 1). Because of their more complicated electron configurations, elements in the central part of the periodic table (the transition metals) cannot easily be represented by electron-dot symbols.

Example 1   Writing Lewis Symbols

Without referring to Table 1, write Lewis symbols for magnesium, oxygen, and phosphorus. You may use the periodic table.

Solution

Magnesium is in group 2A, oxygen is in group 6A, and phosphorus is in group 5A. The Lewis symbols, therefore, have two, six, and five dots, respectively. They are

·Mg·   :Ö: :P̈·

■ EXERCISE 1

Without referring to Table 1, write Lewis symbols for each of the following elements. You may use the periodic table.

   a. Ar   **b.** Ca   **c.** F   **d.** N   **e.** K   **f.** S

In writing a Lewis symbol, only the *number* of dots is important. The dots need not be drawn in any specific positions, except that there should be no more than two dots on any given side of the chemical symbol (right, left, top, or bottom).

Self-Assessment Questions

1. How many dots surround Be in the Lewis symbol for beryllium?
      a. 2   **b.** 4   **c.** 5   **d.** 9

2. How many dots surround F in the Lewis symbol for fluorine?
      a. 1   **b.** 5   **c.** 7   **d.** 9

3. Which of the following Lewis symbols is *incorrect*?
      a. ·Ċ·   **b.** :C̈l·   **c.** Li: **d.** :N̈·

4. Which of the following Lewis symbols is *incorrect*?
      a. ·Ȧs·   **b.** :Ö: **c.** Rb·   **d.** ·Ṡi·

Answers: 1, a; 2, c; 3, c; 4, a

3 The Reaction of Sodium and Chlorine

Learning Objectives   ❯ Distinguish between an ion and an atom. ❯ Describe the nature of the attraction that leads to formation of an ionic bond.

Sodium (Na) is a highly reactive metal. It is soft enough to be cut with a knife. When freshly cut, it is bright and silvery, but it dulls rapidly because it reacts with oxygen in the air. In fact, it reacts so readily in air that it is usually stored under oil or

(a) (b) (c)

◄ **Figure 1** (a) Sodium, a soft, silvery metal, and chlorine, a greenish gas (b). The two react violently, to form sodium chloride (ordinary table salt), a white crystalline solid (c).

Q: *What kinds of particles, ions or molecules, make up sodium chloride?*

kerosene. Sodium reacts violently with water, too, becoming so hot that it melts. A small piece forms a spherical bead after melting and races around on the surface of the water as it reacts.

Chlorine (Cl_2) is a greenish-yellow gas. It is familiar as a disinfectant for drinking water and swimming pools. (The actual substance added is often a compound that reacts with water to form chlorine.) Chlorine is extremely irritating to the eyes and nose. In fact, it was used as a poison gas in World War I.

If a piece of sodium is dropped into a flask containing chlorine gas, a violent reaction ensues, producing sodium chloride, beautiful white crystals that you might sprinkle on your food at the dinner table. These white crystals are ordinary table salt. Sodium chloride has very few properties in common with either sodium or chlorine (Figure 1).

The Reaction of Sodium and Chlorine: Theory

A sodium atom achieves a filled valence shell by losing one electron. A chlorine atom achieves a filled valence shell by adding one electron. What happens when sodium atoms come into contact with chlorine atoms? The obvious: A chlorine atom takes an electron from a sodium atom.

Chlorine gas is composed of Cl_2 molecules, not separate Cl atoms. Each atom of the chlorine molecule takes an electron from a sodium atom. Two sodium ions and two chloride ions are formed.
$$Cl_2 + 2\,Na \rightarrow 2\,Cl^- + 2\,Na^+$$

2. Why does chlorine in a swimming pool have an odor, but chlorine in salt doesn't? Chlorine used in swimming pools is often the element, Cl_2, while the chlorine in salt exists as chlor*ide* ions, Cl^-. An element is chemically quite different from its ions.

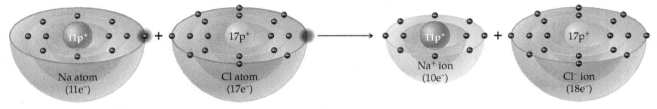

Na atom ($11e^-$) + Cl atom ($17e^-$) → Na^+ ion ($10e^-$) + Cl^- ion ($18e^-$)

With Lewis symbols, this reaction is written as

$$Na\cdot\ +\ :\overset{..}{\underset{..}{Cl}}\cdot\ \longrightarrow\ Na^+\ +\ :\overset{..}{\underset{..}{Cl}}:^-$$

Ionic Bonds

The Na^+ and Cl^- ions formed from sodium and chlorine atoms have opposite charges and are strongly attracted to one another. These ions arrange themselves in an orderly fashion. Each sodium ion attracts (and is attracted to) six chloride ions (above and below, front and back, left and right), as shown in Figure 2a. The arrangement is repeated many times in all directions (Figure 2b). The result is a **crystal** of sodium chloride. The orderly microscopic arrangement of the ions is reflected in the macroscopic shape, a cube, of a salt crystal (Figure 2c). Even the tiniest grain of salt has billions and billions of each type of ion. The forces holding the crystal together—the attractive forces between positive and negative ions—are called **ionic bonds**.

3. My father is on a low-sodium diet. What exactly does that mean? It means that he must restrict his intake of sodium *ions*. For many people, too many sodium ions in the body can increase blood pressure.

▲ **Figure 2** Molecular and macroscopic views of a sodium chloride crystal. (a) Each Na⁺ ion (small purple spheres) is surrounded by six Cl⁻ ions (large green spheres), and each Cl⁻ ion by six Na⁺ ions. (b) This arrangement repeats itself many, many times. (c) The highly ordered pattern of alternating Na⁺ and Cl⁻ ions is observed in the macroscopic world as a crystal of sodium chloride.

▲ **Figure 3** Forms of iron and calcium that are useful to the human body are the ions (usually Fe^{2+} and Ca^{2+}) in ionic compounds such as $FeSO_4$ and $CaCO_3$. The elemental forms (Fe and Ca) are chemically very different from the forms found in ionic compounds.

Atoms and Ions: Distinctively Different

Ions are emphatically different from the atoms from which they are made, much as a whole peach (an atom) and a peach pit (a positive ion) are different from one another. The names and symbols of an atom and its ion may look a lot alike, but the actual entities are very different (Figure 3). Unfortunately, the situation is confusing because people talk about needing iron to perk up "tired blood" and calcium for healthy teeth and bones. What they really need is iron(II) *ions* (Fe^{2+}) and calcium *ions* (Ca^{2+}). You wouldn't think of eating iron nails to get iron (although some enriched cereals do indeed have powdered iron added; the iron metal is readily converted to Fe^{2+} ions in the stomach). Nor would you eat highly reactive calcium metal.

Similarly, if you are warned to reduce your sodium intake, your doctor is not concerned that you are eating too much sodium metal—that would be exceedingly unpleasant—but that your intake of Na⁺ *ions*—usually as sodium chloride—may be too high. Although the names are similar, the atom and the ion are quite different chemically. It is important to make careful distinctions and use precise terminology, as we shall do here.

Self-Assessment Questions

1. A potassium ion and an argon atom have the same
   a. electron configuration
   b. net charge
   c. nuclear charge
   d. properties

2. How many dots are shown on the Lewis symbol for chloride ion, and what is the ion's charge?
   a. five dots, no charge
   b. six dots, + charge
   c. seven dots, − charge
   d. eight dots, − charge

3. The bonding between K⁺ ions and F⁻ ions in potassium fluoride is
   a. covalent   b. ionic   c. nonpolar   d. polar

Answers: 1, a; 2, d; 3, b

4 Using Lewis Symbols for Ionic Compounds

Learning Objectives ❭ Write symbols for common ions and determine their charges.
❭ Describe the relationship between the octet rule and the charge on an ion.

Potassium, a metal in the same family as sodium and therefore similar to sodium in properties, also reacts with chlorine. The reaction yields potassium chloride (KCl).

$$K\cdot \ + \ \cdot\ddot{\underset{..}{Cl}}: \longrightarrow K^+ \ + \ :\ddot{\underset{..}{Cl}}:^-$$

Potassium also reacts with bromine, a reddish-brown liquid in the same family as chlorine and therefore similar to chlorine in properties. The product, potassium bromide (KBr), is a stable, white, crystalline solid.

$$K\cdot \; + \; \cdot \ddot{\underset{..}{Br}}: \longrightarrow K^+ + :\ddot{\underset{..}{Br}}:^-$$

Example 2 Electron Transfer to Form Ions

Use Lewis symbols to show the transfer of electrons from sodium atoms to bromine atoms to form ions with noble gas configurations.

Solution
Sodium has one valence electron, and bromine has seven. Transfer of the single valence electron from sodium to bromine leaves each with a noble gas configuration.

$$Na\cdot \; + \; \cdot \ddot{\underset{..}{Br}}: \longrightarrow Na^+ + :\ddot{\underset{..}{Br}}:^-$$

■ EXERCISE 2A
Use Lewis symbols to show the transfer of electrons from lithium atoms to fluorine atoms to form ions with noble gas configurations.

■ EXERCISE 2B
Use Lewis symbols to show the transfer of electrons from rubidium atoms to iodine atoms to form ions with noble gas configurations.

Magnesium, a group 2A metal, is harder and less reactive than sodium. Magnesium reacts with oxygen, a group 6A element that is a colorless gas, to form a stable, white, crystalline solid called magnesium oxide (MgO).

$$\cdot Mg\cdot \; + \; \cdot \ddot{\underset{..}{O}}: \longrightarrow Mg^{2+} + :\ddot{\underset{..}{O}}:^{2-}$$

Magnesium must give up two electrons and oxygen must gain two electrons for each to have the same configuration as the noble gas neon.

An atom such as oxygen, which needs two electrons to achieve a noble gas configuration, may react with potassium atoms, which have only one electron each to give. In this case, two atoms of potassium are needed for each oxygen atom. The product is potassium oxide (K_2O).

$$\begin{matrix} K\cdot \\ \\ K\cdot \end{matrix} \; + \; \cdot \ddot{\underset{..}{O}}: \longrightarrow \begin{matrix} K^+ \\ \\ K^+ \end{matrix} \; + \; :\ddot{\underset{..}{O}}:^{2-}$$

Through this reaction, each potassium atom achieves the argon configuration. As before, oxygen ends up with the neon configuration.

Example 3 Electron Transfer to Form Ions

Use Lewis symbols to show the transfer of electrons from magnesium atoms to nitrogen atoms to form ions with noble gas configurations.

Solution

$$\begin{matrix} \cdot Mg\cdot \\ \cdot Mg\cdot \\ \cdot Mg\cdot \end{matrix} \quad \begin{matrix} \cdot \ddot{N}\cdot \\ \vdots \\ \cdot N\cdot \end{matrix} \longrightarrow \begin{matrix} Mg^{2+} \\ Mg^{2+} \\ Mg^{2+} \end{matrix} \quad \begin{matrix} :\ddot{\underset{..}{N}}:^{3-} \\ \\ :\ddot{\underset{..}{N}}:^{3-} \end{matrix}$$

When an Mg atom becomes an Mg^{2+} ion, its second shell becomes its outermost shell. The Mg^{2+} ion is isoelectronic with the Ne atom and has the same stable main-shell electron configuration: 2 8.

Each of the three magnesium atoms gives up two electrons (a total of six), and each of the two nitrogen atoms acquires three electrons (a total of six). Notice that the total positive and negative charges on the products are equal (6+ and 6−). Magnesium reacts with nitrogen to yield magnesium nitride (Mg_3N_2).

■ EXERCISE 3

Use Lewis symbols to show the transfer of electrons from aluminum atoms to oxygen atoms to form ions with noble gas configurations.

Generally speaking, metallic elements in groups 1A and 2A (those from the left side of the periodic table) react with nonmetallic elements in groups 6A and 7A (those from the right side) to form ionic compounds. These products are stable crystalline solids.

The Octet Rule

Each atom of a metal tends to give up the electrons in its outer shell, and each atom of a nonmetal tends to take on enough electrons to complete its valence shell. The resulting ions have noble gas configurations. A set of eight valence electrons—an *octet*—is characteristic of all noble gases except helium. When atoms react with each other, they often tend to attain this stable noble-gas electron configuration. Thus, they are said to follow the **octet rule**, or the "rule of eight." (In the case of helium, a maximum of two electrons can occupy its single electron shell, and so hydrogen follows the "rule of two.")

In following the octet rule, atoms of group 1A metals give up one electron to form 1+ ions, those of group 2A metals give up two electrons to form 2+ ions, and those of group 3A metals give up three electrons to form 3+ ions. Group 7A nonmetal atoms take on one electron to form 1− ions, and group 6A atoms tend to pick up two electrons to form 2− ions. Atoms of B group metals can give up various numbers of electrons to form positive ions with various charges. These periodic relationships are summarized in Figure 4.

Table 2 lists symbols and names for some ions formed when atoms gain or lose electrons. (The ion names are explained in the next section.) You can calculate the charge on the negative ions in the table by subtracting 8 from the group number. For example, the charge on the oxide ion (oxygen is in group 6A) is $6 - 8 = -2$. The nitride ion (nitrogen is in group 5A) has a charge of $5 - 8 = -3$.

Example 4 Determining Formulas by Electron Transfer

What is the formula of the compound formed by the reaction of sodium and sulfur?

Solution

Sodium is in group 1A; the sodium atom has one valence electron. Sulfur is in group 6A; the sulfur atom has six valence electrons.

$$Na\cdot \quad \cdot\ddot{\underset{\cdot\cdot}{S}}\cdot$$

▲ It DOES Matter!

Loss of electrons is known as *oxidation*, and gain of electrons is called *reduction*. Oxidation by oxygen gas is both useful and destructive. Oxygen gas oxidizes fuels to produce energy, but it also oxidizes iron metal into familiar orange or red rust (Fe_2O_3), which causes billions of dollars of damage each year.

▶ **Figure 4** Periodic relationships of some simple ions. Many of the transition elements (B groups) can form different ions with different charges.

Q: *Can you write a formula for the simple ion formed from selenium (Se)? For the simple ion formed from indium (In)?*

1A	2A	3B	4B	5B	6B	7B	8B			1B	2B	3A	4A	5A	6A	7A	Noble gases
Li^+														N^{3-}	O^{2-}	F^-	
Na^+	Mg^{2+}											Al^{3+}		P^{3-}	S^{2-}	Cl^-	
K^+	Ca^{2+}						Fe^{2+} Fe^{3+}			Cu^+ Cu^{2+}	Zn^{2+}					Br^-	
Rb^+	Sr^{2+}									Ag^+						I^-	
Cs^+	Ba^{2+}																

Table 2	Symbols and Names for Some Simple (Monatomic) Ions		
Group	Element	Name of Ion	Symbol for Ion
1A	Hydrogen	Hydrogen ion	H^+
	Lithium	Lithium ion	Li^+
	Sodium	Sodium ion	Na^+
	Potassium	Potassium ion	K^+
2A	Magnesium	Magnesium ion	Mg^{2+}
	Calcium	Calcium ion	Ca^{2+}
3A	Aluminum	Aluminum ion	Al^{3+}
5A	Nitrogen	Nitride ion	N^{3-}
6A	Oxygen	Oxide ion	O^{2-}
	Sulfur	Sulfide ion	S^{2-}
7A	Fluorine	Fluoride ion	F^-
	Chlorine	Chloride ion	Cl^-
	Bromine	Bromide ion	Br^-
	Iodine	Iodide ion	I^-
1B	Copper	Copper(I) ion (cuprous ion)	Cu^+
		Copper(II) ion (cupric ion)	Cu^{2+}
	Silver	Silver ion	Ag^+
2B	Zinc	Zinc ion	Zn^{2+}
8B	Iron	Iron(II) ion (ferrous ion)	Fe^{2+}
		Iron(III) ion (ferric ion)	Fe^{3+}

4. If there is iron in blood, why aren't we magnetic? Iron metal is magnetic, but compounds—such as the hemoglobin in blood—that have iron usually have iron(II) ions or iron(III) ions. The ions differ chemically and physically from the metal and are not magnetic.

Sulfur needs two electrons to gain an argon configuration, but sodium has only one to give. The sulfur atom therefore must react with two sodium atoms.

$$\begin{array}{c} Na\cdot \\ Na\cdot \end{array} + \cdot \ddot{\underset{..}{S}}\cdot \longrightarrow \begin{array}{c} Na^+ \\ Na^+ \end{array} + :\ddot{\underset{..}{S}}:^{2-}$$

The formula of the compound, called sodium sulfide, is Na_2S.

■ EXERCISE 4A

What are the formulas of the compounds formed by the reaction of **(a)** calcium with fluorine and **(b)** lithium with oxygen?

■ EXERCISE 4B

Use Figure 4 to predict the formulas of the two compounds that can be formed from iron (Fe) and chlorine.

Self-Assessment Questions

1. Which of the following pairs of elements would be most likely to form an ionic compound?
   a. Ca and Mg   **b.** Cd and Ca   **c.** K and S   **d.** Ne and Na

2. Sulfur forms a simple (monatomic) ion with a charge of
   a. 6−   **b.** 2−   **c.** 2+   **d.** 6+

3. Magnesium forms a simple (monatomic) ion with a charge of
   a. 2−   **b.** 2+   **c.** 4+   **d.** 8+

4. Mg and N react to form Mg_3N_2, an ionic compound. How many electrons are there in the valence shell of the N^{3-} ion?
   a. 2   **b.** 6   **c.** 8   **d.** 18

5. The formula of the ionic compound formed by lithium and oxygen is
   a. LiO   **b.** Li_2O **c.** LiO_2 **d.** Li_2O_3

6. The formula of the ionic compound formed by magnesium and bromine is
   a. MgBr   **b.** Mg_2Br **c.** $MgBr_2$ **d.** Mg_2Br_3

7. Only one of the following ions is likely to be formed in an ordinary chemical reaction; it is
   a. Ar^{3-} **b.** Br^- **c.** K^{2+} **d.** S^-

Answers: 1, c; 2, b; 3, b; 4, c; 5, b; 6, c; 7, b

5 Formulas and Names of Binary Ionic Compounds

Learning Objective ❯ Name and write formulas for binary ionic compounds.

Names of simple positive ions (*cations*) are derived from those of their parent elements by the addition of the word *ion*. A sodium atom, on losing an electron, becomes a *sodium ion* (Na^+). A magnesium atom (Mg), on losing two electrons, becomes a *magnesium ion* (Mg^{2+}). When a metal forms more than one ion, the charges on the different ions are denoted by Roman numerals in parentheses. For example, Fe^{2+} is iron(II) ion and Fe^{3+} is iron(III) ion.

Names of simple negative ions (*anions*) are derived from those of their parent elements by changing the usual ending to *-ide* and adding the word *ion*. A chlor*ine* atom, on gaining an electron, becomes a chlor*ide ion* (Cl^-). A sul*fur* atom gains two electrons, becoming a sul*fide ion* (S^{2-}).

Simple ions of opposite charge can be combined to form **binary** (two-element) **ionic compounds**. To get the correct formula for a binary ionic compound, write each ion with its charge (positive ion to the left), then transpose the charge numbers (but not the plus and minus signs) and write them as subscripts. The process is best learned by practice, which is provided in the following examples and exercises and in the problems at the end of the chapter.

Example 5   Determining Formulas from Ionic Charges

Write the formulas for **(a)** calcium chloride and **(b)** aluminum oxide.

Solution

a. First, we write the symbols for the ions. (We write the charge on chloride ion explicitly as "1−" to illustrate the method. You may omit the "1" when you are comfortable with the process.)

$$Ca^{2+} \quad Cl^{1-}$$

We cross over the charge numbers (without the charges) as subscripts.

$$Ca^{2+} \qquad Cl^{1-}$$

Then we write the formula. The formula for calcium chloride is

$$Ca_1Cl_2 \quad \text{or} \quad \text{(dropping the "1") simply} \quad CaCl_2$$

b. We write the symbols for the ions.

$$Al^{3+} \quad O^{2-}$$

We cross over the charge numbers as subscripts.

We write the formula for aluminum oxide as

$$Al_2O_3$$

■ EXERCISE 5
Write the formulas for **(a)** potassium oxide, **(b)** calcium nitride, and **(c)** calcium sulfide.

The method just described, called the *crossover method*, works because it is based on the transfer of electrons and the conservation of charge. Two Al atoms lose three electrons each (a total of six electrons lost), and three O atoms gain two electrons each (a total of six electrons gained). The electrons lost must equal the electrons gained. Similarly, two Al^{3+} ions have six positive charges (three each), and three O^{2-} ions have six negative charges (two each). The net charge on Al_2O_3 is zero, just as it should be.

Now you are able to translate chemical words, such as aluminum oxide, into a chemical formula, Al_2O_3. You also can translate in the other direction, as shown in Example 6.

A Compound by Any Other Name ...

As you read labels on foodstuffs and pharmaceuticals, you will see some names that are beginning to sound familiar, and some that are confusing or mysterious. For example, why do we have two names for Fe^{2+}? Some names are historical: Iron, copper, gold, silver, and other elements have been known for thousands of years. In naming compounds of these elements, the ending *-ous* came to be used for the ion of smaller charge, and the ending *-ic* for the ion of larger charge. The modern system uses Roman numerals to indicate ionic charge. Although the new system is more logical and easier to apply, the old names persist, especially in everyday life and in some of the biomedical sciences.

▲ Labels for dietary supplements often use older, Latin-derived names.

Example 6   Naming Ionic Compounds

What are the names of **(a)** MgS and **(b)** FeCl₃?

Solution
  a. From Table 2, we can determine that MgS is made up of Mg^{2+} (magnesium ion) and S^{2-} (sulfide ion). The name is simply magnesium sulfide.

b. From Table 2, we can determine that the ions in $FeCl_3$ are

$$Fe^{3+} \ Cl^-$$

How do we know the iron ion in $FeCl_3$ is Fe^{3+} and not Fe^{2+}? Because there are three Cl^- ions, each with a $1-$ charge, the single Fe ion must have a $3+$ charge since the compound, $FeCl_3$, is neutral. The names of these ions are iron(III) ion (or ferric ion) and chloride ion. Therefore, the compound is iron(III) chloride (or, by the older system, ferric chloride).

■ EXERCISE 6
What are the names of **(a)** CaF_2 and **(b)** $CuBr_2$?

Self-Assessment Questions

1. The formula for the binary ionic compound of barium and sulfur is
   a. BaS   **b.** Ba_2S **c.** BaS_2 **d.** Ba_2S_3

2. Which of the following formulas is incorrect?
   a. AlF_3 **b.** K_2S **c.** MgF **d.** NaI

3. Which of the following formulas is incorrect?
   a. $AlCl_3$ **b.** Al_3P_2 **c.** CaS   **d.** Cs_2S

4. The correct name for KCl is
   a. krypton chloride   **b.** krypton chlorine
   c. potassium chloride   **d.** potassium chlorine

5. The correct name for Al_2S_3 is
   a. aluminum sulfide   **b.** aluminum trisulfide
   c. antimony sulfide   **d.** antimony trisulfide

6. The correct name for LiI is
   a. indium lithide   **b.** iodine lithide
   c. lithium indide   **d.** lithium iodide

7. The correct name for $ZnCl_2$ is
   a. dichlorozirconium   **b.** zinc chloride
   c. zinc dichloride   **d.** zirconium chloride

Answers: 1, a; 2, c; 3, b; 4, c; 5, a; 6, d; 7, b

6 Covalent Bonds: Shared Electron Pairs

Learning Objectives ❯ Explain the difference between a covalent bond and an ionic bond. ❯ Name and write formulas for covalent compounds.

We might expect a hydrogen atom, with its one electron, to acquire another electron and achieve the configuration of the noble gas helium. In fact, hydrogen atoms do just that in the presence of atoms of a reactive metal such as lithium—that is, a metal that readily gives up an electron.

$$Li\cdot + H\cdot \longrightarrow Li^+ + H:^-$$

But what if there are no other kinds of atoms around, only hydrogen? One hydrogen atom can't gain an electron from another, for all hydrogen atoms have an equal attraction for electrons. Two hydrogen atoms can compromise, however, by *sharing a pair* of electrons.

$$H\cdot + \cdot H \longrightarrow H:H$$

By sharing electrons, the two hydrogen atoms form a hydrogen molecule. The bond formed when atoms share electrons is called a **covalent bond**. If one pair of electrons is shared, the bond is a **single bond**.

H:H

└─ covalent bond (shared pair of electrons)

Let's consider chlorine next. A chlorine atom readily takes an extra electron from anything willing to give one up. But again, what if the only things around are other chlorine atoms? Chlorine atoms can also attain a more stable arrangement by sharing a pair of electrons.

$$:\ddot{\underset{..}{Cl}}\cdot + \cdot\ddot{\underset{..}{Cl}}: \longrightarrow :\ddot{\underset{..}{Cl}}:\ddot{\underset{..}{Cl}}:$$

The shared pair of electrons in the chlorine molecule is another example of a covalent bond; they are called a **bonding pair**. The electrons that stay on one atom and are not shared are called *nonbonding pairs*, or **lone pairs**.

$$:\ddot{\underset{..}{Cl}}:\ddot{\underset{..}{Cl}}:$$

For simplicity, the hydrogen molecule is often represented as H_2, and the chlorine molecule as Cl_2. In each case, the covalent bond between the atoms is understood. Sometimes the covalent bond is indicated by a dash: H—H and Cl—Cl. Lone pairs of electrons often are not shown. Each chlorine atom in a chlorine molecule has eight electrons around it, an arrangement like that of the noble gas argon. Thus, the atoms involved in a covalent bond follow the octet rule by sharing electrons, just as those linked by an ionic bond follow it by giving up or accepting electrons.

Multiple Bonds

In some molecules, atoms must share more than one pair of electrons to follow the octet rule. In carbon dioxide (CO_2), for example, the carbon atom shares *two* pairs of electrons with each of the two oxygen atoms.

$$:\ddot{O}::C::\ddot{O}:$$

Note that each atom has an octet of electrons around it as a result of this sharing. We say that the atoms are joined by a **double bond**, a covalent linkage in which two atoms share two pairs of electrons. A double bond is indicated by a double dash between atoms (O=C=O).

Two atoms also can share three pairs of electrons. In the nitrogen (N_2) molecule, for example, each nitrogen atom shares three pairs of electrons with the other.

$$:N:::N:$$

The atoms are joined by a **triple bond**, a covalent linkage in which two atoms share three pairs of electrons (N≡N). Note that each of the nitrogen atoms has an octet of electrons around it.

Names of Covalent Compounds

Covalent, or *molecular*, compounds are those in which electrons are shared, not transferred. Such compounds generally have molecules that consist of two or more nonmetals. Many covalent compounds have common and widely used names. Examples are water (H_2O), ammonia (NH_3), and methane (CH_4).

For most other covalent compounds, the naming process is more systematic. The prefixes *mono-*, *di-*, *tri-*, and so on are used to indicate the number of atoms of each element in the molecule. A list of these prefixes for up to 10 atoms is given in Table 3. For example, the compound N_2O_4 is called *dinitrogen tetroxide*. (The ending vowel is often dropped from *tetra-* and other prefixes when they precede another vowel.) We often leave off the prefix *mono-* (NO is nitrogen oxide) but include it when we need to distinguish between two compounds of the same pair of elements (CO is carbon monoxide; CO_2 is carbon dioxide).

Covalent bonds are usually represented as dashes. The three kinds of covalent bonds are simply written as follows:
H—Cl   O=C=O   N≡N

Table 3 Prefixes That Indicate the Number of Atoms of an Element in a Covalent Compound

Prefix	Number of Atoms
Mono-	1
Di-	2
Tri-	3
Tetra-	4
Penta-	5
Hexa-	6
Hepta-	7
Octa-	8
Nona-	9
Deca-	10

Example 7   Naming Covalent Compounds

What are the names of **(a)** SCl_2 and **(b)** P_4S_3?

Solution

a. With one sulfur atom and two chlorine atoms, SCl_2 is sulfur dichloride.
b. With four phosphorus atoms and three sulfur atoms, P_4S_3 is tetraphosphorus trisulfide.

■ **EXERCISE 7**

What are the names of **(a)** BrF_3, **(b)** BrF_5, **(c)** N_2O, and **(d)** N_2O_5?

Example 8   Formulas of Covalent Compounds

Write the formula for tetraphosphorus hexoxide.

Solution

The prefix *tetra*- indicates four phosphorus atoms, and *hex*- specifies six oxygen atoms. The formula is P_4O_6.

■ **EXERCISE 8**

Write the formulas for **(a)** phosphorus trichloride, **(b)** dichlorine heptoxide, **(c)** nitrogen triiodide, and **(d)** disulfur dichloride.

You can have fun with chemical names. Some compounds have strange—even funny—common names. Curious? Curium(III) chloride ($CmCl_3$) is curous chloride. Nickel(II) curate ($NiCmO_3$) is nickelous curate. Titanium(IV) chloride ($TiCl_4$) is titanic chloride. Some ions of uranium, such as UO_2^{2-}, UO_3^{2-}, $U_2O_7^{2-}$, are uranates. The hydrides of group 4 elements include methane (CH_4), silane (SiH_4), and germane (GeH_4). Is GeH_4 relevant?

Self-Assessment Questions

1. A bond formed when two atoms share a pair of electrons is
   a. covalent   **b.** ionic   **c.** nonpolar   **d.** polar

2. The bond in Br_2 is
   a. double covalent   **b.** ionic
   c. single covalent   **d.** triple covalent

3. The bond in N_2 is
   a. double covalent   **b.** ionic
   c. single covalent   **d.** triple covalent

4. The formula for phosphorus trichloride is
   a. KCl_3 **b.** K_3Cl **c.** PCl_3 **d.** P_3Cl

5. The formula for disulfur difluoride is
   a. SF_2 **b.** S_2F_2 **c.** SFe_2 **d.** S_2Fl_2

6. The correct name for N_2S_4 is
   a. dinitrogen disulfide   **b.** dinitrogen tetrasulfide
   c. tetrasulfodinitrogen   **d.** tetrasulfur dinitride

7. The correct name for I_2O_5 is
   a. diiodine pentoxide   **b.** diiodopentoxide
   c. iridium pentoxide   **d.** pentaoxodiiodine

Answers: 1, a; 2, c; 3, d; 4, c; 5, b; 6, b; 7, a

7 Unequal Sharing: Polar Covalent Bonds

Learning Objectives ❭ Classify a covalent bond as polar or nonpolar. ❭ Use electronegativities of elements to determine bond polarity.

So far, we have seen that atoms combine in two different ways. Atoms that are quite different in electron configuration (from opposite sides of the periodic table) react by the complete transfer of one or more electrons from one atom to another to form an ionic bond. Some identical nonmetal atoms (such as two chlorine atoms or two hydrogen atoms) combine by sharing a pair of electrons to form a covalent bond. Now let's consider bond formation between atoms that are different, but not different enough to form ionic bonds.

Hydrogen Chloride

Hydrogen and chlorine react to form a colorless gas called *hydrogen chloride*. This reaction may be represented as

$$\text{H} \cdot \;+\; \cdot \ddot{\underset{..}{\text{Cl}}} : \;\longrightarrow\; \text{H} : \ddot{\underset{..}{\text{Cl}}} :$$

Ignoring the lone pairs of electrons and using a dash to represent the covalent bond, we can write the hydrogen chloride molecule as H—Cl. Both hydrogen and chlorine need an electron to achieve a noble gas configuration—a helium configuration for hydrogen and an argon configuration for chlorine. They achieve these configurations by sharing a pair of electrons to form a covalent bond.

Example 9	Covalent Bonds from Lewis Symbols

Use Lewis symbols to show the formation of a covalent bond **(a)** between two fluorine atoms and **(b)** between a fluorine atom and a hydrogen atom.

Solution

$$: \ddot{\underset{..}{\text{F}}} \cdot \;+\; \cdot \ddot{\underset{..}{\text{F}}} : \;\longrightarrow\; : \ddot{\underset{..}{\text{F}}} : \ddot{\underset{..}{\text{F}}} : \quad \text{bonding pair}$$

$$\text{H} \cdot \;+\; \cdot \ddot{\underset{..}{\text{F}}} : \;\longrightarrow\; \text{H} : \ddot{\underset{..}{\text{F}}} : \quad \text{bonding pair}$$

EXERCISE 9

Use Lewis symbols to show the formation of a covalent bond between **(a)** two bromine atoms, **(b)** a hydrogen atom and a bromine atom, and **(c)** an iodine atom and a chlorine atom.

You might reasonably ask why a hydrogen molecule and a chlorine molecule react at all. Have we not just learned that these molecules form because the result is a stable arrangement of electrons? Yes, indeed, that is the case. But there is stable, and there is *more* stable. The chlorine molecule represents a more stable arrangement than two separate chlorine atoms. However, given the opportunity, a chlorine atom selectively forms a bond with a hydrogen atom rather than with another chlorine atom.

For convenience and simplicity, the reaction of hydrogen (molecule) and chlorine (molecule) to form hydrogen chloride is often represented as

$$\text{H}_2 + \text{Cl}_2 \longrightarrow 2\,\text{HCl}$$

The bonds between the atoms and the lone pairs on the chlorine atoms are not shown explicitly, but remember that they are there.

Each molecule of hydrogen chloride consists of one atom of hydrogen and one atom of chlorine. These unlike atoms share a pair of electrons. *Share*, however, does not necessarily mean "share equally." Chlorine atoms have a greater attraction for a shared pair of electrons than hydrogen atoms do. Chlorine is said to be more *electronegative* than hydrogen.

Electronegativity

The **electronegativity** of an element is a measure of the attraction of an atom of that element *in a molecule* for a pair of shared electrons. The atoms to the right in the periodic table are, in general, more electronegative than those to the left. The ones on the right are precisely the atoms that, in forming ions, tend to gain electrons and form negative ions. The ones on the left—metals—tend to give up electrons and become positive ions. Within a column, electronegativity tends to be higher at the top and lower at the bottom of the column.

► **Figure 5** Pauling electronegativity values for several common
elements.

Q: *Can you estimate a value for
the electronegativity of germanium
(Ge)? For the electronegativity of
rubidium (Rb)?*

1A													3A	4A	5A	6A	7A	Noble gases
H 2.1	2A																	
Li 1.0	Be 1.5												B 2.0	C 2.5	N 3.0	O 3.5	F 4.0	
Na 0.9	Mg 1.2	3B	4B	5B	6B	7B		8B		1B	2B		Al 1.5	Si 1.8	P 2.1	S 2.5	Cl 3.0	
K 0.8	Ca 1.0														As 2.0	Se 2.4	Br 2.8	
																	I 2.5	

(a)   (b)

▲ **Figure 6** Representation
of the polar hydrogen chloride
molecule. (a) The electron-dot formula, with the symbols δ+ and δ−
indicating the partial positive and
partial negative charge, respectively. (b) An *electrostatic potential
diagram* depicting the unequal
distribution of electron density in
the hydrogen chloride molecule.

▲ Chlorine hogs the electron blan-
ket, leaving hydrogen partially, but
positively, exposed.

The more electronegative an atom is, the greater its tendency to pull the electrons in the bond toward its end of the bond when it is involved in covalent bonding. The American chemist Linus Pauling (1901–1994) devised a scale of relative
electronegativity values by assigning fluorine, the most electronegative element, a
value of 4.0. Figure 5 displays the electronegativity values for some of the common
elements that we will encounter in this text.

Chlorine (3.0) is more electronegative than hydrogen (2.1). In the hydrogen
chloride molecule, the shared electrons are held more tightly by the chlorine atom.
Thus, the chlorine end of the molecule is more negative than the hydrogen end.
When the electrons in a covalent bond are not equally shared, the bond is said to
be *polar*. The bond in a hydrogen chloride molecule is described as a **polar covalent
bond**, whereas the bond in a hydrogen molecule or a chlorine molecule is a **nonpolar covalent bond**. A polar covalent bond is not an ionic bond. In an ionic bond, one
atom completely loses an electron. In a polar covalent bond, the atom at the positive
end of the bond (hydrogen in HCl) still has a fractional share in the bonding pair of
electrons (Figure 6). To distinguish this kind of bond from an ionic bond or a nonpolar covalent bond, the following notation is used:

$$\overset{\delta+}{\text{H}} — \overset{\delta-}{\text{Cl}}$$

The line between the atoms represents the covalent bond, a pair of shared electrons.
The δ+ and δ− (read "delta plus" and "delta minus") signify which end of the bond
is partially positive and which is partially negative. (The word *partially* is used to
distinguish these charges from the full charges on ions.)

We can use the electronegativity values for the two atoms joined by a bond to predict the type of bonding. When the electronegativity difference is zero or very small
(<0.5), the bond is *nonpolar covalent*, with nearly equal sharing of the electrons. When
the electronegativity difference is large (>2.0), complete electron transfer occurs and
an *ionic* bond is formed, as in the case of sodium and chlorine. When the electronegativity difference is between 0.5 and 2.0, a *polar covalent* bond is formed.

Example 10 Using Electronegativities to Classify Bonds

Use data from Figure 5 to classify the bond between each of the following pairs of
atoms as nonpolar covalent, polar covalent, or ionic:

a. H, H   **b.** O, H   **c.** C, H

Solution

a. Two H atoms have exactly the same electronegativity. The electronegativity
difference is 0. The bond is nonpolar covalent.

b. The electronegativity difference is 3.5 − 2.1 = 1.4. The bond is polar covalent.

c. The electronegativity difference is 2.5 − 2.1 = 0.4. The bond is nonpolar covalent.

Chemical Bonds

■ EXERCISE 10A

Use data from Figure 5 to classify the bond between each of the following pairs of atoms as nonpolar covalent, polar covalent, or ionic:

a. H, Br   b. Na, O   c. C, C

■ EXERCISE 10B

Use the periodic table to classify the following bonds as nonpolar covalent or polar covalent:

a. C—N   b. C—O   c. C=C

Self-Assessment Questions

1. When HCl is formed,
   a. a Cl atom gives one valence electron to an H atom
   b. an H atom gives one valence electron to a Cl atom
   c. a pair of valence electrons is shared, one each from the H atom and the Cl atom
   d. a pair of valence electrons is shared, none from the H atom and two from the Cl atom

2. Which of the following bonds is least polar?
   a. C—Br   b. C—Cl   c. C—F   d. H—H

3. Which of the following bonds is most polar?
   a. C—C   b. C—F   c. C—O   d. F—F

4. In a polar covalent bond, the atom with greater electronegativity bears a
   a. full negative charge   b. full positive charge
   c. partial negative charge   d. partial positive charge

5. For an ionic bond to exist between two atoms, their difference in electronegativity should be
   a. between 0 and 0.5   b. between 0.5 and 2.0
   c. greater than 2.0   d. zero

Answers: 1, c; 2, d; 3, b; 4, c; 5, c

8 Polyatomic Molecules: Water, Ammonia, and Methane

Learning Objective ❯ Predict the number of bonds formed by common nonmetals (the HONC rules).

To obtain an octet of electrons, an oxygen atom must share electrons with *two* hydrogen atoms, a nitrogen atom must share electrons with *three* hydrogen atoms, and a carbon atom must share electrons with *four* hydrogen atoms. In general, nonmetals tend to form a number of covalent bonds that is equal to eight minus the group number. Oxygen, which is in group 6A, forms $8 - 6 = 2$ covalent bonds in most molecules. Nitrogen, in group 5A, forms $8 - 5 = 3$ covalent bonds in most molecules. Carbon, in group 4A, forms $8 - 4 = 4$ covalent bonds in most molecules, including those of the great host of organic compounds. The following simple guidelines—sometimes called the HONC rules—will enable you to write formulas for many molecules.

- Hydrogen forms 1 bond.
- Oxygen forms 2 bonds.
- Nitrogen forms 3 bonds.
- Carbon forms 4 bonds.

Water

Water is one of the most familiar chemical substances. The electrolysis experiment of Nicholson and Carlisle and the fact that both hydrogen and oxygen are diatomic (two-atom) gases indicate that the molecular formula for water is H_2O. To attain an octet, oxygen shares two pairs of electrons. Because a hydrogen atom

145

shares only one pair of electrons, however, an oxygen atom must bond with two hydrogen atoms, forming a *polyatomic* molecule—a molecule containing more than two atoms.

$$\cdot \ddot{\underset{..}{O}}: + 2\,H\cdot \longrightarrow H:\ddot{\underset{..}{O}}: \text{ or } H-\underset{\underset{H}{|}}{O}$$

This arrangement completes the valence shell octet of the oxygen atom, giving it the neon configuration. It also completes the outer shell of each hydrogen atom, giving each of these atoms the helium configuration. Oxygen has a higher electronegativity than does hydrogen, so the H—O bonds formed are *polar covalent*.

Ammonia

A nitrogen atom has five electrons in its valence shell. It can attain the neon configuration by sharing three pairs of electrons with *three* hydrogen atoms. The result is the compound ammonia.

$$\cdot \ddot{\underset{.}{N}}\cdot + 3\,H\cdot \longrightarrow H:\ddot{\underset{..}{N}}:H \text{ or } H-\underset{\underset{H}{|}}{N}-H$$

In ammonia, the bond arrangement is that of a tripod (see Figure 10) with a hydrogen atom at the end of each leg and the nitrogen atom with its unshared pair of electrons at the top. (We will see why it has this shape in Section 11.) The electronegativity of N is 3.0, and that of H is 2.1, so all three N—H bonds are *polar covalent*.

Methane

A carbon atom has four electrons in its valence shell. It can achieve the neon configuration by sharing pairs of electrons with four hydrogen atoms, forming the compound methane.

$$\cdot \dot{\underset{.}{C}}\cdot + 4\,H\cdot \longrightarrow \underset{\underset{H}{|}}{\overset{\overset{H}{|}}{H:\ddot{\underset{..}{C}}:H}} \text{ or } \underset{\underset{H}{|}}{\overset{\overset{H}{|}}{H-C-H}}$$

The methane molecule, as shown above, appears to be planar but actually is not—as we shall see in Section 11. The electronegativity difference between H and C is so small that the C—H bonds are considered nonpolar.

Self-Assessment Questions

1. When two H atoms each share an electron with an O atom to form H_2O, the bonding is
   a. diatomic
   b. ionic
   c. nonpolar covalent
   d. polar covalent

2. How many electrons are in the valence shell of the N atom in an ammonia molecule?
   a. 2   b. 5   c. 6   d. 8

3. To gain an octet of electrons in forming methane, a carbon atom must share an electron with each of
   a. 2 H atoms
   b. 4 H atoms
   c. 6 H atoms
   d. 8 H atoms

Answers: 1, d; 2, d; 3, b

9 Polyatomic Ions

Learning Objective > Recognize common polyatomic ions and be able to use them in naming and writing formulas for ionic compounds.

Many compounds contain both ionic and covalent bonds. Sodium hydroxide, commonly known as lye, consists of sodium ions (Na^+) and hydroxide ions (OH^-). The hydroxide ion contains an oxygen atom covalently bonded to a hydrogen atom,

Table 4 | **Some Common Polyatomic Ions**

Charge	Name	Formula
1+	Ammonium ion	NH_4^+
	Hydronium ion	H_3O^+
1−	Hydrogen carbonate (bicarbonate) ion	HCO_3^-
	Hydrogen sulfate (bisulfate) ion	HSO_4^-
	Acetate ion	$CH_3CO_2^-$ (or $C_2H_3O_2^-$)
	Nitrite ion	NO_2^-
	Nitrate ion	NO_3^-
	Cyanide ion	CN^-
	Hydroxide ion	OH^-
	Dihydrogen phosphate ion	$H_2PO_4^-$
	Permanganate ion	MnO_4^-
2−	Carbonate ion	CO_3^{2-}
	Sulfate ion	SO_4^{2-}
	Chromate ion	CrO_4^{2-}
	Hydrogen (monohydrogen) phosphate ion	HPO_4^{2-}
	Oxalate ion	$C_2O_4^{2-}$
	Dichromate ion	$Cr_2O_7^{2-}$
3−	Phosphate ion	PO_4^{3-}

Acetate ion

Ammonium ion

Hydrogen carbonate ion (bicarbonate ion)

Carbonate ion   Nitrite ion

plus an "extra" electron. That extra electron gives hydroxide ion a negative charge and gives the O and the H atom each a filled shell.

$$e^- \,+\, \cdot \ddot{O} \cdot \,+\, \cdot H \,\longrightarrow\, :\ddot{O}:H^-$$

The formula for sodium hydroxide is NaOH. For each sodium ion, there is one hydroxide ion.

There are many groups of atoms that (like hydroxide ion) remain together through most chemical reactions. **Polyatomic ions** are charged particles containing two or more covalently bonded atoms. A list of common polyatomic ions is given in Table 4. You can use these ions, in combination with the simple ions in Table 2, to determine formulas for many ionic compounds.

Example 11   Formulas with Polyatomic Ions

What is the formula for ammonium sulfide?

Solution

Ammonium ion is found in Table 4. Sulfide ion is a sulfur atom (group 6A) with two additional electrons. The ions are

$$NH_4^+ \; S^{2-}$$

Crossing over gives

$$NH_4^{①\,+} \quad S^{②\,-}$$

The formula for ammonium sulfide is $(NH_4)_2S$. (Note the parentheses.)

■ EXERCISE 11A

What are the formulas for **(a)** calcium acetate, **(b)** potassium oxide, and **(c)** aluminum sulfate?

■ EXERCISE 11B

How many **(a)** sulfur atoms are in the formula for aluminum sulfate, how many and **(b)** how many carbon atoms are in the formula for calcium acetate?

Example 12   **Naming Compounds with Polyatomic Ions**

What are the names of **(a)** $NaCN$ and **(b)** $Fe(OH)_2$?

Solution

As with compounds containing only monatomic ions, we name the cation and then the anion.

  a. The cation is sodium ion, and the anion is cyanide ion (Table 4). The compound is sodium cyanide.

  b. The cation is an iron ion, and the anion is hydroxide ion (Table 4). There are two hydroxide ions, each with a charge of $1-$, so the iron ion must be a $2+$ ion [iron(II)]. The compound is iron(II) hydroxide.

■ **EXERCISE 12A**
What are the names of **(a)** $CaCO_3$, **(b)** $Mg_3(PO_4)_2$, and **(c)** K_2CrO_4?

■ **EXERCISE 12B**
What are the names of **(a)** $(NH_4)_2SO_4$, **(b)** KH_2PO_4, and **(c)** $CuCr_2O_7$?

Self-Assessment Questions

1. Which of the following compounds incorporates a polyatomic ion?
   a. CO_2 **b.** $C_6H_{12}O_6$ **c.** K_2SO_3 **d.** $SrBr_2$

2. The formula for ammonium phosphate is
   a. NH_4PO_3 **b.** $NH_4(PO_4)_2$ **c.** $(NH_4)_2PO_4$ **d.** $(NH_4)_3PO_4$

3. The formula for sodium hydrogen carbonate is
   a. $NaHCO_3$ **b.** Na_2HCO_3 **c.** NaH_2CO_3 **d.** $NaHCO_4$

4. The formula for copper(I) hydrogen sulfate is
   a. $CuHSO_4$ **b.** Cu_2HSO_3 **c.** Cu_2HSO_4 **d.** $Cu(HSO_4)_2$

5. The formula for calcium nitrate is
   a. $CaNO_3$ **b.** Ca_2NO_3 **c.** $Ca(NO_3)_2$ **d.** $CaNO_4$

6. The correct name for NH_4HCO_3 is
   a. ammonium acetate   **b.** ammonium carbonate
   c. ammonium hydrogen carbonate   **d.** ammonium cyanide

Answers: 1, c; 2, d; 3, a; 4, a; 5, c; 6, c

10 Rules for Writing Lewis Formulas

Learning Objectives   ❯ Write Lewis formulas for simple molecules and polyatomic ions.
❯ Identify free radicals.

As we have seen, electrons are transferred or shared in ways that leave most atoms with octets of electrons in their outermost shells. This section describes how to write **Lewis formulas** for molecules and polyatomic ions. To write a Lewis formula, we first put the atoms of the molecule or ion in their proper places, and then we place all the valence electrons so that each atom has a filled shell.

The *skeletal structure* of a molecule tells us the order in which the atoms are attached to one another. Drawing a skeletal structure takes some practice. However, if there is no experimental evidence, the following guidelines help us to devise likely skeletal structures:

▪ Hydrogen atoms form only single bonds. They are always at the end of a sequence of atoms. Hydrogen is often bonded to carbon, nitrogen, or oxygen.

▪ Oxygen tends to have two bonds, nitrogen usually has three bonds, and carbon has four bonds.

▪ Polyatomic molecules and ions often consist of a central atom surrounded by atoms of higher electronegativity. (Hydrogen is an exception; it is always on the outside, even when bonded to a more electronegative element.) The central atom of a polyatomic molecule or ion is often the *least* electronegative atom.

After choosing a skeletal structure for a polyatomic molecule or ion, we can use the following steps to write the Lewis formula:

1. Determine the total number of valence electrons. This total is the sum of the valence electrons for all the atoms in the molecule or ion. You must also account for the charge(s) on a polyatomic ion. For a polyatomic anion, *add* to its total number of valence electrons the number of negative charges. For a polyatomic cation, *subtract* the number of positive charges.

   Examples:

   N_2O_4 has $(2 \times 5) + (4 \times 6) = 34$ valence electrons.

   NO_3^- has $[(1 \times 5) + (3 \times 6)] + 1 = 24$ valence electrons.

   NH_4^+ has $[(1 \times 5) + (4 \times 1)] - 1 = 8$ valence electrons.

2. Write a reasonable skeletal structure and connect bonded pairs of atoms by a dash (one shared electron pair).
3. Place electrons in pairs around outer atoms so that each (except hydrogen) has an octet.
4. Subtract the number of electrons assigned so far (both in bonds and as lone pairs) from the total calculated in step 1. Any electrons that remain are assigned in pairs to the central atom(s).
5. If a central atom has fewer than eight electrons after step 4, one or more multiple bonds are likely. Move one or more lone pairs from an outer atom to the space between the atoms to form a double or triple bond. A deficiency of two electrons suggests a double bond, and a shortage of four electrons indicates a triple bond or two double bonds to the central atom.

Example 13   Writing Lewis Formulas

Write Lewis formulas for **(a)** methanol (CH_3OH), **(b)** the BF_4^- ion, and **(c)** carbon dioxide (CO_2).

Solution

a. We start by following the preceding rules:
   1. The total number of valence electrons is $4 + (4 \times 1) + 6 = 14$.
   2. The skeletal structure must have all the H atoms on the outside. That means the C and O atoms must be bonded to each other. A reasonable skeletal structure is

$$\begin{array}{c} H \\ | \\ H-C-O-H \\ | \\ H \end{array}$$

   3. Now, we count five bonds with two electrons each, making a total of ten electrons. Thus, four of the 14 valence electrons are left to be assigned. They are placed (as two lone pairs) on the oxygen atom.

$$\begin{array}{c} H \\ | \\ H-C-\ddot{\underset{..}{O}}-H \\ | \\ H \end{array}$$

(The remaining steps are not necessary. Both carbon and oxygen now have octets of electrons.)

b. Again, we start by applying the preceding rules:
1. There are $3 + (4 \times 7) + 1 = 32$ valence electrons.
2. The skeletal structure is

$$
\begin{array}{c}
\text{F} \\
| \\
\text{F} - \text{B} - \text{F} \\
| \\
\text{F}
\end{array}
$$

3. Placing three lone pairs on each fluorine atom gives

$$
\left[
\begin{array}{c}
:\ddot{\text{F}}: \\
| \\
:\ddot{\text{F}} - \text{B} - \ddot{\text{F}}: \\
| \\
:\ddot{\text{F}}:
\end{array}
\right]^{-}
$$

4. We have assigned 32 electrons. None remains to be assigned. Brackets and a negative sign are added to show that this is the structure for an anion, not a molecule. The charge is written outside the brackets to indicate the charge is on the ion as a whole, not necessarily on any particular atom.

c. Again, we start by applying the rules:
1. There are $4 + (2 \times 6) = 16$ valence electrons.
2. The skeletal structure is $\text{O} - \text{C} - \text{O}$.
3. We place three lone pairs on each oxygen atom.

$$
:\ddot{\text{O}} - \text{C} - \ddot{\text{O}}:
$$

4. We have assigned 16 electrons. None remains to be placed.
5. The central carbon atom has only four electrons. It needs to have two double bonds in order to achieve an octet. We move a lone pair from each oxygen atom to the space between the atoms to form a double bond on each side of the carbon atom.

$$
:\ddot{\text{O}} = \text{C} = \ddot{\text{O}}:
$$

■ EXERCISE 13A
Write Lewis formulas for **(a)** oxygen difluoride, OF_2, and **(b)** methyl chloride, CH_3Cl.

■ EXERCISE 13B
Write Lewis formulas for **(a)** the azide ion, N_3^-, and **(b)** the nitryl fluoride molecule, NO_2F (O—N—O—F skeleton).

The rules we have used here lead to the results for selected elements that are summarized in Table 5. Figure 7 relates the number of covalent bonds that a particular element forms to its position on the periodic table.

Odd-Electron Molecules: Free Radicals

There are some classes of molecules in which atoms do not conform to the octet rule. *Free radicals* are one such class. (See Problems 51 and 52 for two other types.) Molecules with odd numbers of valence electrons obviously cannot satisfy the octet rule. Examples of such molecules are nitrogen monoxide (NO, also called nitric oxide), with $5 + 6 = 11$ valence electrons; nitrogen dioxide (NO_2), with 17 valence electrons; and chlorine dioxide (ClO_2), which has 19 valence electrons.

An atom or molecule with unpaired electrons is called a **free radical**. Most free radicals are highly reactive and exist for only a very brief time before reacting with another species. Every atom or molecule with an odd number of electrons must have one unpaired electron. Filled shells and subshells contain all paired electrons, with two electrons in each orbital. Therefore, we need only consider valence electrons to determine whether an atom or molecule is a free radical. Lewis

Table 5 Number of Bonds Formed by Selected Elements

Lewis Symbol	Bond Picture	Number of Bonds	Representative Molecules	Ball-and-Stick Models
H·	H—	1	H—H H—Cl	HCl
He:		0	He	He
·Ċ·	—Ċ—	4	H—C—H (with H above and below) H—C—F (with O double bond above)	CH₄
·N̈·	—N—	3	H—N—H (with H below) N—O—H / H—C—H (with N=O)	NH₃
·Ö:	—O	2	H—O—H (H below) H—C—H (with O double bond above)	H₂O
·F̈:	—F	1	H—F F—F	F₂
·C̈l:	—Cl	1	Cl—Cl H—C—Cl (with H above and below)	CH₃Cl

1A	2A											3A	4A	5A	6A	7A	Noble gases
	—Be—											B—	—C—	N—	O—	F—	
		3B	4B	5B	6B	7B	8B		1B	2B			—Si—	P—	S—	Cl—	
																Br—	
																I—	
										—Hg—							

◀ **Figure 7** Covalent bonding of representative elements on the periodic table.

Q: *What is the relationship between an atom's position on the periodic table and the number of covalent bonds it tends to form? Why are the group 1A and most of the group 2A elements omitted from the table?*

formulas of NO, NO₂, and ClO₂ each have one atom with an unpaired electron. An atom having an unpaired electron cannot have an octet of electrons in its outer shell.

$$:\ddot{N}::\ddot{O}: \qquad :\ddot{O}:N::\ddot{O}: \qquad :\ddot{O}:\ddot{C}l:\ddot{O}:$$

Nitrogen oxides are major components of smog. Chlorine atoms from the breakdown of chlorofluorocarbons in the stratosphere lead to depletion of the ozone layer. Some free radicals are quite stable, however, and have important functions in the body as well as in industrial processes (see the box on the next page).

Useful Applications of Free Radicals

The very reactive nature of free radicals does not preclude their importance and use in a variety of natural and industrial applications.

- Nitric oxide (NO) has been shown to be a signaling molecule in the human cardiovascular system. American scientists Robert F. Furchgott, Louis J. Ignarro, and Ferid Murad won the Nobel Prize in Physiology or Medicine in 1998 for that discovery. Interestingly, one of the physiological effects of sildenafil citrate (Viagra®) is the production of small quantities of NO in the bloodstream.

- Hydroxyl radicals (·OH) are produced in the body in the process of oxidation of foods and by radiation. The decomposition of hydrogen peroxide (HOOH) and other peroxides produces ·OH. These radicals inflict havoc on DNA and other essential substances and they have been implicated in the formation of cancerous cells due to their rapid reaction with DNA. Hydroxyl radicals are also play a role in air pollution.

- Many plastics, including polyethylene and polyvinyl chloride (PVC), are made using free radicals to initiate the reactions. Liquid polyester resin is used to repair automobiles and to construct small boats and surfboards. The resin is converted to hard plastic by the addition of a free-radical catalyst called *methyl ethyl ketone peroxide.*

- The free radical chlorine dioxide (ClO_2) is widely used to bleach paper and other products, including flour. Unbleached flour (left) is a pale cream color; bleached flour (right) is whiter and is considered more attractive to consumers.

Pearson Education/Eric Schrader

▲ Chlorine dioxide (ClO_2) is used to bleach flour. Unbleached flour (left) and bleached flour (right).

Self-Assessment Questions

1. How many lone pairs of electrons are there in the Lewis formula of CF_4?
   a. 4   **b.** 12   **c.** 14   **d.** 16

2. How many unshared electrons are there in the Lewis formula of H_2O_2?
   a. 3   **b.** 8   **c.** 14   **d.** 18

3. The Lewis formula for CCl_4 has
   a. 0 lone pairs   **b.** 1 double bond
   c. 4 ionic bonds   **d.** 24 unshared electrons

4. The correct Lewis formula for carbon dioxide is
   a. O—C—O   **b.** :O—C—O:
   c. :Ö—C—Ö: **d.** :Ö=C=Ö:

5. The correct Lewis formula for the Cl_2O molecule is
   a. :C̈l—C̈l—Ö: b. :C̈l=O=C̈l   c. :Ö—C̈l—Ö: d. :C̈l—Ö—C̈l:

6. In the Lewis formula for CO_2, the number of lone pairs of electrons in the outer shell of the central atom is
   a. 0   **b.** 1   **c.** 2   **d.** 4

7. Which of the following must have a triple bond in order to complete an octet for each atom in its Lewis formula?
   a. F_2 **b.** HCN   **c.** HI   **d.** O_2

8. The Lewis formula for the SO_3^{2-} ion that follows the octet rule is

a. $\left[\begin{array}{c} :\ddot{O}—S—\ddot{O}: \\ | \\ :\ddot{O}: \end{array}\right]^{2-}$ b. $\left[\begin{array}{c} :\ddot{O}—S=\ddot{O}: \\ | \\ :\ddot{O}: \end{array}\right]^{2-}$ c. $\left[\begin{array}{c} :\ddot{O}=S=\ddot{O}: \\ | \\ :\ddot{O}: \end{array}\right]^{2-}$ d. $\left[\begin{array}{c} :\ddot{O}—\ddot{S}—\ddot{O}: \\ | \\ :\ddot{O}: \end{array}\right]^{2-}$

Answers: 1, b; 2, b; 3, d; 4, d; 5, d; 6, a; 7, b; 8, d

11 Molecular Shapes: The VSEPR Theory

Learning Objective > Predict the shapes of simple molecules from their Lewis formulas.

We have represented molecules in two dimensions on paper, but molecules have three-dimensional shapes that are important in determining their properties. For example, the shapes of the molecules that make up gasoline determine its octane rating, and drug molecules must have the right atoms in the right places to be effective. We can use Lewis formulas as part of the process of predicting molecular shapes. Figure 8 shows the shapes that we consider in this book.

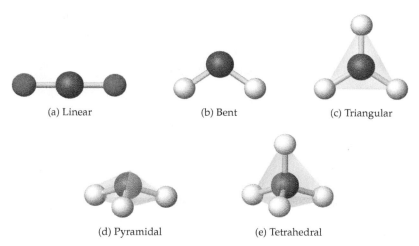

(a) Linear   (b) Bent   (c) Triangular

(d) Pyramidal   (e) Tetrahedral

▲ **Figure 8** Shapes of molecules. In a *linear* molecule (a), all the atoms are along a line; the bond angle is 180°. A *bent* molecule (b) has an angle less than 180°. Connecting the three outer atoms of a *triangular* molecule (c) with imaginary lines produces a triangle with an atom at the center. Imaginary lines connecting all four atoms of a *pyramidal* molecule (d) form a three-sided pyramid. Connecting the four outer atoms of a *tetrahedral* molecule (e) with imaginary lines produces a tetrahedron (a four-sided figure in which each side is a triangle) with an atom at the center.

We use the **valence shell electron pair repulsion (VSEPR) theory** to predict the arrangement of atoms about a central atom in a molecule. The basis of the VSEPR theory is that electron pairs arrange themselves about a central atom in a way that minimizes repulsions between these like-charged particles. This means that electron pairs (both lone pairs and shared pairs in bonds) will be as far apart as possible. In applying the VSEPR theory to predict molecular shapes, we will use the term *electron set* to refer to either a lone pair on a central atom or a bond—single, double, or triple—between the central atom and another atom. Table 6 presents the geometric shapes associated with the arrangement of two, three, or four electron sets about a central atom.

- When *two* electron sets are as far apart as possible, they are on opposite sides of the central atom at an angle of 180°.
- *Three* electron sets assume a triangular arrangement about the central atom, forming angles of separation of 120°.
- *Four* electron sets form a tetrahedral array around the central atom, giving a separation of about 109.5°.

We can determine the shapes of many molecules (and polyatomic ions) by following this simple procedure:

1. Draw a Lewis formula in which a shared electron pair (bonding pair) is indicated by a line. Use dots to show any unshared pairs (lone pairs) of electrons.

153

Table 6 Bonding and the Shapes of Molecules

Number of Bonded Atoms	Number of Lone Pairs	Number of Electron Sets	Molecular Shape	Examples of Molecules	Ball-and-Stick Models
2	0	2	Linear	$BeCl_2$ $HgCl_2$ CO_2 HCN	$BeCl_2$
3	0	3	Triangular	BF_3 $AlBr_3$ CH_2O	BF_3
4	0	4	Tetrahedral	CH_4 CBr_4 $SiCl_4$	CH_4
3	1	4	Pyramidal	NH_3 PCl_3	NH_3
2	2	4	Bent	H_2O H_2S SCl_2	H_2O
2	1	3	Bent	SO_2 O_3	SO_2

2. To determine shape, count the number of electron sets around the *central* atom. Recall that a multiple bond counts only as one electron set. Examples are

$$H-\overset{..}{O}:\;|\;H \quad\quad H-\overset{..}{N}-H\;|\;H \quad\quad \overset{H}{\underset{H}{|}}\;H-C-H$$

Four sets (2 atoms, 2 LPs)   Four sets (3 atoms, 1 LP)   Four sets (4 atoms)

$$H-C\equiv N: \quad :\overset{..}{O}=C=\overset{..}{O}: \quad H-\overset{H}{\underset{|}{B}}-H \quad [:\overset{..}{O}-N=\overset{..}{O}:]^-$$

Two sets (2 atoms)   Two sets (2 atoms)   Three sets (3 atoms)   Three sets (2 atoms, 1 LP)

3. Using the number of electron sets determined in step 2, draw a shape *as if* all the sets were bonding pairs and place these electron sets as far apart as possible (Table 6).

4. If there are *no* lone pairs, the shape from step 3 is the shape of the molecule. If there *are* lone pairs, remove them, leaving the bonding pairs exactly as they were. (This may seem strange, but it stems from the fact that *all* the sets determine the geometry, but only the arrangement of bonded atoms is considered in the shape of the molecule.)

Example 14   Shapes of Molecules

What are the shapes of **(a)** the H_2CO molecule and **(b)** the SCl_2 molecule?

Solution

a. We follow the preceding rules, starting with the Lewis formula.

1. The Lewis formula for H_2CO is

$$H$$
$$|$$
$$C=\ddot{O}$$
$$|$$
$$H$$

2. There are three sets of electrons: two C—H single bonds and one C=O double bond.

3. A triangular arrangement puts the three electron sets as far apart as possible.

H   120°
C=Ö:
H

4. All the electron sets are bonding pairs; the molecular shape is triangular, the same as the arrangement of the electron sets.

b. Again, we follow the rules, starting with the Lewis formula.

1. The Lewis formula for SCl_2 is

:S̈—C̈l:
|
:C̈l:

2. There are four sets of electrons on the sulfur atom.

3. A tetrahedral arrangement around the central atom puts the four sets of electrons as far apart as possible.

A tetrahedral arrangement with a bond angle of about 109.5°

4. Two of the electron sets are bonding pairs and two are lone pairs. Ignore the lone pairs. The molecular shape is *bent*, with a bond angle of about 109.5°.

EXERCISE 14A
What are the shapes of **(a)** the PH_3 molecule and **(b)** the nitrate ion (NO_3^-)?

EXERCISE 14B
What are the shapes of **(a)** the carbonate ion (CO_3^{2-}) and **(b)** the hydrogen peroxide (H_2O_2) molecule?

Self-Assessment Questions

Match the formula in the left column with the molecular shape in the right column.

1. CS_2 **a.** bent
2. H_2S **b.** linear
3. PF_3 **c.** pyramidal
4. SiF_4 **d.** tetrahedral

Answers: 1, b; 2, a; 3, c; 4, d

12 Shapes and Properties: Polar and Nonpolar Molecules

Learning Objective ❯ Classify a simple molecule as polar or nonpolar from its shape and the polarity of its bonds.

▲ **Figure 9** The methane molecule. In (a), black lines indicate covalent bonds; the red lines outline a tetrahedron; and all bond angles are 109.5°. The slightly polar C—H bonds cancel each other (b), resulting in a nonpolar, tetrahedral molecule (c).

Q: *How does the electrostatic potential diagram in (c) look different from the one in Figure 6?*

Section 7 discussed polar and nonpolar bonds. A diatomic molecule is nonpolar if its bond is nonpolar, as in H_2 or Cl_2, and polar if its bond is polar, as in HCl. Recall from Section 7 that the partial charges in a polar bond are indicated by $\delta+$ and $\delta-$. In the case of a **dipole**, a molecule with a positive end and a negative end, the polarity is commonly indicated with an arrow with a plus sign at the tail end (↔). The plus sign indicates the part of the molecule with a partial positive charge, and the head of the arrow signifies the end of the molecule with a partial negative charge.

$$H-H \quad \text{and} \quad Cl-Cl \qquad \overset{\delta+}{H}-\overset{\delta-}{Cl} \quad \text{or} \quad \overset{\longleftrightarrow}{H-Cl}$$

Nonpolar   Polar

For a molecule with three or more atoms, we must consider the polarity of the individual bonds as well as the overall geometry of the molecule to determine whether the molecule as a whole is polar. A **polar molecule** has separate centers of positive and negative charge, just as a magnet has north and south poles. Many properties of compounds—such as melting point, boiling point, and solubility—depend on the polarity of their molecules.

Methane: A Tetrahedral Molecule

There are four electron sets around the central carbon atom in methane, CH_4. Using the VSEPR theory, we would expect a tetrahedral arrangement and bond angles of 109.5° (Figure 9a). The actual bond angles are 109.5°, as predicted by the theory. All four electron sets are shared with hydrogen atoms and, therefore, occupy identical volumes. Each carbon-to-hydrogen bond is slightly polar (Figure 9b), but the methane molecule as a whole is symmetric. The slight bond polarities cancel out, leaving the methane molecule, as a whole, nonpolar (Figure 9c).

Ammonia: A Pyramidal Molecule

In ammonia, NH_3, the central nitrogen atom has three bonds and a lone pair around it. The N—H bonds of ammonia are more polar than the C—H bonds of methane. More important, the NH_3 molecule has a different geometry as a result of the lone pair on the nitrogen atom. The VSEPR theory predicts a tetrahedral arrangement of the four sets of electrons, giving bond angles of 109.5° (Figure 10a). However, the lone pair of electrons occupies a greater volume than a bonding pair, pushing the bonding pairs slightly closer together and resulting in actual bond angles of about 107°. The pyramidal geometry can be envisioned as a tripod with a hydrogen atom at the end of each leg and the nitrogen atom with its lone pair sitting at the top. Each nitrogen-to-hydrogen bond is somewhat polar (Figure 10b). The asymmetric structure makes the ammonia molecule polar, with a partial negative charge on the nitrogen atom and partial positive charges on the three hydrogen atoms (Figure 10c).

Water: A Bent Molecule

The O—H bonds in water are even more polar than the N—H bonds in ammonia because oxygen is more electronegative than nitrogen. (Recall that electronegativity increases from left to right in the periodic table.) Just because a molecule contains polar bonds, however, does not mean that the molecule as a whole is polar. If the atoms in the water molecule were in a straight line (that is, in a linear arrangement, as in CO_2), the two polar bonds would cancel one another and the molecule would be nonpolar.

▲ Figure 10 The ammonia molecule. In (a), black lines indicate covalent bonds. The red lines outline a tetrahedron. The polar N—H bonds do not cancel each other completely in (b), resulting in a polar, pyramidal molecule (c).

Q: *How does the electrostatic potential diagram in Figure 10 (c) resemble the one in Figure 6?*

▲ Figure 11 The water molecule. In (a), black lines indicate covalent bonds, and the red lines outline a tetrahedron. The polar O—H bonds do not cancel each other in (b), resulting in a polar, bent molecule (c).

In its physical and chemical properties, however, water acts like a polar molecule. Molecules such as water and ammonia, in which the polar bonds do not cancel out, act as dipoles. Such molecules have a positive end and a negative end.

We can understand the dipole in the water molecule by using the VSEPR theory. The two bonds and two lone pairs should form a tetrahedral arrangement of electron sets (Figure 11a). Ignoring the lone pairs, the molecular shape has the atoms in a bent arrangement, with a bond angle of about 104.5° (instead of 109.5°). As with ammonia, the actual angle is slightly smaller than the predicted angle because of the greater volume of space occupied by the two lone pairs compared to the bonding pairs. The larger space occupied by the lone pairs reduces the space in which the bonding pairs reside, pushing them closer together. The two polar O—H bonds do not cancel each other (Figure 11b), making the bent water molecule polar (Figure 11c).

Self-Assessment Questions

1. Which of the following molecules is polar?
   a. Br_2 **b.** CH_4 **c.** CO_2 **d.** NH_3

2. Which of the following molecules is polar?
   a. C_2H_2 (linear) **b.** Cl_2 **c.** CCl_4 **d.** PF_3

3. Which of the following molecules is polar?
   a. CF_4 **b.** C_2H_4 (planar) **c.** NF_3 **d.** O_2

4. Which of the following molecules has polar bonds but is not polar?
   a. CCl_4 **b.** Cl_2 **c.** NCl_3 **d.** OF_2

Answers: 1, d; 2, d; 3, c; 4, a

John C. Warner, *Warner Babcock Institute for Green Chemistry*

Amy S. Cannon, *Beyond Benign*

Green Chemistry and Chemical Bonds

You learned in this chapter that atoms bond together to form compounds and these new compounds have properties that differ greatly from the component elements. In molecular compounds (molecules), atoms join by forming covalent bonds that cause the molecules to adopt specific geometric shapes (Sections 6, 7, 12). Each atom is held in a specific position relative to other atoms in the molecule. In ionic compounds, atoms are held together through ionic bonds (Section 3).

Molecular shape and composition of compounds control reactivity and interactions with other substances. As a chemist manipulates the geometry and composition of molecules, the properties can change drastically. A wonderful example of how shape impacts the design of molecules is seen in medicine. Within our bodies, biological molecules have particular shapes that are recognized by enzymes and other receptors, in the same way that a key matches a lock. The molecule and the receptor fit together to form complexes through *noncovalent forces* (intermolecular forces).

Medicinal chemists design new medicines and drug molecules so that they will resemble biological molecules and bind to enzymes or receptors in our body. But these molecule-receptor complexes must behave differently from the biological molecule. The binding triggers a response in our bodies and helps us to heal. Medicinal chemists use the shapes of molecules and forces between them to create new life-saving or life-changing medicines. Interaction between molecules caused by the geometric orientations of their atoms is called **molecular recognition**. The 1987 Nobel Prize in Chemistry was awarded to Donald J. Cram, Jean-Marie Lehn, and Charles J. Pedersen for pioneering work in this area. Scientists are now learning to use molecular recognition to control molecular properties and create not only new medicines but also new materials.

What does this have to do with green chemistry? The processes that chemists rely on to make materials often use large amounts of energy or highly reactive and toxic chemicals. New production methods that take advantage of molecular recognition typically use lower energy, solvent-free processes that do not require harsh conditions.

This way of making materials takes advantage of several of the twelve principles of green chemistry. Principles 3, 5, 6, and 8 focus on the choices we make as chemists as we design new molecules and materials. For example, using less hazardous chemicals to make new medicines means we can reduce the environmental impact of the manufacturing process for these compounds. Doing so ensures that they can change the lives of sick patients as well as provide safer workplaces for the workers making the new medicines.

Typical reactions carried out in laboratories use solvents that dissolve the molecules (solutes) and allow them to react to form new molecules. Many solvents can be hazardous to human health and the environment. Processes for making new noncovalent complexes that rely on molecular recognition often do not require solvents. This drastically reduces the environmental impact of these processes.

Many traditional processes require high temperatures, which translates to high energy use. Noncovalent complexes created through molecular recognition function in much the same way as molecules interact within our bodies at moderate temperatures. Therefore, these new approaches use very little energy, which benefits the environment and reduces the manufacturing cost. Also, many processes that generate new molecules and materials are quite complex. By understanding how molecules interact by shape and noncovalent forces, we can reduce the complexity in these processes and avoid the generation of waste and the reliance on hazardous materials.

By understanding molecular shape, the nature of chemical bonds, and how molecules interact with other molecules through noncovalent forces, chemists are able to design new medicines, molecules, and materials that benefit society and, at the same time, have minimal impact on the environment and human health. Green chemistry allows chemists to use these skills combined with new innovative techniques to design chemicals that do not harm our environment in the process.

The antibiotic *vancomysin* carries out its function using molecular recognition. Vancomysin undergoes strong, selective hydrogen bonding with *peptides* (small protein chains) of bacteria, preventing formation of the cell wall.

A Chemical Vocabulary

Learning chemical symbolism is much like learning a foreign language. Once you have learned the basic "vocabulary," the rest is a lot easier. At first, the task is complicated because different chemical species or definitions sound a lot alike (sodium atoms versus sodium ions). Another complication is that we have several different ways to represent the *same* chemical species (Figure 12).

Ammonia $\longrightarrow$ NH_3 $\longrightarrow$ H—N̈—H $\longrightarrow$
                                              |
                                              H

Name   Chemical   Lewis formula   Molecular
              formula   geometry

▲ **Figure 12** Several representations of the ammonia molecule.

This chapter covered chemical names and chemical formulas. Now you also know how to write Lewis symbols and formulas using dots to represent valence electrons and you can predict the shapes of thousands of different molecules with the VSEPR theory. You will add the mathematics of chemistry to your toolbox.

CRITICAL THINKING 🐝 EXERCISES

Apply knowledge that you have gained in this chapter and one or more of the FLaReS principles to evaluate the following statements or claims.

1 Some people believe that crystals have special powers. Crystal therapists claim that they can use quartz crystals to restore balance and harmony to a person's spiritual energy.

2 A "fuel-enhancer" device is being sold by an entrepreneur. The device contains a powerful magnet and is placed on the fuel line of an automobile. The inventor claims that the device "separates the positive and negative charges in the hydrocarbon fuel molecules, increasing their polarity and allowing them to react more readily with oxygen."

3 Sodium chloride (NaCl) is a metal–nonmetal compound held together by ionic bonds. A scientist has studied mercury(II) chloride ($HgCl_2$) and says that its atoms are held together by covalent bonds. The scientist says that since a solution of this substance in water does not conduct an electric current, it does not contain an appreciable amount of ions.

4 Another scientist, noting that the noble gas xenon does not contain any ions, states that xenon atoms must be held together by covalent bonds.

5 A web page claims, "Fifty years ago, the hydrogen bond angle in water was 108° and you rarely heard of anyone with cancer. Today, it's only 104° and, as a result, cancer is an epidemic!"

SUMMARY

Section 1—Outermost shell electrons are called valence electrons; those in all other shells are core electrons. The noble gases are inert because they (except He) have an octet of valence electrons. Atoms of other elements become more stable by gaining or losing electrons to attain an electron configuration that makes them isoelectronic with (having the same electron configuration as) a noble gas.

Section 2—The number of valence electrons for most main group elements is the same as the group number. Electron-dot symbols, or Lewis symbols, use dots singly or in pairs to represent valence electrons of an atom or ion.

Section 3—The element sodium reacts violently with elemental chlorine to give sodium chloride, or table salt. In this reaction, an electron is transferred from a sodium atom to a chlorine atom, forming ions.

The ions formed have opposite charges and are strongly attracted to one another; this attraction results in an ionic bond. The positive and negative ions arrange themselves in a regular array, forming a crystal of sodium chloride. The ions of an element have very different properties from the atoms of that element.

Section 4—Metal atoms tend to give up their valence electrons to become positively changed ions, and nonmetal atoms tend to accept (8 − group number) electrons to become negatively changed ions. In either case, the ions formed (except hydrogen ions and lithium ions) tend to have eight valence electrons. The formation of ions is thus said to follow the octet rule. The symbol for an ion is the element symbol with a superscript that indicates the number and type (+ or −) of charge. Some elements, especially the transition metals, can form ions of different charges. The formula of an ionic compound always has the same number of positive charges as negative charges.

Section 5—A binary ionic compound contains two different elements; it has a cation of a metal and an anion of a nonmetal. The formula of a binary ionic compound represents the numbers and types of ions in the compound. The formula is found by crossing over the charge numbers of the ions (without the plus and minus signs).

Binary ionic compounds are named by naming the cation first, and then putting an -ide ending on the stem of the anion name. Examples are calcium chloride, potassium oxide, aluminum nitride, and so on. Differently charged cations of a metal are named with Roman numerals to indicate the charge: Fe^{2+} is iron(II) ion and Fe^{3+} is iron(III) ion.

Section 6—Nonmetal atoms can bond by sharing one or more pairs of electrons, forming a covalent bond. A single bond is one pair of shared electrons; a double bond is two pairs; and a triple bond is three pairs. Shared pairs of electrons are called bonding pairs, and unshared pairs are called nonbonding pairs, or lone pairs. Most binary covalent compounds are named by naming the first element in the formula, followed by the stem of the second element with an -ide ending. Prefixes such as mono-, di-, tri-, and so on, are used to indicate the number of atoms of each element.

Section 7—Bonding pairs are shared equally when the two atoms are the same but may be unequally shared when the atoms are different. The electronegativity of an element is the attraction of an atom in a molecule for a bonding pair. Electronegativity generally increases toward the right and up on the periodic table, so fluorine is the most electronegative element. When electrons of a covalent bond are shared unequally, the more electronegative atom takes on a partial negative charge (δ−), the other atom takes on a partial positive charge (δ+), and the bond is said to be a polar covalent bond. The greater the difference in electronegativity, the more polar is the bond. A bonding pair shared equally is a nonpolar covalent bond.

Section 8—Carbon tends to form four covalent bonds, nitrogen three, and oxygen two; hydrogen can form only

one bond. A water molecule has two bonding pairs (O—H bonds) and two lone pairs, an ammonia molecule has three bonding pairs (N—H bonds) and one lone pair, and a methane molecule has four bonding pairs (C—H bonds).

Section 9—A polyatomic ion is a charged particle containing two or more covalently bonded atoms. Compounds containing polyatomic ions are named, and their formulas written, in the same fashion as compounds containing monatomic ions, except that parentheses are placed around the formula for a polyatomic ion if there is more than one of it in the compound. Names of polyatomic ions often end in -ate or -ite.

Section 10—A Lewis formula shows the arrangement of atoms, bonds, and lone pairs in a molecule or polyatomic ion. To draw a Lewis formula, we (a) count the valence electrons; (b) draw a reasonable skeletal structure, showing the arrangement of atoms; (c) connect bonded atoms with a dash (one electron pair); (d) place electron pairs around outer atoms to give each an octet; and (e) place remaining electrons in pairs on the central atom. A multiple bond is included if there are not enough electrons to give each atom (except hydrogen) an octet. There are exceptions to the octet rule. Atoms and molecules with unpaired electrons are called free radicals. They are highly reactive and short-lived. Examples of free radicals are NO and ClO_2.

Section 11—The shape of a molecule can be predicted with the VSEPR theory, which assumes that sets of electrons (either lone pairs or electrons in a bond) around a central atom will get as far away from each other as possible. Two sets of electrons are 180° apart, three sets are about 120° apart, and four sets are about 109° apart. Once these angles have been established, we determine the shape of the molecule by examining only the bonded atoms. Simple molecules have shapes described as linear, bent, triangular, pyramidal, or tetrahedral.

Section 12—Like a polar bond, a polar molecule has separation between its centers of positive charge and negative charge. A molecule with nonpolar bonds is nonpolar. A molecule with polar bonds is nonpolar if its shape causes the polar bonds to cancel one another. If the polar bonds do not cancel, the molecule is polar or is said to be a dipole. The water molecule has polar O—H bonds and is bent, so it is polar.

Green chemistry Chemists manipulate the geometry and composition of molecules to change the properties of both molecules and materials. Typical methods for making these molecules and materials use highly reactive and toxic chemicals and high-energy processes. Greener approaches that take advantage of molecular recognition can instead use low energy, solvent-free processes that do not require harsh conditions.

Learning Objectives

> Determine the number of electrons in an ion. (1) Problems 1–4

> Write the Lewis symbol for an atom or ion. (2) Problems 7, 8

> Distinguish between an ion and an atom. (3) Problems 1, 2, 59

> Describe the nature of the attraction that leads to formation of an ionic bond. (3) Problems 41, 42

> Write symbols for common ions, and determine their charges. (4) Problems 3, 11–16

> Describe the relationship between the octet rule and the charge on an ion. (4)

Problem 4

> Name and write formulas for binary ionic compounds. (5)

Problems 9, 10, 17–20, 55, 67

> Explain the difference between a covalent bond and an ionic bond. (6)

Problems 23–28, 41, 42

> Name and write formulas for covalent compounds. (6)

Problems 23–30

> Classify a covalent bond as polar or nonpolar. (7)

Problems 35–42

> Use electronegativities of elements to determine bond polarity. (7)

Problem 57

> Predict the number of bonds formed by common nonmetals (the HONC rules). (8)

Problems 5, 6

> Recognize common polyatomic ions and be able to use them in naming and writing formulas for compounds. (9)

Problems 21, 22, 65

> Write Lewis formulas for simple molecules and polyatomic ions. (10)

Problems 31–34, 56, 66

> Identify free radicals. (10)

Problems 49, 50

> Predict the shapes of simple molecules from their Lewis formulas. (11)

Problems 43–44

> Classify a simple molecule as polar or nonpolar from its shape and the polarity of its bonds. (12)

Problems 45–48

> Explain how shape and composition change the properties of molecules.

Problem 68

> Describe the concept of molecular recognition.

Problems 68, 69

> Explain the green chemistry advantages of using production methods based on molecular recognition.

Problems 70, 71

REVIEW QUESTIONS

1. How does sodium metal differ from sodium ions (in sodium chloride, for example) in properties?

2. What are the structural differences among chlorine atoms, chlorine molecules, and chloride ions? How do their properties differ?

3. What are the charges on simple ions formed from atoms of the following?
   a. group 1A elements
   b. group 6A elements
   c. group 5A elements
   d. group 2A elements

4. In what group of the periodic table would elements that form ions with the following charges likely be found?
   a. 2–   b. 3+
   c. 1+   d. 2+

5. How many covalent bonds do each of the following usually form? You may refer to the periodic table.
   a. H   b. Cl
   c. S   d. F
   e. N   f. P

6. Of the elements H, O, N, and C, which one(s) can readily form triple bonds?

PROBLEMS

Lewis Symbols for Elements

7. Write Lewis symbols for each of the following elements. You may use the periodic table.
   a. calcium   b. sulfur
   c. silicon

8. Write Lewis symbols for each of the following elements. You may use the periodic table.
   a. phosphorus   b. fluorine
   c. boron

Lewis Formulas for Ionic Compounds

9. Write Lewis formulas for each of the following.
   a. sodium iodide   b. potassium sulfide
   c. calcium chloride   d. aluminum fluoride

10. Write Lewis formulas for each of the following.
    a. lithium bromide
    b. strontium sulfide
    c. sodium nitride
    d. aluminum oxide

Names and Symbols for Simple Ions

11. Without referring to Table 2, supply a symbol given the name or a name given the symbol for each of the following ions:
    a. magnesium ion   b. Na^+
    c. oxide ion   d. Cl^-
    e. zinc ion   f. Cu^+

12. Without referring to Table 2, supply a symbol given the name or a name given the symbol for each of the following ions:
 a. sulfide ion
 b. K^+
 c. Br^-
 d. fluoride ion
 e. Ca^{2+}
 f. iron(III) ion

13. Use that information to name the following ions:
 a. Cr^{2+}
 b. Cr^{3+}
 c. Cr^{6+}

14. Use that information to name the following ions.
 a. Mo^{4+}
 b. Mo^{6+}

15. Write symbols for:
 a. vanadium(II) ion
 b. titanium(II) ion
 c. titanium(IV) ion

16. Write symbols for:
 a. manganese(II) ion
 b. manganese(III) ion
 c. manganese(VII) ion

Names and Formulas for Binary Ionic Compounds

17. Write a formula to match the name or a name to match the formula of the following binary ionic compounds:
 a. sodium iodide
 b. KCl
 c. copper(I) oxide
 d. MgF_2
 e. iron(II) bromide
 f. $FeBr_3$

18. Write a formula to match the name or a name to match the formula of the following binary ionic compounds:
 a. LiF
 b. calcium chloride
 c. MgS
 d. silver iodide
 e. CuO
 f. copper(I) sulfide

19. There are two common binary ionic compounds formed from chromium and oxygen. One of them contains chromium(III) ions; the other contains chromium(VI) ions. Write the formulas for the two compounds, and name them.

20. One of two binary ionic compounds is often added to toothpaste. One of these compounds contains sodium and fluorine; the other contains tin(II) ions and fluorine. Write the formulas for these two compounds, and name them.

Names and Formulas for Ionic Compounds with Polyatomic Ions

21. Supply a formula to match the name or a name to match the formula for the following:
 a. potassium hydroxide
 b. $MgCO_3$
 c. iron(III) cyanide
 d. iron(II) oxalate
 e. $CuSO_4$
 f. $Na_2Cr_2O_7$

22. Supply a formula to match the name or a name to match the formula for the following:
 a. $AgNO_2$
 b. lithium chromate
 c. $(NH_4)_2SO_3$
 d. magnesium hydrogen carbonate
 e. copper(I) phosphate
 f. $Al(MnO_4)_3$

Molecules: Covalent Bonds

23. Use Lewis symbols to show the sharing of electrons between a hydrogen atom and a fluorine atom.

24. Use Lewis symbols to show the sharing of electrons between two bromine atoms to form a bromine (Br_2) molecule. Label all electron pairs as bonding pairs (BPs) or lone pairs (LPs).

25. Use Lewis symbols to show the sharing of electrons between a phosphorus atom and hydrogen atoms to form a molecule in which phosphorus has an octet of electrons.

26. Use Lewis symbols to show the sharing of electrons between a silicon atom and hydrogen atoms to form a molecule in which silicon has an octet of electrons.

27. Use Lewis symbols to show the sharing of electrons between a carbon atom and chlorine atoms to form a molecule in which each atom has an octet of electrons.

28. Use Lewis symbols to show the sharing of electrons between a nitrogen atom and fluorine atoms to form a molecule in which each atom has an octet of electrons.

Names and Formulas for Covalent Compounds

29. Supply a formula for the name or a name for the formula for the following covalent compounds:
 a. dinitrogen tetroxide
 b. bromine trichloride
 c. OF_2
 d. nitrogen triiodide
 e. CBr_4
 f. N_2S_4

30. Supply a formula for the name or a name for the formula for the following covalent compounds:
 a. carbon disulfide
 b. chlorine trifluoride
 c. PF_5
 d. CI_4
 e. tricarbon dioxide
 f. P_4S_3

Lewis Formulas for Molecules and Polyatomic Ions

31. Write Lewis formulas that follow the octet rule for the following covalent molecules:
 a. SiH_4
 b. N_2F_4
 c. CH_5N
 d. H_2CO
 e. NOH_3
 f. H_3PO_3

32. Write Lewis formulas that follow the octet rule for the following covalent molecules:
 a. NH_2Cl
 b. C_2H_4
 c. H_2SO_4
 d. C_2N_2
 e. $COCl_2$
 f. SCl_2

33. Write Lewis formulas that follow the octet rule for the following ions:
 a. ClO^-
 b. HPO_4^{2-}
 c. BrO_3^-

34. Write Lewis formulas that follow the octet rule for the following ions:
 a. CN^-
 b. ClO_2^-
 c. HSO_4^-

Electronegativity: Polar Covalent Bonds

35. Classify the following covalent bonds as polar or nonpolar.
 a. $H—O$
 b. $N—F$
 c. $Cl—B$

36. Classify the following covalent bonds as polar or nonpolar.
 a. $H—N$
 b. $O—Be$
 c. $P—F$

37. Use the symbol $\leftrightarrow$ to indicate the direction of the dipole in each polar bond in Problem 35.

38. Use the symbol $\leftrightarrow$ to indicate the direction of the dipole in each polar bond in Problem 36.

39. Use the symbols $\delta+$ and $\delta-$ to indicate partial charges, if any, on the following bonds.
    a. Si—O
    b. F—F
    c. F—N

40. Use the symbols $\delta+$ and $\delta-$ to indicate partial charges, if any, on the following bonds.
    a. O—H
    b. C—F
    c. C=C

Classifying Bonds

41. Classify the bonds in the following as ionic or covalent. For bonds that are covalent, indicate whether they are polar or nonpolar.
    a. K_2O
    b. $BrCl$
    c. MgF_2
    d. I_2

42. Classify the bonds in the following as ionic or covalent. For bonds that are covalent, indicate whether they are polar or nonpolar.
    a. Na_2O
    b. $CaCl_2$
    c. NBr_3
    d. CS_2

VSEPR Theory: The Shapes of Molecules

43. Use the VSEPR theory to predict the shape of each of the following molecules:
    a. silane (SiH_4)
    b. hydrogen selenide (H_2Se)
    c. phosphine (PH_3)
    d. silicon tetrafluoride (SiF_4)
    e. oxygen difluoride (OF_2)
    f. formaldehyde (H_2CO)

44. Use VSEPR theory to predict the shape of each of the following molecules:
    a. chloroform ($CHCl_3$)
    b. boron trichloride (BCl_3)
    c. carbon tetrafluoride (CF_4)
    d. sulfur difluoride (SF_2)
    e. nitrogen triiodide (NI_3)
    f. dichlorodifluoromethane (CCl_2F_2)

Polar and Nonpolar Molecules

45. The molecule BeF_2 is linear. Is it polar or nonpolar? Explain.

46. The molecule SF_2 is bent. Is it polar or nonpolar? Explain.

47. Look again at the molecules in Problem 43. For each one, are the bonds polar? What are the approximate bond angles? Is the molecule as a whole polar?

48. Look again at the molecules in Problem 44. For each one, are the bonds polar? What are the approximate bond angles? Is the molecule as a whole polar?

Molecules That Are Exceptions to the Octet Rule

49. Which of the following species (atoms or molecules) are free radicals?
    a. Br
    b. F_2
    c. CCl_3

50. Which of the following species (atoms or molecules) are free radicals?
    a. S
    b. NO_2
    c. N_2O_4

51. Free radicals are one class of molecules in which atoms do not conform to the octet rule. Another exception involves atoms with fewer than eight electrons, as seen in elements of group 3 and in beryllium. In some covalent molecules, these atoms can have six or four electrons, respectively. Write Lewis structures for the following covalent molecules:
    a. $AlBr_3$
    b. BeH_2
    c. BH_3

52. Exceptions to the octet rule include molecules that have atoms with more than eight valence electrons, most typically 10 or 12. Atoms heavier than Si can expand their valence shell, meaning that they can accommodate the "extra" electrons in unoccupied, higher-energy orbitals. Draw Lewis structures for the following molecules or ions:
    a. XeF_4
    b. I_3^-
    c. SF_4
    d. KrF_2

ADDITIONAL PROBLEMS

53. Why does neon tend not to form chemical bonds?

54. Draw an electrostatic potential diagram of the H_2S molecule. Use the symbols $\delta+$ and $\delta-$ to indicate the polarity of the molecule.

55. The gas phosphine (PH_3) is used as a fumigant to protect stored grain and other durable produce from pests. Phosphine is generated where it is to be used by adding water to aluminum phosphide or magnesium phosphide. Give formulas for these two phosphides.

56. There are two different covalent molecules with the formula C_2H_6O. Write Lewis formulas for the two molecules.

57. Solutions of iodine chloride (ICl) are used as disinfectants. Is the compound ICl ionic, polar covalent, or nonpolar covalent?

58. Consider the hypothetical elements X, Y, and Z, which have the following Lewis symbols:

    $:\ddot{X}\cdot$ $:\ddot{Y}\cdot$ $:\dot{\ddot{Z}}\cdot$

    a. To which group in the periodic table would each element belong?
    b. Write the Lewis formula for the simplest compound each would form with hydrogen.
    c. Write Lewis formulas for the ions that would be formed when X reacted with sodium and when Y reacted with sodium.

59. Potassium is a soft, silvery metal that reacts violently with water and ignites spontaneously in air. Your doctor recommends that you take a potassium supplement. Would you take potassium metal? If not, what would you take?

60. What is wrong with the phrase "just a few molecules of potassium iodide"?

61. Use subshell notation to write an electron configuration for the most stable simple ion formed by each of the following elements.
    a. Ca
    b. Rb
    c. S
    d. I
    e. N
    f. Se

62. Why is Na^+ smaller than Na? Why is Cl^- larger than Cl?

63. The halogens (F, Cl, Br, and I) tend to form only one single bond in binary molecules. Explain.

64. A science magazine for the general public contains this statement: "Some of these hydrocarbons are very light, like methane gas—just a single carbon molecule attached to three hydrogen molecules." Evaluate the statement, and correct any inaccuracies.

65. Sodium tungstate is Na_2WO_4. What is the formula for aluminum tungstate?

66. Scientists estimate that the atmosphere of Titan (a moon of Saturn) consists of about 98.4% nitrogen and 1.6% methane. They have also found traces of organic molecules with the molecular formulas C_2H_4, C_3H_4, C_4H_2, HCN, HC_3N, and C_2N_2. Write possible Lewis formulas for each of these molecules.

67. What is the formula for the compound formed by the imaginary ions Q^{2+} and ZX_4^{3-}?

68. Give two design criteria that chemists use to design new medicines.

69. What is the term for the science that explains how molecules interact through geometric orientation of atoms?

70. Give three ways that molecular recognition approaches can support greener methods for making molecules and materials.

71. How can an understanding of enzymes and biological receptors guide medicinal chemists?

COLLABORATIVE GROUP PROJECTS

Prepare a PowerPoint, poster, or other presentation (as directed by your instructor) for presentation to the class. Projects 1 and 2 are best done by a group of four students.

1. Make a form like the one below the column headings "Word" and "Definition" with "Name" and "Lewis Formula." Student 1 should write the name from the list below in the first column of the form and its Lewis formula in the second column. End by comparing the name in the last column with that in the first column. Discuss any differences in the two names. If the name in the last column differs from that in the first column, determine what went wrong in the process.
    a. bromide ion
    b. calcium fluoride
    c. phosphorus trifluoride
    d. carbon disulfide

2. Make a form like that below, using the column headings "Name" and "Structure." Then student 1 should write a name from the list below in the first column of the form and its structure in the second column. End by comparing the name in the last column with that in the first column. Discuss any differences in the two names. If the name in the last column differs from that in the first column, determine what went wrong in the process.
    a. ammonium nitrate
    b. potassium phosphate
    c. lithium carbonate
    d. copper(I) chloride

3. Starting with 20 balloons, blown up to about the same size and tied, tie two balloons together. Next, tie three balloons together. Repeat this with four, five, and six balloons. (*Suggestion*: Three sets of two balloons can be twisted together to form a six-balloon set, and so on.) Show how these balloon sets can be used to illustrate the VSEPR theory.

4. Prepare a brief biographical report on one of the following:
    a. Gilbert N. Lewis
    b. Linus Pauling

5. There are several different definitions and scales for electronegativity. Search for information on these, and write a brief compare-and-contrast essay about two of them.

Text Entry	Student 1	Student 2	Student 3	Student 4
Word	Definition	Word	Definition	Word

BRIEF ANSWERS TO SELECTED PROBLEMS

Answers are provided for *all in-chapter exercises*. Brief answers are given for *odd-numbered Review Questions*; more complete answers can be obtained by reviewing the text. Answers are provided for *all odd-numbered Problems and Additional Problems*.

NOTE: For numerical problems, your answer may differ slightly from ours because of rounding and the use of significant figures.

1 **a.** :Är: **b.** ·Ca· **c.** :Ḟ· **d.** :N· **e.** K· **f.** :S̈·

2 **A.** Li· + :Ḟ· ⟶ Li⁺ + :Ḟ:⁻

   B. Rb· + :Ï· ⟶ Rb⁺ + :Ï:⁻

3 2 ·Al· + 3 :Ö· ⟶ 2 Al³⁺ + 3 :Ö:²⁻

4 **A. a.** CaF_2 **b.** Li_2O
   B. $FeCl_2$ and $FeCl_3$

5 **a.** K_2O **b.** Ca_3N_2 **c.** CaS

6 **a.** calcium fluoride   **b.** copper(II) bromide

7 **a.** bromine trifluoride
   b. bromine pentafluoride
   c. dinitrogen monoxide
   d. dinitrogen pentoxide

8 **a.** PCl_3 **b.** Cl_2O_7
   c. NI_3 **d.** S_2Cl_2

9 **a.** :Br· + ·Br: ⟶ :Br:Br:

   b. H· + ·Br: ⟶ H:Br:

   c. :Ï· + ·Cl: ⟶ :Ï:Cl:

10 **A. a.** polar covalent   **b.** ionic   **c.** nonpolar covalent
   B. a. polar covalent   **b.** polar covalent   **c.** nonpolar covalent

11 **A. a.** $Ca(C_2H_3O_2)_2$ **b.** K_2O **c.** $Al_2(SO_4)_3$
   B. a. 3   **b.** 4

12 **A. a.** calcium carbonate   **b.** magnesium phosphate
      c. potassium chromate
   B. a. ammonium sulfate
      b. potassium dihydrogen phosphate
      c. copper(II) dichromate

13 **A. a.** :Ḟ — Ö — Ḟ: **b.** H—C̈—Cl̈: (with H top and H bottom)

   B. a. [:N═N═N:]⁻   **b.** :Ö═N—Ö—Ḟ:

14 **A. a.** pyramidal   **b.** triangular
   B. a. triangular   **b.** bent (at both O)

1. Sodium metal is quite reactive; sodium ions (as in NaCl) are quite unre-active.

3. a. 1+   **b.** 2−   **c.** 3−   **d.** 2+

5. a. 1   **b.** 1   **c.** 2   **d.** 1
   e. 3   **f.** 3

7. a. ·Ca·   **b.** :S̈:   **c.** ·S̈i·

9. a. Na⁺[:Ï:]⁻   **b.** 2 K⁺ [:S̈:²⁻]

   c. Ca²⁺ 2[:Cl̈:]⁻   **d.** Al³⁺ 3[:Ḟ:]⁻

11. a. Mg^{2+} **b.** sodium ion   **c.** O^{2-}
   d. chloride ion   **e.** Zn^{2+} **f.** copper(I) ion

13. a. chromium(II) ion   **b.** chromium(III) ion
   c. chromium(VI) ion

15. a. V^{2+} **b.** Ti^{2+} **c.** Ti^{4+}

17. a. NaI   **b.** potassium chloride
   c. Cu_2O **d.** magnesium fluoride
   e. $FeBr_2$ **f.** iron(III) bromide

19. Cr_2O_3, chromium(III) oxide, and CrO_3, chromium(VI) oxide

21. a. KOH   **b.** magnesium carbonate
   c. $Fe(CN)_3$ **d.** FeC_2O_4
   e. copper(II) sulfate   **f.** sodium dichromate

23. H· + ·Ḟ: ⟶ H:Ḟ:

25. ·P̈· + 3 H· ⟶ H:P̈:H (with H below)

27. ·C̈· + 4 :Cl̈· ⟶ :Cl̈:C:Cl̈: (with :Cl̈: above and :Cl̈: below)

29. a. N_2O_4 **b.** $BrCl_3$
   c. oxygen difluoride   **d.** NI_3
   e. carbon tetrabromide   **f.** dinitrogen tetrasulfide

31. a. H—Si—H (with H above and H below)
   b. :Ḟ:—N—N:—:Ḟ: (with :F: above both N and :F: below both N)

   c. H—C—N: (with H above, H below on C; H above and H below on N)
   d. H—C—H (with :O: double bonded above)

   e. :N—O: (with H above and H below N)
   f. H—Ö—P̈—Ö—H (with :Ö—H below P)

33. a. [:Cl̈—Ö:]⁻   **b.** [H—Ö—P—Ö:]²⁻ (with :O: above and :O: below P)

   c. [:Ö—Br—Ö:]⁻ (with :O: below Br)

35. a. polar   **b.** polar   **c.** polar

37. a. H—O (⟶)   **b.** N—F (⟶)   **c.** Cl—B (⟵)

39. a. Si — O (δ+ δ−)
   b. is not polar
   c. F — N (δ− δ+)

41. a. ionic   **b.** nonpolar covalent
   c. ionic   **d.** nonpolar covalent

Chemical Bonds

43. **a.** tetrahedral **b.** bent
c. pyramidal **d.** tetrahedral
e. bent **f.** triangular

45. Nonpolar; the two polar Be—F bonds cancel.

47. **a.** nonpolar bonds; 109.5°; nonpolar molecule
b. nonpolar bonds; 109.5°; nonpolar molecule
c. nonpolar bonds; 109.5°; nonpolar molecule
d. polar bonds; 109.5°; nonpolar molecule
e. polar bonds; 109.5°; polar molecule
f. polar bonds; 120°; polar molecule

49. a, c

51. **a.** Al—Br with :Br: above and :Br: below **b.** H—Be—H **c.** H—B—H with H below

53. Neon has an octet of valence electrons (a full outer shell).

55. AlP; Mg_3P_2

57. Polar covalent

59. No; a potassium salt, to avoid having the mouth catch fire!

61. **a.** Ca^{2+}: $1s^2 2s^2 2p^6 3s^2 3p^6$
b. Rb^+: $1s^2 2s^2 2p^6 3s^2 3p^6 3d^{10} 4s^2 4p^6$
c. S^{2-}: $1s^2 2s^2 2p^6 3s^2 3p^6$

d. I^-: $1s^2 2s^2 2p^6 3s^2 3p^6 3d^{10} 4s^2 4p^6 4d^{10} 5s^2 5p^6$
e. N^{3-}: $1s^2 2s^2 2p^6$
f. Se^{2-}: $1s^2 2s^2 2p^6 3s^2 3p^6 3d^{10} 4s^2 4p^6$

63. The halogens have seven valence electrons. Forming single bonds by sharing a bond with one other atom gives them an octet of electrons.

65. $Al_2(WO_4)_3$

67. $Q_3(ZX_4)_2$

69. Molecular recognition

71. Medicinal chemists design new drug molecules to resemble biological molecules that bind to enzymes which recognize the molecules by shapes and partial charges.

Chemical Accounting

andibyte/Shutterstock

Have You Ever Wondered?

1. How can a car make more pollution than the gasoline it uses?

2. What's the difference between 14K gold and 18K gold?

3. Does 2% milk have just 2% of the calories of whole milk?

4. What does a cholesterol level of 200 mean?

STR/AFP/Getty Images/Newscom

Learning Objectives

› Identify balanced and unbalanced chemical equations, and balance equations by inspection. (1)

› Determine volumes of gases that react, using a balanced equation for a reaction. (2)

› Calculate the formula mass, molecular mass, or molar mass of a substance. (3)

› Convert from mass to moles and from moles to mass of a substance. (4)

› Calculate the mass or number of moles of a reactant or product from the mass or number of moles of another reactant or product. (4)

› Calculate the concentration (molarity, percent by volume, or percent by mass) of a solute in a solution. (5)

› Calculate the amount of solute or solution given the concentration and the other amount. (5)

› Explain how the concept of atom economy can be applied to pollution prevention and environmental protection.

› Calculate the atom economy for chemical reactions.

Mass and Volume Relationships

We can look at or represent chemical phenomena on three levels:

1. Macro and tangible: for example, a sample of yellow powder or a blue solution in a beaker.

2. Particle (atom, molecule, or ion) and invisible: for example, a sulfur atom, a carbon dioxide molecule, or a chloride ion.

3. Symbolic and mathematical: for example, S, CO_2, Cl, or $d = m/V$.

Macro-level representations of chemicals are familiar from everyday life. It is easy to visualize salt crystals in a shaker, gold in jewelry, baking soda in a box, aspirin in tablets, and many other common substances, because they are tangible. We can see them and touch them.

Everything that burns fuel requires oxygen, and the human body is no exception. At the top of Mt. Everest, there is not enough oxygen in the air to keep people alive, so climbers making the ascent must bring oxygen with them. But how much oxygen should each climber bring? A knowledge of chemistry allows this question to be answered, thus promoting the safety of the climbers and the success of their venture.

Summit Oxygen International Ltd.

From Chapter 5 of *Chemistry for Changing Times*, Thirteenth Edition. John W. Hill, Terry W. McCreary, Doris K. Kolb. Copyright © 2013 by Pearson Education, Inc. All rights reserved.

Much chemistry can be discussed and understood with little or no mathematics, but the quantitative aspects can shed a great deal of light on properties of matter. In this chapter, we will consider some of the basic calculations used in chemistry and related fields such as biology and medicine. Chemists use many kinds of mathematics, from simple arithmetic to sophisticated calculus and complicated computer algorithms, but our calculations here will require at most a bit of algebra.

1 Chemical Sentences: Equations

Learning Objective ❯ Identify balanced and unbalanced chemical equations, and balance equations by inspection.

Chemistry is a study of matter and the changes it undergoes and of the energy that brings about these changes or is released when these changes happen. The symbols and formulas we have used to represent elements and compounds make up the letters (symbols) and words (formulas) of our chemical language. Using them, we can write sentences (chemical equations). A **chemical equation** uses symbols and formulas to represent the elements and compounds involved in the change.

At the macro level, we can describe a chemical reaction in words. For example,

Carbon reacts with oxygen to form carbon dioxide.

We can describe the same reaction symbolically.

$$C + O_2 \longrightarrow CO_2$$

The plus sign (+) indicates that carbon and oxygen are added together or combined in some way. The arrow ($\longrightarrow$) is read "yield(s)" or "react(s) to produce." Substances on the left of the arrow (C and O_2 in this case) are **reactants**, or *starting materials*. Those on the right (here, CO_2) are the **products** of the reaction. Reactants and products need not be written in any particular order in a chemical equation, except that all reactants must be to the left of the arrow and all products to the right. In other words, we could also write the preceding equation as

$$O_2 + C \longrightarrow CO_2$$

At the atomic or molecular level, the equation means that one carbon (C) atom reacts with one oxygen (O_2) molecule to produce one carbon dioxide (CO_2) molecule.

Sometimes, we indicate the physical states of the reactants and products by writing the initial letter of the state immediately following the formula: (g) indicates a gaseous substance, (l) a liquid, and (s) a solid. The label (aq) indicates that the substance is in an aqueous (water) solution. Using state labels, the above equation becomes

$$C(s) + O_2(g) \longrightarrow CO_2(g)$$

Balancing Chemical Equations

We can represent the reaction of carbon and oxygen to form carbon dioxide quite simply, but many other chemical reactions require more thought. For example, hydrogen reacts with oxygen to form water. Using formulas, we can represent this reaction as

$$H_2 + O_2 \longrightarrow H_2O \quad \text{(not balanced)}$$

However, this representation shows two oxygen atoms in the reactants (as O_2), but only one in the product (in H_2O). Because matter is neither created nor destroyed in a chemical reaction (the law of conservation of mass), the equation must be *balanced* to represent the chemical reaction correctly. That means the same number of each type of atom must appear on both sides of the arrow. To balance the oxygen atoms, we need only place the coefficient 2 in front of the formula for water.

$$H_2 + O_2 \longrightarrow 2\,H_2O \quad \text{(not balanced)}$$

This coefficient means that two molecules of water are produced. As is the case with a subscript 1, a coefficient of 1 is understood when there is no number in front of a formula. *Everything* in a formula is multiplied by the coefficient. In the preceding equation, adding the coefficient 2 before H_2O not only increases the number of oxygen atoms on the product side to two but also increases the number of hydrogen atoms to four.

But the equation is still not balanced. As we took care of the oxygen, we unbalanced the hydrogen. To balance the hydrogen, we place a coefficient 2 in front of H_2.

$$2\,H_2 + O_2 \longrightarrow 2\,H_2O \quad \text{(balanced)}$$

Now there are four hydrogen atoms and two oxygen atoms on each side of the equation. Atoms are conserved: The equation is balanced (Figure 1), and the law of conservation of mass is obeyed. Figure 2 illustrates two common pitfalls in the process of balancing equations, as well as the correct method. Remember not to

= hydrogen
= oxygen

▲ **Figure 1** To balance the equation for the reaction of hydrogen and oxygen to form water, the same number of each kind of atom must appear on each side (atoms are conserved). When the equation is balanced, there are four H atoms and two O atoms on each side.

Q: *Why can't you balance the equation by removing one of the oxygen atoms from the left side of the top balance?*

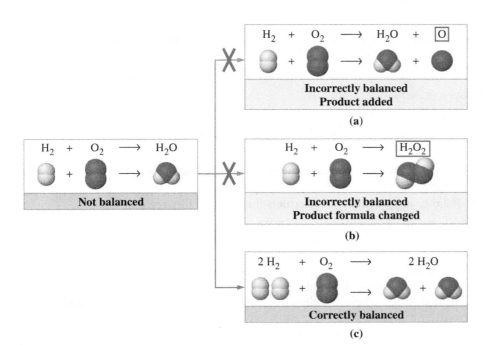

◀ **Figure 2** Balancing the equation for the reaction between hydrogen and oxygen to form water. (a) Incorrect. There is no atomic oxygen (O) as a product. Other products cannot be introduced simply to balance an equation. (b) Incorrect. The product of the reaction is water (H_2O), not hydrogen peroxide (H_2O_2). A formula can't be changed simply to balance an equation. (c) Correct. An equation can be balanced only by using the correct formulas and adjusting the coefficients.

add to or change chemical species on either side, but to use coefficients to equate the numbers of atoms of each type.

Example 1   Balancing Equations

Balance the following chemical equation, which represents the reaction that occurs when an airbag in a car deploys.

$$NaN_3 \longrightarrow Na + N_2$$

Solution

The sodium (Na) atoms are balanced, but the nitrogen atoms are not. To balance this equation, we can use the concept of the least common multiple. There are three nitrogen atoms on the left (reactant side) and two on the right (product side). The least common multiple of 2 and 3 is 6. To get *six* nitrogen atoms on each side, we need *three* N_2 and *two* NaN_3:

We now have *two* sodium atoms on the left. We can get two on the right by placing the coefficient 2 in front of Na.

$$2\,NaN_3 \longrightarrow 2\,Na + 3\,N_2 \quad \text{(balanced)}$$

Checking, we count two Na atoms and six N atoms on each side. The equation is balanced.

■ EXERCISE 1A

The reaction between hydrogen and nitrogen to give ammonia, called the *Haber process*, is typically the first step in the industrial production of nitrogen fertilizers.

$$H_2 + N_2 \longrightarrow NH_3$$

Balance the equation.

■ EXERCISE 1B

Iron ores such as Fe_2O_3 are *smelted* by reaction with carbon to produce metallic iron and carbon dioxide.

$$Fe_2O_3 + C \longrightarrow CO_2 + Fe$$

Balance the equation.

Although simple equations can be balanced by trial and error, a couple of strategies often help:

1. If an element occurs in just one substance on each side of the equation, try balancing that element *first*.
2. Balance any reactants or products that exist as the free element *last*.

Perhaps the most important step in balancing any equation is to check that the result you obtain is indeed balanced. Remember that for each element, the same number of atoms of the element must appear on each side of the equation.

We have made the task of balancing equations appear easy by considering fairly simple reactions. It is more important at this point for you to understand the principle than to be able to balance complicated equations. You should know what is meant by a balanced equation and be able to balance simple equations. It is crucial that you understand the information that is contained in balanced equations.

Self-Assessment Questions

1. Which of the following equations are balanced? (You need not balance the equations. Just determine whether they are balanced as written.)
   - **I.** $Ca + 2 H_2O \longrightarrow Ca(OH)_2 + H_2$
   - **II.** $4 LiH + AlCl_3 \longrightarrow 2 LiAlH_4 + 2 LiCl$
   - **III.** $2 LiOH + CO_2 \longrightarrow Li_2CO_3 + H_2O$
   - **IV.** $2 Sn + 2 H_2SO_4 \longrightarrow 2 SnSO_4 + SO_2 + 2 H_2O$
   - **a.** I and II
   - **b.** I and III
   - **c.** II and III
   - **d.** II and IV

2. Consider the equation for the reaction of phosphine with oxygen to form tetraphosphorus decoxide and water:

$$PH_3 + O_2 \longrightarrow P_4O_{10} + H_2O \quad \text{(not balanced)}$$

   When the equation is balanced, how many molecules of water are produced for each molecule of P_4O_{10} formed?
   - **a.** 1
   - **b.** 4
   - **c.** 6
   - **d.** 12

Items 3–5 refer to the following equation for the reaction of calcium hydroxide [$Ca(OH)_2$] with phosphoric acid (H_3PO_4).

$$Ca(OH)_2 + H_3PO_4 \longrightarrow H_2O + Ca_3(PO_4)_2 \quad \text{(not balanced)}$$

3. When the equation is balanced, how many H_2O molecules will be produced for each H_3PO_4 molecule that reacts?
   - **a.** 1
   - **b.** 2
   - **c.** 3
   - **d.** 6

4. When the equation is balanced, how many H_3PO_4 molecules must react to produce one $Ca_3(PO_4)_2$ formula unit?
   - **a.** 1
   - **b.** 2
   - **c.** 3
   - **d.** 6

5. When the equation is balanced, how many $Ca(OH)_2$ formula units are needed to react with six H_3PO_4 molecules?
   - **a.** 1
   - **b.** 1.5
   - **c.** 6
   - **d.** 9

> Just as a molecule is the smallest unit of a molecular compound, a *formula unit* is the smallest unit of an ionic compound.

Answers: 1, b; 2, c; 3, c; 4, b; 5, d

2 Volume Relationships in Chemical Equations

Learning Objective ❯ Determine volumes of gases that react, using a balanced equation for a reaction.

So far we have looked at chemical reactions in terms of individual atoms and molecules. In the real world, however, chemists work with quantities of matter that contain billions of billions of atoms. John Dalton postulated that atoms of different elements have different masses. Therefore, equal masses of different elements must contain different numbers of atoms. By analogy, a kilogram of golf balls contains a smaller number of balls than a kilogram of Ping-Pong balls, because a golf ball is heavier than a Ping-Pong ball. One could determine the number of balls in each case simply by counting them. For atoms, however, counting is not so straightforward. The smallest visible particle of matter contains more atoms than could be counted in ten lifetimes! Even so, we can determine the number of atoms in a substance, as you will learn in this chapter.

Studies of gases in the eighteenth century advanced our understanding of how to account for atoms involved in chemical reactions. Here we focus on some historical experiments with gases that revealed how chemical equations can be balanced. Experiments with gases led French scientist Joseph Louis Gay-Lussac (1778–1850) to an approach to quantifying atoms. In 1808, he announced the results of some chemical reactions that he had carried out with gases and summarized these experiments in a new law. The **law of combining volumes** states that when all measurements are made at the same temperature and pressure, the volumes of gaseous reactants and products are in small whole-number ratios. One such experiment is illustrated in

▶ **Figure 3** Gay-Lussac's law of combining volumes. Three volumes of hydrogen gas react with one volume of nitrogen gas to yield two volumes of ammonia gas, when measured at the same temperature and pressure.

Q: *Can you sketch a similar figure for the reaction* $2 SO_2(g) + O_2(g) \longrightarrow 2 SO_3(g)$?

Hydrogen gas (three volumes) Nitrogen gas (one volume) Ammonia gas (two volumes)

Figure 3. When hydrogen reacts with nitrogen to form ammonia, three volumes of hydrogen combine with one volume of nitrogen to yield two volumes of ammonia. The small whole-number ratio is 3:1:2.

Gay-Lussac thought there must be some relationship between the numbers of molecules and the volumes of gaseous reactants and products. But it was Amedeo Avogadro who first explained the law of combining volumes in 1811. **Avogadro's hypothesis**, based on a shrewd interpretation of experimental facts, was that equal volumes of all gases, when measured at the same temperature and pressure, contain the same number of molecules (Figure 4).

▶ **Figure 4** Avogadro's explanation of Gay-Lussac's law of combining volumes. Equal volumes of all the gases contain the same number of molecules.

Q: *Can you sketch a similar figure for the reaction* $2 NO(g) + O_2(g) \longrightarrow 2 NO_2(g)$?

Hydrogen gas (three volumes) Nitrogen gas (one volume) Ammonia (two volumes)

The equation for the combination of hydrogen and nitrogen to form ammonia is

$$3 H_2(g) + N_2(g) \longrightarrow 2 NH_3(g)$$

Note that the coefficients of the molecules correlate with the combining ratio of the gas volumes, 3:1:2 (Figure 3). The equation says that three H_2 molecules react with one N_2 molecule to produce two NH_3 molecules. The balanced equation provides the combining ratios. If you had 3 million H_2 molecules, you would need 1 million N_2 molecules to produce 2 million NH_3 molecules. According to the equation, three volumes of hydrogen react with one volume of nitrogen to produce two volumes of ammonia because each volume of hydrogen contains the same number of molecules as that same volume of nitrogen.

Gary J. Shulfer/C. Marvin Lang

▲ Amedeo Avogadro (1776–1856) and his hypothesis. The quotation reads, "Equal volumes of all gases at the same temperature and pressure contain the same number of molecules."

Example 2   Volume Relationships of Gases

What volume of oxygen is required to burn 0.556 L of propane in the following combustion reaction, assuming that both gases are measured at the same temperature and pressure?

$$C_3H_8(g) + 5 O_2(g) \longrightarrow 3 CO_2(g) + 4 H_2O(g)$$

Solution

The coefficients in the equation indicate that each volume of $C_3H_8(g)$ requires five volumes of O_2 gas. Thus, we use $5 L O_2(g)/1 L C_3H_8(g)$ as a conversion factor to find the volume of oxygen required. (Conversion factors are explained in Section A.3 of the Appendix.)

$$? L O_2(g) = 0.556 \, \cancel{L \, C_3H_8(g)} \times \frac{5 L O_2(g)}{1 \, \cancel{L \, C_3H_8(g)}} = 2.78 L O_2(g)$$

■ **EXERCISE 2A**
Using the equation in Example 2, calculate the volume of $CO_2(g)$ produced when 0.492 L of propane is burned if the two gases are compared at the same temperature and pressure.

■ **EXERCISE 2B**
If 10.0 L each of propane and oxygen are combined at the same temperature and pressure, which gas will be left over after reaction? What volume of that gas will remain?

Self-Assessment Questions

1. In the reaction $2 H_2(g) + O_2(g) \longrightarrow 2 H_2O(g)$, with all substances at the same temperature and pressure, the ratio of volumes, for H_2, O_2, and H_2O, respectively, is
   a. 1:0:1   **b.** 2:0:2   **c.** 1:1:1   **d.** 2:1:2

2. How many CO_2 molecules are produced in the following reaction if 50 O_2 molecules react?

$$2 C_8H_{18}(l) + 25 O_2(g) \longrightarrow 16 CO_2(g) + 18 H_2O(l)$$

   a. 25 molecules   **b.** 50 molecules   **c.** 32 molecules   **d.** 16 molecules

3. In the reaction $N_2(g) + 3 H_2(g) \longrightarrow 2 NH_3(g)$, with all substances at the same temperature and pressure, what volume of ammonia is produced when 4.50 L of nitrogen reacts with excess hydrogen?
   a. 3.00 L   **b.** 4.50 L   **c.** 6.75 L   **d.** 9.00 L

Answers: 1, d; 2, c; 3, d

3 Avogadro's Number and the Mole

Learning Objectives ❯ Calculate the formula mass, molecular mass, or molar mass of a substance.

Avogadro's hypothesis, which has been verified many times and in several ways over the years, states that equal volumes of gases at the same temperature and pressure contain equal numbers of molecules. This means that if we weigh equal volumes of different gases, the gases won't weigh the same. The ratio of their masses should be the same as the mass ratio of the molecules themselves.

Avogadro's Number: 6.02×10^{23}

Avogadro had no way of knowing how many molecules were in a given volume of gas. Scientists since his time have determined the number of atoms in various weighed samples of substances. Atoms are so incredibly small that these numbers are extremely large, even for tiny samples. Recall that the mass of a carbon-12 atom is exactly 12 atomic mass units (u) because the carbon-12 atom sets the standard for atomic mass. The number of carbon-12 atoms in a 12-g sample of carbon-12 is called **Avogadro's number** and has been determined experimentally to be 6.0221367×10^{23}. We usually round this number to three significant figures: 6.02×10^{23}.

The Mole: "A Dozen Eggs and a Mole of Sugar, Please"

We buy socks by the pair (2 socks), eggs by the dozen (12 eggs), and pencils by the gross (144 pencils). A dozen is the same number whether we are counting eggs or oranges. But a dozen eggs and a dozen oranges do not weigh the same. If an orange weighs five times as much as an egg, a dozen oranges will weigh five times as much as a dozen eggs.

▶ How big is Avogadro's number?

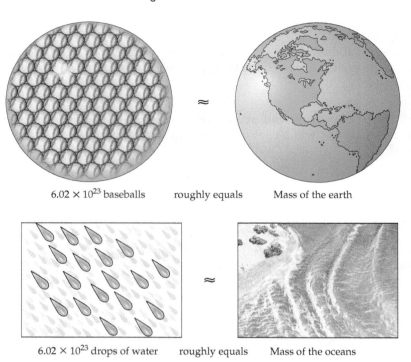

6.02 × 10²³ baseballs   roughly equals   Mass of the earth

6.02 × 10²³ drops of water   roughly equals   Mass of the oceans

Chemists count atoms and molecules by the *mole*. A single carbon atom is much too small to see or weigh, but a mole of carbon atoms fills a tablespoon and weighs 12 g. A mole of carbon and a mole of titanium each contain the same number of atoms. But a titanium atom has a mass four times that of a carbon atom, so a mole of titanium has a mass four times that of a mole of carbon.

A **mole (mol)** is an amount of substance that contains the same number of elementary units as there are atoms in exactly 12 g of carbon-12. That number is 6.02×10^{23}, Avogadro's number. The elementary units may be atoms (such as S or Ca), molecules (such as O_2 or CO_2), ions (such as K^+ or SO_4^{2-}), or any other kind of formula unit. A mole of NaCl, for example, contains 6.02×10^{23} NaCl formula units, which means that it contains 6.02×10^{23} Na^+ ions and 6.02×10^{23} Cl^- ions.

Formula Masses

Each element has a characteristic atomic mass. Because chemical compounds are made up of two or more elements, the masses of compounds are combinations of atomic masses. For any substance, the **formula mass** is the sum of the masses of the atoms represented in the formula. If the formula represents a molecule, the term *molecular mass* is often used. For example, because the formula CO_2 specifies one carbon atom and two oxygen atoms per molecule of carbon dioxide, the formula (or molecular) mass of carbon dioxide (CO_2) is the atomic mass of carbon plus twice the atomic mass of oxygen.

$$\text{Formula mass } CO_2 = 1 \times \text{atomic mass of C} + 2 \times \text{atomic mass of O}$$
$$= 1 \times 12.0\,u + 2 \times 16.0\,u = 44.0\,u$$

Example 3   Calculating Molecular Masses

Calculate **(a)** the molecular mass of nitrogen dioxide (NO_2), an amber-colored gas that is a constituent of smog, and **(b)** the formula mass of ammonium sulfate $[(NH_4)_2SO_4]$, a fertilizer commonly used by home gardeners.

Solution

a. We start with the molecular formula: NO_2. Then, to determine the molecular mass, we simply add the atomic mass of nitrogen to twice the atomic mass of oxygen.

$$1 \times \text{atomic mass of N} = 1 \times 14.0 \text{ u} = 14.0 \text{ u}$$
$$2 \times \text{atomic mass of O} = 2 \times 16.0 \text{ u} = \underline{32.0 \text{ u}}$$
$$\text{Formula mass of } NO_2 = 46.0 \text{ u}$$

b. The formula $(NH_4)_2SO_4$ signifies two nitrogen atoms, eight hydrogen atoms, one sulfur atom, and four oxygen atoms. Combining the atomic masses, we have

$$(2 \times 14.0 \text{ u}) + (8 \times 1.01 \text{ u}) + (1 \times 32.0 \text{ u}) + (4 \times 16.0 \text{ u}) = 132.1 \text{ u}$$

■ EXERCISE 3

Calculate the formula mass of (a) sodium azide (NaN_3), used in automobile airbags, (b) phosphoric acid (H_3PO_4), used to flavor some cola drinks, (c) *para*-dichlorobenzene ($C_6H_4Cl_2$), used as a moth repellent, and (d) calcium dihydrogen phosphate $[Ca(H_2PO_4)_2]$, used as a mineral supplement in foods.

Percent Composition of a Compound from Formula Masses

A formula represents not only an atom ratio, but also a mass ratio. For example, the mass of 1.00 mol CO_2 is 44.0 g, of which 12.0 g is carbon and 32.0 g is oxygen. The composition of CO_2 can be expressed as percents by mass of carbon and of oxygen:

$$\% \text{ by mass C} = \frac{\text{mass C}}{\text{mass } CO_2} \times 100\% = \frac{12.0 \text{ g}}{44.0 \text{ g}} \times 100\% = 27.3\%$$

Because oxygen is the only other element in CO_2, its percent by mass is $100\% - 27.3\% = 72.7\%$ oxygen.

The idea of percent composition by mass is useful in several applications. Dietary sodium limits are usually indicated in milligrams of Na^+. We consume Na^+ mainly as sodium chloride. The American Heart Association (AHA) recommends a maximum intake of 2400 mg Na^+ per day. Example 4 shows how we can relate this amount to the NaCl in one teaspoon of table salt.

Example 4   Calculating Percent Composition from a Formula

What mass of Na^+ is present in one teaspoon (6.0 g) of NaCl? How does this compare to the maximum intake of 2400 mg Na^+ per day recommended by the AHA?

Solution

A mole of sodium chloride has one mole (23.0 g) Na^+ and one mole (35.5 g) Cl^-. The percent by mass of Na^+ is

$$\% \text{ by mass Na} = \frac{\text{mass Na}}{\text{mass NaCl}} \times 100\% = \frac{23.0 \text{ g}}{58.5 \text{ g}} \times 100\% = 39.3\%$$

So in 100 g of NaCl there are 39.3 g of Na^+. One teaspoon (6.0 g) of NaCl has

$$6.0 \text{ g NaCl} \times \frac{39.3 \text{ g Na}^+}{100 \text{ g NaCl}} = 2.4 \text{ g Na}^+$$

That is 2400 mg Na^+, the maximum recommended for one day's intake.

■ EXERCISE 4

Calculate the percent by mass of nitrogen in (a) KNO_3 and (b) $(NH_4)_2S$.

Chemical Accounting

Many environmental pollutants are reported as elements even when the actual pollutant is a compound or a mixture of compounds. For example, nitrates (NO_3^-) in groundwater are reported as parts per million nitrogen, and carbon dioxide emissions often are reported as tons of carbon. The idea of percent by mass is useful in understanding these reported quantities.

Self-Assessment Questions

1. How many carbon-12 atoms are there in exactly 12 g of carbon-12?
   a. 1   **b.** 12   **c.** 144   **d.** 6.02×10^{23}

2. The mass of 1 mol of carbon-12 atoms is
   a. 12 g   **b.** 12.011 g   **c.** 12 u   **d.** 12.011 u

3. Which of the following has the smallest molecular mass?
   a. CH_4 **b.** HF   **c.** H_2O **d.** NH_3

4. How many moles of sulfur atoms are in 1 mol $Fe_2(SO_4)_3$?
   a. 1 mol   **b.** 3 mol   **c.** 15 mol   **d.** 17 mol

5. How many moles of hydrogen atoms are present in 2.00 mol of ammonia (NH_3)?
   a. 2.00 mol   **b.** 3.00 mol   **c.** 6.00 mol   **d.** 8.00 mol

6. Sodium chloride, by mass, is
   a. about 40% Na^+ and 60% Cl^- **b.** 50% Na^+ and 50% Cl^-
   c. about 60% Na^+ and 40% Cl^- **d.** 23.0% Na^+ and 35.5% Cl^-

Answers: 1, d; 2, a; 3, a; 4, b; 5, c; 6, a

4 Molar Mass: Mole-to-Mass and Mass-to-Mole Conversions

Learning Objectives › Convert from mass to moles and from moles to mass of a substance. › Calculate the mass or number of moles of a reactant or product from the mass or number of moles of another reactant or product.

The **molar mass** of a substance is just what the name implies: the mass of one mole of that substance. The molar mass is numerically equal to the atomic mass, molecular mass, or formula mass, but it is expressed in the unit *grams per mole* (g/mol). The atomic mass of sodium is 23.0 u, so its molar mass is 23.0 g/mol. The molecular mass of carbon dioxide is 44.0 u; its molar mass is 44.0 g/mol. The formula mass of ammonium sulfate is 132.1 u; its molar mass is 132.1 g/mol. We can use these facts, together with the definition of the mole, to write the following relationships.

$$1 \text{ mol Na} = 23.0 \text{ g Na}$$
$$1 \text{ mol CO}_2 = 44.0 \text{ g CO}_2$$
$$1 \text{ mol (NH}_4)_2\text{SO}_4 = 132.1 \text{ g (NH}_4)_2\text{SO}_4$$

These relationships supply the conversion factors we need to convert between mass in grams and amount in moles, as illustrated in the following examples.

Example 5 Conversions Involving Moles and Mass

a. What mass in grams of N_2 is 0.400 moles N_2? **(b)** Calculate the number of moles of Na in a 62.5 g sample of sodium metal.

Solution

a. The molecular mass of N_2 is $2 \times 14.0 \text{ u} = 28.0 \text{ u}$. The molar mass of N_2 is therefore 28.0 g/mol. Using this molar mass as a conversion factor (red), we have

$$? \text{ g N}_2 = 0.400 \text{ mol N}_2 \times \frac{28.0 \text{ g N}_2}{1 \text{ mol N}_2} = 11.2 \text{ g N}_2$$

b. The molar mass of Na is 23.0 g/mol. To convert from mass to moles, we must use the *inverse* of the molar mass as a conversion factor (1 mol Na/23.0 g Na) to cancel units of mass. When we start with grams, we must have grams in the denominator of our conversion factor (red).

$$? \text{ mol Na} = 62.5 \text{ g Na} \times \frac{1 \text{ mol Na}}{23.0 \text{ g Na}} = 2.72 \text{ mol Na}$$

■ EXERCISE 5A

Calculate the mass, in grams, of **(a)** 0.0728 mol silicon, **(b)** 55.5 mol H_2O, and **(c)** 0.0728 mol $Ca(H_2PO_4)_2$.

■ EXERCISE 5B

Calculate the amount, in moles, of **(a)** 3.71 g Fe, **(b)** 165 g C_4H_{10}, and **(c)** 0.100 g $Mg(NO_3)_2$.

Figure 5 shows one-mole samples of several different substances. Each container holds Avogadro's number of formula units of the substance. That is, there are just as many sugar molecules in the largest dish as there are helium atoms in the balloon.

◀ **Figure 5** One mole of each of several familiar substances. From left to right on the table are sugar, salt, carbon, and copper. Behind them, the balloon contains helium. Each container holds Avogadro's number of elementary units of the substance. There are 6.02×10^{23} molecules of sugar ($C_{12}H_{22}O_{11}$), 6.02×10^{23} formula units of NaCl, 6.02×10^{23} atoms of carbon, 6.02×10^{23} atoms of copper, and 6.02×10^{23} atoms of helium in the respective samples.

Q: *How many Na^+ ions and how many Cl^- ions are there in the dish of salt? If the balloon was filled with oxygen gas (O_2), how many oxygen atoms would it contain?*

Mole and Mass Relationships in Chemical Equations

Chemists, other scientists, and engineers are often confronted with questions such as "How much iron can be obtained from 1.0 ton of Fe_2O_3?" or "How much carbon dioxide is produced by burning 1000 g of propane?" There is no simple way to calculate the mass of one substance directly from the mass of another in the same reaction. Because chemical reactions involve atoms and molecules, quantities in reactions are calculated in moles of atoms, ions, or molecules. To do such calculations, it is necessary to convert grams of a substance to moles, as we did in Example 5. We also must write balanced equations to determine molar ratios.

Recall that chemical equations provide not only ratios of atoms and molecules but also mole ratios. For example, the equation

$$C + O_2 \longrightarrow CO_2$$

▲ Figure 6 We cannot weigh single atoms or molecules, but we can weigh equal numbers of these tiny particles.

GENT SHKULLAKU/AFP/Getty Images/Newscom

▲ It DOES Matter!

If there is not enough oxygen gas to react completely with burning carbon, some of the carbon will be incompletely oxidized and deadly carbon monoxide will form. Most of the 65 deaths in the Midwestern ice storm in January–February 2009 were the result of burning fuels (charcoal, kerosene, or gasoline, in an electricity generator) indoors without adequate oxygen.

tells us that one C atom reacts with one O_2 molecule (two atoms) to form one CO_2 molecule (one C atom and two O atoms). The equation also means that 1 mol (6.02×10^{23} atoms) of carbon reacts with 1 mol (6.02×10^{23} molecules) of oxygen to yield 1 mol (6.02×10^{23} molecules) of carbon dioxide. Because the molar mass in grams of a substance is numerically equal to the formula mass of the substance in atomic mass units, the equation also tells us (indirectly) that 12.0 g (1 mol) C reacts with 32.0 g (1 mol) O_2 to yield 44.0 g (1 mol) CO_2 (Figure 6).

The important thing is to maintain the *ratio* of masses. For example, in the preceding reaction, the mass ratio of oxygen to carbon is 32.0:12.0, or 8.0:3.0. Thus, 8.0 g O and 3.0 g C will produce 11.0 g CO_2. In fact, to calculate the amount of oxygen needed to react with a given amount of carbon, we need only multiply the amount of carbon by the factor 32.0:12.0. The following examples illustrate these relationships.

CONCEPTUAL Example 6   Molecular, Molar, and Mass Relationships

Nitrogen monoxide (nitric oxide), an air pollutant discharged by internal combustion engines, combines with oxygen to form nitrogen dioxide, a yellowish-brown gas that irritates our respiratory systems and eyes. The equation for this reaction is

$$2\,NO + O_2 \longrightarrow 2\,NO_2$$

State the molecular, molar, and mass relationships indicated by this equation.

Solution

The molecular and molar relationships can be obtained directly from the equation; no calculation is necessary. The mass relationship requires a little calculation.

Molecular: Two molecules of NO react with one molecule of O_2 to form two molecules of NO_2.

Molar: 2 mol NO reacts with 1 mol O_2 to form 2 mol NO_2.

Mass: 60.0 g NO (2 mol NO × 30.0 g/mol) reacts with 32.0 g (1 mol O_2 × 32.0 g/mol) O_2 to form 92.0 g (2 mol NO_2 × 46.0 g/mol) NO_2.

■ EXERCISE 6

Hydrogen sulfide, a gas that smells like rotten eggs, burns in air to produce sulfur dioxide and water according to the equation

$$2\,H_2S + 3\,O_2 \longrightarrow 2\,SO_2 + 2\,H_2O$$

State the molecular, molar, and mass relationships indicated by this equation.

Molar Relationships in Chemical Equations

The quantitative relationship between reactants and products in a chemical reaction is called **stoichiometry**. The ratio of moles of reactants and products is given by the coefficients in a balanced chemical equation. Consider the combustion of propane, the main component of bottled gas.

$$C_3H_8 + 5\,O_2 \longrightarrow 3\,CO_2 + 4\,H_2O$$

The coefficients in the balanced equation allow us to make statements such as

- 1 mol C_3H_8 reacts with 5 mol O_2.
- 3 mol CO_2 is produced for every 1 mol C_3H_8 that reacts.
- 4 mol H_2O is produced for every 3 mol CO_2 produced.

We can turn these statements into conversion factors known as stoichiometric factors. A **stoichiometric factor** relates the amounts, in *moles*, of any two substances involved in a chemical reaction. Note that we can set up stoichiometric factors for any two substances involved in a reaction. Also note that stoichiometric factors, because they come from the balanced equation for a reaction, involve small whole numbers. In the examples that follow, stoichiometric factors are shown in color.

Example 7   Molar Relationships

When 0.105 mol of propane is burned in a plentiful supply of oxygen, how many moles of oxygen are consumed?

$$C_3H_8 + 5\,O_2 \longrightarrow 3\,CO_2 + 4\,H_2O$$

Solution

The equation tells us that 5 mol O_2 is required to burn 1 mol C_3H_8. From this relationship, we can construct conversion factors to relate moles of oxygen to moles of propane. The possible conversion factors are

$$\frac{1\text{ mol } C_3H_8}{5\text{ mol } O_2} \quad \text{and} \quad \frac{5\text{ mol } O_2}{1\text{ mol } C_3H_8}$$

Which one do we use? Only if we multiply the given quantity (0.105 mol C_3H_8) by the factor on the *right* will the answer be expressed in the units requested (moles of oxygen).

$$? \text{ mol } O_2 = 0.105 \text{ mol } C_3H_8 \times \frac{5\text{ mol } O_2}{1\text{ mol } C_3H_8} = 0.525 \text{ mol } O_2$$

■ EXERCISE 7A

Consider the combustion (burning) of propane presented in Example 7. **(a)** How many moles of CO_2 are formed when 0.529 mol C_3H_8 is burned? **(b)** How many moles of CO_2 are produced when 1.010 mol O_2 is consumed?

■ EXERCISE 7B

For the combustion of propane in Example 7, suppose that 50.0 mol O_2 and 25.0 mol propane are combined. After reaction, which reactant will be used up, and how many moles of the other reactant will be left over? (*Hint:* Calculate the number of moles of propane that will react with the oxygen given. Is there enough propane?)

Mass Relationships in Chemical Equations

A chemical equation defines the stoichiometric relationship in terms of moles, but problems are seldom presented in terms of moles. Typically, you are given the mass (grams) of one substance and asked to calculate the mass of another substance that will react or can be produced. Such calculations involve several steps:

1. Write a balanced chemical equation for the reaction.
2. Determine the molar masses of the substances involved in the calculation.
3. Write down the given quantity and use the molar mass to convert this quantity to moles.
4. Use coefficients (stoichiometric relationship) from the balanced chemical equation to convert moles of the given substance to moles of the desired substance.
5. Use the molar mass to convert moles of the desired substance to grams of the desired substance.

If we know the quantity of any substance in an equation, we can determine the quantities of all the other substances. The conversion process is diagrammed in Figure 7. It is best learned by studying examples and working exercises.

▲ **Figure 7** We can use a chemical equation to relate the numbers of *moles* of any two substances represented in the equation. These substances may be a reactant and a product, two reactants, or two products. We cannot directly relate the mass of one substance to the mass of another substance involved in the same reaction. To obtain *mass* relationships, we must convert the mass of each substance to moles, relate moles of one substance to moles of the other through a stoichiometric factor, and then convert moles of the second substance to its mass.

Example 8   Mass Relationships

Calculate the mass of oxygen needed to react with 10.0 g of carbon in the reaction that forms carbon dioxide.

Solution

Step 1: The balanced equation is

$$C + O_2 \longrightarrow CO_2$$

Step 2: The molar masses are 12.0 g/mol for C and $2 \times 16.0 = 32.0$ g/mol for O_2.

Step 3: We convert the given mass of carbon to an amount in moles.

$$? \text{ mol C} = 10.0 \text{ g C} \times \frac{1 \text{ mol C}}{12.0 \text{ g C}} = 0.833 \text{ mol C}$$

Step 4: We use coefficients from the balanced equation to establish the stoichiometric factor (red) that relates the amount of oxygen to that of carbon.

$$0.833 \text{ mol C} \times \frac{1 \text{ mol } O_2}{1 \text{ mol C}} = 0.833 \text{ mol } O_2$$

Step 5: We convert from moles of oxygen to grams of oxygen.

$$0.833 \text{ mol } O_2 \times \frac{32.0 \text{ g } O_2}{1 \text{ mol } O_2} = 26.7 \text{ g } O_2$$

We can also combine the five steps into a single setup. Note that the units in the denominators of the conversion factors are chosen so that each cancels the unit in the numerator of the preceding term.

We start here	This converts g C to mol C	This relates mol C to mol O_2	This converts mol O_2 to g O_2	The answer: the number and the unit

$$10.0 \text{ g C} \times \frac{1 \text{ mol C}}{12.0 \text{ g C}} \times \frac{1 \text{ mol } O_2}{1 \text{ mol C}} \times \frac{32.0 \text{ g } O_2}{1 \text{ mol } O_2} = 26.6 \text{ g } O_2$$

(The answers are slightly different due to rounding in the intermediate steps.)

■ EXERCISE 8A

Calculate the mass of oxygen (O_2) needed to react with 0.334 g nitrogen (N_2) in the reaction that forms nitrogen dioxide.

■ EXERCISE 8B

Calculate the mass of carbon dioxide formed by burning 775 g each of **(a)** methane (CH_4) and **(b)** butane (C_4H_{10}) in oxygen gas. (*Hint*: The reaction in Example 7 may help in balancing the equations.)

Self-Assessment Questions

1. The mass of 4.75 mol H_2SO_4 is
   a. 314 g
   b. 456 g
   c. 466 g
   d. 564 g

2. For which of the following would a 10.0-g sample contain the most moles?
   a. Cu
   b. Fe
   c. Si
   d. S

3. How many moles of CO_2 are there in 1 lb (453.6 g) CO_2?
   a. 0.0969 mol
   b. 9.20 mol
   c. 10.3 mol
   d. 14.2 mol

4. How many moles of benzene (C_6H_6) are there in a 7.81-g sample of benzene?
   a. 0.100 mol
   b. 1.00 mol
   c. 7.81 mol
   d. 610 mol

Items 5–7 refer to the equation $2 H_2 + O_2 \longrightarrow 2 H_2O$.

5. At the molar level, the equation means that
   a. 2 mol H reacts with 1 mol O to form 2 mol H_2O
   b. 4 mol H reacts with 2 mol O to form 4 mol H_2O
   c. 2 mol H_2 reacts with 1 mol O_2 to form 2 mol H_2O
   d. 2 mol O_2 reacts with 1 mol H_2 to form 2 mol H_2O

6. How many moles of water can be formed from 0.500 mol H_2?
   a. 0.500 mol
   b. 1.00 mol
   c. 2.00 mol
   d. 4.00 mol

7. How many moles of oxygen (O_2) are required to form 0.222 mol H_2O?
   a. 0.111 mol
   b. 0.222 mol
   c. 0.444 mol
   d. 1.00 mol

Answers: 1, c; 2, c; 3, c; 4, a; 5, c; 6, c; 7, a

1. How can a car make more pollution than the gasoline it uses? A mole of carbon (12 g) combines with oxygen from the atmosphere to form a mole of carbon dioxide (44 g). Gasoline is mostly carbon by weight, so the mass of carbon dioxide formed is greater than the mass of gasoline burned. Carbon dioxide is a major greenhouse gas.

Margaret Kerr, *Worcester State University*

Atom Economy

Imagine yourself in the future. Your job is related to environmental protection, which requires that you provide information to practicing chemists as they design new processes and reactions. Waste management is one of your top concerns. Although waste typically has been addressed after the production of desired commodities, you realize that a greener approach enables minimizing the waste from the start. What tools would you use in this job? What topics are important? How can chemists provide new products while protecting the environment?

Intrinsic in greener approaches to waste management is the concept of *atom economy*, a calculation of the number of atoms conserved in the desired product rather than in waste. In 1998, Barry Trost (Stanford University) won a Presidential Green Chemistry Challenge Award for his work in developing this concept. By calculating the number of atoms that will not become part of the desired product and, therefore, will enter the waste stream, chemists can precisely determine the minimum amount of waste that will be produced by chemicals used in a reaction before even running the reaction.

You have learned how to write and balance chemical equations (Section 1) and you also can calculate molar mass, convert from mass to moles, and determine the amount of product formed from given amounts of reactants (Sections 3, 4). Other ways of calculating the efficiency of a reaction has traditionally been expressed using *theoretical yield*, *experimental yield*, and *percent yield*. The theoretical yield is the maximum amount of desired product that can be produced by the amounts of reactants used. Under laboratory conditions, the theoretical yield of a reaction is not usually obtained. The actual amount of desired product collected is called the experimental yield. Chemists often express their experimental results in percent yield, which is simply the experimental yield divided by the theoretical yield, then multiplied by 100.

$$\% \text{ yield} = \frac{\text{experimental yield}}{\text{theoretical yield}} \times 100\%$$

A report of a 100% yield for a reaction seems good, but the percent yield considers only the desired product. Any other substance formed (for instance, a byproduct) is not counted in the percent yield. Byproducts often become part of the chemical waste stream. Some reactions actually produce more byproducts than desired products.

Atom economy is a better way to measure reaction efficiency. Percent atom economy (% A.E.) measures the proportion of the atoms in the reaction mixture that actually become part of the desired product. Reactant atoms that do not appear in the product are considered waste. The % A.E. is given by the following relationship:

$$\% \text{ A.E.} = \frac{\text{molar mass of desired product}}{\text{molar masses of all reactants}} \times 100\%$$

A reaction can have a poor atom economy even when the percent yield is near 100%.

Consider the following two ways to make ethyl bromide (C_2H_5Br), a compound used as a solvent, an anesthetic, a refrigerant, and a fumigant. First, ethyl bromide can be made using ethanol (C_2H_5OH) and phosphorus tribromide (PBr_3).

$$3\, C_2H_5OH + PBr_3 \rightarrow 3\, C_2H_5Br + H_3PO_3$$

In this reaction, a Br atom substitutes for the OH group of the alcohol. In reactions like this one, generally only one product is desired and all other products are not utilized. The wasted atoms in the preceding equation are shown in red.

We can calculate the atom economy for this reaction.

$$\% \text{ A.E.} = \frac{3 \times \text{molar mass } C_2H_5Br}{3 \times \text{molar mass } C_2H_5OH + \text{molar mass } PBr_3} \times 100\%$$

$$= \frac{3 \times 108.97 \text{ g/mol}}{(3 \times 46.07 \text{ g/mol}) + 270.69 \text{ g/mol}} \times 100\% = 79.9\%$$

These substitution reactions never have 100% atom economy because there is always a byproduct. This results in some atoms going into the waste stream.

Ethyl bromide can also be made using ethylene (C_2H_4) and hydrogen bromide:

$$C_2H_4 + HBr \rightarrow C_2H_5Br$$

In this reaction, all of the atoms in both reactants appear in the desired product C_2H_5Br and none go into the waste stream. The percent atom economy is 100%.

$$\% \text{ A.E.} = \frac{\text{molar mass } C_2H_5Br}{\text{molar mass } C_2H_4 + \text{molar mass } HBr} \times 100\%$$

$$= \frac{108.97 \text{ g/mol}}{28.05 \text{ g/mol} + 80.91 \text{ g/mol}} \times 100\% = 100\%$$

Because the concept of atom economy offers a way to predict waste, it can lead to innovative design processes that eliminate or minimize waste. By focusing on waste from the beginning of the reaction, we reduce or eliminate cleanup at the end.

5 Solutions

Learning Objectives ❯ Calculate the concentration (molarity, percent by volume, or percent by mass) of a solute in a solution. ❯ Calculate the amount of solute or solution given the concentration and the other amount.

Many chemical reactions take place in solutions. A **solution** is a homogeneous mixture of two or more substances. The substance being dissolved is the *solute*, and the substance doing the dissolving is the *solvent*. The solvent is usually present in greater quantity than the solute. There are many solvents: Kerosene dissolves grease; ethanol dissolves many drugs; isopentyl acetate, a component of banana oil, is a solvent for model airplane glue.

Water is no doubt the most familiar solvent, dissolving as it does many common substances such as sugar, salt, and ethanol. We focus our discussion here on **aqueous solutions**, those in which water is the solvent, and we take a more quantitative look at the relationship between solute and solvent.

Solution Concentrations

We say that some substances, such as sugar and salt, are *soluble* in water. Of course, there is a limit to the quantity of sugar or salt that we can dissolve in a given volume of water. Yet we still find it convenient to say that they are soluble in water because an appreciable quantity dissolves. Other substances, such as an iron nail or sand (silicon dioxide), we consider to be *insoluble* because their solubility in water is near zero. Such terms as *soluble* and *insoluble* are useful, but they are imprecise and must be used with care.

Two other roughly estimated but sometimes useful terms are *dilute* and *concentrated*. A **dilute solution** is one that contains a little bit of solute in lots of solvent. For example, a pinch of sugar in a cup of tea makes a dilute, faintly sweet, sugar solution. A **concentrated solution** is one with a relatively large amount of solute dissolved in a relatively small amount of solvent. Pancake syrup, with lots of sugar solute in a relatively small amount of water, is a concentrated, and very sweet, solution.

Scientific work generally requires more precise concentration units than "a pinch of sugar in a cup of tea." Further, quantitative work often requires the *mole* unit because substances enter into chemical reactions according to *molar* ratios.

Molarity

A concentration unit that chemists often use is *molarity*. For reactions involving solutions, the amount of solute is usually measured in moles and the quantity of solution in liters or milliliters. The **molarity (M)** is the amount of solute, in moles, per liter of solution.

$$\text{Molarity (M)} = \frac{\text{moles of solute}}{\text{liters of solution}}$$

Lynnea Kleinschmidt

▲ It DOES Matter!
The ethanol content of a beverage is almost always expressed by *volume* (see Example 13A). This may be done partly as a marketing ploy. Ethanol is about 20% less dense than water, so a beverage that is labeled "12% alcohol by volume" is only about 10% ethanol by weight. The higher percent by volume may make purchasers think they are getting "more for the money."

Example 9 Solution Concentration: Molarity and Moles

Calculate the molarity of a solution made by dissolving 3.50 mol NaCl in enough water to produce 2.00 L of solution.

Solution

$$\text{Molarity (M)} = \frac{\text{moles of solute}}{\text{liters of solution}} = \frac{3.50 \text{ mol NaCl}}{2.00 \text{ L solution}} = 1.75 \text{ M NaCl}$$

We read 1.75 M NaCl as "1.75 molar sodium chloride."

■ EXERCISE 9A
Calculate the molarity of a solution that has 0.0500 mol NH_3 in 5.75 L of solution.

■ EXERCISE 9B
Calculate the molarity of a solution made by dissolving 0.750 mol H_3PO_4 in enough water to produce 775 mL of solution.

Usually, when preparing a solution, we must *weigh* the solute. Balances do not display units of moles, so we usually work with a given mass and divide by the molar mass of the substance, as illustrated in Example 10.

Example 10   Solution Concentration: Molarity and Mass

What is the molarity of a solution in which 333 g potassium hydrogen carbonate is dissolved in enough water to make 10.0 L of solution?

Solution

First, we must convert grams of $KHCO_3$ to moles of $KHCO_3$.

$$333 \text{ g } KHCO_3 \times \frac{1 \text{ mol } KHCO_3}{100.1 \text{ g } KHCO_3} = 3.33 \text{ mol } KHCO_3$$

Next, we use this value as the numerator in the defining equation for molarity. The solution volume, 10.0 L, is the denominator.

$$\text{Molarity} = \frac{3.33 \text{ mol } KHCO_3}{10.0 \text{ L solution}} = 0.333 \text{ M } KHCO_3$$

■ EXERCISE 10A
Calculate the molarity of **(a)** 18.0 g H_2SO_4 in 2.00 L of solution and **(b)** 3.00 g KI in 2.39 L of solution.

■ EXERCISE 10B
Calculate the molarity of 0.206 g HF in 752 mL of solution (HF is used for etching glass).

Often, we need to know the *mass* of solute required to prepare a given volume of a solution of a particular molarity. In such calculations, we can use molarity as a conversion factor between moles of solute and liters of solution. For instance, in Example 11, the expression "0.15 M NaCl" means 0.15 mol NaCl per liter of solution, expressed as the conversion factor

$$\frac{0.15 \text{ mol NaCl}}{1 \text{ L solution}}$$

Example 11   Solution Preparation: Molarity

What mass in grams of NaCl is required to prepare 0.500 L of typical over-the-counter saline solution (about 0.15 M NaCl)?

Solution

First, we use the molarity as a conversion factor to calculate moles of NaCl.

$$0.500 \text{ L solution} \times \frac{0.15 \text{ mol NaCl}}{1 \text{ L solution}} = 0.075 \text{ mol NaCl}$$

Then, we use the molar mass to calculate grams of NaCl.

$$0.75 \; \text{mol NaCl} \times \frac{58.5 \text{ g NaCl}}{1 \text{ mol NaCl}} = 44 \text{ g NaCl}$$

■ EXERCISE 11

What mass in grams of potassium hydroxide is required to prepare (a) 2.00 L of 6.00 M KOH and (b) 100.0 mL of 1.00 M KOH?

Quite often, solutions of known molarity are available commercially. For example, concentrated hydrochloric acid is 12 M. How would you determine the *volume* of this solution that contains a certain number of moles of solute? We can again rearrange the definition of molarity to obtain the volume.

$$\text{Liters of solution} = \frac{\text{moles of solute}}{\text{molarity}}$$

Example 12   Moles from Molarity and Volume

Concentrated hydrochloric acid is 12.0 M HCl. What volume in milliliters of this solution contains 0.425 mol HCl?

Solution

$$\text{Liters of HCl solution} = \frac{\text{moles of solute}}{\text{molarity}} = \frac{0.425 \text{ mol HCl}}{12.0 \text{ M HCl}}$$

$$= \frac{0.425 \; \text{mol HCl}}{12.0 \; \text{mol HCl}/\text{L}} = 0.0354 \text{ L}$$

In this case, 0.0354 L (35.4 mL) of the solution contains 0.425 mol of the solute. Remember that molarity is moles per liter of *solution*, not per liter of solvent.

■ EXERCISE 12A

What volume in milliliters of 15.0 M aqueous ammonia (NH_3) solution contains 0.445 mol NH_3?

■ EXERCISE 12B

What mass in grams of HNO_3 is in 500 mL of acid rain that has a concentration of 2.00×10^{-5} M HNO_3?

Percent Concentrations

For many practical applications, including those in medicine and pharmacy, solution concentrations are often expressed in percentages. There are different ways to express percentages, depending on whether mass or volume is being measured. If both solute and solvent are liquids, **percent by volume** is often used because liquid volumes are easily measured.

$$\text{Percent by volume} = \frac{\text{volume of solute}}{\text{volume of solution}} \times 100\%$$

In calculating percent by volume, we can measure the solute and solution in any unit of volume as long as we use the same unit for both. For example, we can measure both volumes in milliliters or in gallons. Ethanol (CH_3CH_2OH) for medicinal

▲ Rubbing alcohol is a water–isopropyl alcohol solution that is 70% isopropyl alcohol [$(CH_3)_2CHOH$] by volume.

Pearson Education/Eric Schrader

purposes is 95% by volume. That is, it consists of 95 mL CH_3CH_2OH per 100 mL of aqueous solution.

▲ "Reagent grade" concentrated hydrochloric acid is a 38% by mass solution of HCl in water.

3. Does 2% milk have just 2% of the calories of whole milk? No. Whole milk contains at least 3.25% butterfat by mass. Some of the butterfat is removed to make 2% milk, which is 2% butterfat by mass. Actually, 2% milk has about 75% of the calories of whole milk.

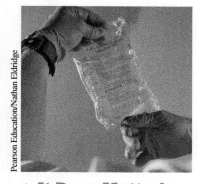

▲ **It Does Matter!**
An isotonic, or "normal," intravenous solution must have the proper concentration of solute to avoid damage to blood cells.

Example 13　Percent by Volume

Two-stroke engines use a mixture of 120 mL of oil dissolved in enough gasoline to make 4.0 L of fuel. What is the percent by volume of oil in this mixture?

Solution

$$\text{Percent by volume} = \frac{120 \text{ mL oil}}{4000 \text{ mL solution}} \times 100\% = 3.0\%$$

■ EXERCISE 13A
What is the volume percent of ethanol in a solution of 625 mL of an ethanol–water solution that contains 58.0 mL of water?

■ EXERCISE 13B
Determine the volume percent of toluene ($C_6H_5CH_3$) in a solution made by mixing 40.0 mL of toluene with 75.0 mL of benzene (C_6H_6). Assume that the volumes are additive.

　　Many commercial solutions are labeled with the concentration in **percent by mass**. For example, sulfuric acid is sold in several concentrations: 35.7% H_2SO_4 for use in storage batteries, 77.7% H_2SO_4 for the manufacture of phosphate fertilizers, and 93.2% H_2SO_4 for pickling steel. Each of these percentages is by mass: 35.7 g of H_2SO_4 per 100 g of sulfuric acid solution, and so on.

$$\text{Percent by mass} = \frac{\text{mass of solute}}{\text{mass of solution}} \times 100\%$$

As with percent by volume, we can express the masses of solute and solution in any mass unit, as long as we use the same unit for both.

Example 14　Percent by Mass

What is the percent by mass of NaCl if 25.5 g of it is dissolved in 425 g (425 mL) of water?

Solution
We use these values in the above percent-by-mass equation:

$$\text{Percent by mass} = \frac{25.5 \text{ g NaCl}}{(25.5 + 425) \text{ g solution}} \times 100\% = 5.66\% \text{ NaCl}$$

■ EXERCISE 14A
Hydrogen peroxide solution for home use is 3.0% by mass of H_2O_2 in water. What is the percent by mass of a solution of 9.40 g H_2O_2 dissolved in 335 g (335 mL) of water?

■ EXERCISE 14B
Sodium hydroxide (NaOH, lye) is used to make soap and is quite soluble in water. What is the percent by mass of NaOH in a solution that contains 1.00 kg NaOH in 950 mL water?

Example 15   Solution Preparation: Percent by Mass

Describe how to make 430 g of an aqueous solution that is 4.85% by mass $NaNO_3$.

Solution

We begin by rearranging the equation for percent by mass to solve for mass of solute.

$$\text{Mass of solute} = \frac{\text{percent by mass} \times \text{mass of solution}}{100\%}$$

Substituting, we have

$$\frac{4.85\% \times 430\,\text{g}}{100\%} = 20.9\,\text{g}$$

We would weigh out 20.9 g $NaNO_3$ and add enough water to make 430 g of solution.

■ **EXERCISE 15A**

Describe how you would prepare 125 g of an aqueous solution that is 4.50% glucose by mass.

■ **EXERCISE 15B**

Describe how you would prepare 1750 g of *isotonic saline*, a commonly used intravenous (IV) solution that is 0.89% sodium chloride by mass.

Note that for percent concentrations, the mass or volume of the solute needed doesn't depend on what the solute is. A 10% by mass solution of NaOH contains 10 g NaOH per 100 g of solution. Similarly, 10% HCl and 10% $(NH_4)_2SO_4$ and 10% $C_{110}H_{190}N_3O_2Br$ each contain 10 g of the specified solute per 100 g of solution. For *molar* solutions, however, the mass of solute in a solution of specified molarity is different for different solutes. A liter of 0.10 M solution requires 4.0 g (0.10 mol) NaOH, 3.7 g (0.10 mol) HCl, 13.2 g (0.10 mol) $(NH_4)_2SO_4$, or 166 g (0.10 mol) $C_{110}H_{190}N_3O_2Br$.

4. What does a cholesterol level of 200 mean? Concentrations of solutes in body fluids are often too low to be expressed conveniently as percentages. A common unit is milligrams (of solute) per deciliter of blood (or other fluid). A cholesterol level of 200 means 200 mg of cholesterol per dL (100 mL) of blood.

Self-Assessment Questions

1. In a solution of 85.0 g water and 5.0 g sucrose ($C_{12}H_{22}O_{11}$), the
   a. solute is sucrose and the solution is the solvent
   b. solute is sucrose and the solvent is water
   c. solute is water and sucrose is the solvent
   d. water and sucrose are both solutes

2. What is the molarity of a sodium hydroxide solution having 0.500 mol NaOH in 250 mL of solution?
   a. 0.00200 M   **b.** 0.200 M   **c.** 2.00 M   **d.** 8.00 M

3. How many moles of sugar are required to make 4.00 L of 0.600 M sugar solution?
   a. 1.20 mol   **b.** 2.40 mol   **c.** 24.0 mol   **d.** 6.67 mol

4. What mass of NaCl in grams is needed to prepare 2.500 L of a 0.800 M NaCl solution?
   a. 2.00 g   **b.** 4.00 g   **c.** 58.5 g   **d.** 117 g

5. What volume of 6.00 M HCl solution contains 1.50 mol HCl?
   a. 250 mL   **b.** 300 mL   **c.** 900 mL   **d.** 9.00 L

6. What is the percent by volume of ethanol in a solution made by adding 50.0 mL of pure ethanol to enough water to make 250 mL of solution?
   a. 16.7%   **b.** 20.0%   **c.** 25.0%   **d.** 80.0%

7. A solution contains 15.0 g sucrose and 60.0 g of water. What is the percent by mass of sucrose in the solution?
   a. 15.0%   **b.** 20.0%   **c.** 25.0%   **d.** 80.0%

8. What volume of water should be added to 23.4 g NaCl to make 100.0 mL of 4.00 M NaCl solution?
   a. 76.6 mL   **b.** 96.0 mL
   c. 100.0 mL   **d.** enough to make 100.0 mL of solution

Answers: 1, b; 2, c; 3, b; 4, d; 5, a; 6, b; 7, b; 8, d

CRITICAL THINKING EXERCISES

Apply knowledge that you have gained in this chapter and one or more of the FLaReS principles to evaluate the following statements or claims.

1 Suppose that someone has published a paper claiming to have established a new value for Avogadro's number. The author says that he has made some very careful laboratory measurements and his calculations indicate that the true value for Avogadro's number is 3.01875×10^{23}. Is this claim credible in your opinion? What questions would you ask the author about his claim?

2 A chemistry teacher asked her students, "What is the mass, in grams, of a mole of bromine?" One student answered 80; another said 160; and several others gave answers of 79, 81, 158, and 162. The teacher stated that all of these answers were correct. Do you believe her statement?

3 A website on fireworks provides directions for preparing potassium nitrate, KNO_3 (molar mass = 101 g/mol), using potassium carbonate (138 g/mol)

and ammonium nitrate (80 g/mol), according to the following equation:

$$K_2CO_3 + 2\,NH_4NO_3 \longrightarrow 2\,KNO_3 + CO_2 \\ + H_2O + NH_3$$

The directions state: "Mix one kilogram of potassium carbonate with two kilograms of ammonium nitrate. The carbon dioxide and ammonia come off as gases, and the water can be evaporated, leaving two kilograms of pure potassium nitrate." Use information from this chapter to evaluate this statement.

4 A battery manufacturer claims that lithium batteries deliver the same power as batteries using nickel, zinc, or lead, but the lithium batteries are much lighter because lithium has a lower atomic mass than does nickel, zinc, or lead.

5 After working Problem 66 of Additional Problems, evaluate the claim that homeopathy is a valid alternative medical treatment.

SUMMARY

Section 1—A chemical equation is shorthand for a chemical change, using symbols and formulas instead of words: for example, $C + O_2 \longrightarrow CO_2$. Substances to the left of the arrow are starting materials, or reactants; those to the right of the arrow are products, or what the reaction produces. Physical states may be indicated with (s), (l), or (g). Because matter is conserved, a chemical equation must be balanced. It must have the same numbers and types of atoms on each side. Equations are balanced by placing coefficients in front of the formula for each reactant or product; we do *not* balance an equation by changing the formulas of reactants or products. The balanced equation $2\,NaN_3 \longrightarrow 2\,Na + 3\,N_2$ means that two formula units of NaN_3 react to give two atoms of Na and three molecules of N_2.

Section 2—Gay-Lussac's experiments led him to the law of combining volumes: At a given temperature and pressure, the volumes of gaseous reactants and products are in a small whole-number ratio (such as 1:1, 2:1, 4:3). Avogadro's hypothesis explained this law by stating that equal volumes of all gases contain the same number of molecules at fixed temperature and pressure.

Section 3—Avogadro's number is defined as the number of ^{12}C atoms in exactly 12 grams of ^{12}C, that is, 6.02×10^{23} atoms. A mole (mol) is the amount of a substance that contains Avogadro's number of elementary units—atoms, molecules, or formula units, depending on the substance. The formula mass is the sum of masses of the atoms represented in the formula of a substance. If the formula represents a molecule, the term *molecular mass* often is used. A formula represents a mass ratio as well as an atom ratio, and the

composition by mass of a compound may be calculated from the formula.

Section 4—The molar mass is the mass of one mole of a substance. Molar mass has the same number as formula mass, molecular mass, or atomic mass but is expressed in units of grams per mole (g/mol). Molar mass is used to convert from grams to moles of a substance, and vice versa. A balanced equation can be read in terms of atoms and molecules or in terms of moles. Stoichiometry, or mass relationships in chemical reactions, can be found by using stoichiometric factors, which relate moles of one substance to moles of another. Stoichiometric factors can be obtained without calculation, directly from the balanced equation. To evaluate mass relationships in chemical reactions, molar masses and stoichiometric factors are both used as conversion factors.

Section 5—A solution is a homogeneous mixture of two or more substances, often consisting of a solute dissolved in a solvent. A substance is soluble in a solvent if some appreciable quantity of the substance dissolves in the solvent. Any substance that does not dissolve significantly in a solvent is insoluble in that solvent. An aqueous solution, indicated by the label (aq), has water as the solvent. The concentration of a solution can be expressed in many ways. A concentrated solution has a relatively large amount of solute compared to solvent, and a dilute solution has only a little solute in a large amount of solvent. One quantitative unit of concentration is molarity (M), moles of solute dissolved per liter of solution.

$$\text{Molarity (M)} = \frac{\text{moles of solute}}{\text{liters of solution}}$$

There are several ways to express concentration using percentages. Two important ones are percent by volume and percent by mass.

$$\text{Percent by volume} = \frac{\text{volume of solute}}{\text{volume of solution}} \times 100\%$$

$$\text{Percent by mass} = \frac{\text{mass of solute}}{\text{mass of solution}} \times 100\%$$

For each concentration unit, if we know two of the three terms in the equation, we can solve for the third.

Green chemistry Atom economy is an important component of green chemistry and waste prevention. By strategically designing reactions to maximize the number of atoms utilized, a chemist has the ability to reduce waste production.

Learning Objectives

> Identify balanced and unbalanced chemical equations, and balance equations by inspection. (1)   Problems 4, 11–16, 51–53, 62

> Determine volumes of gases that react, using a balanced equation for a reaction. (2)   Problems 2, 3, 17–22, 55

> Calculate the formula mass, molecular mass, or molar mass of a substance. (3)   Problems 27–34

> Convert from mass to moles and from moles to mass of a substance. (4)   Problem 71

> Calculate the mass or number of moles of a reactant or product from the mass or number of moles of another reactant or product. (4)   Problems 35–38, 54, 56–58, 62, 69

> Calculate the concentration (molarity, percent by volume, or percent by mass) of a solute in a solution. (5)   Problems 39–50, 60, 61

> Calculate the amount of solute or solution given the concentration and the other amount. (5)   Problems 59, 64, 65

> Explain how the concept of atom economy can be applied to pollution prevention and environmental protection.   Problems 73, 74

> Calculate the atom economy for chemical reactions.   Problems 72–76

REVIEW QUESTIONS

1. Define or illustrate each of the following.
   a. formula unit   b. formula mass
   c. mole   d. Avogadro's number
   e. molar mass   f. molar volume (of a gas)

2. Explain the difference between the atomic mass of chlorine and the formula mass of chlorine gas.

3. What is Avogadro's hypothesis? How does it explain Gay-Lussac's law of combining volumes?

4. Referring to the law of conservation of mass, explain why we must work with balanced chemical equations.

5. Define or explain and illustrate the following terms.
   a. solution   b. solvent
   c. solute   d. aqueous solution

6. Define or explain and illustrate the following terms.
   a. concentrated solution   b. dilute solution
   c. soluble   d. insoluble

PROBLEMS

Interpreting Formulas

7. How many oxygen atoms does each of the following contain?
   a. $Al(H_2PO_4)_3$ b. $HOC_6H_4COOCH_3$
   c. $(BiO)_2SO_4$

8. How many carbon atoms does each of the following contain?
   a. $Fe_2(CO_3)_3$ b. $Al(CH_3COO)_3$
   c. $(CH_3)CCH(CH_3)_2$

9. How many atoms of each element (N, P, H, and O) does the notation $3\ (NH_4)_2HPO_4$ indicate?

10. How many atoms of each element (Fe, C, H, and O) does the notation $4\ Fe(HOOCCH_2COO)_3$ indicate?

Interpreting Chemical Equations

11. Consider the following equation. **(a)** Explain its meaning at the molecular level. **(b)** Interpret it in terms of moles. **(c)** State the mass relationships conveyed by the equation.
$$2\ H_2O_2 \longrightarrow 2\ H_2O + O_2$$

12. Express each chemical equation in terms of moles.
   a. $2\ Ca + O_2 \longrightarrow 2\ CaO$
   b. $CH_4 + 2\ O_2 \longrightarrow CO_2 + 2\ H_2O$

Balancing Chemical Equations

13. Balance the following equations.
    a. $Mg + O_2 \longrightarrow MgO$
    b. $C_3H_8 + O_2 \longrightarrow CO_2 + H_2O$
    c. $H_2 + Ta_2O_3 \longrightarrow Ta + H_2O$

14. Balance the following equations.
    a. $K + O_2 \longrightarrow K_2O_2$
    b. $FeCl_2 + Na_2SiO_3 \longrightarrow NaCl + FeSiO_3$
    c. $F_2 + AlCl_3 \longrightarrow AlF_3 + Cl_2$

15. Write balanced equations for the following processes.
    a. Nitrogen gas and oxygen gas react to form nitrogen oxide (NO).
    b. Ozone (O_3) decomposes into oxygen gas.
    c. Uranium(IV) oxide reacts with hydrogen fluoride (HF) to form uranium(IV) fluoride and water.

16. Write balanced equations for the following processes.
    a. Iron metal reacts with oxygen gas to form rust [iron(III) oxide].
    b. Calcium carbonate (the active ingredient in many antacids) reacts with stomach acid (HCl) to form calcium chloride, water, and carbon dioxide.
    c. Heptane (C_7H_{16}) burns in oxygen gas to form carbon dioxide and water.

Volume Relationships in Chemical Equations

17. Make a sketch similar to Figure 3 to show the reaction of hydrogen gas with oxygen gas to form steam [$H_2O(g)$] at 100 °C.

18. Make a sketch similar to Figure 3 to show that when hydrogen reacts with oxygen to form steam at 100 °C, each volume of gas—hydrogen, oxygen, or steam—contains the same number of molecules.

19. Consider the following equation, which represents the combustion (burning) of hexane (C_6H_{14}).

    $$2\,C_6H_{14}(g) + 19\,O_2(g) \longrightarrow 12\,CO_2(g) + 14\,H_2O(g)$$

    a. What volume, in liters, of $CO_2(g)$ is formed when 20.6 L of $C_6H_{14}(g)$ is burned? Assume that both gases are measured under the same conditions.
    b. What volume, in milliliters, of $C_6H_{14}(g)$ has to burn to react with 29.0 mL $O_2(g)$? Assume that both gases are measured under the same conditions.

20. Consider the following equation, which represents the combustion of ammonia.

    $$4\,NH_3(g) + 3\,O_2(g) \longrightarrow 2\,N_2(g) + 6\,H_2O(g)$$

    a. What volume, in liters, of $N_2(g)$ is formed when 125 L of $NH_3(g)$ is burned? Assume that both gases are measured under the same conditions.
    b. What volume, in liters, of $O_2(g)$ is required to form 36 L of $H_2O(g)$? Assume that both gases are measured under the same conditions.

21. Using the equation in Problem 19, determine the ratio of volume of $CO_2(g)$ formed to volume of $C_6H_{14}(g)$ that reacts, assuming that both gases are measured under the same conditions.

22. Using the equation in Problem 20, determine the ratio of volume of $H_2O(g)$ formed to volume of $NH_3(g)$ that reacts, assuming that both gases are measured under the same conditions.

Avogadro's Number

23. How many (a) sulfur *molecules* and how many (b) sulfur *atoms* are there in 1.00 mol S_8?

24. How many (a) magnesium ions and how many (b) nitride ions are there in 1.00 mol Mg_3N_2?

25. Choose one of the following to complete this statement correctly: One *mole* of bromine (Br_2) gas _____.
    a. has a mass of 79.9 g
    b. contains 6.02×10^{23} Br atoms
    c. contains 12.04×10^{23} Br atoms
    d. has a mass of 6.02×10^{23} g

26. (a) How many barium ions and how many nitrate ions are there in 1.00 mol $Ba(NO_3)_2$? (b) How many nitrogen atoms and how many oxygen atoms are there in 1.00 mol $Ba(NO_3)_2$?

Formula Masses and Molar Masses

You may round atomic masses to one decimal place.

27. Calculate the molar mass of each of the following compounds.
    a. $AgNO_3$
    b. $Mg(ClO)_2$
    c. $Zn(IO_4)_2$
    d. $CH_3(CH_2)_3COF$

28. Calculate the molar mass of each of the following compounds.
    a. Bi_2O_3
    b. $FeSO_4$
    c. $Ca(CH_3COO)_2$
    d. $(NH_4)_2Cr_2O_7$

29. Calculate the mass, in grams, of each of the following.
    a. 7.57 mol $BaSO_4$
    b. 0.0472 mol $CuCl_2$
    c. 0.250 mol $C_{12}H_{22}O_{11}$

30. Calculate the mass, in grams, of each of the following.
    a. 4.61 mol PCl_3
    b. 6.15 mol Cr_2O_3
    c. 0.158 mol IF_5

31. Calculate the amount, in moles, of each of the following.
    a. 6.63 g Sb_2S_3
    b. 19.1 g MoO_3
    c. 434 g $AlPO_4$

32. Calculate the amount, in moles, of each of the following.
    a. 16.3 g SF_6
    b. 25.4 g $Pb(C_2H_3O_2)_2$
    c. 15.6 g $CoCl_3$

33. Calculate the percent by mass of N in (a) $NaNO_3$ and (b) NH_4Cl.

34. Calculate the percent by mass of C, H, and O in glucose ($C_6H_{12}O_6$).

Mole and Mass Relationships in Chemical Equations

35. Consider the reaction for the combustion of butane (C_4H_{10}), a component of liquefied petroleum (LP) gas.

    $$2\,C_4H_{10}(g) + 13\,O_2(g) \longrightarrow 8\,CO_2(g) + 10\,H_2O(g)$$

    a. How many moles of CO_2 are produced when 8.12 mol of butane are burned?
    b. How many moles of oxygen are required to burn 3.13 mol of butane?

36. Consider the reaction for the combustion of octane (C_8H_{18}).

    $$2\,C_8H_{18} + 25\,O_2 \longrightarrow 16\,CO_2 + 18\,H_2O$$

    a. How many moles of H_2O are produced when 0.281 mol of octane is burned?
    b. How many moles of CO_2 are produced when 8.12 mol of oxygen reacts with octane?

37. What mass in grams **(a)** of ammonia can be made from 440 g H_2 and **(b)** of hydrogen is needed to react completely with 892 g N_2?

$$N_2 + H_2 \longrightarrow NH_3 \quad \text{(not balanced)}$$

38. Toluene (C_7H_8) and nitric acid (HNO_3) are used in the production of trinitrotoluene (TNT, $C_7H_5N_3O_6$), an explosive.

$$C_7H_8 + HNO_3 \longrightarrow C_7H_5N_3O_6 + H_2O \quad \text{(not balanced)}$$

What mass in grams **(a)** of nitric acid is required to react with 454 g C_7H_8 and **(b)** of TNT can be made from 829 g C_7H_8?

Molarity of Solutions

39. Calculate the molarity of each of the following solutions.
    a. 23.4 mol HCl in 10.0 L of solution
    b. 0.0875 mol Li_2CO_3 in 632 mL of solution

40. Calculate the molarity of each of the following solutions.
    a. 8.82 mol H_2SO_4 in 7.50 L of solution
    b. 1.22 mol C_2H_5OH in 96.3 mL of solution

41. What mass in grams of solute is needed to prepare **(a)** 3.50 L of 0.500 M NaOH and **(b)** 65.0 mL of 1.45 M $C_6H_{12}O_6$?

42. What mass in grams of solute is needed to prepare **(a)** 0.250 L of 0.167 M $K_2Cr_2O_7$ and **(b)** 625 mL of 0.0200 M $KMnO_4$?

43. What volume in liters of **(a)** 6.00 M NaOH contains 2.50 mol NaOH and **(b)** 0.0500 M KH_2AsO_4 contains 8.10 g KH_2AsO_4?

44. What volume in liters of **(a)** 0.250 M NaOH contains 1.05 mol NaOH and **(b)** 4.25 M $H_2C_2O_4$ contains 0.225 g $H_2C_2O_4$?

Percent Concentrations of Solutions

45. What is the percent by volume concentration of **(a)** 58.0 mL of water in 625 mL of an acetic acid–water solution and **(b)** 79.1 mL of methanol in 755 mL of a methanol–water solution?

46. What is the percent by volume concentration of **(a)** 35.0 mL of water in 725 mL of an ethanol–water solution and **(b)** 78.9 mL of acetone in 1550 mL of an acetone–water solution?

47. Describe how you would prepare 3375 g of an aqueous solution that is 8.2% NaCl by mass.

48. Describe how you would prepare 2.44 kg of an aqueous solution that is 16.3% KOH by mass.

49. Describe how you would prepare 2.00 L of an aqueous solution that is 2.00% acetic acid by volume.

50. Describe how you would prepare 500.0 mL of an aqueous solution that is 30.0% isopropyl alcohol by volume.

ADDITIONAL PROBLEMS

51. Both magnesium and aluminum react with hydrogen ions in aqueous solution to produce hydrogen. Why is it that only one of the following equations correctly describes the reaction?

$$Mg(s) + 2\,H^+(aq) \longrightarrow Mg^{2+}(aq) + H_2(g)$$
$$Al(s) + 2\,H^+(aq) \longrightarrow Al^{3+}(aq) + H_2(g)$$

52. Which of the following correctly represents the decomposition of potassium chlorate to produce potassium chloride and oxygen gas?
    a. $KClO_3(s) \longrightarrow KClO_3(s) + O_2(g) + O(g)$
    b. $2\,KClO_3(s) \longrightarrow 2\,KCl(s) + 3\,O_2(g)$
    c. $KClO_3(s) \longrightarrow KClO(s) + O_2(g)$
    d. $KClO_3(s) \longrightarrow KCl(s) + O_3(g)$

53. Write a balanced chemical equation to represent **(a)** the decomposition, by heating, of solid mercury(II) nitrate to produce pure liquid mercury, nitrogen dioxide gas, and oxygen gas, and **(b)** the reaction of aqueous sodium carbonate with aqueous hydrochloric acid (hydrogen chloride) to produce water, carbon dioxide gas, and aqueous sodium chloride.

54. Joseph Priestley discovered oxygen in 1774 by heating "red calx of mercury" [mercury(II) oxide]. The calx decomposed to its elements. The equation is

$$HgO \longrightarrow Hg + O_2 \quad \text{(not balanced)}$$

What mass of oxygen is produced by the decomposition of 1.08 g HgO?

55. Consider 1.00 mol $H_2(g)$, 2.00 mol He(g), and 0.50 mol $C_2H_2(g)$ at the same temperature and pressure. **(a)** Do the three samples have the same number of atoms? **(b)** Which sample has the greatest mass?

56. What mass in grams of the magnetic oxide of iron (Fe_3O_4) can be made from 24.0 g of pure iron and an excess of oxygen? The equation is

$$Fe + O_2 \longrightarrow Fe_3O_4 \quad \text{(not balanced)}$$

57. When heated above ~ 900 °C, limestone (calcium carbonate) decomposes to quicklime (calcium oxide), which is used to make cement, and carbon dioxide. What mass in grams of quicklime can be produced from 4.72×10^9 g of limestone?

58. Ammonia reacts with oxygen to produce nitric acid (HNO_3) and water. What mass of nitric acid, in grams, can be made from 971 g of ammonia?

59. Hydrogen peroxide solution sold in drugstores is 3.0% H_2O_2 by mass dissolved in water. How many moles of H_2O_2 are in a typical 16-fl. oz. bottle of this solution? (1 fl. oz. = 29.6 mL; density = 1.00 g/mL)

60. What is the mass percent of **(a)** NaOH in a solution of 4.12 g NaOH in 100.0 g of water and **(b)** ethanol in a solution of 5.00 mL of ethanol (density = 0.789 g/mL) in 50.0 g of water?

61. What is the volume percent of **(a)** ethanol in 625 mL of an ethanol–water solution that contains 58.0 mL of water and **(b)** acetone in 1.25 L of an acetone–water solution that contains 10.00 mL of acetone?

62. Laughing gas (dinitrogen monoxide, N_2O, also called nitrous oxide) can be made by very carefully heating ammonium nitrate. The other product is water.
 a. Write a balanced equation for the process.
 b. Draw the Lewis structure for N_2O.
 c. What mass in grams of N_2O can be made from 48.0 g of ammonium nitrate?

63. In Table 1.6 we listed some multiplicative prefixes used with SI base units. In the 1990s, some new prefixes were recommended:
 zetta- (Z, 10^{21})   *yotta-* (Y, 10^{24})
 zepto- (z, 10^{-21})   *yocto-* (y, 10^{-24})
 a. What is the mass of 1.00 ymol of uranium in yoctograms?
 b. How many atoms are in 1.00 zmol of uranium?

64. What volume of 0.0859 M oxalic acid contains 31.7 g of oxalic acid ($H_2C_2O_4$)?

65. In tests for intoxication, blood alcohol levels are expressed as percents by volume. A blood alcohol level of 0.080% by volume means 0.080 mL of ethanol per 100 mL of blood and is considered proof of intoxication. If a person's total blood volume is 5.0 L, what volume of alcohol in the blood gives a blood alcohol level of 0.165% by volume?

66. Homeopathic remedies are prepared using a process of dilution, starting with a substance that causes symptoms of the illness being treated. Some homeopaths use a scale (X) in which the substance is diluted by a factor of ten at each stage. For example, for a 6X remedy, the original substance is diluted tenfold six times, for a total dilution of 10^6. (Many homeopathic remedies are diluted far more than six times.)
 a. If the original substance is in the form of a 1.00 M solution, what would be the yoctomolar concentration of a 24X remedy? (Few starting solutions are 1 M; most are far less concentrated.)
 b. How many molecules of the original substance remain in 1.00 L of a 24X remedy?

67. Evaluate this statement: "One cup of water has more molecules than there are cups of water in all of Earth's oceans" (1 cup = 236 mL = 236 cm³).

68. If a Neanderthal excreted 500 mL of urine into the ocean 50,000 years ago, how many molecules in 500 mL of water you drink today are from that urine? Refer to Problem 67, and assume complete mixing of the waters of Earth over 50,000 years.

69. A truck carrying about 31,000 kg of sulfuric acid (H_2SO_4) is involved in an accident, spilling the acid. What mass of sodium bicarbonate ($NaHCO_3$) is needed to react with and neutralize the sulfuric acid? The products of the reaction are sodium sulfate (Na_2SO_4), water, and carbon dioxide.

70. Referring to Problem 69, determine the mass of sodium carbonate (Na_2CO_3) needed to neutralize the acid. (The products of the reaction are the same.)

71. How many moles of H_2O are in 1.00 L of water? ($d = 1.00$ g/mL)

72. Consider the following equation for the reaction of sodium azide that forms nitrogen gas in airbags. **(a)** What is the atom economy for the production of N_2? **(b)** What is the mass in grams of N_2 that is formed if 2.52 g of NaN_3 are reacted?

$$2\,NaN_3 \longrightarrow 2\,Na + 3\,N_2$$

73. Ethanol (C_2H_5OH) is a very important chemical. In addition to being widely used as an industrial solvent, a gasoline additive, and an alternative fuel, it is well-known as the alcohol in alcoholic beverages. A common name for ethanol is *grain alcohol* because it is formed by the fermentation of glucose ($C_6H_{12}O_6$) and other sugars in grains such as corn, wheat, and barley:

$$C_6H_{12}O_6 \longrightarrow C_2H_5OH + CO_2$$

The previous reaction has been carried out for many centuries and is one of the oldest manufacturing processes. In a more recent development, ethanol can be prepared by reacting ethylene (found in petroleum) with water:

$$C_2H_4 + H_2O \longrightarrow C_2H_5OH$$

 a. Write the *balanced* equation for each of the two reactions above.
 b. Calculate the %A.E. (for the product ethanol) for each of the two reactions.
 c. Explain how you can determine which reaction has the higher atom economy *without* doing the calculation in part (b) above.
 d. Is either method sustainable? Which one? Justify your answer.
 e. Given the results from parts (b) and (d) above, select one of the two methods as the best candidate overall for preparing ethanol. Justify your selection.

74. Formation of butene (C_4H_8) can be accomplished in several different ways. Two are shown below.
Reaction A:

$$C_4H_9Br + NaOH \longrightarrow C_4H_8 + H_2O + NaBr$$

Reaction B:

$$C_4H_6 + H_2 \longrightarrow C_4H_8$$

Which reaction has a higher atom economy?

75. Consider the following equation for the formation of carbon dioxide (CO_2), a known greenhouse gas, from the combustion of hydrocarbons.

$$C_5H_{12} + O_2 \longrightarrow CO_2 + H_2O \text{ (not balanced)}$$

 a. What is the percent atom economy based on carbon dioxide as the target product?
 b. How many grams of CO_2 form if 10.0 g C_5H_{12} is burned?
 c. What is the percent yield of the reaction if 25.4 g CO_2 are formed at the end of the reaction? (Hint: Use the information in the Atom Economy essay for this calculation.)

76. Balance each reaction and calculate the percent atom economy based on the underlined molecule as your desired product.
 a. $CuCl_2(aq) + Na_2CO_3(aq) \longrightarrow \underline{CuCO_3}(s) + NaCl(aq)$
 b. $NH_3(g) + O_2(g) \longrightarrow \underline{NO}(g) + H_2O(g)$
 c. $KMnO_4(aq) + KOH(aq) + KI(aq) \longrightarrow \underline{K_2MnO_4}(aq) + KIO_3(aq) + H_2O(l)$

COLLABORATIVE GROUP PROJECTS

Prepare a PowerPoint, poster, or other presentation (as directed by your instructor) to share with the class.

1. Prepare a brief biographical report on Amedeo Avogadro.

2. In the view of many scientists, hydrogen holds great promise as a source of clean energy. A 2008 report by the U.S. National Research Council suggested that a government subsidy of roughly $4 billion per year through 2023 could make hydrogen cars competitive with petroleum-powered vehicles. Search the web to explore the proposals for using hydrogen as a fuel. Write a brief summary of what you find, and use an appropriate balanced equation to explain why hydrogen is considered a clean, renewable source.

BRIEF ANSWERS TO SELECTED PROBLEMS

Answers are provided for *all in-chapter exercises*. Brief answers are given for *odd-numbered Review Questions*; more complete answers can be obtained by reviewing the text. Answers are provided for *all odd-numbered Problems and Additional Problems*.

NOTE: For numerical problems, your answer may differ slightly from ours because of rounding and the use of significant figures.

1 A. $3 H_2 + N_2 \longrightarrow 2 NH_3$
   B. $2 Fe_2O_3 + 3 C \longrightarrow 3 CO_2 + 4 Fe$

2 A. $1.48 L CO_2$
   B. propane; 8 L

3 A. a. 65.0 u   b. 98.0 u
   c. 147.0 u   d. 234.1 u

4 a. 13.8% N   b. 41.1% N

5 A. a. $2.04 g Si$ b. $1000 g H_2O$
   c. $17.0 g Ca(H_2PO_4)_2$
   B. a. $0.0664 mol Fe$ b. $2.84 mol C_4H_{10}$
   c. $0.000674 mol Mg(NO_3)_2$

6 *Molecular:* 2 molecules H_2S react with 3 molecules O_2 to form 2 molecules SO_2 and 2 molecules H_2O
   Molar: 2 mol H_2S react with 3 mol O_2 to form 2 mol SO_2 and 2 mol H_2O
   Mass: 68.2 g H_2S react with 96.0 g O_2 to form 128.1 g SO_2 and 36.0 g H_2O

7 A. a. $1.59 mol CO_2$ b. $0.168 mol CO_2$
   B. propane; 15 mol

8 A. $0.763 g O_2$
   B. a. $2130 g CO_2$ b. $2350 g CO_2$

9 A. 0.00870 M
   B. 0.968 M

10 A. a. 9.00 M   b. 1.26 M
   B. 0.274 M

11 a. 673 g KOH   b. 5.61 g KOH

12 A. 29.7 mL
   B. $6.30 \times 10^{-4} g HNO_3$

13 A. 90.7% ethanol
   B. 34.8% toluene

14 A. $2.81\% H_2O_2$
   B. 51.3% NaOH

15 A. Dissolve 5.62 g glucose in enough water to make 125 g solution.
   B. Dissolve 15.6 g NaCl in enough water to make 1750 g solution.

1. a. The smallest repeating unit of a substance
   b. The sum of the atomic masses of a chemical compound
   c. The amount of a substance that contains 6.022×10^{23} formula units of the substance
   d. The number of atoms (6.022×10^{23}) in exactly 12 g of pure carbon-12

e. The formula mass of a substance expressed in grams; mass of one mole
   f. The volume occupied by 1 mol of a gas under specified conditions

3. Avogadro's hypothesis states that equal volumes of all gases contain the same number of molecules at fixed temperature and pressure. It explains why volumes of gaseous reactants and products combine in small whole-number ratios.

5. a. A homogeneous mixture of two or more substances
   b. The substance that dissolves another substance (solute) to form a solution
   c. The substance that is dissolved in another substance (solvent) to form a solution
   d. A solution in which the solvent is water.

7. a. 12   b. 3   c. 6

9. 6 N; 3 P; 27 H; 12 O

11. a. Two molecules of H_2O_2 decompose to give two molecules of H_2O and one molecule of O_2.
    b. 2 mol H_2O_2 decompose to give 2 mol H_2O and 1 mol O_2.
    c. 68 g H_2O_2 decompose to give 36 g H_2O and 32 g O_2.

13. a. $2 Mg + O_2 \rightarrow MgO$
    b. $C_3H_8 + 5 O_2 \rightarrow 3 CO_2 + 4 H_2O$
    c. $3 H_2 + Ta_2O_3 \rightarrow 2 Ta + 3 H_2O$

15. a. $N_2 + O_2 \rightarrow 2 NO$
    b. $2 O_3 \rightarrow 3 O_2$
    c. $UO_2 + 4 HF \rightarrow UF_4 + 2 H_2O$

17.

Hydrogen gas (two volumes)   Oxygen gas (one volume)   Steam (two volumes)

19. a. 124 L   b. 3.05 mL

21. 6:1 or 6 times

23. a. $6.02 \times 10^{23} S_8$ molecules   b. 4.82×10^{24} S atoms

25. c

27. a. 169.9 g   b. 127.2 g   c. 447.2 g   d. 104.1 g

29. a. $1770 g BaSO_4$ b. $6.35 g CuCl_2$ c. $85.6 g C_{12}H_{22}O_{11}$

31. a. $0.0195 mol Sb_2S_3$ b. $0.133 mol MoO_3$
    c. $3.56 mol AlPO_4$

33. a. 16.5%   b. 26.2%

35. a. $32.5 mol CO_2$ b. $20.3 mol O_2$

37. a. $2480 g NH_3$ b. $193 g H_2$

39. a. 2.34 M HCl   b. $0.138 M Li_2CO_3$

41. a. 70.0 g NaOH   b. $17.0 g C_6H_{12}O_6$

43. a. 0.416 L   b. 0.900 L

45. a. 9.28% water by vol   b. 10.5% methanol by vol

47. Add 277 g NaCl to 3098 g water.

49. Add 40.0 mL acetic acid to enough water to make 2.00 L of solution.

51. Charge is not balanced in the equation $Al(s) + 2 H^+(aq) \rightarrow Al^{3+}(aq) + H_2(g)$.

53. a. $Hg(NO_3)_2(s) \longrightarrow Hg(l) + 2 NO_2(g) + O_2(g)$
    b. $Na_2CO_3(aq) + 2 HCl(aq) \longrightarrow H_2O(l) + CO_2(g) + 2 NaCl(aq)$

55. a. yes   **b.** 0.50 mol C_2H_2

57. 2.65×10^9 g CaO

59. 0.418 mol H_2O_2

61. a. 90.7% ethanol   **b.** 0.800% acetone

63. a. 2.38×10^{-22} g U   **b.** 602 atoms!

65. 0.00825 L (8.25 mL)

67. There are about 2000 times as many molecules in a cup of water as there are cups of water in Earth's oceans. The statement is valid.

69. 53,000 kg

71. 55.5 mol H_2O

73. a. (1) $C_6H_{12}O_6 \rightarrow 2 C_2H_5OH + 2 CO_2$; (2) $C_2H_4 + H_2O \rightarrow C_2H_5OH$
    b. (1) 51.1%; (2) 100%
    c. (1) CO_2 is a byproduct ("waste"); (2) no byproduct
    d. (1) sustainable; (2) not sustainable
    e. reaction (1) does produce a byproduct, but is sustainable and does not consume valuable, non-renewable petroleum.

75. a. 67.1%   **b.** 30.6 g CO_2 **c.** 83.0%

Acids and Bases

Have You Ever Wondered?

1. **Are all acids corrosive?**

2. **What is an amino acid?**

3. **Is vitamin C really an acid? Are all vitamins acids?**

4. **What is the difference between salt and sodium?**

5. **What is meant by "pH-balanced shampoo"?**

Image Source/Alamy

Learning Objectives

> Distinguish between acids and bases using their chemical and physical properties. (1)

> Explain how an acid–base indicator works. (1)

> Identify Arrhenius and Brønsted–Lowry acids and bases. (2)

> Write a balanced equation for a neutralization or an ionization. (2)

> Identify acidic and basic anhydrides, and write equations showing their reactions with water. (3)

> Define and identify strong and weak acids and bases. (4)

> Identify the reactants and predict the products in a neutralization reaction. (5)

> Describe the relationship between the pH of a solution and its acidity or basicity. (6)

> Find the molar concentration of hydrogen ion, $[H^+]$, from a pH value or the pH value from $[H^+]$. (6)

> Write the formula for the conjugate base of an acid or for the conjugate acid of a base. (7)

> Describe the action of a buffer. (7)

> Describe everyday uses of acids and bases and how they affect daily life. (8)

> Write equations for the production of soap and of biofuel.

> Describe ways by which acids and bases can contribute to greener production of consumer products.

Valentyn Volkov/Shutterstock

Please pass the protons

Have you ever tasted a lemon or a grapefruit? Or felt a burning sensation on your arm after using a cleaning solution containing ammonia? These are but two examples of acids (citric acid in lemons and grapefruit) and bases (ammonia in cleaning solutions) we encounter in our daily lives. Other familiar acids are vinegar (acetic acid), vitamin C (ascorbic acid), and battery acid (sulfuric acid). Some familiar bases are drain cleaner (sodium hydroxide), baking soda (sodium bicarbonate), and antacids.

From "acid indigestion" to "acid rain," the word *acid* appears frequently in the news and in advertisements. Air and water pollution often involve acids

The chemical substances we call acids and bases are all around us. Acids are used in steel production and metal plating, as well as in chemical analysis. Acids are even found in the food we eat. Pancakes and muffins rise because of acids and bases in the ingredients, and the tart taste of fruit comes from the different acids in its flesh. Although the items described and shown here are dramatically different, the acids in them have something in common. All of them can provide hydrogen (hydronium) ions.

From Chapter 7 of *Chemistry for Changing Times*, Thirteenth Edition. John W. Hill, Terry W. McCreary, Doris K. Kolb. Copyright © 2013 by Pearson Education, Inc. All rights reserved.

Lajos Repasi/iStockphoto

▲ Many skin-peel preparations used by cosmetologists contain alpha-hydroxy acids such as glycolic acid or lactic acid.

1. Are all acids corrosive? It is clear from Table 1 that *acid* does not necessarily mean "corrosive." Many acids are harmless enough to be included in foods we eat, and some are necessary to life.

▶ **Figure 1** Some common acids (left), bases (center), and salts (right). Acids, bases, and salts are components of many familiar consumer products.

Q: *How would each of the three classes of compounds affect the indicator dye litmus? (See Figure 2.)*

and bases. Acid rain, for example, is a serious environmental problem. In arid areas, alkaline (basic) water is sometimes undrinkable.

Did you know that our senses recognize four tastes related to acid–base chemistry? Acids taste sour, bases taste bitter, and the compounds formed when acids react with bases (salts) taste salty. The sweet taste is more complicated. To taste sweet, a compound must have both an acidic part and a basic part, plus just the right geometry to fit the sweet-taste receptors of our taste buds.

In this chapter, we discuss some of the chemistry of acids and bases. You use them every day. Your body processes them continuously. You will probably hear and read about them as long as you live. What you learn here can help you gain a better understanding of these important classes of compounds.

1 Acids and Bases: Experimental Definitions

Learning Objectives ❯ Distinguish between acids and bases using their chemical and physical properties. ❯ Explain how an acid–base indicator works.

Acids and bases are chemical opposites, and so their properties are quite different—often opposite. Let's begin by listing a few of these properties.
An *acid* is a compound that

- tastes sour.
- causes litmus indicator dye to turn red.
- dissolves active metals such as zinc and iron, producing hydrogen gas.
- reacts with bases to form water and ionic compounds called *salts*.

A *base* is a compound that

- tastes bitter.
- causes litmus indicator dye to turn blue.
- feels slippery on the skin.
- reacts with acids to form water and salts.

We can identify foods that are acidic by their sour taste. Vinegar and lemon juice are examples. Vinegar is a solution of acetic acid (about 5%) in water. Lemons, limes, and other citrus fruits contain citric acid. Lactic acid gives yogurt its tart taste, and phosphoric acid is often added to carbonated drinks to impart tartness. The bitter taste of tonic water, on the other hand, comes in part from quinine, a base. Figure 1 shows some common acids and bases.

Pearson Education/Eric Schrader

Acids and Bases

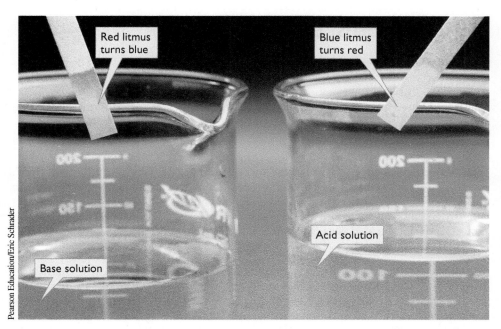

Figure 2 Strips of paper impregnated with litmus dye (extracted from a fungus) are often used to distinguish between acids and bases. The sample on the left turns litmus blue and is therefore basic. The sample on the right turns litmus red and is acidic.

▲ **It DOES Matter!**!
Hydrangea is one of many types of flowers that may show different colors depending on the acidity of the soil in which it is grown. Some varieties are blue (top) when planted in slightly acidic soil and pink (bottom) when planted in more basic soil.

A litmus test is a common way to identify a substance as an acid or a base. Litmus (Figure 2) is an **acid–base indicator**, one of many such compounds. If you dip a strip of neutral (violet-colored) litmus paper into an unknown solution and the strip turns pink, the solution is acidic. If it turns blue, the solution is basic. If the strip does not turn pink or blue, the solution is neither acidic nor basic. Many substances, such as those that give the colors to grape juice, red cabbage, blueberries, and many flower petals, are acid–base indicators.

Self-Assessment Questions

1. Which of the following is *not* a property of acids?
   a. feel slippery on the skin
   b. react with Zn to form hydrogen gas
   c. taste sour
   d. turn litmus red

2. Which of the following is *not* a property of bases?
   a. feel slippery on the skin
   b. react with salts to form acids
   c. taste bitter
   d. turn litmus blue

3. In general, when an acid and a base are mixed,
   a. a new acid and a salt are formed
   b. a new base and a salt are formed
   c. no reaction occurs
   d. a salt and water are formed

4. A common substance that contains lactic acid is
   a. salad oil
   b. soap
   c. vinegar
   d. yogurt

5. The sour taste of grapefruit is due to
   a. acetic acid
   b. ammonia
   c. carbonic acid
   d. citric acid

Richard Megna/Fundamental Photographs

▲ You can make your own indicator dye. Chop about 2 cups of red cabbage. Cover with boiling water. Stir. After about 10 min, filter out the solids with a coffee filter. Use about 50 mL of the liquid to test various household chemicals (vinegar, baking soda, ammonia, and so on) for pH. The indicator changes from red at about pH 2 to purple at pH 4, violet at pH 6, blue at pH 8, blue-green at pH 10, and greenish-yellow at pH 12. Other plant materials that contain indicators include blackberries, black raspberries, red radish peels, red rose petals, and turmeric.

Answers: 1, a; 2, b; 3, d; 4, d; 5, d

197

2 Acids, Bases, and Salts

Learning Objectives ⟩ Identify Arrhenius and Brønsted–Lowry acids and bases.
⟩ Write a balanced equation for a neutralization or an ionization.

▲ Swedish chemist Svante Arrhenius (1859–1927) proposed the theory that acids, bases, and salts in water are composed of ions. He also was the first to relate carbon dioxide in the atmosphere to the greenhouse effect.

Acids and bases have certain characteristic properties. But why do they have these properties? We use several different theories to explain these properties.

The Arrhenius Theory

Svante Arrhenius developed the first successful theory of acids and bases in 1887. According to Arrhenius's concept, an **acid** is a molecular substance that breaks up in aqueous solution into hydrogen ions (H^+) and anions. (Because a hydrogen ion is a hydrogen atom from which the sole electron has been removed, H^+ ions are also called *protons*.) The acid is said to *ionize*. For example, nitric acid ionizes in water.

$$HNO_3(aq) \longrightarrow H^+(aq) + NO_3^-(aq)$$

In water, then, the properties of acids are those of the H^+ ion. It is the hydrogen ion that turns litmus red, tastes sour, and reacts with active metals and bases. Table 1 lists some common acids. Notice that each formula contains one or more hydrogen atoms. Chemists often indicate an acid by writing the formula with the H atom(s) first. HCl, H_2SO_4, and HNO_3 are acids; NH_3 and CH_4 are not. The formula $HC_2H_3O_2$ (acetic acid) indicates that one H atom ionizes when this compound is in aqueous solution, and three do not.

An Arrhenius **base** is defined as a substance that releases hydroxide ions (OH^-) in aqueous solution. Some bases are ionic solids that contain OH^-, such as sodium hydroxide ($NaOH$) and calcium hydroxide [$Ca(OH)_2$]. These compounds simply release hydroxide ions into the solution when the solid is dissolved in water:

$$NaOH(s) \xrightarrow{\text{H}_2\text{O}} Na^+(aq) + OH^-(aq)$$

We write H_2O over the arrow to indicate that it is a solvent, not a reactant.

Other bases are molecular substances such as ammonia that ionize to produce OH^- when placed in water.

Experimental evidence indicates that the properties of bases in water are due to OH^-. Table 2 lists some common bases. Most of these are ionic compounds containing positively changed metal ions, such as Na^+ or Ca^{2+}, and negatively charged hydroxide ions. When these compounds dissolve in water, they all provide OH^- ions, and thus they are all bases. The properties of bases are those of hydroxide ions, just as the properties of acids are those of hydrogen ions.

Table 1	Some Common Acids		
Name	**Formula**	**Acid Strength**	**Common Uses/Notes**
Sulfuric acid	H_2SO_4	Strong	Battery acid; ore processing, fertilizer manufacturing, oil refining
Hydrochloric acid	HCl	Strong	Cleaning of metals and bricks, removing scale from boilers
Phosphoric acid	H_3PO_4	Moderate	Used in colas and rust removers
Lactic acid	$CH_3CHOHCOOH$	Weak	Yogurt; acidulant (food additive to increase tartness), lotion additive
Acetic acid	CH_3COOH	Weak	Vinegar; acidulant
Boric acid	H_3BO_3	Very weak	Antiseptic eyewash, roach poison
Hydrocyanic acid	HCN	Very weak	Plastics manufacture; extremely toxic

Table 2 Some Common Bases

Name	Formula	Classification	Common Uses/Notes
Sodium hydroxide	NaOH	Strong	Acid neutralization; soap making
Potassium hydroxide	KOH	Strong	Making liquid soaps and biodiesel fuels
Lithium hydroxide	LiOH	Strong	Alkaline storage batteries
Calcium hydroxide	$Ca(OH)_2$	Strong[a]	Plaster, cement; soil neutralizer
Magnesium hydroxide	$Mg(OH)_2$	Strong[a]	Antacid, laxative
Ammonia	NH_3	Weak	Fertilizer, household cleansers

[a]Although these bases are classified as strong, they are not very soluble in water. Calcium hydroxide is only slightly soluble, and magnesium hydroxide is practically insoluble.

Arrhenius further proposed that the essential reaction between an acid and a base, **neutralization**, is the combination of H^+ and OH^- to form water. The cation that was originally associated with the OH^- combines with the anion that was associated with the H^+ to form an ionic compound, a **salt**.

$$\text{An acid} + \text{a base} \longrightarrow \text{a salt} + \text{water}$$

CONCEPTUAL Example 1   Ionization of Acids and Bases

Write equations showing (a) the ionization of nitric acid (HNO_3) in water and (b) the ionization of solid potassium hydroxide (KOH) in water.

Solution

a. An HNO_3 molecule ionizes to form a hydrogen ion and a nitrate ion. Because this reaction occurs in water, we can use the label "(aq)" to indicate that the substances involved are in aqueous solution.

$$HNO_3(aq) \longrightarrow H^+(aq) + NO_3^-(aq)$$

b. Potassium hydroxide (KOH), an ionic solid, simply dissolves in the water, forming separate $K^+(aq)$ and $OH^-(aq)$ ions.

$$KOH(s) \xrightarrow{H_2O} K^+(aq) + OH^-(aq)$$

■ EXERCISE 1A

Write equations showing (a) the ionization of HBr (hydrobromic acid) in water and (b) the ionization of solid calcium hydroxide in water.

■ EXERCISE 1B

Historically, formulas for carboxylic acids (compounds containing a —COOH group) are often written with the ionizable hydrogen *last*. For example, instead of writing the formula for acetic acid as $HC_2H_3O_2$, it can be written as CH_3COOH. Write an equation showing the ionization of CH_3COOH in water.

2. What is an amino acid? An amino acid is a molecule that contains both —COOH, which is acidic, and —NH_2 (an *amino group*), which is basic. Amino acids undergo acid-base reactions with one another and link together to form the proteins in living tissue.

Limitations of the Arrhenius Theory

The Arrhenius theory is limited in several ways.

■ A simple free proton does not exist in water solution. The H^+ ion has such a high positive charge density that it is immediately attracted to a lone pair of electrons on an O atom of an H_2O molecule, forming a *hydronium ion*, H_3O^+.

- It does not explain the basicity of ammonia and related compounds. Ammonia seems out of place in Table 2 because it contains no hydroxide ions.
- It applies only to reactions in aqueous solution.

As with many scientific theories, a better one based on newer data has supplanted Arrhenius's theory.

The Brønsted–Lowry Acid–Base Theory

The shortcomings of the Arrhenius theory were largely overcome by a theory proposed in 1923, by J. N. Brønsted in Denmark and T. M. Lowry in Great Britain, who were working independently. In the Brønsted–Lowry theory,

- an acid is a *proton donor*, and
- a base is a *proton acceptor*.

The theory portrays the ionization of hydrogen chloride in this way:

$$HCl(aq) + H_2O \longrightarrow H_3O^+(aq) + Cl^-(aq)$$

Here, water is a reactant. The acid molecules donate hydrogen ions (protons) to the water molecules, so the acid (HCl) acts as a proton donor.

$$H:\ddot{C}l: \ + \ H:\ddot{O}: \longrightarrow \left[H:\ddot{O}: \atop H \right]^+ + \ :\ddot{C}l:^-$$

Acid
(proton donor)   Hydrochloric acid

The HCl molecule donates a proton to a water molecule, producing a hydronium ion and a chloride ion and forming a solution called *hydrochloric acid*. Other acids react similarly; they donate hydrogen ions to water molecules to produce hydronium ions. If we let HA represent any acid, the reaction is written as

$$HA(aq) + H_2O \longrightarrow H_3O^+(aq) + A^-(aq)$$

Even when the solvent is something other than water, the acid acts as a proton donor, transferring H^+ ions to the solvent molecules.

In water, an H^+ ion is associated with several H_2O molecules—for example, four H_2O molecules in the ion $H(H_2O)_4{}^+$, or $H_9O_4{}^+$. For most purposes, we simply use H^+ and ignore the associated water molecules. However, keep in mind that the notation H^+ is a simplification of the real situation: Protons in water actually exist associated with water molecules.

CONCEPTUAL Example 2   Brønsted–Lowry Acids

Write an equation showing the reaction with water of HNO_3 as a Brønsted–Lowry acid. What is the role of water in the reaction?

Solution
As a Brønsted–Lowry acid, HNO_3 donates a proton to a water molecule, forming a hydronium ion and a nitrate ion.

$$HNO_3(aq) + H_2O \longrightarrow H_3O^+(aq) + NO_3{}^-(aq)$$

The water molecule accepts a proton from HNO_3. Water is a Brønsted–Lowry base in this reaction.

■ EXERCISE 2A
Write an equation showing the reaction with water of HBr as a Brønsted–Lowry acid.

■ EXERCISE 2B
Write an equation showing the reaction of methanol (CH_3OH) with $HClO_4$ as a Brønsted–Lowry acid.

Where does the OH^- come from when bases such as ammonia (NH_3) are dissolved in water? The Arrhenius theory proved inadequate in answering this question, but the Brønsted–Lowry theory explains how ammonia acts as a base in water.

Ammonia is a gas at room temperature. When it is dissolved in water, some of the ammonia molecules react as shown by the following equation.

$$NH_3(aq) + H_2O \longrightarrow NH_4^+(aq) + OH^-(aq)$$

An ammonia molecule accepts a proton from a water molecule; NH_3 acts as a Brønsted–Lowry base. (Recall that the N atom of ammonia has a lone pair of electrons, which it can share with a proton.) The water molecule acts as a proton donor—an acid. The ammonia molecule accepts the proton and becomes an ammonium ion. When a proton leaves a water molecule, it leaves behind the electron pair that it shared with the O atom. The water molecule becomes a negatively charged hydroxide ion.

In general, then, *a base is a proton acceptor* (Figure 3). This definition includes not only hydroxide ions but also neutral molecules such as ammonia and *amines* (organic compounds such as CH_3NH_2 that are derived from ammonia). It also includes other negative ions such as the oxide (O^{2-}), carbonate (CO_3^{2-}), and bicarbonate (HCO_3^-) ions. The idea of an acid as a proton donor and a base as a proton acceptor greatly expands our concept of acids and bases.

Acid   Base

◀ Figure 3 A Brønsted–Lowry acid is a proton donor. A base is a proton acceptor.

Q: *Can you write an equation in which the acid is represented as HA and the base as :B⁻?*

Salts

Salts, formed from the neutralization reactions of acids and bases, are ionic compounds composed of cations and anions. These ions can be simple ions, such as sodium ion (Na^+) and chloride ion (Cl^-), or polyatomic ions, such as ammonium ion (NH_4^+), sulfate ion (SO_4^{2-}), and acetate ion (CH_3COO^-). Sodium chloride, ordinary table salt, is probably the most familiar salt.

Salts that conduct electricity when dissolved in water are called *electrolytes*. Various electrolytes, in certain amounts, are critical for many bodily functions including nerve conduction, heartbeat, and fluid balance. Medical blood tests often check levels of Na^+, K^+, Cl^-, HCO_3^-, and other electrolyte ions.

There are many common salts with familiar uses. Sodium chloride and calcium chloride are used to melt ice on roads and sidewalks in winter. Copper(II) sulfate is used to kill tree roots in sewage lines. We will encounter many other examples as dietary minerals, fertilizers, and more. Table 3 lists some salts used in medicine.

Table 3 Some Salts with Present or Past Uses in Medicine

Name	Formula	Uses
Silver nitrate	$AgNO_3$	Germicide and antiseptic
Stannous fluoride [tin(II) fluoride]	SnF_2	Toothpaste additive to prevent dental cavities
Calcium sulfate (plaster of Paris)	$(CaSO_4)_2 \cdot H_2O^a$	Plaster casts
Magnesium sulfate (Epsom salts)	$MgSO_4 \cdot 7H_2O^a$	Laxative, foot baths
Potassium permanganate	$KMnO_4$	Cauterizing agent, antiseptic
Ferrous sulfate [iron(II) sulfate]	$FeSO_4$	Prescribed for iron deficiency (anemia)
Zinc sulfate	$ZnSO_4$	Skin treatment (eczema)
Barium sulfate	$BaSO_4$	Provides the contrast material in "barium cocktail" given for gastrointestinal X-rays
Mercurous chloride [mercury(I) chloride; calomel]	Hg_2Cl_2	Laxative; no longer used'

[a] These compounds are hydrates, substances containing water molecules combined in a definite ratio as an integral part of the compound.

Irv Levy, *Gordon College*

Sustainability: It's Basic (and Acidic)

Green chemistry is a part of sustainable chemistry. Sustainability, often defined as "meeting the needs of the present generation without compromising the ability of future generations to meet their needs," is much in the news these days. Green chemistry is one of the critical means of attaining sustainability. Understanding of acids and bases has led to greener, more sustainable methods for producing consumer products. Two important examples are soap and renewable biofuels.

Soap traditionally has been made from fats left from cooking meats and from vegetable oils. Fats and oils contain substances composed of three long chains of carbon atoms connected to a central set of three carbon atoms, an arrangement called a *triglyceride*. To make soap, the fats are heated and mixed with lye solution (aqueous sodium hydroxide—a base). Each mole of triglyceride reacts with three moles of base to produce three moles of soap and one mole of the byproduct glycerol (also called glycerin). Soaps are salts (Section 2) of carboxylic acids that usually have a long chain of carbon atoms. An example of a typical soap is sodium palmitate. Its chemical formula is shown here.

$$CH_3(CH_2)_{14}COO^-Na^+$$

The byproduct glycerol has a number of uses, including as a moisturizing ingredient in soap. Chemists at Gordon College (Wenham, MA) found that adding glycerol to the fats and oils traditionally used in soap-making decreased the quantity of starting materials required for soap production. Much more glycerol byproduct is produced industrially than can be used by the soap industry, however, so the search continues for other green uses for glycerol.

The chemistry of biodiesel fuel production is much like that of soap-making. In both processes, bases are used and glycerol is formed. With the use of methanol (CH_3OH) in place of water and a catalytic amount of base, though, the triglycerides are converted to compounds called *esters*. An example of a typical biodiesel molecule is shown here.

$$CH_3(CH_2)_{14}COOCH_3$$

Although the long chains of carbon atoms in biodiesel often are the same as in soap molecules, biodiesel molecules have a different group on one end of the chain. Compare these compounds to a typical diesel molecule from petroleum that does not contain any atoms other than carbon and hydrogen.

$$CH_3(CH_2)_{14}CH_3$$

What do soap, biodiesel, and glycerol have to do with sustainability and green chemistry? The first principle of green chemistry encourages the prevention of waste. Sometimes wastes also are harmful to the environment. Wouldn't it be better to redirect apparently useless materials into something useful?

Consider this: Each year billions of gallons of fats and oils are used to fry foods. Fryer oils degrade fairly quickly in commercial kitchens. For many years the used oils were carted off by disposal companies as waste. Today, much of that used oil is converted into biodiesel fuel, providing an alternative fuel that doesn't deplete fossil petroleum reserves. This approach satisfies the green chemistry principle of using renewable resources while providing new use for what was once considered waste. And it gets better! Petroleum diesel fuel is hazardous to humans and toxic to the environment. Biodiesel is much safer.

Acids also are involved in green processes such as cleaning. For example, polylactic acid (PLA) is a type of biodegradable and renewable plastic made from chemicals derived from corn (see green chemistry essay. PLA plastic, made by companies such as NatureWorks, is found in many consumer materials, such as plastic cups. Research at Simmons College in Boston has led to a new way to convert used PLA cups into an antimicrobial cleaning solution containing lactic acid ($CH_3CHOHCOOH$). The shredded plastic is mixed with alcohol and base to break down the polymer to sodium lactate ($CH_3CHOHCOONa$). The basic sodium lactate solution is neutralized with acid to form the lactic acid cleaner, which is useful for wiping away soap scum.

In the quest for sustaisnability, acids and bases are an essential part of the toolbox that will continue to be used as chemists search for better ways to prevent waste and use renewable starting materials. You might argue that sustainability is basic—not to mention acidic.

a11/ZUMA Press/Newscom

▲ Biodiesel is made from waste fats and oils used in cooking. In the past, those wastes would require disposal; now, they are useful. Biodiesel is an excellent example of sustainable chemistry.

Self-Assessment Questions

For Questions 1–5, match each formula with the compound's application.

1. CH_3COOH (a) battery acid
2. H_3BO_3 (b) soap making
3. HCl   (c) antiseptic eyewash
4. H_2SO_4 (d) remove boiler scale
5. NaOH   (e) vinegar
6. Which of the following equations best represents what happens when hydrogen bromide dissolves in water?

     a. $2\ HBr \xrightarrow{H_2O} Br_2 + H_2$ **b.** $HBr(g) \xrightarrow{H_2O} H(aq) + Br(aq)$

     c. $HBr \longrightarrow H^+(aq) + Br^-(aq)$ **d.** $HBr(g) + H_2O \longrightarrow Br^-(aq) + H_3O^+(aq)$

For Questions 7–10, match each term with the correct definition.

7. Arrhenius acid   (a) proton acceptor
8. Arrhenius base   (b) proton donor
9. Brønsted acid   (c) produces H^+ in water
10. Brønsted base   (d) produces OH^- in water

Answers: 1, e; 2, c; 3, d; 4, a; 5, b; 6, d; 7, c; 8, d; 9, b; 10, a

3 Acidic and Basic Anhydrides

Learning Objective ❯ Identify acidic anhydrides and basic anhydrides, and write equations showing their reactions with water.

Certain metal and nonmetal oxides are well known for their ability to produce or to neutralize acids or bases. For example, nitrogen dioxide (NO_2) and sulfur dioxide (SO_2) are notorious for producing acid rain. Calcium oxide (quicklime, CaO) is widely used to neutralize acidic soils. In the Brønsted–Lowry view, many metal oxides act directly as bases because the oxide ion can accept a proton. These metal oxides also react with water to form metal hydroxides, compounds that are bases in the Arrhenius sense. And many nonmetal oxides react with water to form acids.

Nonmetal Oxides: Acidic Anhydrides

Many acids are made by reacting nonmetal oxides with water. For example, sulfur trioxide reacts with water to form sulfuric acid.

$$SO_3 + H_2O \longrightarrow H_2SO_4$$

Similarly, carbon dioxide reacts with water to form carbonic acid.

$$CO_2 + H_2O \longrightarrow H_2CO_3$$

In general, nonmetal oxides react with water to form acids.

$$\text{Nonmetal oxide} + H_2O \longrightarrow \text{acid}$$

Nonmetal oxides that act in this way are called **acidic anhydrides**. *Anhydride* means "without water." These reactions explain why rainwater is acidic (Section 8).

CONCEPTUAL **Example 3**   Acidic Anhydrides

Give the formula for the acid formed when sulfur dioxide reacts with water.

Solution

The formula for the acid, H_2SO_3, is obtained by adding the two H atoms and one O atom of water to SO_2. The equation for the reaction is simply

$$SO_2 + H_2O \longrightarrow H_2SO_3$$

▲ **It DOES Matter!**
Slaked lime is inexpensive, easily made from cheap raw materials, and low in toxicity. These properties make it the most widely used base for neutralizing acids. It is an ingredient in such diverse materials as bricklayer's mortar, plaster, glues, and even pickles and corn tortillas. The whitewash made famous in Mark Twain's *Adventures of Tom Sawyer* was a simple mixture of slaked lime and water.

■ EXERCISE 3A
Give the formula for the acid formed when selenium dioxide (SeO_2) reacts with water.

■ EXERCISE 3B
Give the formula for the acid formed when dinitrogen pentoxide (N_2O_5) reacts with water. (*Hint:* Two molecules of acid are formed.)

Metal Oxides: Basic Anhydrides

Just as acids can be made from nonmetal oxides, many common hydroxide bases can be made from metal oxides. For example, calcium oxide reacts with water to form calcium hydroxide ("slaked lime").

$$CaO + H_2O \longrightarrow Ca(OH)_2$$

Another example is the reaction of lithium oxide with water to form lithium hydroxide.

$$Li_2O + H_2O \longrightarrow 2\,LiOH$$

In general, metal oxides react with water to form bases (Figure 4). These metal oxides are called **basic anhydrides**.

$$\text{Metal oxide} + H_2O \longrightarrow \text{base}$$

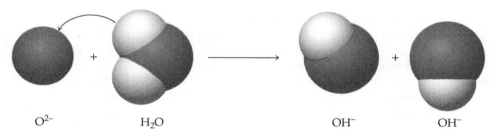

O^{2-} H_2O OH^- OH^-

▲ **Figure 4** Metal oxides are basic because the oxide ion reacts with water to form two hydroxide ions.

Q: *Can you write an equation that shows how solid sodium oxide (Na_2O) reacts with water to form sodium hydroxide?*

CONCEPTUAL Example 4   Basic Anhydrides

Give the formula for the base formed by the addition of water to barium oxide (BaO).

Solution
Again, we add the atoms of a water molecule to BaO. Because a barium ion has a 2+ charge, the formula for the base has *two* hydroxide (1−) ions.

$$BaO + H_2O \longrightarrow Ba(OH)_2$$

■ EXERCISE 4A
Give the formula for the base formed by the addition of water to strontium oxide (SrO).

■ EXERCISE 4B
What base is formed by the addition of water to potassium oxide (K_2O)? (*Hint:* Two moles of base are formed for each mole of potassium oxide.)

Self-Assessment Questions

1. Selenic acid (H_2SeO_4) is an extremely corrosive acid that when heated is capable of dissolving gold. It is quite soluble in water. The anhydride of selenic acid is
   a. SeO
   b. SeO_2
   c. SeO_3
   d. SeO_4

2. Zinc hydroxide [$Zn(OH)_2$] is used as an absorbent in surgical dressings. The anhydride of zinc hydroxide is
   a. ZnO
   b. ZnOH
   c. ZnO_2
   d. Zn_2O_3

Answers: 1, c; 2, a

4 Strong and Weak Acids and Bases

Learning Objective > Define and identify strong and weak acids and bases.

When gaseous hydrogen chloride (HCl) reacts with water, it reacts completely to form hydronium ions and chloride ions.

$$HCl + H_2O \longrightarrow H_3O^+ + Cl^-$$

For many purposes, we simply write this reaction as the ionization of HCl and use (aq) to indicate a solution in water.

$$HCl(aq) \longrightarrow H^+(aq) + Cl^-(aq)$$

Most acids do not ionize completely, however. The poisonous gas hydrogen cyanide (HCN) also ionizes in water to produce hydrogen ions and cyanide ions. But HCN ionizes only to a slight extent. In a solution that has 1 mol of HCN in 1 L of water, only one HCN molecule in 40,000 ionizes to produce a hydrogen ion.

$$HCN(aq) \rightleftharpoons H^+(aq) + CN^-(aq)$$

We represent this slight ionization by using a double arrow. The opposite-pointing arrows indicate that the reaction is reversible; the ions can also combine to form HCN molecules. A short arrow points to the right and a longer arrow points to the left to indicate that most of the HCN remains intact as HCN molecules.

Clearly, acids can be classified according to their extent of ionication.

- An acid such as HCl that ionizes completely in (reacts completely with) water is called a **strong acid**.
- An acid such as HCN that ionizes only slightly in water is a **weak acid**.

There are only a few strong acids. The first two acids listed in Table 1 (sulfuric and hydrochloric) are the common ones. The other strong acids are nitric acid (HNO_3), hydrobromic acid (HBr), hydroiodic acid (HI), and perchloric acid ($HClO_4$). Most acids are weak acids.

Bases are also classified as strong or weak.

- A **strong base** is completely ionized in water.
- A **weak base** is only slightly ionized in water.

Perhaps the most familiar strong base is sodium hydroxide (NaOH), commonly called *lye*. It exists as sodium ions and hydroxide ions even in the solid state. Other strong bases include potassium hydroxide (KOH) and the hydroxides of all the other group 1A metals. Except for $Be(OH)_2$, the hydroxides of group 2A metals are also strong bases. However, $Ca(OH)_2$ is only slightly soluble in water, and $Mg(OH)_2$ is nearly insoluble. The concentration of hydroxide ions in a solution of $Ca(OH)_2$ or $Mg(OH)_2$ is, therefore, not very high.

The word *strong* does not refer to the *amount* of acid or base in a solution. A solution that contains a relatively large amount of an acid or a base, whether strong or weak, as the solute in a given volume of solution is called a *concentrated* solution. A solution with only a little solute in that same volume of solution is a *dilute* solution.

3. Is vitamin C really an acid? Are all vitamins acids?
Yes, vitamin C is a complex organic compound known as *ascorbic acid*. Some, but not all, vitamins are acids (including folic acid and niacin). Like most acids, these vitamins are weak acids. Not only are they not corrosive but they are necessary to health.

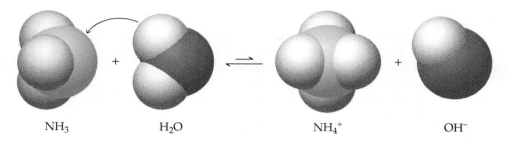

NH₃   H₂O   NH₄⁺   OH⁻

▲ **Figure 5** Ammonia is a base because it accepts a proton from water. A solution of ammonia in water contains ammonium ions and hydroxide ions. Only a small fraction of the ammonia molecules react, however; most remain unchanged. Ammonia is therefore a *weak* base.

Q: *Amines are related to ammonia; in an amine, one or more of the H atoms of NH₃ is replaced by a carbon-containing group. Amines react in the same way as ammonia does. Can you write an equation that shows how the amine CH₃NH₂ reacts with water? One product is hydroxide ion.*

The most familiar weak base is ammonia (NH_3). It reacts with water to a slight extent to produce ammonium ions (NH_4^+) and hydroxide ions (Figure 5).

$$NH_3 + H_2O \rightleftharpoons NH_4^+ + OH^-$$

In its reaction with HCl, water acts as a base (proton acceptor). In its reaction with NH_3, water acts as an acid (proton donor). A substance such as water that can either donate a proton or accept a proton is said to be *amphiprotic* (see also Additional Problem 65).

Self-Assessment Questions

For Questions 1–7, select the correct classification (more than one substance may fit into a given classification).

1. $Ca(OH)_2$
2. HCN
3. HF
4. HNO_3
5. H_3PO_4
6. KOH
7. NH_3

(a) strong acid
(b) strong base
(c) weak acid
(d) weak base

8. Acetic acid reacts with water to form
   a. $CH_3COO^+ + H_2O$
   c. $CH_3COO^- + H_3O^-$
   b. $CH_3COOH + OH^-$
   d. $CH_3COO^+ + OH^-$

9. Ammonia reacts with water to form
   a. $NH_3 + H_2O$
   c. $NH_2^- + H_3O^+$
   b. $NH_4^+ + OH^-$
   d. $NH_3 + OH^-$

Answers: 1, b; 2, c; 3, c; 4, a; 5, c; 6, b; 7, d; 8, c; 9, b

5 Neutralization

Learning Objective > Identify the reactants and predict the products in a neutralization reaction.

When an acid reacts with a base, the products are water and a salt. If a solution containing hydrogen ions (an acid) is mixed with another solution containing exactly the same amount of hydroxide ions (a base), the resulting solution does not change the color of litmus, dissolve zinc or iron, or feel slippery on the skin. It is no longer either acidic or basic. It is neutral. As was mentioned earlier, the reaction of an acid with a base is called *neutralization* (Figure 6).

$$H^+ + OH^- \longrightarrow H_2O$$

(a)

(b)

(c)

Richard Megna/Fundamental Photographs

◀ **Figure 6** The amount of acid (or base) in a solution is determined by careful neutralization. Here a 5.00-mL sample of vinegar, some water, and a few drops of phenolphthalein (an acid–base indicator) are placed in a flask (a). A solution of 0.1000 M NaOH is added to the flask slowly from a buret (a device for precise measurement of volumes of solutions) (b). As long as the acid is in excess, the solution is colorless. When the acid has been neutralized and a tiny excess of base is present, the phenolphthalein indicator turns pink (c).

Q: *Can you write an equation for the reaction of acetic acid (CH_3COOH), the acid in vinegar, with aqueous NaOH?*

If sodium hydroxide is neutralized by hydrochloric acid, the products are water and sodium chloride (ordinary table salt)

$$NaOH(aq) + HCl(aq) \longrightarrow NaCl(aq) + H_2O$$

A base · An acid · A salt · Water

Example 5   Neutralization Reactions

Potassium nitrate, a component of black powder gunpowder and some fertilizers, was obtained from the late Middle Ages through the nineteenth century by precipitation from urine. Commonly called *saltpeter*, it can be prepared by the reaction of nitric acid with potassium hydroxide. Write the equation for this neutralization reaction.

Solution

The OH^- from the base and the H^+ from the acid combine to form water. The cation of the base (K^+) and the anion of the acid (NO_3^-) form a solution of the salt (potassium nitrate, KNO_3).

$$KOH(aq) + HNO_3(aq) \longrightarrow KNO_3(aq) + H_2O(l)$$

■ EXERCISE 5A

Countertop spills of lye solutions (aqueous sodium hydroxide) can be neutralized with vinegar (aqueous acetic acid; see Table 1). Write the equation for the neutralization reaction.

■ EXERCISE 5B

A toilet-bowl cleaner contains hydrochloric acid. An emergency first-aid treatment for accidental ingestion is a teaspoon of milk of magnesia (magnesium hydroxide). Write the equation for the neutralization reaction between magnesium hydroxide and hydrochloric acid. (*Hint:* Be sure to write the correct formulas for the reactants and the salt before attempting to balance the equation.)

4. What is the difference between salt and sodium? A salt is any ionic compound formed by reacting an acid and a base. In everyday life, *salt* usually means table salt—sodium chloride (NaCl). Sodium is a highly reactive metal element. Sodium ions are essential for life, but you wouldn't want to eat pure sodium. It reacts violently with water.

Self-Assessment Questions

1. When equal amounts of acids and bases are mixed,
   a. the acid becomes stronger
   b. the base becomes stronger
   c. no reaction occurs
   d. they neutralize each other

2. What amount in moles of hydrochloric acid is needed to neutralize 1.5 mol of sodium hydroxide?
   a. 1 mol
   b. 1.5 mol
   c. 3.0 mol
   c. 4.5 mol

3. What amount in moles of hydrochloric acid is needed to neutralize 2.4 mol of calcium hydroxide?
   a. 1.2 mol
   b. 2.4 mol
   c. 3.0 mol
   d. 4.8 mol

4. What amount in moles of sodium hydroxide is needed to neutralize 1.5 mol of phosphoric acid?
   a. 0.5 mol
   b. 3.0 mol
   c. 4.5 mol
   d. 6.0 mol

Answers: 1, d; 2, b; 3, d; 4, c

Concentration of H^+ (mol/L)	pH
1×10^{-0}	0
1×10^{-1}	1
1×10^{-2}	2
1×10^{-3}	3
1×10^{-4}	4
1×10^{-5}	5
1×10^{-6}	6
1×10^{-7}	7
1×10^{-8}	8
1×10^{-9}	9
1×10^{-10}	10
1×10^{-11}	11
1×10^{-12}	12
1×10^{-13}	13
1×10^{-14}	14

Table 4 Relationship between pH and Concentration of H^+ Ion

The relationship between pH and $[H^+]$ is perhaps easier to see when the equation is written in the following form.
$[H^+] = 10^{-pH}$

6 The pH Scale

Learning Objectives ❯ Describe the relationship between the pH of a solution and its acidity or basicity. ❯ Find the molar concentration of hydrogen ion, $[H^+]$, from a pH value or the pH value from $[H^+]$.

In solutions, the concentrations of ions are expressed in moles per liter (molarity). Because hydrogen chloride is completely ionized in water, a 1 molar solution of hydrochloric acid (1 M HCl), for example, contains 1 mol H^+ ions per liter of solution. Likewise, 1 L of 3 M HCl contains 3 mol H^+ ions, and 0.500 L of 0.00100 M HCl contains 0.500 L × 0.00100 mol/L = 0.000500 mol H^+ ions.

We can describe the acidity of a particular solution in moles per liter: The hydrogen ion concentration of a 0.00100 M HCl solution is 1×10^{-3} mol/L. However, exponential notation isn't very convenient. More often, the acidity of this solution is reported simply as pH 3.

We usually use the **pH** scale, first proposed in 1909 by the Danish biochemist S. P. L. Sørensen, to describe the degree of acidity or basicity. Most solutions have a pH that lies in the range from 0 to 14. The neutral point on the scale is 7, with values below 7 indicating increasing acidity and those above 7 increasing basicity. Thus, pH 6 is slightly acidic, whereas pH 12 is strongly basic (Figure 7).

The numbers on the pH scale are directly related to the hydrogen ion concentration. We might expect pure water to be completely in the form of H_2O molecules, but it turns out that about 1 out of every 500 million water molecules splits into H^+ and OH^- ions. This gives a concentration of hydrogen ion and of hydroxide ion in pure water of 0.0000001 mol/L, or 1×10^{-7} M. Can you see why 7 is the pH of pure water? It is simply the power of 10 for the molar concentration of H^+, with the negative sign removed. (The H in pH stands for "hydrogen," and the p for "power.") Thus, pH is defined as the negative logarithm of the molar concentration of hydrogen ion (refer to Table 4):

$$pH = -\log[H^+]$$

The brackets around H^+ mean "molar concentration."

▲ **Figure 7** The pH scale. A change in pH of one unit means a tenfold change in the hydrogen ion concentration.

Q: *Are tomatoes more acidic or less acidic than oranges? About how many times more (or less) acidic?*

Table 5 Approximate pH Values of Some Common Solutions

Solution	pH
Hydrochloric acid (4%)	0
Gastric juice	1.6–1.8
Soft drink	2.0–4.0
Lemon juice	2.1
Vinegar (4%)	2.5
Urine	5.5–7.0
Rainwater[a]	5.6
Saliva	6.2–7.4
Milk	6.3–6.6
Pure water	7.0
Blood	7.4
Fresh egg white	7.6–8.0
Bile	7.8–8.6
Milk of magnesia	10.5
Washing soda	12.0
Sodium hydroxide (4%)	13.0

[a] Saturated with carbon dioxide from the atmosphere but unpolluted.

▲ A pH meter is a device for determining pH quickly and accurately.

Q: *Is the solution in the beaker more basic or less basic than household ammonia? (Refer to Figure 7.)*

Although pH is an acidity scale, note that its value goes down when acidity goes up. Not only is the relationship an inverse one, but it is also logarithmic. A decrease of 1 pH unit represents a tenfold increase in acidity, and when pH goes down by 2 units, acidity increases by a factor of 100. This relationship may seem strange at first, but once you understand the pH scale, you will appreciate its convenience.

Table 4 summarizes the relationship between hydrogen ion concentration and pH. A pH of 4 means a hydrogen ion concentration of 1×10^{-4} mol/L, or 0.0001 M. If the concentration of hydrogen ions is 0.01 M, or 1×10^{-2} M, the pH is 2. Typical pH values for various common solutions are listed in Table 5.

5. What is meant by "pH-balanced shampoo"? Shampoo on either end of the pH scale would damage hair (and probably skin as well!). Most shampoos are formulated to be neutral (pH 7) or slightly basic.

Example 6 pH from Hydrogen Ion Concentration

What is the pH of a solution that has a hydrogen ion concentration of 1×10^{-5} M?

Solution

The hydrogen ion concentration is 1×10^{-5} M. The exponent is −5; the pH is, therefore, the negative of this exponent: −(−5) or 5.

■ EXERCISE 6A

What is the pH of a solution that has a hydrogen ion concentration of 1×10^{-9} M?

■ EXERCISE 6B

What is the pH of a solution that is 0.010 M HCl? (*Hint:* HCl is a strong acid.)

Example 7 Finding Hydrogen Ion Concentration from pH

What is the hydrogen ion concentration of a solution that has a pH of 4?

Solution

A pH value of 4 means that the exponent of 10 is −4. The hydrogen ion concentration is, therefore, 1×10^{-4} M.

■ EXERCISE 7A
What is the hydrogen ion concentration of a solution that has a pH of 2?

■ EXERCISE 7B
What is the hydrogen ion concentration of a HI solution that has a pH of 3? (*Hint:* HI is a strong acid.)

CONCEPTUAL **Example 8** Estimating pH from Hydrogen Ion Concentration

Which of the following is a reasonable pH for a solution that is 8×10^{-4} M in H^+?
  a. 2.9   **b.** 3.1   **c.** 4.2   **d.** 4.8

Solution
The $[H^+]$ is greater than 1×10^{-4} M, and so the pH must be less than 4. That rules out answers (c) and (d). The $[H^+]$ is less than 10×10^{-4} (or 1×10^{-3} M), and so the pH must be greater than 3. That rules out answer (a). The only reasonable answer is (b), a value between 3 and 4.

  (With a scientific calculator, you can calculate the actual pH, usually with the following keystrokes: ⑧ (exp) ④ (±) (log) This gives a value of -3.1 for the log of 8×10^{-4}. Because pH is the *negative* log of the H^+ concentration, the pH value is 3.1.)

■ EXERCISE 8
Which of the following is a reasonable pH for a solution that is 2×10^{-10} M in H^+?
a. 2.0   **b.** 8.7   **c.** 9.7   **d.** 10.2

It's not obvious right away, but every aqueous solution contains *both* hydrogen ions and hydroxide ions. An acidic solution contains more H^+ ions than OH^- ions. For example, a solution with a pH of 4 is 1×10^{-4} M in H^+ ions but only 1×10^{-10} M in OH^- ions. On the other hand, a basic solution contains more OH^- ions than H^+ ions. A solution with a pH of 12 is 1×10^{-12} M in H^+ ions and 1×10^{-2} M in OH^- ions. And a neutral solution contains equal concentrations of H^+ ions and OH^- ions; both are 1×10^{-7} M.

CONCEPTUAL **Example 9** Hydrogen and Hydroxide Ions in Acids and Bases

Classify the three aqueous solutions shown below as acidic, basic, or neutral. (Water molecules are not shown.)

Solution
Beaker I contains equal numbers of OH^- ions and H^+ ions—six of each—so that solution is neutral. Beaker II contains more OH^- ions (seven) than H^+ ions (one), so its solution is basic. Beaker III contains six H^+ ions and one OH^- ion; the solution is acidic.

■ EXERCISE 9
What is the formula of the compound that was dissolved in Beaker III of Example 9? What is the formula of the compound that was dissolved in Beaker II?

Self-Assessment Questions

1. The hydrogen ion concentration, $[H^+]$, of a 0.0010 M HNO_3 solution is
   a. 1.0×10^{-4} M
   b. 1.0×10^{-3} M
   c. 1.0×10^{-2} M
   d. 10 M

2. What is the pH of a solution that has a hydrogen ion concentration of 1.0×10^{-11} M?
   a. 1.0
   b. 3
   c. 10
   d. 11

3. Swimming pool water with a pH of 8 has a hydrogen ion concentration of
   a. 8.0 M
   b. 8.0×10^{-8} M
   c. 1.0×10^{-8} M
   d. 1.0×10^8 M

4. The pH of pure water is
   a. 0
   b. 1
   c. 7
   d. 10
   e. 14

5. Which of the following is a reasonable pH for 0.15 M HCl?
   a. 0.15
   b. 0.82
   c. 8.24
   d. 13.18

6. Which of the following is a reasonable pH for 0.15 M NaOH?
   a. 0.15
   b. 0.82
   c. 8.24
   d. 13.18

7. Physiological pH (4) is the average pH of blood. Which of the following is a reasonable hydrogen ion concentration of a solution at physiological pH?
   a. -7.4 M
   b. 0.6 M
   c. 6×10^{-7} M
   d. 1×10^{-8} M
   e. 4×10^{-8}

Answers: 1. b; 2. d; 3. c; 4. c; 5. b; 6. d; 7. e

7 Buffers and Conjugate Acid–Base Pairs

Learning Objectives › Write the formula for the conjugate base of an acid or for the conjugate acid of a base. › Describe the action of a buffer.

In the Brønsted–Lowry theory, a pair of compounds or ions that differ by one proton (H^+) is called a **conjugate acid–base pair**. HF and F^- are a conjugate acid-base pair, as are NH_3 and NH_4^+. When a base (for example, NH_3) accepts a proton, it becomes an acid because it now has a proton that it can donate. NH_4^+ is an acid; it can donate its "extra" proton. Similarly, when an acid (for example, HF) donates a proton, it becomes a base, because it can now accept a proton. F^- is a base; it can accept a proton.

CONCEPTUAL Example 10   Conjugate Acid–Base Pairs

What is the conjugate base **(a)** of HBr and **(b)** of HNO_3? What is the conjugate acid **(c)** of OH^- and **(d)** of HSO_4^-?

Solution
   a. Removing a proton from HBr leaves Br^-; the conjugate base of HBr is Br^-.
   b. Removing a proton from HNO_3 leaves NO_3^-; the conjugate base of HNO_3 is NO_3^-.
   c. Adding a proton to OH^- gives H_2O; the conjugate acid of OH^- is H_2O.
   d. Adding a proton to HSO_4^- gives H_2SO_4; the conjugate acid of HSO_4^- is H_2SO_4.

■ EXERCISE 10
What is the conjugate base **(a)** of HCN and **(b)** of H_3O^+? What is the conjugate acid **(c)** of SO_4^{2-} and **(d)** of HCO_3^-?

Buffer Solutions

A **buffer solution** maintains an almost constant pH when small amounts of a strong acid or a strong base are added to it. Buffer solutions have many important applications in industry, in the laboratory, and in living organisms because some chemical reactions consume acids, others produce acids, and many are catalyzed by acids[1]. A buffer solution consists of a weak acid and its conjugate base (for example, $HC_2H_3O_2$ and $C_2H_3O_2^-$) or a weak base and its conjugate acid (for example, NH_3 and NH_4^+).

Consider the equation for the ionization of acetic acid, in which the double arrow indicates the slight extent to which the acid ionizes.

$$HC_2H_3O_2(aq) \rightleftharpoons H^+(aq) + C_2H_3O_2^-(aq)$$

If we add sodium acetate to a solution of acetic acid, we are adding the conjugate base of acetic acid—that is, acetate ion—thus forming a buffer solution. If we add a little strong base to this solution, it will react with the weak acid.

$$OH^- + HC_2H_3O_2 \longrightarrow H_2O + C_2H_3O_2^-$$

Do you see that the solution no longer contains the strong base? Instead, it has a little more weak base and a little less weak acid than it did before the strong base was added. The pH remains very nearly constant. Likewise, if a little strong acid is added, it will react with the weak base.

$$H^+ + C_2H_3O_2^- \longrightarrow HC_2H_3O_2$$

The strong acid is consumed, a weak acid is formed, and the solution pH increases slightly. This behavior of buffered solutions contrasts sharply with that of unbuffered solutions, in which any added strong acid or base changes the pH greatly.

A dramatic and essential example of the action of buffers is found in our blood. Blood must maintain a pH very close to 7.4 or it cannot carry oxygen from the lungs to cells. The most important buffer for maintaining acid–base balance in the blood is the carbonic acid–bicarbonate ion (H_2CO_3/HCO_3^-) buffer.

Self-Assessment Questions

1. Which of the following pairs is a conjugate acid–base pair?
   - **a.** CH_3COOH and OH^-
   - **b.** HCN and CN^-
   - **c.** HCN and OH^-
   - **d.** HCl and OH^-

2. Which of the following is *not* a conjugate acid–base pair?
   - **a.** CH_3COO^- and CH_3COOH
   - **b.** F^- and HF
   - **c.** H_2O and H_3O^+
   - **d.** NH_3 and H_3O^+

3. A buffer solution is made from formic acid ($HCOOH$) and sodium formate ($HCOONa$). Added acid will react with
   - **a.** $HCOO^-$
   - **b.** $HCOOH$
   - **c.** Na^+
   - **d.** OH^-

4. Which of the following pairs could form a buffer?
   - **a.** C_6H_5COOH and C_6H_5COONa
   - **b.** HCl and $NaCl$
   - **c.** HCl and $NaOH$
   - **d.** NH_3 and NO_3^-

Answers: 1, b; 2, d; 3, a; 4, a

8 Acids and Bases in Industry and in Daily Life

Learning Objective ❯ Describe everyday uses of acids and bases and how they affect daily life.

Acids and bases play an important role in our bodies, in medicine, in our homes, and in industry, they are useful products in many ways, As industrial by-products, they can damage the environment. Their use requires caution, and their misuse can be dangerous to human health.

---

[1]A *catalyst* is a substance or mixture that speeds up a reaction. Unlike a reactant, a catalyst can be recovered unchanged after the reaction is complete, and ordinarily it can be reused. For example, the breakdown of some flavoring components of fruits is catalyzed by acid, and the formation of biodiesel fuel from waste oil is catalyzed by a strong base such as sodium hydroxide.

Acid Rain

Carbon dioxide is the anhydride of carbonic acid (Section 3). Raindrops falling through the air absorb CO_2, which is converted to H_2CO_3 in the drops. Rainwater is thus a dilute solution of carbonic acid, a weak acid. Rain saturated with carbon dioxide has a pH of 5.6. In many areas of the world, particularly those downwind from industrial centers, rainwater is much more acidic, with a pH as low as 3 or less. Rain with a pH below 5.6 is called **acid rain**.

Acid rain is due to acidic pollutants in the air. Several air pollutants are acid anhydrides. These include sulfur dioxide (SO_2), mainly from the burning of high-sulfur coal in power plants and metal smelters, and nitrogen dioxide (NO_2) and nitric oxide (NO), from automobile exhaust fumes.

Some acid rain is due to natural pollutants, such as those resulting from volcanic eruptions and lightning. Volcanoes give off sulfur oxides and sulfuric acid, and lightning produces nitrogen oxides and nitric acid from nitrogen, oxygen, and water in the air.

Acid rain is an important environmental problem that involves both air pollution and water pollution. It can have serious effects on plant and animal life.

Antacids: A Basic Remedy

The stomach secretes hydrochloric acid to aid in the digestion of food. Sometimes overindulgence or emotional stress leads to *hyperacidity* (too much acid is secreted). Hundreds of brands of antacids (Figure 8) are sold in the United States to treat this condition. Despite the many brand names, there are only a few different antacid ingredients, all of which are bases. Common ingredients are sodium bicarbonate, calcium carbonate, aluminum hydroxide, magnesium carbonate, and magnesium hydroxide. Even a single brand name often encompasses a variety of products. For example, there are more than a dozen varieties of Alka-Seltzer®.

Sodium bicarbonate ($NaHCO_3$), commonly called *baking soda*, was one of the first antacids and is still used occasionally. It is the principal antacid in most forms of Alka-Seltzer for heartburn relief. The bicarbonate ions react with the acid in the stomach to form carbonic acid, which then breaks down to carbon dioxide and water.

$$HCO_3^-(aq) + H^+(aq) \longrightarrow H_2CO_3(aq)$$

$$H_2CO_3(aq) \longrightarrow CO_2(g) + H_2O(l)$$

The $CO_2(g)$ is largely responsible for the burps that bicarbonate-containing antacids produce. Overuse of sodium bicarbonate can make the blood too alkaline,

You can make your own aspirin-free "Alka-Seltzer." Simply place half a teaspoon of baking soda in a glass of orange juice. (What is the acid and what is the base in this reaction?)

◄ **Figure 8** Claims that antacids are "fast acting" are almost meaningless because most common acid–base reactions are almost instantaneous. Some tablets may dissolve a little more slowly than others. You can speed their action by chewing them.

Why Doesn't Stomach Acid Dissolve the Stomach?

We know that strong acids are corrosive to skin. Look back at Table 1 and you will see that the gastric juice in your stomach is extremely acidic. Gastric juice is a solution containing about 0.5% hydrochloric acid. Why doesn't the acid in your stomach destroy your stomach lining? The cells that line the stomach are protected by a layer of mucus, a viscous solution of a sugar–protein complex called *mucin* and other substances in water. The mucus serves as a physical barrier, but its role is broader than that. The mucin acts like a sponge that soaks up bicarbonate ions from the cells lining the stom-ach and hydrochloric acid from within the stomach. The bicarbonate ions neutralize the acid within the mucus.

It used to be thought that stomach acid was the cause of ulcers, but it is now known that the acid plays only a minor role in ulcer formation. Research has shown that most ulcers develop as a result of infection with a bacterium called *Helicobacter pylori* (*H. pylori*) that damages the mucus, exposing cells in the stomach lining to the harsh stomach acid. Other agents, such as aspirin and alcohol, may be contributing factors to the development of ulcers. Treatment usually involves antibiotics that kill *H. pylori*.

Pearson Education/Eric Schrader

▲ Drugs such as ranitidine (Zantac™), famotidine (Pepcid AC™), cimetidine (Tagamet HB™), and omeprazole (Prilosec) are not antac-ids. Rather than neutralizing stomach acid, these drugs act on cells in the lining of the stomach, reducing the amount of acid that is produced.

a condition called **alkalosis**. Also, antacids that contain sodium ion are not recommended for people with hypertension (high blood pressure).

Calcium carbonate ($CaCO_3$) is safe in small amounts, but regular use can cause constipation. Also, taking large amounts of calcium carbonate can actually result in increased acid secretion after a few hours. Tums® and many store brands of antacids have calcium carbonate as the only active ingredient.

Aluminum hydroxide $[Al(OH)_3]$, like calcium carbonate, can cause constipation. There is also some concern that antacids containing aluminum ions can deplete the body of essential phosphate ions. Aluminum hydroxide is the active ingredient in Amphojel®.

A suspension of magnesium hydroxide $[Mg(OH)_2]$ in water is sold as *milk of magnesia*. Magnesium carbonate ($MgCO_3$) is also used as an antacid. These magnesium compounds act as antacids in small doses, but as laxatives in large doses.

Many antacid products have a mixture of antacids. Rolaids® and Mylanta® contain calcium carbonate and magnesium hydroxide. Maalox® liquid has aluminum hydroxide and magnesium hydroxide. These products balance the tendency of magnesium compounds to cause diarrhea with that of aluminum and calcium compounds to cause constipation.

Although antacids are generally safe for occasional use, they can interact with other medications. Anyone who has severe or repeated attacks of indigestion should consult a physician. Self-medication can sometimes be dangerous.

Acids and Bases in Industry and at Home

Sulfuric acid is by far the leading chemical product in both the United States (average production of about 40 billion kg each year) and the world (over 200 billion kg annually). Most of it is used for making fertilizers and other industrial chemicals. Around the home, we use sulfuric acid in automobile batteries and in some special kinds of drain cleaners.

Hydrochloric acid is used in industry to remove rust from metal, in construction to remove excess mortar from bricks and etch concrete for painting, and in the home to remove lime deposits from fixtures and toilet bowls. The product used in the home is often called *muriatic acid*, an old name for hydrochloric acid. Concentrated solutions (about 38% HCl) cause severe burns, but dilute solutions can be used safely in the home if handled carefully. Yearly production of hydrochloric acid is more than 4 billion kg in the United States and about 20 billion kg worldwide.

Lime (CaO) is the cheapest and most widely used commercial base. It is made by heating limestone ($CaCO_3$) to drive off CO_2.

$$CaCO_3(s) + heat \longrightarrow CaO(s) + CO_2(g)$$

Yearly production of calcium oxide is about 22 billion kg in the United States and about 280 billion kg worldwide. Adding water to lime forms calcium hydroxide $[Ca(OH)_2]$, or slaked lime, which is generally safer to handle. Slaked lime is used in agriculture and to make mortar and cement.

Sodium hydroxide ($NaOH$, lye) is the strong base most often used in the home. It is employed in products such as Easy Off® for cleaning ovens, in products such as Drano® for unclogging drains, and to make both commercial and homemade soaps. Yearly U.S. production of sodium hydroxide is about 9 billion kg.

Ammonia (NH_3) is produced in huge volume, mainly for use as fertilizer. Yearly U.S. production is nearly 11 billion kg. Ammonia is used around the home in a variety of cleaning products.

Acids and Bases in Health and Disease

When they are misused, acids and bases can be damaging to human health. Concentrated strong acids and bases are corrosive poisons that can cause serious chemical burns. Once the chemical agents are removed, these injuries resemble burns caused by heat and are often treated in the same way. Besides being a strong acid, sulfuric acid is also a powerful dehydrating agent that can react with water in the cells.

Strong acids and bases, even in dilute solutions, break down, or *denature*, the protein molecules in living cells, much as cooking does. Generally, the fragments are not able to carry out the functions of the original proteins. If exposure to the acid or base is sustained, this fragmentation continues until the tissue has been completely destroyed.

Acids and bases affect human health in more subtle ways. A delicate balance between acids and bases must be maintained in the blood, other body fluids, and cells. If the acidity of the blood changes too much, the blood loses its capacity to carry oxygen. In living cells, proteins function properly only at an optimal pH. If the pH changes too much in either direction, the proteins can't carry out their functions. Fortunately, the body has a complex but efficient mechanism for maintaining a proper acid–base balance.

Michael Page Gadomski/Photo Researchers, Inc.

▲ It DOES Matter!

The proper pH is as important for plant growth as fertilizer is. Soil that is "sour," or too acidic, is "sweetened" by adding slaked lime (calcium hydroxide). A few plants, such as blueberries and citrus fruit, require acidic soil, and an acid such as vinegar may have to be periodically added to the soil they grow in.

Tom McNemar/Shutterstock

▲ Safety Alert

Concentrated acids and bases can cause severe burns and are especially damaging to the eyes. Use great care in working with them. Always follow directions carefully. Wear chemical-splash safety goggles to protect your eyes and clothing that will protect your skin and clothes.

Self-Assessment Questions

1. Which of the following is a common ingredient in antacids?
   a. $CaCO_3$
   b. $Ca(OH)_2$
   c. HCl
   d. KOH

2. When a person with excess stomach acid takes an antacid, the pH of the person's stomach changes
   a. from a low value to a value nearer 7
   b. from 7 to a much higher value
   c. from a low value to an even lower value
   d. from a high value to a lower value

3. The leading chemical product of U.S. industry is
   a. ammonia
   b. lime
   c. pesticides
   d. sulfuric acid

4. The acid used in automobile batteries is
   a. citric acid
   b. hydrochloric acid
   c. nitric acid
   d. sulfuric acid

5. The base often used in soap making is
   a. $Ca(OH)_2$
   b. $Mg(OH)_2$
   c. $NaOH$
   d. NH_3

Answers: 1, a; 2, a; 3, d; 4, d; 5, c

CRITICAL THINKING EXERCISES

Apply knowledge that you have gained in this chapter and one or more of the FLaReS principles (Chapter 1) to evaluate the following statements or claims.

1   A television advertisement claimed that the antacid Maalox neutralizes stomach acid faster and, therefore, relieves heartburn faster than Pepcid AC®, a drug that inhibits the release of stomach acid. To illustrate this claim, two flasks of acid were shown. In one, Maalox rapidly neutralized the acid. In the other, Pepcid AC did not neutralize the acid.

2   Some people claim that putting salt on grapefruit takes away a little of the acidity.

3   Testifying in a court case, a witness makes the following statement: "Although runoff from our plant did appear to contaminate a stream, the pH of the stream before the contamination was 6.4, and after contamination it was 5.4. So the stream is now only slightly more acidic than before."

4   A Jamaican fish recipe calls for adding the juice of several limes to the fish, but no heat is used to cook the fish. The directions state that the lime juice in effect "cooks" the fish.

5   An advertisement claims that vinegar in a glass-cleaning product will remove the spots left on glasses by tap water. The spots are largely calcium carbonate deposits.

SUMMARY

Section 1—Acids taste sour, turn litmus red, and react with active metals to form hydrogen. Bases taste bitter, turn litmus blue, and feel slippery to the skin. Acids and bases react to form salts and water. An acid–base indicator such as litmus has different colors in acid and in base and is used to determine whether solutions are acidic or basic.

Section 2—According to Arrhenius's definition, an *acid* produces hydrogen ions (H^+, also called protons) in aqueous solution, and a *base* produces hydroxide ions (OH^-). Neutralization is the combination of H^+ and OH^- to form water. The anion and cation that were associated with H^+ and OH^- ions combine to form an ionic salt. In the more general Brønsted–Lowry acid–base theory, an acid is a proton donor and a base is a proton acceptor. When a Brønsted–Lowry acid dissolves in water, the H_2O molecules pick up H^+ to form hydronium ions (H_3O^+). A Brønsted–Lowry base in water accepts a proton from a water molecule, forming OH^-.

Section 3—Some nonmetal oxides (such as CO_2 and SO_3) are acidic anhydrides in that they react with water to form acids. Some metal oxides (such as Li_2O and CaO) are basic anhydrides; they react with water to form bases.

Section 4—A strong acid is one that ionizes completely in water to form H^+ ions and anions. A weak acid ionizes only slightly in water; most of the acid exists as intact molecules. Common strong acids are sulfuric, hydrochloric, and nitric acids. Likewise, a strong base is completely ionized in water, and a weak base is only slightly ionized. Sodium hydroxide and potassium hydroxide are common strong bases.

Section 5—The reaction between an acid and a base is called *neutralization*. In aqueous solution, it is the combination of H^+ and OH^- that forms water. The other anions and cations form an ionic salt.

Section 6—The pH scale indicates the degree of acidity or basicity; pH is defined as $pH = -\log[H^+]$, where $[H^+]$ is the molar concentration of hydrogen ion. A pH of 7 ($[H^+] = 1 \times 10^{-7}$ M) is neutral; pH values lower than 7 represent increasing acidity, and pH values greater than 7 represent increasing basicity. A change in pH of one unit represents a tenfold change in $[H^+]$.

Section 7—A pair of compounds or ions that differ by one proton (H^+) is called a conjugate acid–base pair. A buffer solution is a mixture of a weak acid and its conjugate base or a weak base and its conjugate acid. A buffer maintains a nearly constant pH when a small amount of a strong acid or a strong base is added.

Section 8—An antacid is a base such as sodium bicarbonate, magnesium hydroxide, aluminum hydroxide, or calcium carbonate that is taken to relieve hyperacidity. Overuse of some antacids can make the blood too alkaline (basic), a condition called alkalosis. Acid rain is rain with a pH less than 5.6. The acidity is due to sulfur oxides and nitrogen oxides from natural sources as well as industrial air pollution and automobile exhaust fumes. Acid rain can have serious effects on plant and animal life. Sulfuric acid is the number one chemical produced in the United States and is used for making fertilizers and other industrial chemicals. Hydrochloric acid is used for rust removal and etching mortar and concrete. Lime (calcium oxide) is made from limestone and is the cheapest and most widely used base. It is an ingredient in plaster and cement and is used in agriculture. Sodium hydroxide is used to make many industrial products, as well as soap. Ammonia is a weak base produced mostly for use as fertilizer. Concentrated strong acids and bases are corrosive poisons that can cause serious burns. Living cells have an optimal pH that is necessary for the proper functioning of proteins.

Green chemistry Base is used to convert renewable fats and oils into products such as soaps and biofuels. Treatment with acid can decompose special plastics (such as polylactic acid, PLA) into a useful antimicrobial cleaner. Application of the Twelve Principles of Green Chemistry can guide us to find practical uses for materials that were once considered waste.

Learning Objectives

> Distinguish between acids and bases using their chemical and physical properties. (1) — Problems 1, 26, 27

> Explain how an acid–base indicator works. (1) — Problem 2

> Identify Arrhenius and Brønsted–Lowry acids and bases. (2) — Problems 4, 12–22, 59

> Write a balanced equation for a neutralization or an ionization. (2) — Problems 8, 39–46, 60, 67

> Identify acidic and basic anhydrides, and write equations showing their reactions with water. (3) — Problems 7, 29, 30

> Define and identify strong and weak acids and bases. (4) — Problems 5, 9, 10, 31–38, 61

> Identify the reactants and predict the products in a neutralization reaction. (5) — Problems 43–46

> Describe the relationship between the pH of a solution and its acidity or basicity. (6) — Problems 47–54

> Find the molar concentration of hydrogen ion, $[H^+]$, from a pH value or the pH value from $[H^+]$. (6) — Problems 49–54

> Write the formula for the conjugate base of an acid or for the conjugate acid of a base. (7) — Problems 55, 56

> Describe the action of a buffer. (7) — Problem 65

> Describe everyday uses of acids and bases and how they affect daily life. (8) — Problems 11, 57, 58

> Write equations for the production of soap and of biofuel. — Problem 73

> Describe ways by which acids and bases can contribute to greener production of consumer products. — Problems 71, 72, 74

REVIEW QUESTIONS

1. Define the following terms, and give an example of each.
   a. acid   **b.** base   **c.** salt

2. Describe the effect on litmus and the action on iron or zinc of a solution that has been neutralized.

3. List four general properties **(a)** of acidic solutions and **(b)** of basic solutions.

4. Can a substance be a Brønsted–Lowry acid if it does not contain H atoms? Are there any characteristic atoms that must be present in a Brønsted–Lowry base?

5. Both strong bases and weak bases have properties characteristic of hydroxide ions. How do strong bases and weak bases differ?

6. What is meant by a proton in acid–base chemistry? How does it differ from a nuclear proton?

7. What is an acidic anhydride? A basic anhydride?

8. Describe the neutralization of an acid or a base.

9. Magnesium hydroxide is completely ionic, even in the solid state, yet it can be taken internally as an antacid. Explain why taking it does not cause injury although taking sodium hydroxide would.

10. What are the effects of strong acids and strong bases on the skin?

11. What is alkalosis? What antacid ingredient might cause alkalosis if taken in excess?

12. According to the Arrhenius theory, all acids have one element in common. What is that element? Are all compounds containing that element acids? Explain.

PROBLEMS

Acids and Bases: The Arrhenius Theory

13. Write an equation that represents how perchloric acid $(HClO_4)$ behaves as an Arrhenius acid.

14. Write an equation that represents how dihydrogen phosphate ion $(H_2PO_4^-)$ behaves as an Arrhenius acid. (Be sure to include the correct charges for ions.)

15. Write an equation showing that rubidium hydroxide $(RbOH)$ acts as an Arrhenius base in water.

16. Write an equation showing that calcium hydroxide acts as an Arrhenius base in water.

Acids and Bases: The Brønsted–Lowry Acid–Base Theory

17. Use the Brønsted–Lowry definitions to identify the first compound in each equation as an acid or a base. (*Hint:* What is produced by the reaction?)
    a. $(CH_3)_2NH + H_2O \longrightarrow (CH_3)_2NH_2^+ + OH^-$
    b. $C_6H_5NH_2 + H_2O \longrightarrow C_6H_5NH_3^+ + OH^-$
    c. $C_6H_5CH_2NH_2 + H_2O \longrightarrow C_6H_5CH_2NH_3^+ + OH^-$

18. Use the Brønsted–Lowry definitions to identify the first compound in each equation as an acid or a base.
    a. $CH_3NH_2 + H_2O \longrightarrow CH_3NH_3^+ + OH^-$
    b. $H_2O_2 + H_2O \longrightarrow H_3O^+ + HO_2^-$
    c. $NH_2Cl + H_2O \longrightarrow NH_3Cl^+ + OH^-$

19. Write the equation that shows hydrogen chloride gas reacting as a Brønsted–Lowry acid in water. What is the name of the acid formed?

20. Write the equation that shows hydrogen iodide gas reacting as a Brønsted–Lowry acid in water. Based on the answer to Problem 19, suggest a name for the acid formed.

21. Write the equation that shows how ammonia acts as a Brønsted–Lowry base in water.

22. Hydroxylamine ($HONH_2$) is not an Arrhenius base, even though it contains OH, but it *is* a Brønsted–Lowry base. Write an equation that shows how hydroxylamine acts as a Brønsted–Lowry base in water.

Acids and Bases: Names and Formulas

23. For the following acids and bases, supply a formula to match the name or a name to match the formula.
    a. HCl
    b. strontium hydroxide
    c. KOH
    d. boric acid

24. For the following acids and bases, supply a formula to match the name or a name to match the formula.
    a. rubidium hydroxide
    b. $Al(OH)_3$
    c. hydrocyanic acid
    d. HNO_3

25. Name the following, and classify each as an acid or a base.
    a. H_3PO_4
    b. CsOH
    c. H_2CO_3

26. Name the following, and classify each as an acid or a base.
    a. $Mg(OH)_2$
    b. NH_3
    c. CH_3COOH

27. When an acid name ends in -*ic acid*, there is often a related acid whose name ends in -*ous acid*. The formula of the -*ous* acid has one less oxygen atom than that of the -*ic* acid. With this information, write formulas for (a) nitrous acid and (b) phosphorous acid.

28. Refer to Problem 27 and Table 1. Tellurium is chemically similar to sulfur. Use this information to write the formulas for (a) telluric acid and (b) tellurous acid.

Acidic and Basic Anhydrides

29. Give the formula for the compound formed when (a) sulfur trioxide reacts with water and (b) magnesium oxide reacts with water. In each case, is the product an acid or a base?

30. Give the formula for the compound formed when (a) potassium oxide reacts with water and (b) carbon dioxide reacts with water. In each case, is the product an acid or a base?

Strong and Weak Acids and Bases

31. When 1.0 mol of hydrogen iodide (HI) gas is dissolved in a liter of water, the resulting solution contains 1.0 mol of hydronium ions and 1.0 mol of iodide ions. Classify HI as a strong acid, a weak acid, a weak base, or a strong base.

32. Thallium hydroxide (TlOH) is a water-soluble ionic compound. Classify TlOH as a strong acid, a weak acid, a weak base, or a strong base.

33. Methylamine (CH_3NH_2) gas reacts slightly with water to form relatively few hydroxide ions and methylammonium ions ($CH_3NH_3^+$). Classify CH_3NH_2 as a strong acid, a weak acid, a weak base, or a strong base.

34. When 1 mol of hydrogen sulfide (H_2S) gas is dissolved in a liter of water, the resulting solution contains about 0.0004

mol of H^+ ions and about 3×10^{-11} mol of OH^- ions. Classify H_2S as a strong acid, a weak acid, a weak base, or a strong base.

35. Identify each of the following substances as a strong acid, a weak acid, a strong base, a weak base, or a salt.
    a. LiOH
    b. HBr
    c. HNO_2
    d. $CuSO_4$

36. Identify each of the following substances as a strong acid, a weak acid, a strong base, a weak base, or a salt.
    a. K_3PO_4
    b. $CaBr_2$
    c. $Mg(OH)_2$
    d. $BaCO_3$

37. Which of the following aqueous solutions has the highest concentration of H^+ ions? Which has the lowest?
    a. 0.10 M HNO_3
    b. 0.10 M NH_3
    c. 0.10 M CH_3COOH

38. Consider 0.10 M solutions of acetic acid, ammonia, hydrochloric acid, and sodium hydroxide. Rank these solutions in order of increasing pH.

Ionization of Acids and Bases

39. Write equations showing the ionization of the following as Arrhenius acids or bases.
    a. HNO_2
    b. $Ba(OH)_2$
    c. HBr

40. Write equations showing the ionization of the following as Arrhenius acids or bases.
    a. HI
    b. LiOH
    c. $HClO_2$

41. Write equations showing the ionization of the following as Brønsted–Lowry acids in water.
    a. HClO
    b. HNO_2
    c. H_2S

42. Write equations showing the ionization of the following as Brønsted–Lowry acids in water.
    a. HI
    b. $HClO_3$
    c. $CFH_2CHOHCOOH$

Neutralization

43. Write equations for the reaction (a) of potassium hydroxide with hydrochloric acid and (b) of lithium hydroxide with nitric acid.

44. Write equations for the reaction (a) of 1 mol of calcium hydroxide with 2 mol of hydrochloric acid and (b) of 1 mol of sulfuric acid with 2 mol of potassium hydroxide.

45. Write the equation for the reaction of 1 mol of sulfurous acid (H_2SO_3) with 1 mol of magnesium hydroxide.

46. Write the equation for the reaction of 1 mol of phosphoric acid with 1 mol of aluminum hydroxide.

The pH Scale

47. Indicate whether each of the following pH values represents an acidic, basic, or neutral solution.
    a. 4
    b. 7
    c. 3.5
    d. 9

48. Lime juice is quite sour. Which of the following is a reasonable pH for lime juice?
    a. 2
    b. 6
    c. 7.8
    d. 12

49. What is the pH of a solution that has a hydrogen ion concentration of 1.0×10^{-5} M?

50. What is the pH of a solution that has a hydrogen ion concentration of 1.0×10^{-9} M?

51. What is the hydrogen ion concentration of a solution that has a pH of 3?

52. What is the hydrogen ion concentration of a solution that has a pH of 11?

53. Milk of magnesia has a hydrogen ion concentration between 1.0×10^{-10} M and 1.0×10^{-11} M. What two whole-number values is the pH of milk of magnesia between?

54. Oven cleaner has a pH between 13 and 14. What two whole-number values of x should be used in 1.0×10^{-x} M to express the range of hydrogen ion concentration?

Conjugate Acid–Base Pairs

55. In the following reaction in aqueous solution, identify (a) which of the reactants is the acid and which is the base, (b) the conjugate base of the acid, and (c) the conjugate acid of the base.

$$HNO_3\,(aq) + NH_3(aq) \longrightarrow NO_3^-\,(aq) + NH_4^+\,(aq)$$

56. In the following reaction in aqueous solution, identify (a) which of the reactants is the acid and which is the base, (b) the conjugate base of the acid, and (c) the conjugate acid of the base.

$$CH_3CH_2COOH + H_2O \longrightarrow CH_3CH_2COO^- + H_3O^+$$

Antacids

57. Mylanta liquid has 200 mg of $Al(OH)_3$ and 200 mg of $Mg(OH)_2$ per teaspoonful. Write the equation for the neutralization of stomach acid [represented as HCl(aq)] by each of these substances.

58. What is the Brønsted–Lowry base in each of the following compounds, which are ingredients in antacids?
   a. $NaHCO_3$
   b. $Mg(OH)_2$
   c. $MgCO_3$
   d. $CaCO_3$

ADDITIONAL PROBLEMS

59. According to the Arrhenius theory, is every compound that contains OH a base? Explain.

60. Lime deposits on brass faucets are mostly $CaCO_3$. The deposits can be removed by soaking the faucets in hydrochloric acid. Write an equation for the reaction that occurs.

61. The conjugate base of a very weak acid is a strong base, and the conjugate base of a strong acid is a weak base. (a) Is Cl^- ion a strong base or a weak base? (b) Is CN^- a strong base or a weak base?

62. Strontium iodide can be made by the reaction of solid strontium carbonate $(SrCO_3)$ with an acid. Identify the acid, and write the balanced equation for the reaction.

63. The pOH is related to $[OH^-]$ just as pH is related to $[H^+]$. What is the pOH (a) of a solution that has a hydroxide ion concentration of 1.0×10^{-3} M? (b) Of a 0.01 M KOH solution?

64. Rank 0.1 M solutions of (a) acetic acid $(HC_2H_3O_2)$, (b) ammonia (NH_3), (c) nitric acid (HNO_3), (d) sodium chloride (NaCl), and (e) sodium hydroxide (NaOH) from the highest pH to the lowest pH.

65. Human blood contains buffers that minimize changes in pH. One blood buffer is the hydrogen phosphate ion (HPO_4^{2-}). Like water, HPO_4^{2-} is amphiprotic. That is, it can act either as a Brønsted–Lowry acid or as a Brønsted–Lowry base. Write equations that illustrate the reaction with water of HPO_4^{2-} as an acid and as a base.

66. Three varieties of Tums have calcium carbonate as the only active ingredient: Regular Tums tablets have 500 mg; Tums E-X, 750 mg; and Tums ULTRA, 1000 mg. How many regular Tums would you have to take to get the same quantity of calcium carbonate as you would get with two Tums E-X? With two Tums ULTRA tablets?

67. The active ingredient in the antacid Basaljel is a gel of solid aluminum carbonate. Write the equation for the neutralization of aluminum carbonate by stomach acid (aqueous HCl).

68. Milk of magnesia has 400 mg of $Mg(OH)_2$ per teaspoon. Calculate the mass of stomach acid that can be neutralized by 1.00 teaspoon of milk of magnesia, assuming that the stomach acid is 0.50% HCl by mass.

69. When a well is drilled into rock that contains sulfide minerals, some of the minerals may dissolve in the well water, yielding "sulfur water" that smells like rotten eggs. The water from these wells feels slightly slippery, contains HS^- ions, and turns litmus paper blue. From this information, write an equation representing the reaction of HS^- ions with water.

70. Sulfuric acid is produced from elemental sulfur by a three-step process: (1) Sulfur is burned to produce sulfur dioxide. (2) Sulfur dioxide is oxidized to sulfur trioxide using oxygen and a vanadium (V) oxide catalyst. (3) Finally, the sulfur trioxide is reacted with water to produce 98% sulfuric acid. Write equations for the three reactions.

71. The pH of soap is sometimes adjusted by adding citric acid before the raw soap is formed into bars. Would citric acid increase or decrease the pH of the finished soap?

72. Write an equation to show soap [as $CH_3(CH_2)_{14}COO^-Na^+$] acting as a base with sulfuric acid.

73. Write an equation for the neutralization reaction of a fatty acid $(HC_{16}H_{31}O_2)$ with potassium hydroxide (KOH) in water. Is the product of this reaction a fuel or a soap?

74. Most soaps have a bitter taste and a slippery feel. What does this hint indicate about the pH of most soaps?

COLLABORATIVE GROUP PROJECTS

Prepare a PowerPoint, poster, or other presentation (as directed by your instructor) to share with the class.

1. Prepare a brief report on one of the following acids or bases. List sources (including local sources for the acid or base, if available) and commercial uses.
   a. ammonia
   b. hydrochloric acid
   c. phosphoric acid
   d. nitric acid
   e. sodium hydroxide
   f. sulfuric acid

2. Examine the labels of at least five antacid preparations. Make a list of the ingredients in each. Look up the properties (medical use, side effects, toxicity, and so on) of

each ingredient on the Web or in a reference book such as *The Merck Index*.

3. Examine the labels of at least five toilet-bowl cleaners and five drain cleaners. Make a list of the ingredients in each. Look up the formulas and properties of each ingredient on the Web or in a reference book such as *The Merck Index*. Which ingredients are acids? Which are bases?

4. A web page on making biodiesel claims that any water in the waste oil must be removed before starting the reaction.

BRIEF ANSWERS TO SELECTED PROBLEMS

Answers are provided for *all in-chapter exercises*. Brief answers are given for *odd-numbered Review Questions*; more complete answers can be obtained by reviewing the text. Answers are provided for *all odd-numbered Problems and Additional Problems.*

NOTE: For numerical problems, your answer may differ slightly from ours because of rounding and the use of significant figures.

1 **A. a.** $HBr(aq) \xrightarrow{H_2O} H^+(aq) + Br^-(aq)$

   b. $Ca(OH)_2(s) \xrightarrow{H_2O} Ca^{2+}(aq) + 2 OH^-(aq)$

   B. $CH_3COOH(aq) \xrightarrow{H_2O} H^+(aq) + CH_3COO^-(aq)$

2 **A.** $HBr(aq) + H_2O \longrightarrow H_3O^+(aq) + Br^-(aq)$

   B. $HBr(aq) + CH_3OH \longrightarrow CH_3OH_2^+(aq) + Br^-(aq)$

3 **A.** H_2SeO_3 **B.** HNO_3

4 **A.** $Sr(OH)_2$ **B.** KOH

5 **A.** $NaOH(aq) + HC_2H_3O_2(aq) \longrightarrow NaC_2H_3O_2(aq) + H_2O$

   B. $2 HCl(aq) + Mg(OH)_2(aq) \longrightarrow MgCl_2(aq) + 2 H_2O$

6 **A.** $pH = 11$ **B.** $pH = 3$

7 **A.** 1.0×10^{-2} M (0.010 M)   **B.** 1.0×10^{-3} M (0.0010 M)

8 (c)

9 Beaker III: HNO_3; Beaker II: KOH

1. **a.** Arrhenius: forms H^+ in water; Brønsted–Lowry: proton donor
   b. Arrhenius: forms OH^- in water; Brønsted–Lowry: proton acceptor
   c. Ionic compound from acid-base neutralization

3. An acid turns litmus red, tastes sour, dissolves active metals, and neutralizes bases. A base turns litmus blue, tastes bitter, feels slippery, and neutralizes acids.

5. A strong base in water ionizes to a much greater extent than does a weak base.

7. Acidic anhydrides react with water to form acids. Basic anhydrides react with water to form bases.

9. $Mg(OH)_2$ is insoluble in water, so that few $OH^-(aq)$ ions form.

11. A condition in which the blood is too alkaline

13. $HClO_4(aq) \xrightarrow{H_2O} H^+(aq) + ClO_4^-(aq)$

15. $RbOH(s) \xrightarrow{H_2O} Rb^+(aq) + OH^-(aq)$

17. base: a, b, c; acid: none

19. $HCl(g) + H_2O \longrightarrow H_3O^+(aq) + Cl^-(aq)$; hydrochloric acid

21. $NH_3(aq) + H_2O \longrightarrow NH_4^+(aq) + OH^-(aq)$

23. **a.** hydrochloric acid   **b.** $Sr(OH)_2$
    c. potassium hydroxide   **d.** H_3BO_3

25. **a.** phosphoric acid (an acid)
    b. cesium hydroxide (a base)
    c. carbonic acid (an acid)

27. **a.** HNO_2 **b.** H_3PO_3

29. **a.** H_2SO_4 (an acid)   **b.** $Mg(OH)_2$ (a base)

31. strong acid

33. weak base

35. **a.** strong base   **b.** strong acid
    c. weak acid   **d.** salt

37. highest: a; lowest, b

39. **a.** $HNO_2(aq) \xrightarrow{H_2O} H^+(aq) + NO_2^-(aq)$
    b. $Ba(OH)_2(s) \xrightarrow{H_2O} Ba^{2+}(aq) + 2 OH^-(aq)$
    c. $HBr(aq) \xrightarrow{H_2O} H^+(aq) + Br^-(aq)$

41. **a.** $HClO(aq) + H_2O \rightleftharpoons H_3O^+(aq) + ClO^-(aq)$
    b. $HNO_2(aq) + H_2O \rightleftharpoons H_3O^+(aq) + NO_2^-(aq)$
    c. $H_2S(aq) + H_2O \rightleftharpoons H_3O^+(aq) + HS^-(aq)$

43. **a.** $KOH(aq) + HCl(aq) \longrightarrow KCl(aq) + H_2O$
    b. $LiOH(aq) + HNO_3(aq) \longrightarrow LiNO_3(aq) + H_2O$

45. $H_2SO_3(aq) + Mg(OH)_2(aq) \longrightarrow MgSO_3(aq) + 2 H_2O$

47. acidic: a, c; basic: d; neutral: b

49. $pH = 5$

51. 1.0×10^{-3} M H^+

53. 10 and 11

55. **a.** acid: HNO_3; base: NH_3
    b. NO_3^-
    c. NH_4^+

57. $3 HCl(aq) + Al(OH)_3(s) \longrightarrow AlCl_3(aq) + 3 H_2O$
    $2 HCl(aq) + Mg(OH)_2(s) \longrightarrow MgCl_2(aq) + 2 H_2O$

59. No. Covalent OH-containing compounds do not produce OH^- ions in water.

61. **a.** weak base   **b.** strong base

63. **a.** 3   **b.** 2

65. $HPO_4^{2-}(aq) + H_2O \longrightarrow H_3O^+(aq) + PO_4^{3-}(aq)$
    $HPO_4^{2-}(aq) + H_2O \longrightarrow OH^-(aq) + H_2PO_4^-(aq)$

67. $Al_2(CO_3)_3(s) + 6 HCl(aq) \longrightarrow 2 AlCl_3(aq) + 3 CO_2(g) + 3 H_2O(l)$

69. $HS^-(aq) + H_2O \longrightarrow H_2S(g) + OH^-(aq)$

71. Decrease

73. $HC_{16}H_{31}O_2(s) + KOH(aq) \longrightarrow KC_{16}H_{31}O_2 + H_2O(l)$; a soap

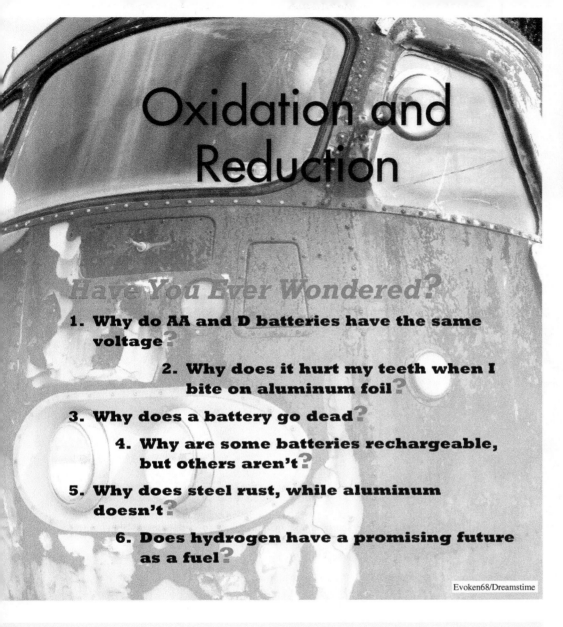

Oxidation and Reduction

Have You Ever Wondered?

1. Why do AA and D batteries have the same voltage?

2. Why does it hurt my teeth when I bite on aluminum foil?

3. Why does a battery go dead?

4. Why are some batteries rechargeable, but others aren't?

5. Why does steel rust, while aluminum doesn't?

6. Does hydrogen have a promising future as a fuel?

Evoken68/Dreamstime

eyecraveeyecrave/iStockphoto

Learning Objectives

> Identify an oxidation–reduction reaction. (1)

> Classify a particular change within a redox reaction as either oxidation or reduction. (1)

> Identify the oxidizing agent and the reducing agent in a redox reaction. (2)

> Balance redox equations. (3)

> Identify and write the half-reactions in an electrochemical cell. (3)

> Describe the reactions that occur when iron rusts. (4)

> Explain why an explosive reaction is so energetic. (4)

> Write equations for reactions in which oxygen is an oxidizing agent. (5)

> List some of the common oxidizing agents encountered in daily life. (5)

> Identify some common reducing agents. (6)

> Write the overall equations for the metabolism of glucose and for photosynthesis. (7)

> Distinguish between the objectives of chemists producing industrial chemicals and those of chemists producing specialty chemicals.

> Explain how green chemistry can be applied to the design of new catalysts.

Burn and Unburn From a simple campfire to the most advanced electric battery, from the trees in a rainforest that consume carbon dioxide and make oxygen to the people hurrying along a city street, we depend on an important group of reactions called *oxidation–reduction reactions*, or *redox reactions* (a shortening of *reduction–oxidation*). These reactions are extremely diverse: charcoal burns, iron rusts, bleach removes stains, the food we eat is converted to energy for our brain and muscles, and plants use the sun's energy to produce food.

We see the long-term product of automotive steel and our atmosphere above: rust. The orange color is from iron(III) oxide. Steel is mostly iron, and iron undergoes an undesirable oxidation-reduction (redox) reaction in the presence of air and water. That reaction costs almost $10 billion every year, as engineers and manufacturers look for ways to minimize or prevent that redox reaction. Other redox reactions are desirable, or even necessary, to life itself. In this chapter, we will examine the nature of redox reactions, and we will look at some of their applications in life and in modern technology.

Ben Willmore/Digital Mastery

From Chapter 8 of *Chemistry for Changing Times*, Thirteenth Edition. John W. Hill, Terry W. McCreary, Doris K. Kolb. Copyright © 2013 by Pearson Education, Inc. All rights reserved.

Oxidation and reduction always occur together. They are opposite aspects of a single process, a redox reaction. You can't have one without the other (Figure 1). When one substance is oxidized, another is reduced. However, it is sometimes convenient to discuss only a part of the process—the oxidation part or the reduction part.

Reduced forms of matter—foods, coal, and gasoline—are high in energy. *Oxidized* forms—carbon dioxide and water—are low in energy. The energy in foods and fossil fuels is released when these materials are oxidized. In this chapter, we examine the processes of oxidation and reduction in some detail to better understand the chemical reactions that keep us alive and maintain our civilization.

Paul Silverman/Fundamental Photographs

Paul Silverman/Fundamental Photographs

▲ **Figure 1** Oxidation and reduction always occur together. Pictured here on the left is a reaction called the ammonium dichromate volcano. In the reaction, the ammonium ion (NH_4^+) is oxidized and the dichromate ion ($Cr_2O_7^{2-}$) is reduced. Considerable heat and light are evolved. The equation for the reaction is

$$(NH_4)_2Cr_2O_7 \longrightarrow Cr_2O_3 + N_2 + 4\,H_2O$$

The water is driven off as vapor, and the nitrogen gas escapes, leaving pure Cr_2O_3 as the visible product (right).

1 Oxidation and Reduction: Three Views

Learning Objectives ❯ Identify an oxidation–reduction reaction. ❯ Classify a particular change within a redox reaction as either oxidation or reduction.

The term *oxidation* stems from the early recognition of oxygen's involvement in oxide formation; *reduction* originally meant removal of oxygen from an oxide. When oxygen combines with other elements or compounds, the process is called **oxidation**. The substances that combine with oxygen are said to have been *oxidized*. Originally, the term *oxidation* was limited to reactions involving combination with oxygen. As chemists came to realize that combination with chlorine (or bromine or another active nonmetal) was not all that different from combination with oxygen, they broadened the definition of oxidation to include reactions involving these other substances—as we shall shortly see.

Reduction is the opposite of oxidation. When hydrogen burns, it combines with oxygen to form water.

$$2\,H_2 + O_2 \longrightarrow 2\,H_2O$$

The hydrogen is oxidized in this reaction, but at the same time the oxygen is reduced. Whenever oxidation occurs, reduction must also occur. Oxidation and reduction always happen at the same time and in exactly equivalent amounts.

Because oxidation and reduction are chemical opposites and constant companions, their definitions are linked. We can view oxidation and reduction in at least three different ways (Figure 2).

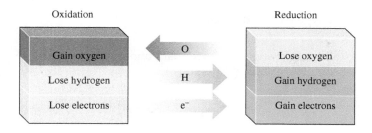

1. *Oxidation* is a gain of oxygen atoms.
   Reduction is a loss of oxygen atoms.

At high temperatures (such as those in automobile engines), nitrogen, which is normally quite unreactive, combines with oxygen to form nitric oxide.

$$N_2 + O_2 \longrightarrow 2\,NO$$

Nitrogen gains oxygen atoms; there are no O atoms in the N_2 molecule and one O atom in each of the NO molecules. Therefore, nitrogen is oxidized.

Now consider what happens when methane is burned to form carbon dioxide and water. Both carbon and hydrogen gain oxygen atoms, and so both elements are oxidized.

When lead dioxide is heated at high temperatures, it decomposes as follows:

$$2\,PbO_2 \longrightarrow 2\,PbO + O_2$$

| This Pb atom has two O atoms attached | This Pb atom has only one O atom attached |

The lead dioxide loses oxygen, so it is reduced.

CONCEPTUAL Example 1 | **Redox Processes—Gain or Loss of Oxygen Atoms**

In each of the following changes, is the reactant undergoing oxidation or reduction? (These are not complete chemical equations.)

a. $Pb \longrightarrow PbO_2$ b. $SnO_2 \longrightarrow SnO$

c. $KClO_3 \longrightarrow KCl$ d. $Cu_2O \longrightarrow 2\,CuO$

Solution

a. Lead gains oxygen atoms (it has none on the left and two on the right); it is oxidized.

b. Tin loses an oxygen atom (it has two on the left and only one on the right); it is reduced.

c. There are three O atoms on the left and none on the right. The compound loses oxygen; it is reduced.

d. The two copper atoms on the left share a single oxygen atom, that is, half an oxygen atom each. On the right, each Cu atom has an O atom all its own. Cu has gained oxygen; it is oxidized.

■ EXERCISE 1

In each of the following changes, is the reactant undergoing oxidation or reduction? (These are not complete chemical equations.)

a. $3 Fe \longrightarrow Fe_3O_4$

b. $NO \longrightarrow NO_2$

c. $CrO_3 \longrightarrow Cr_2O_3$

d. $C_3H_6O \longrightarrow C_3H_6O_2$

A second view of oxidation and reduction involves hydrogen atoms.

2. *Oxidation* is a loss of hydrogen atoms.

   Reduction is a gain of hydrogen atoms.

   Look once more at the burning of methane:

$$CH_4 + 2 O_2 \longrightarrow CO_2 + 2 H_2O$$

The oxygen gains hydrogen to form water, so the oxygen is reduced. Methane loses hydrogen and is oxidized. (We see that the carbon and hydrogens of CH_4 also gain oxygen, so our two views of oxidation and reduction are consistent with one another.)

Methyl alcohol (CH_3OH), when passed over hot copper gauze, forms formaldehyde and hydrogen gas.

| The C and O atoms have 4 H atoms attached | The C and O atoms have only two H atoms attached |

Because the methyl alcohol loses hydrogen, it is oxidized in this reaction.

Methyl alcohol can be made by reaction of carbon monoxide with hydrogen.

$$CO + 2 H_2 \rightarrow CH_3OH$$

Because the carbon monoxide gains hydrogen atoms, it is reduced.

Biochemists often find the gain or loss of hydrogen atoms a useful way to look at oxidation–reduction processes. For example, a substance called NAD^+ is changed to NADH in a variety of biochemical redox reactions. The actual molecules are rather complex, but we can write the equation for the oxidation of ethyl alcohol to acetaldehyde, one step in the metabolism of the alcohol, as follows.

$$CH_3CH_2OH + NAD^+ \longrightarrow CH_3CHO + NADH + H^+$$

We can see that ethyl alcohol is oxidized (loses hydrogen) and NAD^+ is reduced (gains hydrogen).

CONCEPTUAL **Example 2**   Redox Processes—Gain or Loss of Hydrogen Atoms

In each of the following changes, is the reactant undergoing oxidation or reduction? (These are not complete chemical equations.)

a. $C_2H_6O \longrightarrow C_2H_4O$

b. $C_2H_2 \longrightarrow C_2H_6$

Solution

a. There are six H atoms in the reactant on the left and only four in the product on the right. The reactant loses H atoms; it is oxidized.

b. There are two H atoms in the reactant on the left and six in the product on the right. The reactant gains H atoms; it is reduced.

■ EXERCISE 2

In each of the following changes, is the reactant undergoing oxidation or reduction? (These are not complete chemical equations.)

a. $C_3H_6O \longrightarrow C_3H_8O$ **b.** $C_3H_6 \longrightarrow C_3H_4$

A third view of oxidation and reduction involves gain or loss of electrons.

3. *Oxidation* is a loss of electrons.

Reduction is a gain of electrons.

When magnesium metal reacts with chlorine, magnesium ions and chloride ions are formed.

$$Mg + Cl_2 \longrightarrow Mg^{2+} + 2Cl^-$$

Because the magnesium atom loses electrons, it is oxidized, and because the chlorine atoms gain electrons, they are reduced.

It is easy to see that when magnesium atoms become Mg^{2+} ions, they lose electrons, and that when chlorine atoms become Cl^- ions, they must gain electrons. But which is oxidation and which is reduction? Perhaps Figure 3 can help. The charge on a simple ion is often referred to as its *oxidation number*. An increase in oxidation number (increase in positive charge) is oxidation; a decrease in oxidation number is reduction. The charge on an Mg atom is zero, therefore, conversion to Mg^{2+} is an increase in oxidation number (oxidation). For Cl atoms, the charge is also zero, and a change to Cl^- is a decrease in oxidation number (reduction).

This view of oxidation and reduction as a gain or loss of electrons is especially useful in electrochemistry (Section 3).

| CONCEPTUAL Example 3 | Redox Processes—Gain or Loss of Electrons |

In each of the following changes, is the reactant undergoing oxidation or reduction? (These are not complete chemical equations.)

a. $Zn \longrightarrow Zn^{2+}$ **b.** $Fe^{3+} \longrightarrow Fe^{2+}$
c. $S^{2-} \longrightarrow S$ **d.** $AgNO_3 \longrightarrow Ag$

Solution

a. In forming a 2+ ion, a Zn atom loses two electrons. Its oxidation number increases from 0 to +2. Zinc is oxidized.

b. To change from a 3+ ion to a 2+ ion, Fe gains an electron. Its oxidation number decreases from +3 to +2. The Fe^{3+} ion is reduced.

c. To change from a 2− ion to an atom with no charge, S loses two electrons. Its oxidation number increases. Sulfide ion is oxidized.

d. To answer this question, you must recognize that $AgNO_3$ is an ionic compound consisting of Ag^+ and NO_3^- ions. In changing from Ag^+ to Ag, silver gains an electron. Its oxidation number decreases. Silver ion is reduced.

■ EXERCISE 3

In each of the following changes, is the reactant undergoing oxidation or reduction? (These are not complete chemical equations.)

a. $Cr^{6+} \rightarrow Cr^{3+}$ **b.** $Sn^{2+} \longrightarrow Sn^{4+}$
c. $MnO_4^{2-} \longrightarrow MnO_4^-$ **d.** $Ti \rightarrow TiO_2$

Why do we have different ways to look at oxidation and reduction? Oxidation as a gain of oxygen is historical and specific, but the definition in terms of electrons applies more broadly. Which one should we use? Ordinarily, the definitions are consistent with one another, so we use the most convenient one. For the combustion (burning) of carbon,

$$C + O_2 \longrightarrow CO_2$$

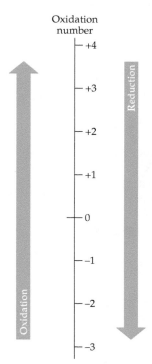

▲ **Figure 3** An increase in oxidation number means a loss of electrons and is therefore oxidation. A decrease in oxidation number means a gain of electrons and is therefore reduction.

Q: *Manganese's oxidation number changes from +4 in MnO_2 to +7 in MnO_4^-. Is it oxidized or reduced? Sulfur's oxidation number changes from 0 in S_8 to −2 in S^{2-}. Is it oxidized or reduced?*

Two mnemonics:

LEO the lion says GER.

Loss of
  Electrons is
    Oxidation.
Gain of
  Electrons is
    Reduction.
      OIL RIG
Oxidation
  Is
    Loss of electrons.
Reduction
  Is
    Gain of electrons.

it is most convenient to see that carbon is oxidized by gaining oxygen atoms. Similarly, for the reaction

$$CH_2O + H_2 \longrightarrow CH_4O$$

it is easy to see that the reactant CH_2O gains hydrogen atoms and is thereby reduced. Finally, in the case of the reaction

$$3\,Sn^{2+} + 2\,Bi^{3+} \longrightarrow 3\,Sn^{4+} + 2\,Bi$$

it is clear that tin is oxidized because it loses electrons, increasing its oxidation number from +2 to +4. Similarly, we see that bismuth is reduced because it gains electrons, decreasing its oxidation number from +3 to 0.

Self-Assessment Questions

1. Which of the following is *not* one of the ways we can view oxidation?
   a. electrons gained   **b.** electrons lost
   c. hydrogen atoms lost   **d.** oxygen atoms gained

2. Which of the following partial equations represents an oxidation of nitrogen?
   a. $NH_3 \rightarrow NH_4^+$ **b.** $N_2O_4 \rightarrow NI_3$ **c.** $NO_3^- \rightarrow NO$ **d.** $NO_2 \rightarrow N_2O_5$

3. When CrO_4^- reacts to form Cr^{3+}, the chromium in CrO_4^- is
   a. reduced; it loses electrons
   b. reduced; it loses oxygen
   c. oxidized; its oxidation number increases
   d. oxidized; it gains positive charge

4. Which of the following partial equations best represents a reduction of molybdenum?
   a. $MoO_2 + H_2O \rightarrow H_2MoO_3$ **b.** $MoO_2 + 4\,H_2 \rightarrow Mo + 2\,H_2O$
   c. $2\,MoO_2 + O_2 \rightarrow 2\,MoO_3$ **d.** $MoO_2 + 4\,H^+ \rightarrow Mo^{4+} + 2\,H_2O$

5. According to the following partial equation, Cl_2 is
   $$3\,Cl_2 + 2\,Al \rightarrow 2\,AlCl_3$$
   a. both oxidized and reduced   **b.** neither oxidized nor reduced
   c. oxidized, only   **d.** reduced only

6. According to the following partial equation, manganese
   $$Mn \rightarrow Mn^{2+} + 2\,e^-$$
   a. gains electrons and is oxidized   **b.** gains electrons and is reduced
   c. loses electrons and is oxidized   **d.** loses electrons and is reduced

7. When an element is oxidized, its oxidation number
   a. decreases, as electrons are gained   **b.** decreases, as electrons are lost
   c. increases, as electrons are gained   **d.** increases, as electrons are lost

Answers: 1, a; 2, d; 3, b; 4, b; 5, d; 6, c; 7, d

2 Oxidizing and Reducing Agents

Learning Objective > Identify the oxidizing agent and the reducing agent in a redox reaction.

Oxidation and reduction occur together. However, in looking at oxidation–reduction reactions, we often find it convenient to focus on the role played by a particular reactant. For example, in the reaction

$$CuO + H_2 \longrightarrow Cu + H_2O$$

we see that copper oxide is reduced and hydrogen is oxidized. We can conclude that if one substance is oxidized, the other must *cause* it to be oxidized. In the above reaction, CuO causes H_2 to be oxidized. Therefore, CuO is called the **oxidizing agent**. Conversely, H_2 causes CuO to be reduced, so H_2 is the **reducing agent**. Each oxidation–reduction reaction has an oxidizing agent and a reducing agent among the reactants. The reducing agent is the substance being oxidized; the oxidizing agent is the substance being reduced.

Reduction: CuO is reduced; CuO is the oxidizing agent.

$$CuO + H_2 \longrightarrow Cu + H_2O$$

Oxidation: H_2 is oxidized; H_2 is the reducing agent.

CONCEPTUAL Example 4   Oxidizing and Reducing Agents

Identify the oxidizing agents and reducing agents in the following reactions.

a. $2\,C + O_2 \longrightarrow 2\,CO$ b. $N_2 + 3\,H_2 \longrightarrow 2\,NH_3$

c. $SnO + H_2 \longrightarrow Sn + H_2O$ d. $Mg + Cl_2 \longrightarrow Mg^{2+} + 2Cl^-$

Solution

We can determine the answers by applying the three definitions of oxidation and reduction.

a. C gains oxygen and is oxidized, so it must be the reducing agent. O_2 is therefore the oxidizing agent.

b. N_2 gains hydrogen and is reduced, so it is the oxidizing agent. H_2 therefore is the reducing agent.

c. SnO loses oxygen and is reduced, so it is the oxidizing agent. H_2 is therefore the reducing agent.

d. Mg loses electrons and is oxidized, so it is the reducing agent. Cl_2 is therefore the oxidizing agent.

■ EXERCISE 4

Identify the oxidizing agents and reducing agents in the following reactions.

a. $Se + O_2 \longrightarrow SeO_2$ b. $2\,K + Br_2 \longrightarrow 2\,K^+ + 2\,Br^-$

c. $CH_3CN + 2\,H_2 \longrightarrow CH_3CH_2NH_2$ d. $V_2O_5 + 2\,H_2 \longrightarrow V_2O_3 + 2H_2O$

Self-Assessment Questions

1. A reducing agent
   a. gains electrons
   b. gains protons
   c. loses electrons
   d. loses protons

2. Which substance is the oxidizing agent in the following reaction?
   $$Cu(s) + 2\,Ag^+(aq) \rightarrow Cu^{2+}(aq) + 2\,Ag(s)$$
   a. Ag   b. Ag^+ c. Cu   d. Cu^{2+}

3. In the following reaction, the reducing agent is
   $$Al(s) + Cr^{3+}(aq) \rightarrow Al^{3+}(aq) + Cr(s)$$
   a. Al(s)   b. $Al^{3+}(aq)$ c. $Cr^{3+}(aq)$ d. Cr(s)

4. What is the oxidizing agent in the following reaction?
   $$Zn(s) + 2\,Tl^+(aq) \rightarrow Zn^{2+}(aq) + 2\,Tl(s)$$
   a. Tl(s)   b. $Tl^+(aq)$ c. Zn(s)   d. $Zn^{2+}(aq)$

5. What is the reducing agent in the following reaction?
   $$12\,H^+(aq) + 2\,IO_3^-(aq) + 10\,Fe^{2+}(aq) \rightarrow 10\,Fe^{3+}(aq) + I_2(s) + 6\,H_2O(l)$$
   a. $Fe^{2+}(aq)$ b. $H^+(aq)$ c. $I_2(s)$ d. $IO_3^-(aq)$

Answers: 1, c; 2, b; 3, a; 4, b; 5, a

3 Electrochemistry: Cells and Batteries

Learning Objectives > Balance redox equations. > Identify and write the half-reactions in an electrochemical cell.

Electricity can produce chemical change, a process called *electrolysis*. For example, an electric current passed through molten sodium chloride produces sodium metal and chlorine gas. Here we focus on the reverse process, in which chemical change produces electricity.

An electric current in a wire is simply a flow of electrons. Oxidation–reduction reactions in which electrons are transferred from one substance to another can be used to produce electricity. This is what happens in dry cell and storage batteries.

When a coil of copper wire is placed in a solution of silver nitrate (Figure 4a), the copper atoms give up their outer electrons to the silver ions. (We can omit the nitrate ions from the equation because they do not change.) The copper metal dissolves, going into solution as copper(II) ions that color the solution blue. The silver ions come out of solution as beautiful needles of silver metal (Figure 4b). The copper is oxidized; the silver ions are reduced.

▶ **Figure 4** A coil of copper wire is immersed in a colorless solution of Ag^+ ions (a). As the reaction progresses, the more active copper displaces the less active silver from solution, producing needle-like crystals of silver metal (b) and a blue solution of Cu^{2+} ions. The equation for the reaction is $2Ag^+(aq) + Cu(s) \longrightarrow 2Ag(s) + Cu^{2+}(aq)$.

(a)   (b)

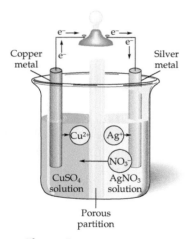

▲ **Figure 5** A simple electrochemical cell. The half-reactions are
Oxidation (anode):

$$Cu(s) \longrightarrow Cu^{2+}(aq) + 2\ e^-$$

Reduction (cathode):

$$Ag^+(aq) + e^- \longrightarrow Ag(s)$$

Q: *To balance the equation for the overall reaction, you need to add a coefficient of 2 before Ag^+ and $Ag(s)$. Why?*

Because the reaction involves only the transfer of electrons, it can occur even when the silver ions are separated from the copper metal. If we place the reactants in separate compartments and connect them with a wire, the electrons will flow through the wire to get from the copper metal to the silver ions. This flow of electrons constitutes an electric current, and it can be used to run a motor or light a lamp.

In the **electrochemical cell** pictured in Figure 5, there are two separate compartments. One contains copper metal in a blue solution of copper(II) sulfate, and the other contains silver metal in a colorless solution of silver nitrate. Copper atoms give up electrons much more readily than silver atoms do, so electrons flow away from the copper compartment and toward the silver. The copper metal slowly dissolves as copper atoms give up electrons to form copper(II) ions. The electrons flow through the wire to the silver compartment, where silver ions pick them up to become silver atoms.

As time goes by, the copper bar slowly disappears and the silver bar gets bigger. The blue solution becomes darker blue as Cu atoms are converted to Cu^{2+} ions. Those Cu^{2+} ions give the left compartment a positive charge, so (negative) nitrate ions move from the right compartment, through the porous partition, into the copper sulfate solution. (That is why the partition is porous. If the nitrate ions were unable to move through it, the cell would not work.) For each copper atom that gives up two electrons, two silver ions each pick up one electron, and two nitrate ions move from the right compartment to the left compartment.

The two pieces of metal where electrons are transferred are called **electrodes**. The electrode where oxidation occurs is called the **anode**. The one where reduction occurs is the **cathode**. In our example cell, copper gives up electrons, it is oxidized, and the copper bar is therefore the anode. Silver ions gain electrons and are reduced, so the silver bar is the cathode.

Electrochemical reactions are often represented as two *half-reactions*. The following representation shows the two half-reactions for the copper–silver cell and their addition to give the overall cell reaction.

Oxidation: $Cu(s) \longrightarrow Cu^{2+}(aq) + 2\,\cancel{e}$
Reduction: $2\,Ag^{+}(aq) + 2\,\cancel{e} \longrightarrow 2\,Ag(s)$
———————————————————————————————
Overall reaction: $Cu(s) + 2\,Ag^{+}(aq) \longrightarrow Cu^{2+}(aq) + 2\,Ag(s)$

Note that the electrons cancel when the two half-reactions are added.

CONCEPTUAL Example 5   Oxidation and Reduction Half-Reactions

Represent the following reaction as two half-reactions, and label them as an oxidation half-reaction and a reduction half-reaction.

$$Mg + Cl_2 \longrightarrow Mg^{2+} + 2\,Cl^-$$

Solution
Magnesium is oxidized from Mg to Mg^{2+}, a process that involves loss of two electrons from the Mg atom. The oxidation half-reaction is therefore

Oxidation: $Mg \longrightarrow Mg^{2+} + 2\,e^-$

The reduction half-reaction involves chlorine. Each of the two Cl atoms in the Cl_2 molecule must gain an electron to form a Cl^- ion. The reduction half-reaction is therefore

Reduction: $Cl_2 + 2\,e^- \longrightarrow 2\,Cl^-$

■ EXERCISE 5
Represent the following reaction as two half-reactions, and label them as an oxidation half-reaction and a reduction half-reaction.

$$2\,Co + 3\,S \rightarrow 2\,Co^{3+} + 3\,S^{2-}$$

Example 6   Balancing Redox Equations

Balance the following half-reactions, and combine them to give a balanced overall reaction.

$$Sn^{2+} \longrightarrow Sn^{4+}$$
$$Bi^{3+} \longrightarrow Bi$$

Solution
Atoms are balanced in both half-reactions, but electric charge is not. To balance charge in the first half-reaction, we add two electrons on the right side.

$$Sn^{2+} \longrightarrow Sn^{4+} + 2\,e^-$$

The second half-reaction requires three electrons on the left side.

$$Bi^{3+} + 3\,e^- \longrightarrow Bi$$

1. Why do AA and D batteries have the same voltage? Cell voltage depends almost entirely on the overall cell reaction. Cells with the same cell reaction will have virtually the same voltage. However, a larger cell (D or flashlight battery) contains more reactants and will last longer in a particular device than would a smaller cell (AA or penlight battery).

2. Why does it hurt my teeth when I bite on aluminum foil? If you have an amalgam (metal) filling, aluminum touching the metal can cause a redox reaction in which the aluminum is oxidized. Only a small voltage is produced, but it can be enough to irritate the tooth's nerve causing a lot of discomfort!

Before we can combine the two, however, we must set electron loss equal to electron gain. Electrons lost by the substance being oxidized must be gained by the substance being reduced. To make electron loss and gain equal, we multiply the first half-reaction by 3 and the second by 2.

$$3 \times (Sn^{2+} \longrightarrow Sn^{4+} + 2\,e^-) = 3\,Sn^{2+} \longrightarrow 3\,Sn^{4+} + 6\,e^-$$
$$2 \times (Bi^{3+} + 3\,e^- \longrightarrow Bi) = \underline{2\,Bi^{3+} + 6\,e^- \longrightarrow 2\,Bi}$$
$$3\,Sn^{2+} + 2\,Bi^{3+} \longrightarrow 3\,Sn^{4+} + 2\,Bi$$

Note that both atoms and charges balance in the overall reaction.

■ EXERCISE 6A

Balance the following half-reactions, and combine them to give a balanced overall reaction.

$$Fe \longrightarrow Fe^{3+}$$
$$Mg^{2+} \longrightarrow Mg$$

■ EXERCISE 6B

Balance the following half-reactions, and combine them to give a balanced overall reaction.

$$Pb \longrightarrow Pb^{2+}$$
$$Ag(NH_3)_2^+ \longrightarrow Ag + 2\,NH_3$$

Photochromic Glass

Eyeglasses with photochromic lenses eliminate the need for sunglasses because the lenses darken when exposed to bright light. This response to light is the result of oxidation–reduction reactions. Ordinary glass is a complex matrix of silicates that is transparent to visible light. Photochromic lenses have silver chloride (AgCl) and copper(I) chloride (CuCl) crystals uniformly embedded in the glass. Silver chloride is susceptible to oxidation and reduction by light. First, the light displaces an electron from a chloride ion.

$$Cl^- \xrightarrow{\text{oxidation}} Cl + e^-$$

The electron then reduces a silver ion to a silver atom.

$$Ag^+ + e^- \xrightarrow{\text{reduction}} Ag$$

Clusters of silver atoms block the transmittance of light, causing the lenses to darken. This process occurs quite quickly. The degree of darkening depends on the intensity of the light.

To be useful in eyeglasses, the photochromic process must be reversible. The darkening process is reversed by the copper(I) chloride. When the lenses are removed from light, the chlorine atoms formed by the exposure to light are reduced by the copper(I) ions, which are oxidized to copper(II) ions.

$$Cl + Cu^+ \longrightarrow Cu^{2+} + Cl^-$$

The copper(II) ions then oxidize the silver atoms.

$$Cu^{2+} + Ag \longrightarrow Cu^+ + Ag^+$$

The net effect is that the silver and chlorine atoms are converted to their original oxidized and reduced states, and the lenses become transparent once more.

Spencer Grant/PhotoEdit

▲ Photochromic glass darkens in the presence of light.

Dry Cells

The familiar *dry cell* (Figure 6) is used in flashlights and some small portable devices. It has a cylindrical zinc case that acts as the anode. A carbon rod in the center of the cell is the cathode. The space between the cathode and the anode contains a moist paste of graphite powder (carbon), manganese dioxide (MnO_2), and ammonium chloride (NH_4Cl). The anode reaction is the oxidation of the zinc cylinder to zinc ions. The cathode reaction involves reduction of manganese dioxide. A simplified version of the overall reaction is

$$Zn + 2 MnO_2 + H_2O \longrightarrow Zn^{2+} + Mn_2O_3 + 2 OH^-$$

The ordinary dry cell has largely been replaced by the alkaline cell, which is similar but contains potassium hydroxide instead of ammonium chloride. Alkaline cells are more expensive than zinc–carbon dry cells, but they last longer—both in storage and in use.

Lead Storage Batteries

Although we often refer to dry cells as batteries, a **battery** is actually a collection of electrochemical cells. The 12-volt (V) storage battery used in automobiles, for example, is a series of six 2-V cells. Each cell (Figure 7) contains a pair of electrodes, one lead and the other lead dioxide, in a chamber filled with sulfuric acid. Lead–acid batteries have been known for 150 years. They are used mainly in automobiles. Three hundred million of them are made per year.

An important feature of the lead storage battery is that it can be recharged. It discharges as it supplies electricity when the ignition is turned on to start a car or when the motor is off and the lights are on. It is recharged when the car is moving and an electric current created by the mechanical action of the car is supplied to the battery. The net reaction during discharge is

$$Pb + PbO_2 + 2 H_2SO_4 \longrightarrow 2 PbSO_4 + 2 H_2O$$

The reaction during recharge is the reverse.

$$2 PbSO_4 + 2 H_2O \longrightarrow Pb + PbO_2 + 2 H_2SO_4$$

Lead storage batteries are durable, but they are heavy, contain corrosive sulfuric acid, and lead is a toxic environmental problem.

▲ **Figure 6** Cross section of a zinc–carbon cell. The half-reactions are

Oxidation (anode):

$$Zn(s) \longrightarrow Zn^{2+}(aq) + 2 e^-$$

Reduction (cathode):

$$2MnO_2(s) + H_2O + 2 e^- \longrightarrow$$
$$Mn_2O_3(s) + 2 OH^-(aq)$$

Marianne de Jong/ Shutterstock

▲ **It DOES Matter!**
Batteries labeled "Heavy Duty" or "Super" may be ordinary dry cells and may not have the longer shelf life and operating life of alkaline cells. Usually, alkaline cells are labeled as such and are only slightly higher in cost, making them a better buy.

3. Why does a battery go dead? When one or more of the reactants (zinc and MnO_2 in a dry cell) is essentially used up, the cell can no longer provide useful energy.

◄ **Figure 7** One cell of a lead-storage battery has two anode plates and two cathode plates. Six such cells make up the common 12-V car battery. The half-reactions are

Oxidation (anode):

$$Pb(s) + SO_4{}^{2-}(aq) \longrightarrow$$
$$PbSO_4(s) + 2 e^-$$

Reduction (cathode):

$$PbO_2(s) + 4 H^+(aq) +$$
$$SO_4{}^{2-}(aq) + 2 e^- \longrightarrow$$
$$PbSO_4(s) + 2 H_2O$$

4. Why are some batteries rechargeable, but others aren't? A rechargeable battery uses a *reversible* redox reaction. The normal, forward reaction provides electrical energy. Applying electrical energy in the opposite direction using a charger reverses the reaction, and the starting materials are reformed. Not all redox reactions can be reversed in this manner.

Other Batteries

Much current battery technology involves the use of lithium, which has an extraordinarily low density and provides a higher voltage than other metals. Lithium cells make today's lightweight laptop computers possible. Lithium–SO_2 cells are used in submarines and rockets; lithium–iodine cells are used in pacemakers; and lithium–FeS_2 batteries are used in cameras, radios, and compact disc players.

Lithium cells provide so much energy and have such a compact volume that there have been incidents when the cells burst or even caught fire while being rapidly charged or discharged. Several manufacturers recalled millions of computer and telephone batteries between 2005 and 2011 because of the potential for such incidents.

The rechargeable NiCad cell (Cd anode, NiO cathode) has long been popular for portable radios and cordless tools. Its biggest competitor is the nickel–metal hydride cell, in which cadmium is replaced by a hydrogen-absorbing nickel alloy, such as $ZrNi_2$ or $LaNi_5$.

The button batteries used in hearing aids and hand calculators formerly contained mercury (zinc anode, HgO cathode), but these cells are gradually being phased out and replaced with zinc–air cells. Tiny silver oxide cells (zinc anode, Ag_2O cathode) are used mainly in watches and cameras.

Fuel Cells

An interesting kind of battery is the fuel cell. In a **fuel cell**, the oxidizing agent (usually oxygen) and the reducing agent are supplied continuously to the cell. Unlike other cells, a fuel cell does not "go dead" as long as the reactants are supplied. Moreover, when fossil fuels such as coal are burned to generate electricity, at most 35–40% of the energy from the combustion is actually harnessed. In a fuel cell, the fuel is oxidized and oxygen is reduced with 70–75% efficiency. Most present-day fuel cells use hydrogen as the fuel with platinum, nickel, or rhodium electrodes, in a solution of potassium hydroxide.

Electrolysis

Dry cells and fuel cells produce electricity from chemical reactions. Sometimes, we can reverse the process. In electrolysis, electricity supplied externally causes a chemical reaction to occur. The charging reaction of the lead storage cell shown in Figure 7 is one type of electrolysis. The car's alternator provides electric current, causing lead(II) sulfate to be converted back to lead metal and PbO_2. Other rechargeable cells undergo the reverse of their electricity-producing reaction when they are recharged.

Electrolysis is very important in industry. About 1% of all of the electricity in the United States is used to convert aluminum oxide to the aluminum metal we use for pots, foil, and cans. Chrome plating is performed by passing electricity through a solution of chromium ions (Cr^{6+}); electrons convert the ions to shiny chromium metal. Crude copper metal is purified by electrolysis, which converts the copper metal at the anode into copper(II) ions and then deposits nearly pure copper metal at the cathode. Many other materials—including sodium hydroxide, chlorine bleach, and magnesium metal—are produced by electrolysis.

▲ Some carbon monoxide detectors use an electrochemical cell in which carbon monoxide is oxidized to carbon dioxide at the anode, and oxygen is consumed at the cathode. Sulfuric acid serves as the electrolyte. The cell produces current related to the CO concentration in the air, and the current triggers an alarm or produces a readout of the CO concentration.

Self-Assessment Questions

1. In the electrochemical cell whose overall reaction is represented by the following equation, the negative electrode is

$$Zn(s) + Cu^{2+}(aq) \rightarrow Zn^{2+}(aq) + Cu(s)$$

   a. Cu(s)   **b.** Cu^{2+}(aq)   **c.** Zn(s)   **d.** Zn^{2+}(aq)

2. In one kind of electrochemical cell, the anode is ____ and the cathode is ____.
   a. Zn, MnO_2 **b.** Zn, C   **c.** C, Zn   **d.** C, MnO_2

3. In an electrochemical cell composed of two half-cells, ions flow from one half-cell to another through
   a. electrodes
   b. an external conductor
   c. a porous partition
   d. a voltmeter

4. For the following reaction, the oxidation half-reaction is

$$Mg + CuO \rightarrow MgO + Cu$$

   a. $Cu^{2+} + 2 e^- \rightarrow CuO$
   b. $CuO \rightarrow Cu^{2+} + 2 e^-$
   c. $Mg^{2+} + 2 e^- \rightarrow MgO$
   d. $Mg \rightarrow Mg^{2+} + 2 e^-$

5. In a lead storage battery, the product of both cathode and anode half-reactions is
   a. H_2SO_4
   b. Pb
   c. PbO_2
   d. $PbSO_4$

6. The fluid in the chamber of a lead storage battery is
   a. hydrochloric acid
   b. hydrofluoric acid
   c. methanol
   d. sulfuric acid

7. The overall electricity-producing reaction in the H_2/O_2 fuel cell is

$$2 H_2(g) + O_2(g) \rightarrow 2 H_2O(g)$$

   The half-reaction at the cathode is
   a. $H_2 \rightarrow 2 H^+ + 2 e^-$
   b. $2 H^+ + 2 e^- \rightarrow H_2$
   c. $O_2(g) + 4 H^+ + 4 e^- \rightarrow 2 H_2O$
   d. $2 H_2O \rightarrow O_2(g) + 4 H^+ + 4 e^-$

Answers: 1. c; 2. b; 3. c; 4. d; 5. d; 6. d; 7. c

4 Corrosion and Explosion

Learning Objectives ❯ Describe the reactions that occur when iron rusts. ❯ Explain why an explosive reaction is so energetic.

You might think *corrosion* and *explosion* have little in common except that they rhyme. However, both processes involve redox reactions. Corrosion of metals is of great economic importance. In the United States alone, corrosion costs about $276 billion a year. Perhaps 20% of all the iron and steel produced in the United States each year goes to replace corroded items. Explosions can bring economic benefit when used in mining and road building. Or they can cause enormous loss in war and accidents.

The Rusting of Iron

In moist air, iron is oxidized, particularly at a nick or scratch.

$$Fe(s) \longrightarrow Fe^{2+}(aq) + 2 e^-$$

As iron is oxidized, oxygen is reduced.

$$O_2(g) + 2 H_2O(l) + 4 e^- \longrightarrow 4 OH^-(aq)$$

The net result, initially, is the formation of insoluble iron(II) hydroxide, which appears dark green or black.

$$2 Fe(s) + O_2(g) + 2 H_2O(l) \longrightarrow 2 Fe(OH)_2(s)$$

This product is usually further oxidized to iron(III) hydroxide.

$$4 Fe(OH)_2(s) + O_2(g) + 2 H_2O(l) \longrightarrow 4 Fe(OH)_3(s)$$

Iron(III) hydroxide $[Fe(OH)_3]$, sometimes written as $Fe_2O_3 \cdot 3 H_2O$, is the familiar iron rust.

Oxidation and reduction often occur at separate points on the metal's surface. Electrons are transferred through the iron metal. The circuit is completed by an electrolyte in aqueous solution. In the Snow Belt, this solution is often the slush from road salt and melting snow. The metal is pitted in an anodic area, where iron is oxidized to Fe^{2+}. These ions migrate to the cathodic area, where they react with hydroxide ions formed by the reduction of oxygen.

$$Fe^{2+}(aq) + 2\,OH^-(aq) \longrightarrow Fe(OH)_2(s)$$

As noted previously, the iron(II) hydroxide is then oxidized to $Fe(OH)_3$, or rust. This process is diagrammed in Figure 8. Note that the anodic area is protected from oxygen by a water film, while the cathodic area is exposed to air.

▶ **Figure 8** The corrosion of iron requires water, oxygen, and an electrolyte.

Protection of Aluminum

Aluminum is more reactive than iron, yet corrosion is not a serious problem with aluminum. We use aluminum foil, we cook with aluminum pots, and we buy beverages in aluminum cans. Even after many years, they do not corrode. How is this possible?

The aluminum at the surface reacts with oxygen in the air to form a thin layer of oxide. Instead of being porous and flaky like iron oxide, however, aluminum oxide is hard and tough and adheres strongly to the surface of the metal, protecting if from further oxidation.

Nonetheless, corrosion can sometimes be a problem with aluminum. Certain substances, such as salt, can interfere with the protective oxide coating on aluminum, allowing the metal to oxidize. This problem has caused mag wheels on automobiles to crack, and some planes with aluminum landing gear have had wheels shear off.

Silver Tarnish

The tarnish on silver results from oxidation of the silver surface by hydrogen sulfide (H_2S) in the air or from food. It produces a film of black silver sulfide (Ag_2S) on the metal surface. You can use silver polish to remove the tarnish, but in doing so, you also lose part of the silver. An alternative method involves the use of aluminum metal.

$$3\,Ag^+(aq) + Al(s) \longrightarrow 3\,Ag(s) + Al^{3+}(aq)$$

This reaction also requires an electrolyte, and sodium bicarbonate ($NaHCO_3$) is usually used. The tarnished silver is placed in contact with aluminum metal (often in the form of foil) and covered with a hot solution of sodium bicarbonate. The silver ions are reduced to silver metal at the expense of the cheaper metal.

Explosive Reactions

Corrosive reactions are often quite slow. A chemical explosion (that is, not one based on nuclear fission or fusion) is usually an extremely rapid redox reaction, often accompanied by a considerable increase in volume. The redox reaction often involves a compound of nitrogen, such as nitroglycerin (the active ingredient in dynamite), ammonium nitrate (NH_4NO_3, a common fertilizer), or trinitrotoluene (TNT). These compounds can decompose readily, yielding nitrogen gas as one of the products.

Explosive mixtures are used for mining, earthmoving projects, and the demolition of buildings. *ANFO* (*Ammonium Nitrate mixed with Fuel Oil*) is an inexpensive and effective explosive, widely used for mining salt, coal, and other minerals. When ANFO explodes, ammonium ion is the reducing agent and nitrate ion is the

5. Why does steel rust, while aluminum doesn't? Both steel (iron) and aluminum undergo oxidation. But the product from iron flakes off, exposing a fresh iron surface that will rust again. The aluminum oxide formed when aluminum "rusts" adheres strongly to the surface of the metal, protecting it from further oxidation.

▲ Silver tarnish (Ag_2S) is readily removed from silver metal brought into contact with aluminum metal in a baking soda solution. Working in a sink, add about 1 cup of baking soda to 1 gal of hot water. Immerse a piece of aluminum and then the tarnished silver object so it touches the aluminum.

Q: To what is the Ag_2S converted? To what is the Al converted?

oxidizing agent. The fuel oil provides additional oxidizable material. Using $C_{17}H_{36}$ as the formula for a typical molecule in fuel oil, we can write the equation for the explosive reaction.

$$52\ NH_4NO_3(s) + C_{17}H_{36}(l) \longrightarrow 52\ N_2(g) + 17\ CO_2(g) + 122\ H_2O(g)$$

Notice that the starting materials, 53 mol of a solid and a liquid, generate 191 mol of gaseous products. This reaction produces a huge volume increase, which becomes part of the explosive force.

Unfortunately, ANFO has also been used in terrorist attacks around the world. Ammonium nitrate is a widely used fertilizer, and fuel oil is used in many home furnaces. The fact that both these materials are readily accessible to potential terrorists is cause for some concern.

Self-Assessment Questions

1. What type of reaction is the corrosion of iron?
   a. acid–base
   b. addition
   c. oxidation–reduction
   d. neutralization

2. Corrosion of aluminum is not as big a problem as corrosion of iron because aluminum
   a. forms an oxide layer that adheres to the metal's surface
   b. is less reactive than Fe
   c. needs water to corrode
   d. has a higher oxidation number

3. Silver tarnish is mainly
   a. AgCl
   b. Ag_2O
   c. Ag_2S
   d. Fe_2O_3

4. In a typical explosive reaction, which of the following usually occurs?
   a. Gases are converted from one form to another.
   b. Liquids or solids are converted to aqueous solutions.
   c. Liquids or solids are converted to gases.
   d. Nitrogen nuclei are split.

5. Black powder is a mixture of charcoal (carbon), potassium nitrate, and sulfur. The oxidizing agent in black powder is
   a. charcoal
   b. nitroglycerin
   c. potassium nitrate
   d. sulfur

Answers: 1, c; 2, a; 3, c; 4, c; 5, c

5 Oxygen: An Abundant and Essential Oxidizing Agent

Learning Objectives > Write equations for reactions in which oxygen is an oxidizing agent. > List some of the common oxidizing agents encountered in daily life.

Oxygen itself is the most common oxidizing agent. Many other oxidizing agents—sometimes called *oxidants*—are important in the laboratory, in industry, and in the home. They are used as antiseptics, disinfectants, and bleaches and play a role in many chemical syntheses.

Oxygen: Occurrence and Properties

Certainly one of the most important elements on Earth, oxygen is one of about two dozen elements essential to life. Making up one-fifth of the air, it oxidizes the wood in our campfires and the gasoline in our automobiles. It even "burns" the food we eat to give us the energy to move and to think. It is found in most compounds that are important to living organisms. Foodstuffs—carbohydrates, fats, and proteins—all contain oxygen. The human body is approximately 65% water (by mass). Because water is 89% oxygen by mass and many other compounds in your body also contain oxygen, almost two-thirds of your body mass is oxygen.

▲ It DOES Matter!
Physical activity under conditions in which plenty of oxygen is available to body tissues is called *aerobic* exercise. When the available oxygen is insufficient, the exercise is called *anaerobic*, and it often leads to weakness and pain resulting from "oxygen debt."

Oxygen comprises about half of the accessible portion of Earth by mass. It occurs in all three subdivisions of Earth's outermost structure. Oxygen occurs as O_2 molecules in the atmosphere (the gaseous mass surrounding Earth). In the hydrosphere (the oceans, seas, rivers, and lakes), oxygen is combined with hydrogen in water. In the lithosphere (the outer solid portion of the Earth's crust), oxygen is combined with silicon (sand is SiO_2), aluminum (in clays), and other elements.

The atmosphere is about 21% elemental oxygen (O_2) by volume. The rest is about 78% nitrogen (N_2) and 1% argon (Ar), both of which are quite unreactive. The free, uncombined oxygen in the air is taken into our lungs, passes into our bloodstreams, is carried to our body tissues, and reacts with the food we eat. This is the process that provides us with all our energy.

Fuels such as natural gas, gasoline, and coal also need oxygen to burn and release their stored energy. Oxidation, or combustion, of these fossil fuels currently supplies about 86% of the energy that turns the wheels of civilization.

Pure oxygen is obtained by liquefying air and then letting the nitrogen and argon boil off. Nitrogen boils at $-196\,°C$, argon at $-186\,°C$, and oxygen at $-183\,°C$. About 20 billion kg of oxygen is produced annually in the United States, but most of it is used directly by industry, much of it in steel plants. About 1% is compressed into tanks for use in welding, hospital respirators, and other purposes.

Not everything that oxygen does is desirable. In addition to causing corrosion (Section 4), it promotes food spoilage and wood decay.

Oxygen: Reactions with Other Elements

Many oxidation reactions involving atmospheric oxygen are quite complicated, but we can gain some understanding by looking at some of the simpler ones. For example, as we have seen, oxygen combines with many metals to form metal oxides and with nonmetals to form nonmetal oxides.

Example 7	Writing Equations: Reaction of Oxygen with Other Elements

Magnesium combines readily with oxygen when ignited in air. Write the equation for this reaction.

Solution
Magnesium is a group 2A metal. Oxygen occurs as diatomic molecules (O_2). The two react to form MgO. The reaction is

$$Mg(s) + O_2(g) \longrightarrow MgO(s) \quad \text{(not balanced)}$$

To balance the equation, we need 2 MgO and 2 Mg.

$$2\,Mg(s) + O_2(g) \longrightarrow 2\,MgO(s)$$

■ **EXERCISE 7**
Write equations for the following reactions.
  a. Zinc burns in air to form zinc oxide (ZnO).
  b. Selenium (Se) burns in air to form selenium dioxide.

▲ Fuels burn more rapidly in pure oxygen than in air. Huge quantities of liquid oxygen are used to burn the fuels that blast rockets into orbit.

Oxygen: Reactions with Compounds

Oxygen reacts with many compounds, oxidizing one or more of the elements in the compound. As we have seen, combustion of a fuel is oxidation and produces oxides. There are many other examples. Hydrogen sulfide, a gaseous compound with a rotten-egg odor, burns to produce oxides of hydrogen (water) and of sulfur (sulfur dioxide).

$$2\,H_2S(g) + 3\,O_2(g) \longrightarrow 2\,H_2O(l) + 2\,SO_2(g)$$

Example 8   Writing Equations: Reaction of Oxygen with Compounds

Carbon disulfide, a highly flammable liquid, combines readily with oxygen, burning with a blue flame. What products are formed? Write the equation.

Solution

Carbon disulfide is CS_2. The products are oxides of carbon (carbon dioxide) and of sulfur (sulfur dioxide). The balanced equation is

$$CS_2(g) + 3\,O_2(g) \longrightarrow CO_2(g) + 2\,SO_2(g)$$

■ EXERCISE 8A

When heated in air, lead sulfide (PbS) combines with oxygen to form lead(II) oxide (PbO) and sulfur dioxide. Write a balanced equation for the reaction.

■ EXERCISE 8B

Write a balanced equation for the combustion (reaction with oxygen) of ethanol (C_2H_5OH).

Ozone: Another Form of Oxygen

In addition to diatomic O_2, oxygen also has a triatomic form (O_3) called *ozone*. Ozone is a powerful oxidizing agent and a harmful air pollutant. It can be extremely irritating to both plants and animals and is especially destructive to rubber. On the other hand, a layer of ozone in the upper stratosphere serves as a shield that protects life on Earth from ultraviolet radiation from the sun. Ozone clearly illustrates that the same substance can be extremely beneficial or quite harmful, depending on the context.

Other Common Oxidizing Agents

Oxidizing agents used around the home include antiseptics, disinfectants, and bleaches. Many others are used in workplaces and in laboratories.

Disinfectants and antiseptics are alike in that both are materials used to destroy microorganisms (that is, they are germicidal), but antiseptics are applied mainly to living tissue and disinfectants to nonliving things. A good example of a disinfectant is chlorine, which is used to kill disease-causing microorganisms in drinking water and some swimming pools. The actual disinfecting agent is hypochlorous acid (HOCl), formed by the reaction of chlorine with water.

$$Cl_2(g) + H_2O(l) \longrightarrow HOCl(aq) + HCl(aq)$$

In recent years, concern has been raised over by-products that form when chlorine is used to disinfect water containing certain impurities. Although chlorine kills harmful microorganisms, it can also oxidize certain small molecules to form harmful by-products, such as chloroform.

Swimming pools are often chlorinated with calcium hypochlorite $[Ca(OCl)_2]$. Because calcium hypochlorite is alkaline, it also raises the pH of the water. (When a pool becomes too alkaline, the pH is lowered by adding hydrochloric acid. Swimming pools are usually maintained at pH 7.2–7.8.)

Hydrogen peroxide (H_2O_2) is a common oxidizing agent that has the advantage of being converted to water in most reactions. Pure hydrogen peroxide is a syrupy liquid. It is available (in laboratories) as a dangerous 30% solution that has powerful oxidizing power or as a 3% solution (sold in stores) for various uses around the home. When combined with a specially designed catalyst, hydrogen peroxide can be used to oxidize colored compounds and water impurities.

As a dilute aqueous solution, hydrogen peroxide is used to bleach hair (which gave rise to the phrase "peroxide blonde"). Dilute H_2O_2 is used medically to clean and deodorize wounds and ulcers.

Iodine is used as an antiseptic, either in an alcoholic solution (called *tincture of iodine*) or in Lugol's iodine solution (which contains no alcohol).

▲ Hydrogen peroxide is a powerful oxidizing agent. Dilute solutions are used as disinfectant and to bleach hair.

⚠ **SAFETY ALERT**

Strong oxidizing agents such as 30% aqueous hydrogen peroxide can cause severe burns. In general, strong oxidizing agents are corrosive, and many are highly toxic. They can also initiate a fire or increase the severity of a fire when brought into contact with combustible materials.

Solutions of potassium perman-ganate ($KMnO_4$), a common laboratory oxidizing agent, are good disinfectants. Such solutions are a deep purplish pink. Highly diluted solutions are pale pink (called "pinky water" in India) and are used in developing countries to disinfect foods. Their use is limited because the permanganate ion is reduced to brown manganese dioxide, leaving a brown stain on the treated substance.

▲ Pure water (left) has little effect on a dried tomato sauce stain. Sodium hypochlorite bleach (right) removes the stain by oxidizing the colored tomato pigments to colorless products.

An oxidizing agent sometimes used in the laboratory is potassium dichromate ($K_2Cr_2O_7$). It is an orange substance that turns green when it is reduced to chromium(III) compounds. One of the compounds that potassium dichromate oxidizes is ethyl alcohol. The early Breathalyzer test for intoxication made use of a dichromate solution. The exhaled breath of the person being tested was mixed with the acidic dichromate, and the degree of color change indicated the level of alcohol.

Ointments for treating acne often contain 5–10% benzoyl peroxide, a powerful antiseptic and also a skin irritant. It causes old skin to slough off and be replaced by new, fresher-looking skin. When used on areas exposed to sunlight, however, benzoyl peroxide may promote skin cancer.

Bleaches are oxidizing agents, too. A **bleach** removes unwanted color from fabrics or other material. Most bleaches work by oxidizing carbon-carbon double bonds in the colored substances to single bonds. This renders the stain colorless or nearly so. Almost any oxidizing agent could do the job, but some might be unsafe to use, or harmful to fabrics, or perhaps too expensive.

Bleaches are usually sodium hypochlorite (NaOCl) in aqueous solution (in laundry products such as Purex® and Clorox®), often called *chlorine bleaches*, or calcium hypochlorite $[Ca(OCl)_2]$, known as *bleaching powder*. The powder is usually preferred for large industrial operations, such as the whitening of paper or fabrics. Nonchlorine bleaches, often called *oxygen bleaches*, contain sodium percarbonate (a combination of Na_2CO_3 and H_2O_2) or sodium perborate (a combination of $NaBO_2$ and H_2O_2).

Stain removal is more complicated than bleaching. A few stain removers are oxidizing agents, but some are reducing agents, some are solvents or detergents, and some have quite different action. Stains often require rather specific stain removers.

Self-Assessment Questions

1. When CH_4 is burned in plentiful air, the products are
   a. $C + H_2$ **b.** $CH_2 + H_2O$ **c.** $CO_2 + H_2$ **d.** $CO_2 + H_2O$

2. When sulfur burns in plentiful air, the product is
   a. CO_2 **b.** H_2S **c.** H_2SO_4 **d.** SO_2

3. Which of the following is a common oxidizing agent?
   a. HCl   **b.** H_2O_2 **c.** NaOH   **d.** NaCl

4. Which of the following is a common oxidizing agent?
   a. Cl_2 **b.** H_2 **c.** HCl   **d.** KOH

5. The main active ingredient in common household bleach, often called *chlorine bleach*, is
   a. HCl   **b.** NaOCl   **c.** NaOH   **d.** NaCl

6. Bleach for hair usually contains
   a. ammonia   **b.** hydrochloric acid
   c. hydrogen peroxide   **d.** sodium hypochlorite

7. Many disinfectants are
   a. oxidizing agents   **b.** reducing agents
   c. strong acids   **d.** strong bases

Answers: 1, d; 2, d; 3, b; 4, a; 5, b; 6, c; 7, a

6 Some Common Reducing Agents

Learning Objective ❯ Identify some common reducing agents.

In every reaction involving oxidation, the oxidizing agent is reduced, and the substance undergoing oxidation acts as a reducing agent. Let's now consider reactions in which the purpose of the reaction is reduction.

Metals

Most metals occur in nature as compounds. To prepare the free metals, the compounds must be reduced. Metals are often freed from their ores by using coal or *coke* (elemental carbon obtained by heating coal to drive off volatile matter). Tin(IV) oxide is one of the many ores that can be reduced with coal or coke.

$$SnO_2(s) + C(s) \longrightarrow Sn(s) + CO_2(g)$$

Sometimes a metal can be obtained by heating its ore with a more active metal. Chromium oxide, for example, can be reduced by heating it with aluminum.

$$Cr_2O_3(s) + 2\,Al(s) \longrightarrow Al_2O_3(s) + 2\,Cr(s)$$

Antioxidants

In food chemistry, certain reducing agents are called **antioxidants**. Ascorbic acid (vitamin C) can prevent the browning of fruit (such as sliced apples or pears) by inhibiting air oxidation. Vitamin C is water soluble, but tocopherol (vitamin E) and beta-carotene (a precursor of vitamin A) are fat-soluble antioxidants. All these vitamins are believed to retard various oxidation reactions that are potentially damaging to vital components of living cells.

Hydrogen as a Reducing Agent

Hydrogen is an excellent reducing agent that can free many metals from their ores, but it is generally used to produce more expensive metals, such as tungsten (W).

$$WO_3(s) + 3\,H_2(g) \longrightarrow W(s) + 3\,H_2O(l)$$

Hydrogen can be used to reduce many kinds of chemical compounds. Ethylene, for example, can be reduced to ethane.

$$C_2H_4(g) + H_2(g) \longrightarrow C_2H_6(g)$$

The reaction requires a **catalyst**, a substance that increases the rate of a chemical reaction without itself being used up. (Catalysts lower the *activation energy*—the minimum energy needed to get a reaction started.) Nickel is the catalyst used in this case.

Hydrogen also reduces nitrogen, from air, in the industrial production of ammonia.

$$N_2(g) + 3\,H_2(g) \longrightarrow 2\,NH_3(g)$$

Ammonia is the source of most nitrogen fertilizers in modern agriculture. The reaction that produces ammonia employs an iron catalyst.

A stream of pure hydrogen burns quietly in air with an almost colorless flame, but when a mixture of hydrogen and oxygen is ignited by a spark or a flame, an explosion results. The product in both cases is water.

$$2\,H_2(g) + O_2(g) \longrightarrow 2\,H_2O(l)$$

Certain metals, including platinum and palladium, have an unusual affinity for hydrogen. They absorb large volumes of the gas. Palladium can absorb up to 900 times its own volume of hydrogen. It is interesting to note that hydrogen and oxygen can be mixed at room temperature with no perceptible reaction. If a piece of platinum gauze is added to the mixture, however, the gases react violently. The platinum acts as a catalyst. The heat from the initial reaction heats up the platinum, making it glow; it then ignites the hydrogen–oxygen mixture, causing an explosion.

Nickel, platinum, and palladium are often used as catalysts for reactions involving hydrogen. These metals have the greatest catalytic activity when they are finely divided and have lots of active surface area. Hydrogen adsorbed on the surface of these metals is more reactive than ordinary hydrogen gas.

Catalysts are an important area of research in green chemistry. Chemists are able to develop more energy-efficient and sustainable processes by designing catalysts that enable chemical reactions to occur at lower temperatures or pressures.

▲ It DOES Matter!
In making a black-and-white photograph, silver bromide in the film is exposed to light. The silver ions so exposed can then be reduced to black silver metal, forming a photographic negative.

A nickel catalyst is used in converting unsaturated fats to saturated fats. Unsaturated fats ordinarily react very slowly with hydrogen, but in the presence of nickel metal, the reaction proceeds readily. The nickel increases the rate of the reaction, but it does not increase the amount of product formed.

Colin P. Horwitz, *GreenOx Catalysts, Inc.*

Green Oxidation Catalysts

A catalyst provides a pathway for chemicals (reactants) to combine in a more effective manner than is possible without it. Catalysis is also central to green chemistry (Green Chemistry Principle 9). Catalysts increase efficiency and efficacy of chemical and energy resources and reduce reaction time, which also lead to cost savings.

Catalysts are widely used in oxidation reactions, especially those reactions that produce industrial and specialty chemicals. Industrial chemicals are produced on a scale of millions of tons per year and generally cost less than $0.50/lb. They are often building blocks for more sophisticated chemicals. On the other hand, specialty chemicals are produced on a smaller scale. They generally are more complex than industrial chemicals and have higher value in the marketplace.

There is great reliance on catalysts in the production of industrial chemicals because they must be made cheaply. For example, to produce terephthalic acid, *p*-xylene is oxidized with oxygen using a Co/Mn/Br catalyst. The terephthalic acid can then be converted to polyethylene terephthalate (PET), the major component of soft-drink bottles.

Another example is the oxidation of propylene to propylene oxide. Attempts to make this process greener began in the early 1990s and included using hydrogen peroxide, H_2O_2, as the oxidizing agent (Section 5). A titanium silicalite, TS-1, was the catalyst. Green benefits of this catalyst include the fact that Ti is both earth-abundant and nontoxic. This research resulted in the HPPO process, which uses hydrogen peroxide and propylene oxide and is much greener than currently used methods. The propylene is oxidized under mild reaction conditions in aqueous methanol, and high selectivity for product over byproducts is reported. The methanol also is recycled. This process received a 2010 Presidential Green Chemistry Challenge Award and is being commercialized by a BASF–Dow Chemical Company partnership.

The complexity of specialty chemicals makes their synthesis challenging. Many reactions are based on oxidation, and a need for efficient routes has led to the development of an array of catalytic and noncatalytic methods. These approaches have often relied on chemical reagents that lead to the desired product but are environmentally harmful. A classic example of a noncatalytic method is the dichromate oxidation of an alcohol to an aldehyde.

$$3\ C_2H_6O + Cr_2O_7^{2-} + 8\ H^+ \rightarrow 3\ C_2H_4O + 2\ Cr^{3+} + 7\ H_2O$$

In this reaction, Cr^{6+} in the dichromate ion, $Cr_2O_7^{2-}$, is reduced to Cr^{3+}, and the alcohol is oxidized to an aldehyde. Although the product is formed, Cr^{6+} is a likely carcinogen, the noncatalytic reaction produces lots of waste, and the atom economy is poor.

There are many opportunities to employ green chemistry through the development of catalysts that make oxidations like the example above unnecessary. Many oxidation catalysts rely on transition metals attached to organic molecules. Catalyst design can be difficult because the organic part can become a target for oxidation during reactions. When this happens, complex protection schemes for the organic portion or high quantities of catalyst are required.

Professor Terry Collins at Carnegie Mellon University took a unique design approach in which weak links in the organic framework were replaced with more robust ones. An earth-abundant and nontoxic element, iron, was chosen as the metal, and the organic portions were designed to bind strongly to iron. The organic parts also contain biochemically common elements, C, H, N, and O. The resulting catalysts are soluble in water and can survive thousands of catalytic cycles. Also, the greener oxidant hydrogen peroxide, H_2O_2, can be used, which leads to oxidation products with low or no toxicity. The design process has yielded an expanding family of iron-based TAML® catalysts that can rapidly oxidize and thus destroy pollutants in water. This work garnered Collins a 1997 Presidential Green Chemistry Challenge Award.

Recent work with the TAML® catalysts has shown that they are effective at levels as low as a single part per million, are efficient users of H_2O_2, function in water over a wide pH range, and offer an alternative to other processes that also use H_2O_2 but much less efficiently. In some applications, the temperature of the reaction can be lowered, which saves energy, and the amounts of chemicals can be decreased because of the efficiency of the TAML® catalyst.

Using a catalyst can also allow a reaction to occur using milder reactants, such as oxygen or hydrogen peroxide instead of chlorine for oxidizing stains on clothes or destroying harmful microorganisms in drinking water.

A Closer Look at Hydrogen

Hydrogen is an especially vital element because it and oxygen are the components of water. By mass, hydrogen makes up only about 0.9% of the Earth's crust and oceans. However, because it has such a low atomic mass, it ranks third in abundance by number of atoms. A random sample of 10,000 atoms from this portion of Earth would have 1510 hydrogen atoms.

Unlike oxygen, hydrogen is rarely found as a free, uncombined element on Earth. Most of it is combined with oxygen in water. Some is combined with carbon in petroleum and natural gas, which are mixtures of hydrocarbons. Nearly all compounds derived from plants and animals contain hydrogen.

Because hydrogen has the lowest atomic number ($Z = 1$) and the smallest atoms of any element, it is first in the periodic table. However, it is difficult to know exactly where to place it. Hydrogen is usually shown as the first member of group 1A because it has the same valence electronic structure (ns^1) as alkali metals. Like the atoms of elements in group 1A, a hydrogen atom can lose an electron to form a 1+ ion; but, unlike the other group 1A elements, hydrogen is not a metal. Like the atoms of group 7A elements, a hydrogen atom can pick up an electron to become a 1− ion; but, unlike the other group 7A elements, hydrogen is not a halogen. We place hydrogen in group 1A in the periodic table on the inside front cover, but you should keep in mind that it is a unique element, and is in a class by itself.

Small amounts of elemental hydrogen can be made for laboratory use by reacting zinc with hydrochloric acid (Figure 9).

$$Zn(s) + 2\,HCl(aq) \longrightarrow ZnCl_2(aq) + H_2(g)$$

Hydrogen ranks low in abundance by mass on Earth. If we look beyond our home planet, however, hydrogen becomes much more significant. The sun, for example, is made up largely of hydrogen. The planet Jupiter is also mainly hydrogen. In fact, the universe is about 72% by mass H, 26% He, and 1% O.

◀ **Figure 9** Hydrogen gas can be prepared in the laboratory by the reaction of zinc metal with hydrochloric acid.

Commercial quantities of hydrogen are obtained as by-products of petroleum refining or from the reaction of natural gas with steam. About 8 billion kg of hydrogen is produced each year in the United States. At present, hydrogen is used mainly to make ammonia and methanol.

Hydrogen is a colorless, odorless gas and the lightest of all substances. Its density is only one-fourteenth that of air, and for this reason it was once used in lighter-than-air craft (Figure 10). Unfortunately, hydrogen can be ignited by a spark, as occurred in 1937 when the German airship *Hindenburg* was destroyed in a disastrous fire and explosion while landing in Lakehurst, New Jersey. The use of hydrogen in airships was discontinued after that, and the industry never recovered. Today, the few airships that are still in service are filled with nonflammable helium, but they are used mainly in advertising.

▲ **Figure 10** Hydrogen is the most buoyant gas, but it is highly flammable. The disastrous fire that destroyed the hydrogen-filled German airship *Hindenburg* led to the replacement of hydrogen by nonflammable helium, which buoys the Goodyear blimp.

Q: *What is the equation for the reaction pictured on the left? Would a similar reaction occur if lightning struck the Goodyear blimp? Explain.*

6. Does hydrogen have a promising future as a fuel? Gram for gram, hydrogen provides more energy than any other chemical fuel. Also, when hydrogen is oxidized by oxygen, the product is ordinary water. Unfortunately, it takes more energy to produce hydrogen than we get from burning the hydrogen. Until we can use renewable energy to generate hydrogen, its future as a fuel will remain in question.

Self-Assessment Questions

1. Which of the following is a common reducing agent?
   a. Cl_2 **b.** F_2 **c.** H_2 **d.** I_2

2. Which of the following is a common reducing agent?
   a. C   **b.** Cl_2 **c.** F_2 **d.** I_2

3. All the following metals are used as catalysts for reactions involving hydrogen gas *except*
   a. aluminum   **b.** nickel   **c.** palladium   **d.** platinum

4. A catalyst changes the rate of a chemical reaction by
   a. changing the products of the reaction
   b. changing the reactants involved in the reaction
   c. increasing the frequency of molecular collisions
   d. lowering the activation energy

5. By number of atoms, what is the rank of hydrogen in abundance in the accessible portion of Earth?
   a. first   **b.** second   **c.** tenth   **d.** third

6. Hydrogen gas can be produced by reacting an active metal such as zinc with
   a. an acid   **b.** ammonia
   c. an oxidizing agent   **d.** a reducing agent

7. Although helium gas is twice as dense as hydrogen gas, modern blimps are filled with helium because hydrogen is
   a. highly flammable   **b.** more expensive
   c. rarer   **d.** toxic

Answers: 1, c; 2, a; 3, a; 4, d; 5, d; 6, a; 7, a

7 Oxidation, Reduction, and Living Things

Learning Objective ❯ Write the overall equations for the metabolism of glucose and for photosynthesis.

Perhaps the most important oxidation–reduction processes are the ones that maintain life on this planet. We obtain energy for all our physical and mental activities by metabolizing food in a process called *cellular respiration*. The process has many steps, but eventually the food we eat is converted mainly into carbon dioxide, water, and energy.

Bread and many of the other foods we eat are largely made up of carbohydrates, composed of carbon, hydrogen, and oxygen. If we represent carbohydrates with the simple example of glucose ($C_6H_{12}O_6$), we can write the overall equation for their metabolism as follows.

$$C_6H_{12}O_6 + 6\,O_2 \longrightarrow 6\,CO_2 + 6\,H_2O + energy$$

This process occurs constantly in animals, including humans. The carbohydrate is oxidized in the process.

Meanwhile, plants need carbon dioxide, water, and energy from the sun to produce carbohydrates. The process by which plants synthesize carbohydrates is called **photosynthesis** (Figure 11). The overall chemical equation is

$$6\,CO_2 + 6\,H_2O + energy \longrightarrow C_6H_{12}O_6 + 6\,O_2$$

◀ **Figure 11** Photosynthesis occurs in green plants. The chlorophyll pigments that catalyze the photosynthesis process give the green color to much of the land area of Earth.

Notice that this process in plant cells is exactly the reverse of the process going on inside animals. In food metabolism in animals, we focus on an oxidation process. In photosynthesis, we focus on a reduction process.

The carbohydrates produced by photosynthesis are the ultimate source of all our food because fish, fowl, and other animals either eat plants or eat other animals that eat plants. Note that the photosynthesis process not only makes carbohydrates but also yields free elementary oxygen (O_2). In other words, photosynthesis does not just provide the food we eat, it also provides the oxygen we breathe.

There are many oxidation reactions that occur in nature (with oxygen being reduced in the process). The net photosynthesis reaction is unique in that it is a natural reduction of carbon dioxide (with oxygen being oxidized). Many processes in nature use oxygen. Photosynthesis is the only natural process that produces it.

Self-Assessment Questions

1. The main process by which animals obtain energy from food is
   a. acidification
   b. cellular respiration
   c. photosynthesis
   d. reduction of CO_2

2. The only natural process that produces O_2 is
   a. acidification of carbonates
   b. photosynthesis
   c. oxidation of CO_2
   d. reduction of metal oxide

CRITICAL THINKING EXERCISES

Apply knowledge that you have gained in this chapter and one or more of the FLaReS principles to evaluate the following statements or claims.

1   Over the years, some people have claimed that someone has invented an automobile engine that burns water instead of gasoline. They say that we have not heard about it because the oil companies have bought the rights to the engine from the inventor so that they can keep it from the public and people will continue to burn gasoline in their cars.

2   In January 2011, Italian scientists claimed to have constructed an apparatus to produce energy. The apparatus uses hydrogen and nickel and is supposed to give several hundred times as much energy as would be obtained by merely burning the hydrogen.

3   A Web site claims that electricity can remove rust. The procedure is described as follows: Connect a wire to the object to be derusted, and immerse in a bath of sodium carbonate (washing soda) solution.

Immerse a second wire in the bath. Connect the wires to a battery so that the object to be derusted is the cathode. The site claims that hydrogen gas is produced at the cathode and oxygen at the anode. The hydrogen then changes the rust back to iron metal.

4   A friend claims that an automobile can be kept free of rust simply by connecting the negative pole of the car's battery to the car's body. He reasons that this action makes the car the cathode, and oxidation does not occur at the cathode. He claims that for years he has kept his car from rusting by doing this.

5   A salesman claims that your tap water is contaminated. As evidence, he connects a battery to a pair of "special electrodes" and dips the electrodes in a glass of your tap water. Within a few minutes, white and brown "gunk" appears in the water. The salesman sells a special purifying filter that he claims will remove the contaminants and leave the water pure and clear.

SUMMARY

Section 1—Oxidation and reduction are processes that occur together. They may be defined in three ways. Oxidation occurs when a substance gains oxygen atoms or loses hydrogen atoms or loses electrons. Reduction is the opposite of oxidation; it occurs when a substance loses oxygen atoms or gains hydrogen atoms or gains electrons. We usually use the definition that is most convenient for the situation.

Section 2—In an oxidation–reduction (or redox) reaction, the substance that causes oxidation is the oxidizing agent. The substance that causes reduction is the reducing agent. In a redox reaction, the oxidizing agent is reduced, and the reducing agent is oxidized.

Section 3—A redox reaction involves a transfer of electrons. That transfer can be made to take place in an electrochemical cell, which has two solid electrodes where the electrons are transferred. The electrode where oxidation occurs is the anode, and the one where reduction occurs is the cathode. Electrons are transferred from anode to cathode through a wire; their flow is an electric current. When the oxidation half-reaction is added to the reduction half-reaction, the electrons in the half-reactions cancel and we get the overall cell reaction. Knowing this, we can balance many redox reactions.

A dry cell (flashlight battery) has a zinc case and a central carbon rod and contains a paste of manganese dioxide with graphite powder and ammonium chloride. Alkaline cells are similar but contain potassium hydroxide instead of ammonium chloride. A battery is a series of connected cells. An automobile's lead storage battery contains six cells.

Each cell contains lead and lead dioxide electrodes in sulfuric acid, and the battery can be recharged. A fuel cell generates electricity by oxidizing a fuel in a cell to which the fuel and oxygen are supplied continuously.

Section 4—Corrosion of metals is ordinarily an undesirable redox reaction. When iron corrodes, the iron is first oxidized to Fe^{2+} ions, and oxygen gas is reduced to hydroxide ions. The $Fe(OH)_2$ that forms is further oxidized to $Fe(OH)_3$, or rust. Oxidation and reduction often occur in separate places on the metal surface, and an electrolyte (such as salt) on the surface can intensify the corrosion reaction. Aluminum corrodes, but the oxide layer is tough and adherent and protects the underlying metal. Silver corrodes in the presence of sulfur compounds, forming black silver sulfide, which can be removed electrochemically. An explosive reaction is a redox reaction that occurs rapidly and with a considerable increase in volume (due to the formation of gases).

Section 5—Oxygen is an oxidizing agent that is essential to life. It makes up about one-fifth of the air and about two-thirds of our body mass. Our food is "burned" in oxygen as we breathe, and fuels such as coal react with oxygen when they burn and release most of the energy used in civilization. Pure oxygen is obtained from liquefied air, and most of it is used in industry. Oxygen reacts with metals and nonmetals to form oxides. It reacts with many compounds to form oxides of the elements in the compound. Ozone, O_3, is a form of oxygen that is an air pollutant in the lower atmosphere but provides a shield from ultraviolet radiation in the upper atmosphere. Other oxidizing agents include hydrogen peroxide, potassium dichromate, benzoyl peroxide, and chlorine. A bleach is an oxidizing agent that removes unwanted color from fabric or other material.

Section 6—Most metals are reducing agents. An antioxidant is a reducing agent that retards damaging oxidation reactions in living cells. Vitamins C and E and beta-carotene are antioxidants. Common reducing agents include carbon, hydrogen, and active metals. Carbon in the form of coal or coke is often used as a reducing agent to obtain metals from their oxides. Active metals such as aluminum are also used for this purpose. Hydrogen can free many metals from their ores. Some reactions of hydrogen require a catalyst, which speeds up a reaction without itself being used up. Formation of ammonia from hydrogen and nitrogen uses a catalyst.

Hydrogen is a vital element because it is a component of water and of living tissue. Because it has the lowest atomic number and the smallest atoms, its behavior is unique among the elements. Hydrogen is produced in petroleum refining or from the reaction of natural gas with steam; it is used to make ammonia and methanol. Hydrogen was once used for lighter-than-air craft but its flammability caused it to be replaced by helium.

Section 7—Oxidation of carbohydrates and other substances in foods produces the energy humans and other animals need to survive. The reduction of carbon dioxide in photosynthesis is the most important reduction process on Earth. We could not exist without it. Photosynthesis provides the food we eat and the oxygen we breathe.

Green chemistry When a chemist needs to use an oxidation reaction to produce a chemical, it is important to find a catalyst that makes the reaction proceed efficiently so that energy and chemical resources are used wisely. To further the principles of green chemistry, the catalyst should be composed of nontoxic and earth-abundant elements.

Learning Objectives

❯ Identify an oxidation–reduction reaction. (1)	Problems 13–16
❯ Classify a particular change within a redox reaction as either oxidation or reduction. (1)	Problems 1, 4, 13, 14, 41–43, 47, 50, 54
❯ Identify the oxidizing agent and the reducing agent in a redox reaction. (2)	Problems 17–22, 27–36, 39, 48, 49
❯ Balance redox equations. (3)	Problems 25, 26, 51
❯ Identify and write the half-reactions in an electrochemical cell. (3)	Problems 2, 3, 5–8, 15, 16, 23, 24
❯ Describe the reactions that occur when iron rusts. (4)	Problem 9
❯ Explain why an explosive reaction is so energetic. (4)	
❯ Write equations for reactions in which oxygen is an oxidizing agent. (5)	Problems 37, 38
❯ List some of the common oxidizing agents encountered in daily life. (5)	Problems 10, 11
❯ Identify some common reducing agents. (6)	Problems 29–36
❯ Write the overall equations for the metabolism of glucose and for photosynthesis. (7)	Problems 12, 46, 53
❯ Distinguish between the objectives of chemists producing industrial chemicals and those of chemists producing specialty chemicals.	Problem 55
❯ Explain how green chemistry can be applied to the design of new catalysts.	Problems 56–58

REVIEW QUESTIONS

1. What happens to the oxidation number of one of its elements when a compound is oxidized? When it is reduced?

2. What is an electrochemical cell? A battery?

3. What is the purpose of a porous partition between the two electrode compartments in an electrochemical cell?

4. What is a half-reaction? How are half-reactions combined to give an overall cell reaction?

5. From what material is the case of a zinc–carbon dry cell made? What purpose does this material serve? What happens to it as the cell discharges?

6. How does an alkaline cell differ from a zinc–carbon dry cell?

7. What happens when a lead storage battery is charged?

8. Describe what happens when a lead storage battery discharges.

9. Describe what happens when iron corrodes. How does road salt intensify this process?

10. Describe how a bleaching agent, such as hypochlorite (ClO⁻), works.

11. How does silver tarnish? How can the tarnish be removed without the loss of silver?

12. Relate the chemistry of photosynthesis to the chemical process that provides energy for your heartbeat.

PROBLEMS

Recognizing Oxidation and Reduction

13. Indicate whether the reactant in each of the following partial equations is being oxidized or reduced. Explain.
    a. $Fe \rightarrow Fe^{3+}$
    b. $H_2O \rightarrow O_2$
    c. $Sr \rightarrow Sr^{2+}$
    d. $P_4 \rightarrow 4\,P^{3-}$
    e. $CH_4O \rightarrow CH_2O$

14. In which of the following changes is the reactant undergoing oxidation? Explain.
    a. $C_2H_4 \rightarrow C_2H_6$
    b. $CrO_3 \rightarrow Cr$
    c. $Fe^{3+} \longrightarrow Fe^{2+}$
    d. $C_{27}H_{33}N_9O_{15}P_2 \longrightarrow C_{27}H_{35}N_9O_{15}P_2$
    e. $2\,Cl^- \rightarrow Cl_2$

15. Write a balanced oxidation half-reaction similar to $Na \longrightarrow Na^+ + e^-$ for each of the following metals.
    a. Ca
    b. Al
    c. Cu (two different equations)

16. Write a balanced reduction half-reaction similar to $Cl_2 + 2\,e^- \longrightarrow 2\,Cl^-$ for each of the following nonmetals.
    a. I_2
    b. N_2
    c. S_8

Oxidizing Agents and Reducing Agents

17. Identify the oxidizing agent and the reducing agent in each reaction.
    a. $3\,C + Fe_2O_3 \longrightarrow 3\,CO + 2\,Fe$
    b. $P_4 + 5\,O_2 \longrightarrow P_4O_{10}$
    c. $C + H_2O \longrightarrow CO + H_2$
    d. $H_2SO_4 + Zn \longrightarrow ZnSO_4 + H_2$

18. Identify the oxidizing agent and the reducing agent in each reaction.
    a. $CuS + H_2 \longrightarrow Cu + H_2S$
    b. $4\,K + CCl_4 \longrightarrow C + 4\,KCl$
    c. $C_3H_4 + 2\,H_2 \longrightarrow C_3H_8$
    d. $Fe^{3+} + Ce^{3+} \longrightarrow Fe^{2+} + Ce^{4+}$

19. Look again at Figure 4. What is the reducing agent?

20. What is the oxidizing agent in Figure 4?

21. Look again at Figure 6. Identify the oxidizing and reducing agents.

22. Look again at Figure 7. **(a)** Is SO_4^{2-} the oxidizing agent, the reducing agent, both, or neither? **(b)** When the cell is being charged, the discharge half-reactions are reversed. During charging, is Pb^{2+} being oxidized, reduced, both, or neither?

Half-Reactions

23. Separate the following redox reactions into half-reactions, and label each half-reaction as oxidation or reduction.
    a. $Fe(s) + 2\,H^+(aq) \longrightarrow Fe^{2+}(aq) + H_2(g)$
    b. $2\,Al(s) + 3\,Cr^{2+}(aq) \longrightarrow 3\,Cr(s) + 2\,Al^{3+}(aq)$

24. Separate the following redox reactions into half-reactions, and label each half-reaction as oxidation or reduction.
    a. $2\,Al(s) + 6\,H^+(aq) \longrightarrow 2\,Al^{3+}(aq) + 3\,H_2(g)$
    b. $2\,Cu^+(aq) + Mg(s) \longrightarrow Mg^{2+}(aq) + 2\,Cu(s)$

25. Label each of the following half-reactions as oxidation or reduction, and then combine them to obtain a balanced overall redox reaction.
    a. $2\,H_2O_2 \longrightarrow 2\,O_2 + 4\,H^+ + 4\,e^-$ and
       $Fe^{3+} + e^- \longrightarrow Fe^{2+}$
    b. $WO_3 + 6\,H^+ + 6\,e^- \longrightarrow W + 3\,H_2O$ and
       $C_2H_6O \longrightarrow C_2H_4O + 2\,H^+ + 2\,e^-$

26. Label each of the following half-reactions as oxidation or reduction, and then combine them to obtain a balanced overall redox reaction.
    a. $2\,I^- \longrightarrow I_2 + 2\,e^-$ and $Cl_2 + 2\,e^- \longrightarrow 2\,Cl^-$
    b. $HNO_3 + H^+ + e^- \longrightarrow NO_2 + H_2O$ and
       $SO_2 + 2\,H_2O \longrightarrow H_2SO_4 + 2\,H^+ + 2\,e^-$

Oxidation and Reduction: Chemical Reactions

27. In the following reactions, which substance is oxidized? Which is the oxidizing agent?
    a. $2\,HNO_3 + SO_2 \longrightarrow H_2SO_4 + 2\,NO_2$
    b. $2\,CrO_3 + 6\,HI \longrightarrow Cr_2O_3 + 3\,I_2 + 3\,H_2O$

28. In the following reactions, which element is oxidized and which is reduced?
    a. $CH_3CHO + H_2O_2 \rightarrow CH_3COOH + H_2O$
    b. $5\,C_2H_6O + 4\,MnO_4^- + 12\,H^+ \longrightarrow$
       $5\,C_2H_4O_2 + 4\,Mn^{2+} + 11\,H_2O$

29. Ethylene (C_2H_4) reacts with hydrogen to form ethane (C_2H_6). Is the ethylene oxidized or reduced? Explain.

30. Unsaturated vegetable oils react with hydrogen to form saturated fats. A typical reaction is

    $$C_{57}H_{104}O_6 + 3\,H_2 \longrightarrow C_{57}H_{110}O_6$$

    Is the unsaturated oil oxidized or reduced? Explain.

31. Tantalum, a metal used in electronic devices such as cellular phones and computers, can be manufactured by the reaction of its oxide with molten sodium metal.

    $$Ta_2O_5 + 10\,Na \rightarrow 2\,Ta + 5\,Na_2O$$

    Which substance is reduced? Which is the reducing agent?

32. To test for iodide ions (for example, in iodized salt), a solution is treated with chlorine to liberate iodine.

    $$2\,I^- + Cl_2 \longrightarrow I_2 + 2\,Cl^-$$

    Which substance is oxidized? Which is reduced?

33. In the Fukushima nuclear reactor that failed in March 2011, zirconium metal reacted with steam to produce hydrogen gas.

    $$Zr + 2\,H_2O \longrightarrow ZrO_2 + 2\,H_2$$

    What substance was oxidized in the reaction? What was the oxidizing agent?

34. Unripe grapes are exceptionally sour because of a high concentration of tartaric acid $(C_4H_6O_6)$. As the grapes

ripen, this compound is converted to glucose ($C_6H_{12}O_6$). Is the tartaric acid oxidized or reduced?

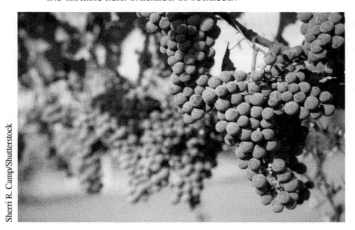

Sherri R. Camp/Shutterstock

35. Vitamin C (ascorbic acid) is thought to protect our stomachs from the carcinogenic effect of nitrite ions (NO_2^-) by converting the ions to nitric oxide (NO). Is the nitrite ion oxidized or reduced? Is ascorbic acid an oxidizing agent or a reducing agent?

36. In the reaction in Problem 35, ascorbic acid ($C_6H_8O_6$) is converted to dehydroascorbic acid ($C_6H_6O_6$). Is ascorbic acid oxidized or reduced in this reaction?

Combination with Oxygen

37. Write formula(s) for the product(s) formed when each of the following substances reacts with oxygen (O_2).
    a. S
    b. CH_3OH
    c. C_3H_6O

38. Write formula(s) for the product(s) formed when each of the following substances reacts with oxygen (O_2). (There may be more than one correct answer.)
    a. N_2
    b. CS_2
    c. C_5H_{12}

Additional Problems

39. The dye indigo (used to color blue jeans) is formed by exposure of indoxyl to air.

$$2\,C_8H_7ON + O_2 \longrightarrow C_{16}H_{10}N_2O_2 + 2\,H_2O$$
Indoxyl   Indigo

What substance is oxidized? What is the oxidizing agent?

Jacob Kearns/Shutterstock

40. Why do some mechanics lightly coat their tools with grease or oil before storing them?

41. When an aluminum wire is placed in a blue solution of copper(II) chloride, the blue solution turns colorless and reddish-brown copper metal comes out of solution. Write an equation for the reaction. (Chloride ion is not involved in the reaction.)

42. Researchers led by Elisabeth Bouwman, a chemist at Leiden University in the Netherlands, discovered a copper-based catalyst that can convert CO_2 from the air to oxalate ion ($C_2O_4{}^{2-}$). Write the equation for the half-reaction. Is the CO_2 oxidized or reduced?

43. When exposed to air containing hydrogen sulfide, lead-based paints turn black because the Pb^{2+} ions react with the H_2S to form black lead sulfide (PbS). This has caused the darkening of old oil-based paintings. Hydrogen peroxide lightens the paints by oxidizing the black sulfide (S^{2-}) to white sulfates ($SO_4{}^{2-}$). (a) Write the equation for the darkening reaction. (b) Write the equation for this reaction that lightens the paints.

44. The oxidizing agent our bodies use to obtain energy from food is oxygen (from the air). If you breathe 15 times a minute (at rest), taking in and exhaling 0.5 L of air with each breath, what volume of air do you breathe each day? Air is 21% oxygen by volume. What volume of oxygen do you breathe each day?

45. To oxidize 1.0 kg of fat, our bodies require about 2000 L of oxygen. A healthy diet contains not more than about 80 g of fat per day. What volume (at STP) of oxygen is required to oxidize that fat?

46. The photosynthesis reaction can be expressed as the net result of two processes, one of which requires light and is called the *light reaction*. This reaction may be written as

$$12\,H_2O \xrightarrow{\text{light}} 6\,O_2 + 24\,H^+ + 24\,e^-$$

    a. Is the light reaction an oxidation or reduction?
    b. Write the equation for the other half-reaction, called the *dark reaction*, for photosynthesis.

47. Indicate whether the first-named substance in each change undergoes an oxidation, a reduction, or neither. Explain your reasoning.
    a. A violet solution of vanadium(II) ions, V^{2+}(aq), is converted to a green solution of V^{3+}(aq).
    b. Nitrogen dioxide converts to dinitrogen tetroxide when cooled.
    c. Carbon monoxide reacts with hydrogen to form methanol.

48. As a rule, metallic elements act as reducing agents, not as oxidizing agents. Explain. (*Hint:* Consider the charges on metal ions.) Do nonmetals act only as oxidizing agents and not as reducing agents? Explain your answer.

49. If a stream of hydrogen gas is ignited in air, the flame can be immersed in a jar of chlorine gas and it will still burn. Write the balanced equation for the reaction that occurs in the jar. What is the oxidizing agent in the reaction?

50. Consider the following reaction of calcium hydride (CaH_2) with molten sodium metal. Identify the species being oxidized and the species being reduced according to (a) the second definition shown in Figure 2 and (b) the third definition in Figure 2. What difficulty arises?

$$CaH_2(s) + 2\,Na(l) \longrightarrow 2\,NaH(s) + Ca(l)$$

51. Aluminum metal can react with water, but the oxide coating normally found on the metal prevents that reaction. In 2007, a Purdue University researcher found that adding gallium to aluminum prevented the formation of the oxide coating, allowing the aluminum to react with water to form hydrogen gas. This process might lead to a compact source of hydrogen gas for fuel. Write a balanced equation for the reaction of aluminum with water (aluminum hydroxide is the other product), and identify the oxidizing and reducing agents in the reaction.

52. Refer to Problem 51. Aluminum has a density of 2.70 g/cm^3. What volume in cubic centimeters of aluminum metal would be needed to produce 2.0×10^4 L of hydrogen gas at STP? How many times smaller is this volume of aluminum than is the volume of hydrogen gas? (Recall that at STP, 1 mol of gas occupies 22.4 L.)

53. Consider the oxidation of ethanol (CH_3CH_2OH) to acetaldehyde (CH_3CHO) by NAD^+. **(a)** Write half-reactions for the process. **(b)** NADH is a biochemical reducing agent, in the reverse of the oxidation reaction. Write half-reactions for the reduction of pyruvic acid (CH_3CO-$COOH$) to lactic acid ($CH_3CHOHCOOH$) by NADH, and then combine these two half-reactions to get the equation for the overall reaction.

54. Following are some organic chemistry processes. Classify each as an oxidation or a reduction. R represents a hydrocarbon group, and does not change in the process.
   a. RCH_3 (alkane) $\rightarrow$ RCH_2OH (alcohol)
   b. $RCHO$ (aldehyde) $\rightarrow$ RCH_2OH (alcohol)
   c. $RCHO$ (aldehyde) $\rightarrow$ $RCOOH$ (carboxylic acid)
   d. $RCOOH$ (carboxylic acid) $\rightarrow$ $RCHO$ (aldehyde)
   e. RCH_2OH (alcohol) $\rightarrow$ $RCHO$ (aldehyde)

55. Which of the following describe industrial chemicals, and which describe specialty chemicals?
   a. made on a large scale
   b. complex molecules
   c. high-value chemicals
   d. building blocks for other chemicals

56. A green catalyst is one that
   a. contains earth-abundant elements
   b. makes reagents react more efficiently
   c. decreases the cost of producing a chemical
   d. does all of the above

57. Give one reason why it can be difficult to design a long-lived oxidation catalyst.

58. Identify the oxidizing agent and the substance that is oxidized in the following reaction.
$$3 \, C_2H_6O + Cr_2O_7^{2-} + 8 \, H^+ \longrightarrow 3 \, C_2H_4O + 2 \, Cr^{3+} + 7 \, H_2O$$

COLLABORATIVE GROUP PROJECTS

Prepare a PowerPoint, poster, or other presentation (as directed by your instructor) to share with the class.

1. Prepare a brief report on one of the following types of electrochemical cells or batteries. If possible, give the half-reactions, the overall reaction, and typical uses.
   a. lithium–SO_2 cell   **b.** lithium–iodine cell
   c. lithium–FeS_2 battery   **d.** Ni–Cad cell
   e. silver oxide cell   **f.** nickel–metal hydride cell

2. Prepare a brief report on one of the following methods of protecting steel from corrosion. Identify the chemical reactions involved in the process, and tell how the process is related to oxidation and reduction.
   a. galvanization   **b.** coating with tin
   c. cathodic protection

3. Batteries contain toxic substances and should be recycled rather than thrown in the trash. Prepare a brief report on battery recycling. Are there facilities in your area for recycling batteries?

4. Military personnel, outdoor recreation enthusiasts such as wilderness campers and trekkers, and others often have to drink water from untreated streams or lakes. People who temporarily lack safe drinking water after a natural disaster also need a way to purify water. A variety of water purification tablets are available to treat contaminated water. Research several such tablets, and list their ingredients.

5. Visit one or more Web sites about fuel cells. Write the reactions that occur in the different types of fuel cells in development. Prepare a brief report on one of the following topics:
   a. a cost–benefit analysis of using fuel cells in automobiles versus using gasoline, electricity from batteries, or natural gas
   b. safety considerations about the hydrogen–oxygen fuel cell
   c. political–economic factors that may be hindering or promoting fuel cell research

BRIEF ANSWERS TO SELECTED PROBLEMS

Answers are provided for *all in-chapter exercises*. Brief answers are given for *odd-numbered Review Questions*; more complete answers can be obtained by reviewing the text. Answers are provided for *all odd-numbered Problems and Additional Problems*.

NOTE: For numerical problems, your answer may differ slightly from ours because of rounding and the use of significant figures.

1 oxidation: a, b, d; reduction: c
2 reduction: a; oxidation: b
3 reduction: a; oxidation: b, c, d
4 a. oxidizing agent: O_2; reducing agent: Se
  b. oxidizing agent: CH_3CN; reducing agent: H_2

c. oxidizing agent: V_2O_5; reducing agent: H_2
d. oxidizing agent: Br_2; reducing agent: K
5 oxidation: Al $\longrightarrow$ Al^{3+} + 3 e^-; reduction: Br_2 + 2 e^- $\longrightarrow$ 2 Br^-
6 A. Half-reactions: Fe $\longrightarrow$ Fe^{3+} + 3 e^-; Mg^{2+} + 2 e^- $\longrightarrow$ Mg
   Overall: 2 Fe + 3 Mg^{2+} $\longrightarrow$ 2 Fe^{3+} + 3 Mg
  B. Half-reactions:
   Pb $\longrightarrow$ Pb^{2+} + 2 e^-; $Ag(NH_3)_2^+$ + e^- $\longrightarrow$ Ag + 2 NH_3
   Overall: Pb + 2 $Ag(NH_3)_2^+$ $\longrightarrow$ Pb^{2+} + 2 Ag + 4 NH_3
7 A. 2 Zn + O_2 $\longrightarrow$ 2 ZnO
  B. Se + O_2 $\longrightarrow$ SeO_2
8 A. 2 PbS + 3 O_2 $\longrightarrow$ 2 PbO + 2 SO_2
  B. C H OH + 3 O $\longrightarrow$ 2 CO + 3 H O

1. Oxidation: oxidation number increases; reduction: oxidation number decreases

3. To allow ions to flow from one compartment to the other and thus keep the solutions electrically neutral

5. Zinc; it is the anode; oxidized to Zn^{2+}

7. $PbSO_4$ is converted to Pb and PbO_2.

9. Iron is oxidized to iron(III) hydroxide; salt water acts as an electrolyte.

11. Silver is oxidized by hydrogen sulfide to (black) silver sulfide; use aluminum to reduce the silver sulfide back to metallic silver.

13. a. oxidized (Fe loses e^-)
    b. oxidized (H_2O loses H)
    c. oxidized (Sr loses e^-)
    d. reduced (P_4 gains e^-)
    e. oxidized (CH_4O loses H)

15. a. $Ca \longrightarrow Ca^{2+} + 2\,e^-$
    b. $Al \longrightarrow Al^{3+} + 3\,e^-$
    c. $Cu \longrightarrow Cu^+ + e^-$; $Cu \longrightarrow Cu^{2+} + 2\,e^-$

17. a. oxidizing agent: Fe_2O_3; reducing agent: C
    b. oxidizing agent: O_2; reducing agent: P_4
    c. oxidizing agent: H_2O; reducing agent: C
    d. oxidizing agent: H_2SO_4; reducing agent: Zn

19. Cu

21. oxidizing agent: MnO_2; reducing agent: Zn

23. a. oxidation: $Fe \longrightarrow Fe^{2+} + 2\,e^-$; reduction: $2\,H^+ + 2\,e^- \longrightarrow H_2$
    b. oxidation: $Al \longrightarrow Al^{3+} + 3\,e^-$ reduction: $Cr^{2+} + 2\,e^- \longrightarrow Cr$

25. a. oxidation: $2\,H_2O_2 \longrightarrow 2\,O_2 + 4\,H^+ + 4\,e^-$ reduction: $Fe^{3+} + e^- \longrightarrow Fe^{2+}$
    overall: $2\,H_2O_2 + 4\,Fe^{3+} \longrightarrow 2\,O_2 + 4\,Fe^{2+} + 4\,H^+$
    b. oxidation: $C_2H_6O \longrightarrow C_2H_4O + 2\,H^+ + 2\,e^-$
    reduction: $WO_3 + 6\,H^+ + 6\,e^- \longrightarrow W + 3\,H_2O$
    overall: $3\,C_2H_6O + WO_3 \longrightarrow 3\,C_2H_4O + W + 3\,H_2O$

27. a. SO_2 is oxidized; HNO_3 is the oxidizing agent
    b. HI is oxidized, CrO_3 is the oxidizing agent

29. Reduced; ethylene gains hydrogen.

31. Ta_2O_5 is reduced; the reducing agent is Na.

33. Zr was oxidized; water was the oxidizing agent.

35. Nitrite ion is reduced; ascorbic acid is the reducing agent.

37. a. SO_2 b. $CO_2 + H_2O$ c. $CO_2 + H_2O$

39. Indoxyl is oxidized; O_2 is the oxidizing agent.

41. $2\,Al(s) + 3\,Cu^{2+}(aq) \longrightarrow 2\,Al^{3+}(aq) + 3\,Cu(s)$

43. $H_2S + Pb^{2+} \longrightarrow PbS + 2\,H^+$
    $S^{2-} + 4\,H_2O_2 \longrightarrow SO_4^{2-} + 4\,H_2O$

45. $160\ L\ O_2$

47. a. V^{2+} is oxidized; it loses an electron when forming V^{3+}.
    b. neither; there are two O atoms per N atom in both NO_2 and N_2O_4.
    c. CO is reduced; C gains H.

49. $H_2 + Cl_2 \longrightarrow 2\,HCl$; Cl_2 is the oxidizing agent.

51. $2\,Al(s) + 6\,H_2O(l) \longrightarrow 2\,Al(OH)_3 + 3\,H_2$; H_2O is the oxidizing agent and Al is the reducing agent.

53. a. $NAD^+ + H^+ + 2\,e^- \longrightarrow NADH$; $CH_3CH_2OH \longrightarrow CH_3CHO + 2\,H^+ + 2\,e^-$
    b. $NADH \longrightarrow NAD^+ + H^+ + 2\,e^-$; $CH_3COCOOH + 2\,H^+ + 2\,e^- \longrightarrow CH_3CHOHCOOH$
    Overall: $NADH + CH_3COCOOH + H^+ \longrightarrow NAD^+ + CH_3CHOHCOOH$

55. a. industrial   b. specialty
    c. specialty   d. industrial

57. Organic parts may undergo oxidation, inactivating the catalyst.

The Scoville Food Institute

Organic Chemistry

Paul Paladin/Shutterstock

Have You Ever Wondered?

1. **Does organic food have anything to do with organic chemistry?**

2. **What is the "petroleum distillate" that I see listed on some product labels?**

3. **If a compound has *benzene* in its name, is the compound a carcinogen?**

4. **Why do some mouthwashes taste "medicine-y"?**

5. **Why does fresh fruit smell so good and rotting fruit so bad?**

6. **Why do dead animals smell so bad?**

Learning Objectives

> Define *hydrocarbon*, and recognize structural features of alkanes, alkenes, and alkynes. (1)

> Identify hydrocarbon molecules as alkanes, alkenes, or alkynes, and name them. (1)

> Define *aromatic compound*, and recognize the structural feature such compounds share. (2)

> Name simple aromatic hydrocarbons. (2)

> Name a halogenated hydrocarbon given its formula, and write the formula for such a compound given its name. (3)

> Classify an organic compound according to its functional group(s), and explain why the concept of a functional group is useful in the study of organic chemistry. (4)

> Recognize and write the formulas of simple alkyl groups. (4)

> Recognize the general structure for an alcohol, a phenol, and an ether. (5)

> Name simple alcohols, phenols, and ethers. (5)

> Name simple aldehydes and ketones, and list their important properties. (6)

> Name simple carboxylic acids and esters, and list their important properties. (7)

> Name and write the formulas of simple amines and amides. (8)

> Recognize a structure as that of a heterocyclic compound. (8)

> Identify greener solvents that can replace those from nonrenewable fossil fuels, methods for incorporating renewable resources into organic synthesis, and efficient energy sources for enhancing chemical reactions.

The Infinite Variety of Carbon Compounds

The definition of organic chemistry has changed over the years. The changes exemplify the dynamic character of science and exemplify how scientific concepts change in response to experimental evidence. Until the nineteenth century, chemists believed that *organic* chemicals originated only in tissues of living *organisms* and required a "vital force" for their production. All chemicals not manufactured by living tissue were regarded as *inorganic*.

The compound capsaicin, a molecular model of which is shown here, is the principal compound responsible for the "hotness" of chili peppers. Capsaicin is organic in the original sense because it is obtained from a plant. It is also organic in the modern sense in that it is a compound containing carbon. Numerous organic chemicals are obtained from plants and animals, but many of the millions of organic compounds known today are synthetic.

Abel Tumik/Shutterstock

From Chapter 9 of *Chemistry for Changing Times*, Thirteenth Edition. John W. Hill, Terry W. McCreary, Doris K. Kolb.

Some chemists even believed that organic and inorganic chemicals followed different laws. This all changed in 1828, when Friedrich Wöhler synthesized the organic compound urea (found in urine) from ammonium cyanate, an inorganic compound. This important event led other chemists to attempt synthesis of organic chemicals from inorganic ones and changed the very definition of organic chemicals.

Organic chemistry is now defined as the chemistry of carbon-containing compounds. Most of these compounds do come from living things or from things that were once living, but some do not. Perhaps the most remarkable thing about organic compounds is their sheer number. Of the tens of millions of known chemical compounds, more than 95% are compounds of carbon.

One reason for the huge number of organic compounds is the carbon atom itself. Carbon is unique in that its atoms bond readily to each other and form long chains. (Silicon and a few other elements can form chains, but only short ones.) Carbon chains can also have branches or form rings of various sizes. When we consider that carbon atoms also bond strongly to other elements, particularly nonmetals such as hydrogen, oxygen, and nitrogen, and that these atoms can be arranged in many different ways, it soon becomes obvious why there are so many organic compounds.

In addition to the millions of carbon compounds already known, new ones are being discovered every day. Carbon can form an almost infinite number of molecules of various shapes, sizes, and compositions. We use thousands of carbon compounds every day without even realizing it because they are silently carrying out important chemical reactions within our bodies. Many of these carbon compounds are so vital that we cannot live without them.

1 Aliphatic Hydrocarbons

Learning Objectives > Define *hydrocarbon*, and recognize structural features of alkanes, alkenes, and alkynes. > Identify hydrocarbon molecules as alkanes, alkenes, or alkynes, and name them.

The simplest organic compounds are hydrocarbons. A **hydrocarbon** contains only hydrogen and carbon. There are several kinds of hydrocarbons, classified according to the type of bonding between carbon atoms. We divide hydrocarbons into two main classes. Those discussed in this section are **aliphatic compounds** (the Greek word *aleiphar* means "fat" or "oil"), usually defined as nonaromatic. The other category, benzene-like *aromatic compounds*, is discussed in Section 2.

Alkanes

Each carbon atom forms four bonds, and each hydrogen atom forms only one bond, so the simplest hydrocarbon molecule possible is methane, CH_4. Methane is the main component of natural gas. It has the structure

$$H-\overset{\displaystyle H}{\underset{\displaystyle H}{C}}-H$$

◀ **Figure 1** Ball-and-stick
(a) and space-filling (b) models of
methane (left) and ethane (right).

Methane is the first member of a group of related compounds called **alkanes**, hydrocarbons that contain only single bonds. Alkanes can have from one to several hundred or more carbon atoms. The next member of the series is ethane,

$$\begin{array}{ccc} & H & H \\ & | & | \\ H- & C- & C-H \\ & | & | \\ & H & H \end{array}$$

Ethane is a minor constituent of natural gas. It is seldom encountered as a pure compound in everyday life, but many common compounds are derived from it.

The methane molecule is tetrahedral, in accord with the VSEPR theory. In fact, the tetrahedral shape results whenever a carbon atom is connected to four other atoms, whether they are hydrogen, carbon, or other elements. Figure 1 shows models of methane and ethane. The ball-and-stick models show the bond angles best, but the space-filling models more accurately reflect the shapes of the molecules. Ordinarily, we use simple structural formulas such as the one shown previously for ethane because they are much easier to draw. A **structural formula** shows which atoms are bonded to each other, but it does not attempt to show the actual shape of the molecule.

Alkanes are often called **saturated hydrocarbons** because each carbon atom is *saturated* with hydrogen atoms; that is, each carbon is bonded to the maximum number of hydrogen atoms. In constructing a formula, we connect the carbon atoms to each other through single bonds; then we add enough hydrogen atoms to give each carbon atom four bonds. All alkanes have two more than twice as many hydrogen atoms as carbon atoms. That is, alkanes can be represented by a general formula C_nH_{2n+2}, in which n is the number of carbon atoms.

The three-carbon alkane is propane. Models of propane are shown in Figure 2. To draw its structural formula, we place three carbon atoms in a row.

$$C-C-C$$

Then we add enough hydrogen atoms (eight in this case) to give each carbon atom a total of four bonds. Therefore, the structural formula of propane is

$$\begin{array}{cccc} & H & H & H \\ & | & | & | \\ H- & C- & C- & C-H \\ & | & | & | \\ & H & H & H \end{array}$$

Condensed Structural Formulas

The complete structural formulas that we have used so far show all the carbon and hydrogen atoms and how they are attached to one another. But these formulas take up a lot of space, and they can be a bit of trouble to draw. For these reasons, chemists usually prefer to use **condensed structural formulas**. These formulas show how

(a)

(b)

▲ **Figure 2** Ball-and-stick
(a) and space-filling (b) models of
propane.

▲ A propane torch. Propane burns in air with a hot flame.

VladimirB/Shutterstock

253

many hydrogen atoms are attached to each carbon atom without showing the bond to each hydrogen atom. For example, the condensed structural formulas for ethane and propane are written $CH_3—CH_3$ and $CH_3—CH_2—CH_3$, respectively. These formulas can be simplified even further by omitting some (or all) of the remaining bond lines, resulting in CH_3CH_3 and $CH_3CH_2CH_3$.

Homologous Series

Note that methane, ethane, and propane form a pattern. We can build alkanes of any length simply by joining carbon atoms together in long chains and adding enough hydrogen atoms to give each carbon atom four bonds. Even the naming of these compounds follows a pattern (Table 1), with a stem name indicating the number of carbon atoms. For compounds of five carbon atoms or more, each stem is derived from the Greek or Latin name for the number. The compound names end in -*ane*, signifying that the compounds are *alkanes*. Table 2 gives condensed structural formulas and names for the continuous-chain (straight-chain, or unbranched) alkanes with up to ten carbon atoms.

Notice that the molecular formula for each alkane in Table 2 differs from the one preceding it by precisely one carbon atom and two hydrogen atoms—that is, by a CH_2 unit. Such a series of compounds has properties that vary in a regular and predictable manner. This principle, called *homology*, gives order to organic chemistry in much the same way that the periodic table gives organization to the chemistry of the elements. Instead of studying the chemistry of a bewildering array of individual carbon compounds, organic chemists study a few members—called *homologs*—of a **homologous series**, from which they can deduce the properties of other compounds in the series.

We need not stop at ten carbon atoms as Table 2 does. Hundreds, thousands, even millions of carbon atoms can be linked together. We can make an infinite number of alkanes simply by lengthening the chain. But lengthening the chain is not the only option. Beginning with alkanes having four carbon atoms, chain branching is also possible.

Isomerism

When we extend the carbon chain to four atoms and add enough hydrogen atoms to give each carbon atom four bonds, we get $CH_3CH_2CH_2CH_3$. This formula represents butane, a compound that boils at about 0 °C. A second compound, which has a boiling point of −12 °C, has the same molecular formula, C_4H_{10}, as butane. The structure of this compound, however, is not the same as that of butane. Instead of having four carbon atoms connected in a continuous chain, this compound has a continuous chain of only three carbon atoms. The fourth carbon is branched off the

Table 1 — Stems for Organic Molecule Names

Stem	Number of Carbon Atoms
Meth-	1
Eth-	2
Prop-	3
But-	4
Pent-	5
Hex-	6
Hept-	7
Oct-	8
Non-	9
Dec-	10

Table 2 — The First Ten Continuous-Chain Alkanes

Name	Molecular Formula	Condensed Structural Formula	Number of Possible Isomers
Methane	CH_4	CH_4	—
Ethane	C_2H_6	CH_3CH_3	—
Propane	C_3H_8	$CH_3CH_2CH_3$	—
Butane	C_4H_{10}	$CH_3CH_2CH_2CH_3$	2
Pentane	C_5H_{12}	$CH_3CH_2CH_2CH_2CH_3$	3
Hexane	C_6H_{14}	$CH_3CH_2CH_2CH_2CH_2CH_3$	5
Heptane	C_7H_{16}	$CH_3CH_2CH_2CH_2CH_2CH_2CH_3$	9
Octane	C_8H_{18}	$CH_3CH_2CH_2CH_2CH_2CH_2CH_2CH_3$	18
Nonane	C_9H_{20}	$CH_3CH_2CH_2CH_2CH_2CH_2CH_2CH_2CH_3$	35
Decane	$C_{10}H_{22}$	$CH_3CH_2CH_2CH_2CH_2CH_2CH_2CH_2CH_2CH_3$	75

middle carbon of the three-carbon chain. To show the two structures more clearly, let's use complete structural formulas, showing all the bonds to hydrogen atoms.

(a)

Branch point

Compounds that have the same molecular formula but different structural formulas are called **isomers**. Because it is an isomer of butane, the branched four-carbon alkane is sometimes called *isobutane*. Condensed structural formulas for the two isomeric butanes are written as follows.

CH₃CH₂CH₂CH₃   CH₃CHCH₃
                                    |
                                   CH₃

Butane   Isobutane

(b)

▲ **Figure 3** Ball-and-stick models of (a) butane and (b) isobutane.

Figure 3 shows ball-and-stick models of the two compounds.

The number of isomers increases rapidly with the number of carbon atoms (Table 2). There are three pentanes, five hexanes, nine heptanes, and so on. Isomerism is common in carbon compounds and provides another reason for the existence of millions of organic compounds.

Propane and the butanes are familiar fuels. Although they are gases at ordinary temperatures and under normal atmospheric pressure, they are liquefied under pressure and are usually supplied in tanks as liquefied petroleum gas (LPG). Gasoline is a mixture of hydrocarbons, mostly alkanes, with 5–12 carbon atoms.

Not all the possible isomers of the larger molecules have been isolated. Indeed, the task rapidly becomes more and more prohibitive going up the series. There are, for example, 4,111,846,763 possible isomers with the molecular formula $C_{30}H_{62}$.

Example 1   Hydrocarbon Formulas

Without referring to Table 2, write the molecular formula, the complete structural formula, and the condensed structural formula for heptane.

Solution

The stem *hept-* means seven carbon atoms, and the ending *-ane* indicates an alkane. For the complete structural formula, we write a string of seven carbon atoms.

C—C—C—C—C—C—C

Then we attach enough hydrogen atoms to the carbon atoms to give each carbon four bonds. This requires three hydrogens on each end carbon and two hydrogens on each of the other carbons.

For the condensed form, we simply write each set of hydrogen atoms following the carbon atom to which they are bonded.

CH₃CH₂CH₂CH₂CH₂CH₂CH₃

For the molecular formula, we can simply count the carbon and hydrogen atoms to arrive at C_7H_{16}. Alternatively, we could use the general formula C_nH_{2n+2}, with $n = 7$, to get C_7H_{16}.

▲ Gasoline is a mixture containing dozens of hydrocarbons, many of which are alkanes.

2. What is the "petroleum distillate" that I see listed on some product labels? Petroleum distillates are various components of crude oil, most of which are hydrocarbons. Paint thinner, lighter fluid, paraffin wax, petroleum jelly, and asphalt are all petroleum distillates.

Recall that water has a density of 1.00 g/mL at room temperature. All the alkanes listed in Table 3 have densities less than that.

⚠ SAFETY ALERT

Hydrocarbons and most other organic compounds are flammable or combustible. Volatile ones may form explosive mixtures with air. Hydrocarbons are the main ingredients in gasoline, motor oils, fuel gases (natural gas and bottled gas), and fuel oils. They are also ingredients, identified on labels as "petroleum distillates" and "mineral spirits," of products such as floor cleaners, furniture polishes, paint thinners, wood stains and varnishes, and car waxes and polishes. Some products also contain flammable alcohols, esters, and ketones. Products containing flammable substances can be dangerous but may be used safely with proper precautions. Use only as directed and keep all such products away from open flames.

■ **EXERCISE 1**
Write the molecular, complete structural, and condensed structural formulas for **(a)** hexane and **(b)** octane.

Properties of Alkanes

Note in Table 3 that after the first few members of the alkane series, the rest show an increase in boiling point of about 30° with each added CH_2 group. Note also that at room temperature alkanes that have 1 to 4 carbon atoms per molecule are gases, those with 5 to about 16 carbon atoms per molecule are liquids, and those with more than 16 carbon atoms per molecule are solids. The densities of liquid and solid alkanes are less than that of water. Alkanes are nonpolar molecules and are insoluble in water; thus, they float on top of water. They dissolve many organic substances of low polarity—such as fats, oils, and waxes.

Alkanes undergo few chemical reactions, but one important chemical property is that they burn, producing a lot of heat. Alkanes have many uses, but they mainly serve as fuels.

The effects of alkanes on the human body vary. Methane appears to be physiologically inert. We probably could breathe a mixture of 80% methane and 20% oxygen without ill effect. This mixture would be flammable, however, and no fire or spark of any kind could be permitted in such an atmosphere. Breathing an atmosphere of pure methane (the "gas" of a gas-operated stove) can lead to death—not because of the presence of methane but because of the absence of oxygen, a condition called *asphyxia*.

Light liquid alkanes such as those in gasoline will dissolve and wash away body oils when spilled on the skin. Repeated contact may cause dermatitis. (Other components of gasoline are less innocuous.) If swallowed, most alkanes do little harm in the stomach; in fact, mineral oil is a mixture of long-chain liquid alkanes that has been used for many years as a laxative.

Heavier liquid alkanes act as emollients (skin softeners). Petroleum jelly (Vaseline™ is one brand) is a semisolid mixture of hydrocarbons that can be applied as an emollient or simply as a protective film. However, in the lungs, alkanes cause chemical pneumonia by dissolving fatlike molecules from the cell membranes in the alveoli, allowing the lungs to fill with fluid.

Table 3 — Physical Properties, Uses and Occurrences of Selected Alkanes

Name	Molecular Formula	Melting Point (°C)	Boiling Point (°C)	Density[a] at 20 °C (g/mL)	Use/Occurrence
Methane	CH_4	−183	−162	(Gas)	Natural gas (main component); fuel
Ethane	C_2H_6	−172	−89	(Gas)	Natural gas (minor component); plastics
Propane	C_3H_8	−188	−42	(Gas)	LPG (bottled gas); plastics
Butane	C_4H_{10}	−138	0	(Gas)	LPG; lighter fuel
Pentane	C_5H_{12}	−130	36	0.626	Gasoline component
Hexane	C_6H_{14}	−95	69	0.659	Gasoline component; extraction solvent for food oils
Heptane	C_7H_{16}	−91	98	0.684	Gasoline component
Octane	C_8H_{18}	−57	126	0.703	Gasoline component
Decane	$C_{10}H_{22}$	−30	174	0.730	Gasoline component
Dodecane	$C_{12}H_{26}$	−10	216	0.749	Gasoline component
Tetradecane	$C_{14}H_{30}$	6	254	0.763	Diesel fuel component
Hexadecane	$C_{16}H_{34}$	18	280	0.775	Diesel fuel component
Octadecane	$C_{18}H_{38}$	28	316	(Solid)	Paraffin wax component
Eicosane	$C_{20}H_{42}$	37	343	(Solid)	Paraffin wax and asphalt component

[a]Densities of the gaseous alkanes vary with pressure. Densities of the solids are not available.

Cyclic Hydrocarbons: Rings and Things

The hydrocarbons we have encountered so far (alkanes) have open-ended chains of carbon atoms. Carbon atoms can also connect to form closed rings. The simplest possible ring-containing hydrocarbon, or **cyclic hydrocarbon**, has the molecular formula C_3H_6 and is called *cyclopropane* (Figure 4).

$$
\begin{array}{c}
\text{H}\quad\text{H} \\
\diagdown\diagup \\
\text{C} \\
\diagup\backslash \\
\text{H}-\text{C}-\text{C}-\text{H} \qquad or \qquad \text{CH}_2 \\
\vert\quad\vert \qquad\qquad\qquad \diagup\backslash \\
\text{H}\quad\text{H} \qquad\qquad \text{CH}_2-\text{CH}_2
\end{array}
$$

▲ **Figure 4** Ball-and-stick model of cyclopropane. Cyclopropane is a potent, quick-acting anesthetic with few undesirable side effects. It is no longer used in surgery, however, because it forms an explosive mixture with air at nearly all concentrations.

Names of *cycloalkanes* (cyclic hydrocarbons containing only single bonds) are formed by adding the prefix *cyclo-* to the name of the open-chain compound with the same number of carbon atoms as are in the cycloalkane's ring.

Chemists often use geometric shapes to represent cyclic compounds (Figure 5). For example, a triangle is used to represent the cyclopropane ring, and a hexagon represents cyclohexane. Each corner of such a shape represents a carbon atom with its associated hydrogen atoms.

◀ **Figure 5** Structural formulas and symbolic representations of some cyclic hydrocarbons.

Cyclopropane   Cyclohexane   Cyclohexene

Example 2	Structural Formulas of Cyclic Hydrocarbons

Write the structural formula for cyclobutane. What geometric figure is used to represent cyclobutane?

Solution

Cyclobutane has four carbon atoms arranged in a ring.

$$
\begin{array}{c}
\text{C}-\text{C} \\
\vert\quad\vert \\
\text{C}-\text{C}
\end{array}
$$

Each carbon atom needs two hydrogen atoms to complete its set of four bonds.

$$
\begin{array}{c}
\text{CH}_2-\text{CH}_2 \\
\vert\qquad\vert \\
\text{CH}_2-\text{CH}_2
\end{array}
$$

Cyclobutane can also be represented by a square.

■ EXERCISE 2A

Write the structural formula for cyclopentane and the geometric shape used to represent it.

■ EXERCISE 2B

What is the general formula for a cycloalkane?

Unsaturated Hydrocarbons: Alkenes and Alkynes

(a)

(b)

▲ **Figure 6** Ball-and-stick (a) and space-filling (b) models of ethylene.

Two carbon atoms can share more than one pair of electrons. In ethylene (C_2H_4), the two carbon atoms share two pairs of electrons and are therefore joined by a double bond (Figure 6).

$$\overset{H}{\underset{H}{..}}C::\overset{..}{\underset{H}{C}}\overset{H}{} \quad \text{or} \quad \overset{H}{\underset{H}{}}C=C\overset{H}{\underset{H}{}} \quad \text{or} \quad CH_2{=}CH_2$$

(Ethylene is the common name; the systematic, or IUPAC, name is *ethene*.) Ethylene is the simplest member of the alkene family. An **alkene** is a hydrocarbon that contains one or more carbon-to-carbon double bonds. Alkenes with one double bond have the general formula C_nH_{2n}, where n is the number of carbon atoms.

Ethylene is the most important organic chemical commercially. Annual U.S. production is over 20 billion kg. More than half goes into the manufacture of polyethylene, one of the most familiar plastics. Another 15% or so is converted to ethylene glycol, the major component of many formulations of antifreeze used in automobile radiators.

In acetylene (C_2H_2), the two carbon atoms share three pairs of electrons. The carbon atoms are joined by a triple bond (Figure 7).

$$H:C:::C:H \quad \text{or} \quad H{-}C{\equiv}C{-}H$$

Acetylene (IUPAC name, ethyne) is the simplest member of the alkyne family. An **alkyne** is a hydrocarbon that contains one or more carbon-to-carbon triple bonds. Alkynes with one triple bond have the general formula C_nH_{2n-2}, where n is the number of carbon atoms.

▶ **Figure 7** Ball-and-stick (a) and space-filling (b) models of acetylene.

(a)   (b)

Acetylene is used in oxyacetylene torches for cutting and welding metals. Such torches can produce very high temperatures. Acetylene is also converted to a variety of other chemical products.

Collectively, alkenes and alkynes are called *unsaturated hydrocarbons*. Recall that a *saturated hydrocarbon* (alkane) has the maximum number of hydrogen atoms attached to each carbon atom; it has no double or triple bonds. An **unsaturated hydrocarbon** can have more hydrogen atoms added to it.

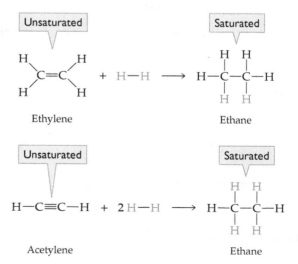

Example 3 — Molecular Formulas of Unsaturated Hydrocarbons

What is the molecular formula for 1-hexene? (The "1-" is a part of a systematic name that indicates the location of the double bond, which in this case connects the first carbon atom of the chain to the second.)

Solution

The stem *hex-* indicates six carbon atoms, the ending *-ene* tells us that the compound is an alkene. Using the general formula C_nH_{2n} for an alkene, with $n = 6$, we see that an alkene with six carbon atoms has the molecular formula C_6H_{14}.

■ EXERCISE 3

What are the molecular formulas for **(a)** 2-hexene and **(b)** 3-heptyne?

Properties of Alkenes and Alkynes

The physical properties of alkenes and alkynes are much like those of the corresponding alkanes. Unsaturated hydrocarbons with 2 to 4 carbon atoms per molecule are gases at room temperature, those with 5 to 18 carbon atoms are liquids, and most of those with more than 18 carbon atoms are solids. Like alkanes, alkenes and alkynes are insoluble in, and float on, water.

Like alkanes, both alkenes and alkynes burn. However, these unsaturated hydrocarbons undergo many more chemical reactions than alkanes do. An alkene or alkyne can undergo an **addition reaction** to the double or triple bond, in which all the atoms of the reactants are incorporated into a single product. In the preceding reactions, ethylene (C_2H_4) adds hydrogen (H_2) to form ethane (C_2H_6), and acetylene (C_2H_2) adds two moles of hydrogen (2 H_2) to form ethane. Chlorine, bromine, water, and many other kinds of small molecules also add to double and triple bonds.

One of the most unusual features of alkene (and alkyne) molecules is that they can add *to each other* to form large molecules called *polymers*.

Bon Appetit/Alamy

▲ It DOES Matter!

Fats are probably the best-known examples of compounds that can be saturated or unsaturated. In saturated fats, all the carbon-carbon bonds are single bonds. These fats are found mostly in milk, meats, and eggs, and their consumption tends to increase low-density lipoproteins ("bad" cholesterol) in the human bloodstream. Most plant oils are unsaturated fats, with one or more carbon-carbon double bonds. Consumption of unsaturated fats tends to increase high-density lipoproteins ("good" cholesterol) in the blood.

Self-Assessment Questions

1. Which of the following is *not* a reason for the great number of carbon compounds?
   a. Carbon atoms can form chains.
   b. Carbon compounds are easily oxidized.
   c. Carbon atoms can form rings.
   d. The same carbon atoms can be arranged different ways.

2. A saturated hydrocarbon is one that
   a. contains only carbon-carbon single bonds
   b. has the maximum number of carbon atoms
   c. has a vapor pressure equal to atmospheric pressure
   d. is solid at room temperature

3. Successive members of the alkane series differ from the preceding member by one additional
   a. C atom and one H atom
   b. C atom and two H atoms
   c. C atom and three H atoms
   d. H atom and two C atoms

4. Isomers are compounds whose molecules have the same
   a. numbers of C atoms but different numbers of H atoms
   b. numbers of H atoms but different numbers of C atoms
   c. numbers and kinds of atoms but different structures
   d. kinds of atoms but different numbers of these atoms

5. As the molecular mass of the members of the alkane series increases, their boiling points
   a. decrease   b. increase   c. remain the same   d. vary randomly

6. A cyclic compound with 6 C atoms and 12 H atoms is
   a. cyclobutane   b. cycloheptane   c. cyclohexane   d. cyclosexane

An unsaturated hydrocarbon tends to burn with a smoky flame, especially if the oxygen supply is limited. Saturated hydrocarbons usually burn with a clean yellow flame. Burning of natural gas, propane, and butane is almost soot-free, but paint thinner, gasoline, and kerosene (all containing unsaturated hydrocarbons) burn with sooty flames.

7. The family of hydrocarbons whose molecules have a triple bond between carbon atoms is the
   a. alkanes   **b.** alkenes   **c.** alkynes   **d.** aromatic hydrocarbons
8. Addition reactions occur with alkenes but not with alkanes because alkenes have
   a. double bonds   **b.** a greater molecular mass
   c. more C atoms per molecule   **d.** a tetrahedral arrangement of bonds
9. The following equation is an example of what kind of reaction?
   $$C_2H_4 + H_2 \longrightarrow C_2H_6$$
   a. addition   **b.** neutralization   **c.** oxidation   **d.** ionization

Answers: 1, b; 2, a; 3, b; 4, c; 5, b; 6, c; 7, c; 8, a; 9, a

2 Aromatic Compounds: Benzene and its Relatives

Learning Objectives ❯ Define *aromatic* compound, and recognize the structural feature such compounds share. ❯ Name simple aromatic hydrocarbons.

Clive Freeman/The Royal Institution/SPL/ Photo Researchers, Inc.

▲ **Figure 8** A computer-generated model of the benzene molecule. The six unassigned electrons occupy the yellow and blue areas above and below the plane of the ring of carbon atoms.

A circle inside a ring indicates that a compound is aromatic. It does not always mean six electrons. The structural formula for naphthalene (Figure 9), for example, has a circle in each ring, indicating that it is an aromatic hydrocarbon. The total number of unassigned electrons, however, is only ten. Some chemists still prefer to represent naphthalene (and other aromatic compounds) with alternating double and single bonds.

An important and interesting hydrocarbon is benzene. Discovered by Michael Faraday in 1825, benzene has the molecular formula C_6H_6. The structure of benzene puzzled chemists for decades. The formula seems to indicate an unsaturated compound, but benzene does not react as if it contains any double or triple bonds. It does not readily undergo addition reactions the way unsaturated compounds usually do.

Finally, in 1865, August Kekulé proposed a structure with a ring of six carbon atoms, each attached to one hydrogen atom.

The two structures shown appear to contain double bonds, but in fact they do not. Both structures represent the same molecule, and the actual structure of this molecule is a *hybrid* of these two structures. The benzene molecule actually has six identical carbon-to-carbon bonds that are neither single bonds nor double bonds but something in between. In other words, the three pairs of electrons that would form the three double bonds are not tied down in one location but are spread around the ring (Figure 8). Today, we usually represent the benzene ring with a circle inside a hexagon.

The hexagon represents the ring of six carbon atoms, and the inscribed circle represents the six unassigned electrons. Because its ring of electrons resists being disrupted, the benzene molecule is exceptionally stable.

Benzene and similar compounds are called *aromatic hydrocarbons*, because quite a few of the first benzene-like substances to be discovered had strong aromas. Even though many compounds derived from benzene have turned out to be odorless, the name has stuck. Today, an **aromatic compound** is any compound that contains a benzene ring or has certain properties like those of benzene. All other compounds are said to be aliphatic (Section 1).

Structures of some common aromatic hydrocarbons are shown in Figure 9. Benzene, toluene, and the xylenes are all liquids that float on water. They are used mainly as solvents and fuels but are also used to make other benzene derivatives. Their vapors can act as narcotics when inhaled. Because benzene may cause leukemia after long exposure, its use has been restricted. Naphthalene is a volatile, white, crystalline solid used as an insecticide, especially as a moth repellant.

Monosubstituted benzenes—in which one hydrogen is replaced by another atom or group, called a **substituent**—are often represented in by condensed formulas—for example, toluene is $C_6H_5CH_3$ and ethylbenzene is $C_6H_5CH_2CH_3$. Similar designations are sometimes used for disubstituted aromatic rings, indicating the relative positions of substituents with numbers, as in $1,4\text{-}C_6H_4(CH_3)_2$ for 1,4-dimethylbenzene.

3. If a compound has *benzene* in its name, is the compound a carcinogen? No. Aromatic compounds are often named as derivatives of benzene simply because their structures contain a benzene ring. In fact, many compounds that are useful or even necessary to life contain benzene rings, including penicillin, aspirin, and the amino acids phenylalanine and tryptophan.

Toluene

Ethylbenzene

Naphthalene

ortho-Xylene
(1,2-Dimethylbenzene)

meta-Xylene
(1,3-Dimethylbenzene)

para-Xylene
(1,4-Dimethylbenzene)

◀ **Figure 9** Some aromatic hydrocarbons. Like benzene, toluene and the three xylenes are components of gasoline and also serve as solvents. All these compounds are intermediates in the synthesis of polymers and other organic chemicals.

Self-Assessment Questions

1. The molecular formula of benzene is
   a. C_4H_4 **b.** C_4H_{10} **c.** C_6H_6 **d.** C_6H_{10}

2. Which compound is an aromatic hydrocarbon?
   a. acetylene   **b.** butadiene   **c.** chlorobenzene   **d.** cyclohexene

3. Which organic molecule is represented as a hybrid of two structures?
   a. benzene   **b.** butadiene   **c.** 1-butene   **d.** propyne

4. Naphthalene is an
   a. alkane   **b.** alkene   **c.** alkyne   **d.** aromatic hydrocarbon

5. The reactivity of the benzene ring reflects
   a. its aromatic odor
   b. the presence of carbon-carbon double bonds
   c. its saturated structure
   d. the spreading of six electrons over all six carbon atoms

Answers: 1, c; 2, c; 3, a; 4, d; 5, d

3 Chlorinated Hydrocarbons: Many Uses, Some Hazards

Learning Objective ❯ Name a chlorinated hydrocarbon given its formula, and write the formula for such a compound given its name.

Many other organic compounds are derived from hydrocarbons by replacing one or more hydrogen atoms by another atom or group of atoms. For example, replacement of hydrogen atoms by chlorine atoms gives chlorinated hydrocarbons. When chlorine gas (Cl_2) is mixed with methane gas (CH_4) in the presence of ultraviolet (UV) light, a reaction takes place at a very rapid, even explosive, rate. The result is a mixture of products, some of which may be familiar to you (see Example 4 and Exercise 4). Several billion kilograms of chlorinated methanes are produced each year for use as solvents and as starting materials for other commercially valuable compounds. We can write an equation for the reaction in which one hydrogen atom of methane is replaced by a chlorine atom to give methyl chloride (chloromethane).

$$CH_4(g) + Cl_2(g) \longrightarrow CH_3Cl(g) + HCl(g)$$

Example 4   Formulas of Chlorinated Hydrocarbons

What is the formula for dichloromethane (also known as methylene chloride)?

Solution

The prefix *dichloro-* indicates two chlorine atoms. The rest of the name indicates that the compound is derived from methane (CH_4). We conclude that two hydrogen atoms of methane have been replaced by chlorine atoms; the formula for dichloromethane is therefore CH_2Cl_2.

■ EXERCISE 4

What are the formulas for **(a)** trichloromethane (also known as chloroform) and **(b)** tetrachloromethane (carbon tetrachloride)?

Methyl chloride is used mainly in making silicone polymers. Methylene chloride (dichloromethane) is a solvent used, for example, as a paint remover. Chloroform (trichloromethane), also a solvent, was once used as an anesthetic, but such use is now considered dangerous. The dosage required for effective anesthesia is too close to a lethal dose. Carbon tetrachloride (tetrachloromethane) has been used as a dry-cleaning solvent and in fire extinguishers, but it is no longer recommended for either use. Exposure to carbon tetrachloride or most other chlorinated hydrocarbons can cause severe damage to the liver. The use of a carbon tetrachloride fire extinguisher in conjunction with water to put out a fire can be deadly. Carbon tetrachloride reacts with water at elevated temperatures to form phosgene ($COCl_2$), an extremely poisonous gas that was used against troops during World War I.

A number of chlorinated hydrocarbons are of considerable interest. Vinyl chloride ($CH_2\!=\!CHCl$) is the starting material for manufacture of polyvinylchloride.

Many chlorinated hydrocarbons have similar properties. Most are only slightly polar and do not dissolve in (highly polar) water. Instead, they dissolve (and dissolve in) fats, oils, greases, and other substances of low polarity. This is why certain chlorinated hydrocarbons make good degreasing and dry-cleaning solvents; they remove grease and oily stains from fabrics. This is also why DDT (dichlorodiphenyltrichloroethane) and PCBs (polychlorinated biphenyls) cause problems for fish and birds and perhaps for people; these toxic substances are concentrated in fatty animal tissues rather than being easily excreted in (aqueous) urine.

Chlorofluorocarbons and Fluorocarbons

Compounds containing carbon and both fluorine and chlorine are called *chlorofluorocarbons (CFCs)*. CFCs have been used as the dispersing gases in aerosol cans, for making foamed plastics, and as refrigerants. Three common CFCs are best known by their industrial code designations:

$$CFCl_3 \quad CF_2Cl_2 \quad CF_2ClCF_2Cl$$
$$\text{CFC 11} \quad \text{CFC 12} \quad \text{CFC 114}$$

At room temperature, CFCs are gases or liquids with low boiling points. They are insoluble in water and inert toward most other substances. These properties make them ideal propellants in aerosol cans for deodorant, hair spray, and food products. CFCs are being phased out because their inertness allows them to persist in the environment and diffuse into the stratosphere, where they participate in chemical reactions that lead to depletion of the ozone layer that protects Earth from harmful UV radiation.

Fluorinated compounds have found some interesting uses. Some have been used as blood extenders. Oxygen is quite soluble in certain *perfluorocarbons*. (The prefix *per-* means that all hydrogen atoms have been replaced, in this case, by fluorine atoms.) These compounds can therefore serve as temporary substitutes for hemoglobin, the oxygen-carrying protein in blood. Perfluoro compounds have been used to treat premature babies, whose lungs are often underdeveloped.

Polytetrafluoroethylene (PTFE, or Teflon®) is a perfluorinated polymer. It has many interesting applications because of its resistance to corrosive chemicals and to high temperatures. It is especially noted for its unusual nonstick properties.

Pearson Education/Eric Schrader

▲ Perfluorinated lubricants are used where highly corrosive or reactive conditions would cause most hydrocarbon greases to burst into flame.

Self-Assessment Questions

1. The compound CH_3Cl is named
   a. chloroform
   b. methyl chloride
   c. methylene chloride
   d. methyl formate

2. The compound CF_2Cl_2 is
   a. a chlorofluorocarbon
   b. chloroform
   c. methyl chloride
   d. methylene chloride

3. Which of the following is an isomer of 2-chloropropane ($CH_3CHClCH_3$)?
   a. butane   b. 2-chlorobutane
   c. 1-chloropropane   d. propane

Answers: 1, b; 2, a; 3, c

4 The Functional Group

Learning Objectives   ❯ Classify an organic compound according to its functional group(s), and explain why the concept of a functional group is useful in the study of organic chemistry. ❯ Recognize and write the formulas of simple alkyl groups.

Many organic compounds contain oxygen as well as carbon and hydrogen. This section introduces several important families of oxygen-containing organic compounds. First, however, we need to cover a fundamental concept of organic chemistry.

Double and triple carbon–carbon bonds and halogen substituents are examples of **functional groups**, atoms or groups of atoms that give a family of organic compounds its characteristic chemical and physical properties. Table 4 lists a number of common functional groups found in organic molecules. Each of these groups is the basis for its own homologous series.

In many simple molecules, a functional group is attached as a substituent to a hydrocarbon stem called an *alkyl group*. An **alkyl group** is derived from an alkane by removing a hydrogen atom. The methyl group (CH_3—), for example,

Table 4 Selected Organic Functional Groups

Name of Class	Functional Group[a]	General Formula of Class
Alkane	None	R—H
Alkene	—C=C—	$R_2C=CR_2$
Alkyne	—C≡C—	RC≡CR
Alcohol	—C—OH	R—OH
Ether	—C—O—C—	R—O—R'
Aldehyde	O ‖ —C—H	O ‖ R—C—H
Ketone	O ‖ —C—	O ‖ R—C—R'
Carboxylic acid	O ‖ —C—OH	O ‖ R—C—O—H
Ester	O ‖ —C—O—C—	O ‖ R—C—O—R'
Amine	—C—N—	H | R—N—H ; H | R—N—R' ; R' | R—N—R''
Amide	O ‖ —C—N—	O ‖ R—C—N—H | H ; O ‖ R—C—N—R' | H ; O ‖ R—C—N—R' | R''

[a] Neutral functional groups are shown in green, acidic groups in red, and basic groups in blue.

is derived from methane (CH_4), and the ethyl group (CH_3CH_2—) from ethane (CH_3CH_3). Propane yields two different alkyl groups, depending on whether the hydrogen atom is removed from an end or from the middle carbon atom; see Table 5. Table 5 also lists the four alkyl groups derived from the two butanes.

Often the letter R is used to stand for an alkyl group in general. Thus, ROH is a general formula for an alcohol, and RCl represents any alkyl chloride.

Table 5 **Common Alkyl Groups**

	Name	Structural Formula	Condensed Structural Formula
Derived from Propane	Propyl		$CH_3CH_2CH_2$—
	Isopropyl		CH_3CHCH_3
Derived from Butane	Butyl		$CH_3CH_2CH_2CH_2$—
	Secondary butyl (*sec*-butyl)		$CH_3CHCH_2CH_3$
Derived from Isobutane	Isobutyl		CH_3 CH_3CHCH_2—
	Tertiary butyl (*tert*-butyl)		CH_3 CH_3—C—CH_3

Self-Assessment Questions

1. A specific arrangement of atoms that gives characteristic properties to an organic molecule is called a(n)
   a. alkyl group
   b. carbonyl group
   c. functional group
   d. hydroxyl group

2. The formula $CH_3CH_2CH_2$— represents
   a. an alkyl group
   b. a functional group
   c. propane
   d. propylene

3. How many carbon atoms are there in a butyl group?
   a. 2   b. 3   c. 4   d. 6

4. The formula $CH_3CH_2CH_2CH_2$— represents a(n)
   a. butyl group
   b. isobutyl group
   c. isopropyl group
   d. propyl group

Organic Chemistry

5 Alcohols, Phenols, and Ethers

Learning Objectives ❭ Recognize the general structure for an alcohol, a phenol, and an ether. ❭Name simple alcohols, phenols, and ethers.

When a hydroxyl group (—OH) is substituted for any hydrogen atom in an alkane (R—H), the molecule becomes an **alcohol** (ROH). Like many organic compounds, alcohols can be called by their common names or by the systematic names of IUPAC. The IUPAC names for alcohols are based on those of alkanes, with the ending changed from -*e* to -*ol*. Methanol, ethanol, and 1-propanol are the first three members of the homologous series of straight-chain alcohols.

A number designates the carbon to which the —OH group is attached when more than one location is possible. For example, the 1 in 1-propanol indicates that —OH is attached to an end carbon atom of the three-carbon chain; the isomeric compound, 2-propanol, has the —OH group on the second (middle) carbon atom of the chain.

CH_3—OH	CH_3CH_2—OH	$CH_3CH_2CH_2$—OH	$CH_3\underset{\underset{\text{OH}}{|}}{C}HCH_3$
Methanol	Ethanol	1–Propanol	2–Propanol

Common names for these alcohols are methyl alcohol, ethyl alcohol, and propyl alcohol. The IUPAC names are the ones used in most scientific literature.

Methyl Alcohol (Methanol)

The simplest alcohol is *methanol*, or *methyl alcohol* (Figure 10). Methanol is sometimes called *wood alcohol* because it was once made from wood. The modern industrial process makes methanol from carbon monoxide and hydrogen at high temperature and pressure in the presence of a catalyst.

$$CO(g) + 2\,H_2(g) \longrightarrow CH_3OH(l)$$

Methanol is important as a solvent and as a chemical intermediate. It is also a gasoline additive and a potential replacement for gasoline in automobiles.

Ethyl Alcohol (Ethanol)

The next member of the homologous series of alcohols is *ethyl alcohol* (CH_3CH_2OH), also called ethanol or *grain alcohol* (Figure 11). Ethanol is made by fermentation of grain (or other starchy or sugary materials). If the sugar is glucose, the reaction is

$$C_6H_{12}O_6(aq) \xrightarrow{\text{yeast}} 2\,CH_3CH_2OH(aq) + 2\,CO_2(g)$$

Ethanol for beverages and for automotive fuel is made in this way. Ethanol for industrial use is made by reacting ethylene with water.

$$CH_2{=}CH_2(g) + H_2O(l) \xrightarrow{H^+} CH_3CH_2OH(l)$$

This industrial alcohol is identical to that made by fermentation and is generally cheaper, but by law, it cannot be used in alcoholic beverages. Because it carries no excise tax, the law requires that noxious substances be added to this alcohol to prevent people from drinking it. The resulting *denatured alcohol* is not fit to drink. This is the kind of alcohol commonly found on the shelves in chemical laboratories.

(a) (b)

▲ **Figure 10** Ball-and-stick (a) and space-filling (b) models of methanol.

(a) (b)

▲ **Figure 11** Ball-and-stick (a) and space-filling (b) models of ethanol.

Is it poisonous? That seems to be a simple question, but it is a difficult one to answer. Toxicity depends on the nature of the substance, the amount, and the route by which it is taken into the body.

266

Table 6	Approximate Relationship among Drinks Consumed, Blood-Alcohol Level, and Behavior[a]	
Number of Drinks[b]	Blood-Alcohol Level (percent by volume)	Behavior[c]
2	0.05	Mild sedation; tranquility
4	0.10	Lack of coordination
6	0.15	Obvious intoxication
10	0.30	Unconsciousness
20	0.50	Possible death

[a]Data are for a 70-kg (154-lb) moderate drinker.

[b]Rapidly consumed 30-mL (1-oz) shots of 90-proof whiskey, 360-mL (12-oz) bottles of beer, or 150-mL (5-oz) glasses of wine.

[c]An inexperienced drinker would be affected more strongly, or more quickly, than someone who is ordinarily a moderate drinker. Conversely, an experienced heavy drinker would be affected less.

Gasoline in many parts of the United States contains up to 10% ethanol that is produced by fermentation. Because the United States has a large corn (maize) surplus, there is a generous government subsidy for gasoline producers who use ethanol made this way. As a result, many factories now make ethanol by fermentation of corn.

Toxicity of Alcohols

Although ethanol is an ingredient in wine, beer, and other alcoholic beverages, alcohols in general are rather toxic. Methanol, for example, is oxidized in the body to formaldehyde (HCHO). Drinking as little as 1 oz (about 30 mL or 2 tablespoonfuls) can cause blindness and even death. Several poisonings each year result when people mistake methanol for the less toxic ethanol.

Ethanol is not as poisonous as methanol, but it is still toxic. About 50,000 cases of ethanol poisoning are reported each year in the United States, and dozens of people die of acute ethanol poisoning.

Generally, ethanol acts as a mild depressant; it slows down both physical and mental activity. Table 6 lists the effects of various doses. Although ethanol generally is a depressant, small amounts of it seem to act as a stimulant, perhaps by relaxing tensions and relieving inhibitions.

Ingesting too much ethanol over a long period of time can alter brain-cell function, cause nerve damage, and shorten life span by contributing to diseases of the liver, cardiovascular system, and practically every other organ of the body. In addition, about half of fatal automobile accidents involve at least one drinking driver. Babies born to alcoholic mothers often are small, deformed, and mentally retarded. Some investigators believe that this *fetal alcohol syndrome* can occur even if mothers drink only moderately. Ethanol, is by far the most abused drug in the United States.

Rubbing alcohol is a 70% solution of isopropyl alcohol. Because isopropyl alcohol is also more toxic than ethanol, it is not surprising that people become ill, and sometimes die, after drinking rubbing alcohol.

Multifunctional Alcohols

Several alcohols have more than one hydroxyl group. Examples are ethylene glycol, propylene glycol, and glycerol.

The *proof* of an alcoholic beverage is twice the percentage of alcohol by volume. The term originated in a seventeenth-century English method for testing whiskey to ensure that a dealer was not increasing profits by adding water to the booze. A qualitative test was to pour some of the whiskey on gunpowder and ignite it. Ignition of the gunpowder after the alcohol had burned away was considered "proof" that the whiskey did not contain too much water.

Pearson Education/Eric Schrader

▲ Warning labels on alcoholic beverages alert consumers to the hazards of consumption.

Ethylene glycol

Propylene glycol

Glycerol

Ethylene glycol is the main ingredient in many permanent antifreeze mixtures. Its high boiling point keeps it from boiling away in automobile radiators. Ethylene glycol is a syrupy liquid with a sweet taste, but it is quite toxic. It is oxidized in the liver to oxalic acid.

$$\underset{\text{Ethylene glycol}}{\overset{\overset{\displaystyle OH \quad\ OH}{|\qquad |}}{CH_2—CH_2}} \xrightarrow{\text{liver enzymes}} \underset{\substack{\text{Oxalic acid}\\(\text{toxic})}}{\overset{\overset{\displaystyle O \quad\ O}{\ \ ||\quad ||}}{HO—C—C—OH}}$$

Oxalic acid forms crystals of its calcium salt, calcium oxalate (CaC_2O_4), which can damage the kidneys, leading to kidney failure and death. Propylene glycol, a high-boiling substance that is not poisonous, is now marketed as a safer permanent anti-freeze.

Glycerol (or glycerin) is a sweet, syrupy liquid that is a by-product from fats during soap manufacture. It is used in lotions to keep the skin soft and as a food additive to keep cakes moist. Its reaction with nitric acid makes nitroglycerin, the explosive material in dynamite. Nitroglycerin is also important as a vasodilator, a medication taken by heart patients to relieve angina pain.

▲ It DOES Matter!
Antifreeze containing ethylene glycol should always be drained into a container and disposed of properly. Pets have been known to die from licking the sweet, but toxic, ethylene glycol mixture from a driveway or open container.

Example 5   Structural Formulas of Alcohols

Write the structural formula for *tert*-butyl alcohol, sometimes used as an octane booster in gasoline.

Solution
An alcohol consists of an alkyl group joined to a hydroxyl group. From Table 5, we see that the *tert*-butyl group is

$$\underset{}{\overset{\overset{\displaystyle CH_3}{|}}{CH_3—\underset{\underset{\displaystyle CH_3}{|}}{C}—}}$$

Connecting this group to an OH group gives *tert*-butyl alcohol.

$$\underset{}{\overset{\overset{\displaystyle CH_3}{|}}{CH_3—\underset{\underset{\displaystyle CH_3}{|}}{C}—OH}}$$

■ **EXERCISE 5**
Write the structural formulas for **(a)** butyl alcohol and **(b)** *sec*-butyl alcohol.

4. Why do some mouthwashes taste "medicine-y"? Some mouthwashes and sore-throat remedies contain certain phenols, which often have what might be termed a "hospital" odor and a medicinal taste.

Phenols

When a hydroxyl group is attached to a benzene ring, the compound is called a **phenol**. Although a phenol may appear to be an alcohol, it is not. The benzene ring greatly alters the properties of the hydroxyl group. Unlike alcohols, phenol is a weak acid (sometimes called *carbolic acid*), and it is quite poisonous compared to most simple alcohols.

Phenol

Phenol was the first antiseptic used in an operating room—by Joseph Lister in 1867. Up until that time, surgery was not antiseptic, and many patients died from infections following surgical operations. Although phenol has a strong germicidal action, it is far from an ideal antiseptic because it causes severe skin burns and kills healthy cells along with harmful microorganisms.

Phenol is still sometimes employed as a disinfectant for floors and furniture, but other phenolic compounds are now used as antiseptics. Hexylresorcinol, for example, is a more powerful germicide than phenol, and it is less damaging to the skin and has fewer other side effects.

Ethers

Compounds with two alkyl or aromatic groups attached to the same oxygen atom are called **ethers**. The general formula is ROR (or ROR' because the alkyl groups need not be alike). The best-known ether is *diethyl ether* ($CH_3CH_2OCH_2CH_3$), often called simply *ether*.

Diethyl ether was once used as an anesthetic but is now used mainly as a solvent. It dissolves many organic substances that are insoluble in water. It boils at 36 °C, which means that it evaporates readily, making it easy to recover dissolved materials. Although diethyl ether has little chemical reactivity, it is highly flammable. Great care must be taken to avoid sparks or flames when it is in use.

Another problem with ethers is that they can react slowly with oxygen to form unstable peroxides, which may decompose explosively. Beware of previously opened containers of ether, especially old ones.

The ether produced in the largest amount commercially is a cyclic compound called *ethylene oxide*. Its two carbon atoms and one oxygen atom form a three-membered ring. Ethylene oxide is a toxic gas, used mainly to make ethylene glycol.

$$H_2C\overset{\displaystyle|}{-}CH_2 \;+\; H_2O \;\xrightarrow{H^+}\; \underset{\overset{|}{OH}}{CH_2}-\underset{\overset{|}{OH}}{CH_2}$$

Ethylene oxide   Water   Ethylene glycol

Ethylene oxide is also used to sterilize medical instruments and as an intermediate in the synthesis of some detergents. Most of the ethylene glycol produced is used in making polyester fibers and antifreeze.

Hexylresorcinol

▲ Phenolic compounds help to ensure antiseptic conditions in hospital operating rooms.

Diethyl ether was introduced in 1842 as a general anesthetic for surgery and was once the most widely used anesthetic. It is rarely used for humans today because it has undesirable side effects, such as postanesthetic nausea and vomiting.

Like cyclic hydrocarbons, cyclic ethers can be represented by geometric shapes. Each corner of such a shape (except the O) stands for a C atom with enough H atoms attached to give the carbon four bonds. For example, ethylene oxide is represented as

CONCEPTUAL Example 6   Identifying Functional Groups

Classify each of the following as an alcohol, an ether, or a phenol.

HO—⟨◯⟩—Cl $CH_3CH_2OCH_3$ $\underset{\overset{|}{OH}}{CH_3CHCH_2CH_3}$

(a)   (b)   (c)

⟨◯⟩—CH_2OH ⬠O

(d)   (e)

Solution

a. The OH functional group, is attached directly to the benzene ring; the compound is a phenol.

b. The O atom is between two alkyl groups; the compound is an ether.

   c. The OH group is attached to an alkyl group; the compound is an alcohol.

   d. The compound is an alcohol; the OH is not attached directly to the benzene ring.

   e. The compound is an ether; the O atom is between two C atoms.

■ EXERCISE 6

Classify each of the following as an alcohol, an ether, or a phenol.

$$CH_3CH_2CHOH$$
$$|$$
$$CH_3$$

(a)

$$CH_3O - \bigcirc$$

(b)

$$CH_3CH_2CHOCH_3$$
$$|$$
$$CH_3$$

(c)

$$HO - \bigcirc$$
$$Br$$

(d)

(e)

Example 7   Formulas for Ethers

What is the formula for isopropyl methyl ether?

Solution

Isopropyl methyl ether has an oxygen atom joined to an isopropyl group (three carbons joined to oxygen by the middle carbon) and a methyl group. The formula is

$$CH_3CHOCH_3 \quad \boxed{\text{Methyl group}}$$
$$\boxed{\text{Isopropyl group}} \quad CH_3$$

■ EXERCISE 7

Write formulas for **(a)** methyl propyl ether and **(b)** ethyl *tert*-butyl ether.

Self-Assessment Questions

1. Which of the following formulas represents an alcohol?
   a. $CH_3CHOHCH_2CH_3$ **b.** CH_3COCH_3
   c. CdOH   **d.** CH_3CHO

2. Which of the following alcohols has molecules with more than one hydroxyl group?
   a. 2-butanol   **b.** glycerol   **c.** 4-octanol   **d.** 3-pentanol

3. The formula for ethylene glycol is
   a. CH_3CH_2OH **b.** $CH_3CH(OH)_2$
   c. $C_3H_5(OH)_3$ **d.** $HOCH_2CH_2OH$

4. A structural formula that has a hydroxyl (OH) group attached to a benzene ring represents a(n)
   a. alcohol   **b.** ether   **c.** hexanol   **d.** phenol

5. An important use of phenols is as
   a. anesthetics   **b.** antiseptics   **c.** flavors   **d.** solvents

6. The general formula R—O—R′ represents a(n)
   a. ester   **b.** ether   **c.** ketone   **d.** phenol

7. The formula $CH_3CH_2OCH_2CH_3$ represents
   a. 2-butanol   **b.** 2-butanone   **c.** butyraldehyde   **d.** diethyl ether

8. The formula for butyl ethyl ether is
   a. $CH_3CH_2OCH_2CH_3$ **b.** $CH_3OCH_2CH_2CH_3$
   c. $CH_3CH_2CH_2OCH_2CH_3$ **d.** $CH_3CH_2OCH_2CH_2CH_2CH_3$

9. The compound $CH_3CHOHCH_2CH_3$ is an isomer of
    a. $CH_3COCH_2CH_2CH_3$ **b.** $CH_3CH_2OCH_2CH_3$
    c. $CH_3COOCH_2CH_3$ **d.** $CH_3CH_2CH_2COOH$

Answers: 1, a; 2, b; 3, d; 4, d; 5, b; 6, b; 7, d; 8, d; 9, b

6 Aldehydes and Ketones

Learning Objective ❯ Name simple aldehydes and ketones, and list their important properties.

Two families of organic compounds that share the same functional group are **aldehydes** and **ketones**. Both types of compounds contain the **carbonyl group** (C=O), but aldehydes have at least one hydrogen atom attached to the carbonyl carbon, whereas ketones have two other carbon atoms joined to the carbonyl carbon.

A carbonyl group   An aldehyde   A ketone

To simplify typing, these structures are often written on one line with the C=O bond omitted.

—C(=O)— or —CO—   R—CH(=O) or R—CHO   R—C(=O)—R′ or R—CO—R′

A carbonyl group   An aldehyde   A ketone

Models of three familiar carbonyl compounds are shown in Figure 12.

Some Common Aldehydes

The simplest aldehyde is *formaldehyde* (HCHO). It is a gas at room temperature but is readily soluble in water. As a 40% solution called *formalin*, it is used as a preservative for biological specimens and in embalming fluid. Systematic names for aldehydes are based on those of alkanes, with the ending changed from *-e* to *-al*. Thus, by the IUPAC system, formaldehyde is named methanal. IUPAC names are seldom used for simple aldehydes because of possible confusion with the corresponding alcohols. For example, "methanal" is easily confused with "methanol," when spoken or (especially) when handwritten.

◀ **Figure 12** Ball-and-stick (a) and space-filling (b) models of formaldehyde (left), acetaldehyde (center), and acetone (right).

(a)

(b)

Formaldehyde is used in making certain plastics. It also is used to disinfect homes, ships, and warehouses. Commercially, formaldehyde is made by the oxidation of methanol. The same net reaction occurs in the human body when methanol is ingested and accounts for the high toxicity of that alcohol.

The next member of the homologous series of aldehydes is acetaldehyde (ethanal), formed by the oxidation of ethanol.

The next two members of the aldehyde series are propionaldehyde (propanal) and butyraldehyde (butanal). Both have strong, unpleasant odors. Benzaldehyde has an aldehyde group attached to a benzene ring. Also called (synthetic) oil of almond, benzaldehyde is used in perfumery, and is the flavor ingredient in maraschino cherries.

Some Common Ketones

The simplest ketone is *acetone*, made by the oxidation of isopropyl alcohol.

Acetone is a common solvent for such organic materials as fats, rubbers, plastics, and varnishes. It is also used in paint and varnish removers and is a major ingredient in some fingernail polish removers. By the IUPAC system, acetone is named propanone. The systematic names for ketones are based on those of alkanes, with the ending changed from -e to -one. When necessary, a number is used to indicate the location of the carbonyl group. For example, $CH_3CH_2COCH_2CH_2CH_3$ is 3-hexanone.

Two other familiar ketones are ethyl methyl ketone and isobutyl methyl ketone, which, like acetone, are frequently used as solvents.

CONCEPTUAL Example 8   Aldehyde or Ketone?

Identify each of the following compounds as an aldehyde or a ketone.

A ketone is a carbon chain
With a carbonyl inside.
If the carbonyl is on the end,
Then it's an aldehyde.

272

Solution

a. A hydrogen atom is attached to the carbonyl carbon atom; the compound is an aldehyde.

b. The carbonyl group is between two other (ring) carbon atoms; the compound is a ketone.

c. The compound is a ketone. (Remember that the corner of the hexagon stands for a carbon atom.)

■ EXERCISE 8
Identify each of the following compounds as an aldehyde or a ketone.

$$CH_3CH_2CH_2CCH_3$$

(a)   (b)   (c)

Self-Assessment Questions

1. The aldehyde functional group has a carbonyl group attached to
   a. an H atom   **b.** an N atom   **c.** an OH group   **d.** two other C atoms

2. The ketone functional group has a carbonyl group attached to
   a. an OH group   **b.** an OR group
   c. two other C atoms   **d.** two OR groups

3. The general formula R—CO—R' represents a(n)
   a. ester   **b.** ether   **c.** ketone   **d.** phenol

4. A name for $CH_3COCH_2CH_3$ is
   a. 2-butanal   **b.** ethyl methyl ether
   c. ethyl methyl ketone   **d.** 2-propanone

5. A name for $CH_3CH_2CH_2CHO$ is
   a. 1-butanone   **b.** butyraldehyde   **c.** propanone   **d.** propylaldehyde

6. Which alcohol is oxidized to produce formaldehyde?
   a. CH_3OH **b.** CH_3CH_2OH
   c. $CH_3CH_2CH_2OH$ **d.** $CH_3CHOHCH_3$

7. Which alcohol is oxidized to produce acetone?
   a. CH_3OH **b.** CH_3CH_2OH
   c. $CH_3CH_2CH_2OH$ **d.** $CH_3CHOHCH_3$

Answers: 1, a; 2, c; 3, c; 4, c; 5, b; 6, a; 7, d

7 Carboxylic Acids and Esters

Learning Objective ＞ Name simple carboxylic acids and esters, and list their important properties.

Carboxylic Acids

The functional group of organic acids is called the **carboxyl group**, and the acids are called **carboxylic acids**.

A carboxyl group   A carboxylic acid

As with aldehydes and ketones, these formulas are often written on one line:

$$-\text{C}(=\text{O})\text{OH} \text{ or } -\text{COOH} \qquad \text{R}-\text{C}(=\text{O})\text{OH} \text{ or } \text{R}-\text{COOH}$$

A carboxyl group   A carboxylic acid

The simplest carboxylic acid is formic acid (HCOOH). The systematic (IUPAC) names for carboxylic acids are based on those of alkanes, with the ending changed from *-e* to *-oic acid*. For example, the IUPAC name for formic acid is methanoic acid, and $CH_3CH_2CH_2CH_2COOH$ is pentanoic acid.

Formic acid was first obtained by the destructive distillation of ants (the Latin word *formica* means "ant"). It smarts when an ant bites because the ant injects formic acid into the skin. The stings of wasps and bees also contain formic acid (as well as other poisonous compounds).

Acetic acid (ethanoic acid, CH_3COOH) can be made by the aerobic fermentation of a mixture of cider and honey. This produces a solution (vinegar) containing about 4–10% acetic acid plus a number of other compounds that add flavor. Acetic acid is probably the most familiar weak acid used in academic and industrial chemistry laboratories.

The third member of the homologous series of acids, propionic acid (propanoic acid, CH_3CH_2COOH), is seldom encountered in everyday life. The fourth member is more familiar, at least by its odor. If you've ever smelled rancid butter, you know the odor of butyric acid (butanoic acid, $CH_3CH_2CH_2COOH$). It is one of the most foul-smelling substances imaginable. Butyric acid can be isolated from butterfat or synthesized in the laboratory. It is one of the ingredients of body odor, and extremely small quantities of this acid and other chemicals enable bloodhounds to track lost people and fugitives.

The acid with a carboxyl group attached directly to a benzene ring is called *benzoic acid*.

▲ Acetic acid is a familiar weak acid in chemistry laboratories. It is also the principal active ingredient in vinegar.

Benzoic acid

Carboxylic acid salts—calcium propionate, sodium benzoate, and others—are widely used as food additives to prevent mold.

Example 9   Structural Formulas of Oxygen-Containing Organic Compounds

Write the structural formula for each of the following compounds.

  a. propionaldehyde   **b.** ethanoic acid   **c.** ethyl methyl ketone

Solution

  a. Propionaldehyde has three carbon atoms with an aldehyde function.

$$\text{C}-\text{C}-\overset{\overset{\textstyle O}{\|}}{\text{C}}-\text{H}$$

Adding the proper number of hydrogen atoms to the other two carbon atoms gives the structure

$$\text{H}-\overset{\overset{\textstyle H}{|}}{\underset{\underset{\textstyle H}{|}}{\text{C}}}-\overset{\overset{\textstyle H}{|}}{\underset{\underset{\textstyle H}{|}}{\text{C}}}-\overset{\overset{\textstyle O}{\|}}{\text{C}}-\text{H} \quad \text{ or } \quad CH_3CH_2CHO$$

b. Ethanoic acid has two carbon atoms with a carboxylic acid function.

$$\begin{array}{ccc} & H & O \\ & | & \| \\ H-&C-&C-OH \\ & | & \\ & H & \end{array} \quad \text{or} \quad CH_3COOH$$

c. Ethyl methyl ketone has a ketone function between an ethyl and a methyl group.

$$\begin{array}{cccc} H & H & O & H \\ | & | & \| & | \\ H-C-&C-&C-&C-H \\ | & | & & | \\ H & H & & H \end{array} \quad \text{or} \quad CH_3CH_2COCH_3$$

■ EXERCISE 9
Write the structural formula for each of the following compounds.
  a. butyric acid   **b.** acetaldehyde   **c.** diethyl ketone
  d. 3-octanone   **e.** heptanal   **f.** hexanoic acid

Esters: The Sweet Smell of RCOOR′

Esters are derived from carboxylic acids and alcohols or phenols. The general reaction involves splitting out a molecule of water.

$$\begin{array}{ccccccc} & O & & & & O & \\ & \| & & & H^+ & \| & \\ R-&C-&OH & + & R'OH & \rightleftharpoons & R-C-OR' & + & HOH \end{array}$$

An acid   An alcohol   An ester

The name of an ester ends in *-ate* and is formed by naming the part from the alcohol first and the part from the carboxylic acid last. For example, the ester derived from butyric acid and methyl alcohol is methyl butyrate.

This four-carbon group is derived from butyric acid	This one-carbon group is derived from methyl alcohol

$$CH_3CH_2CH_2COOCH_3$$

Although carboxylic acids often have strongly unpleasant odors, the esters derived from them are usually quite fragrant, especially when dilute. Many esters have fruity odors and tastes. Some examples are given in Table 7. Esters are widely used as flavorings in cakes, candies, and other foods and as ingredients in perfumes.

5. Why does fresh fruit smell so good and rotting fruit so bad? Esters are often the main components of fruity flavors. When fruit is broken down by bacteria, the esters are often broken down into their corresponding alcohols and (unpleasant!) carboxylic acids.

Table 7   Ester Flavors and Fragrances

Ester	Formula	Flavor/Fragrance
Methyl butyrate	$CH_3CH_2CH_2COOCH_3$	Apple
Ethyl butyrate	$CH_3CH_2CH_2COOCH_2CH_3$	Pineapple
Propyl acetate	$CH_3COOCH_2CH_2CH_3$	Pear
Pentyl acetate	$CH_3COOCH_2CH_2CH_2CH_2CH_3$	Banana
Pentyl butyrate	$CH_3CH_2CH_2COOCH_2CH_2CH_2CH_2CH_3$	Apricot
Octyl acetate	$CH_3COOCH_2CH_2CH_2CH_2CH_2CH_2CH_2CH_3$	Orange
Methyl benzoate	$C_6H_5COOCH_3$	Ripe kiwifruit
Ethyl formate	$HCOOCH_2CH_3$	Rum
Methyl salicylate	$o\text{-}HOC_6H_4COOCH_3$	Wintergreen
Benzyl acetate	$CH_3COOCH_2C_6H_5$	Jasmine

GREEN CHEMISTRY

Thomas E. Goodwin, *Hendrix College*

The Art of Organic Synthesis: Green Chemists Find a Better Way

At one time or another, most of us have taken medicines purchased over the counter or obtained by prescription. Many of these are synthetic drugs prepared by an organic chemist at a pharmaceutical company or in a research lab at a college or university, not compounds that occur in nature. These drugs are synthesized via chemical transformations that make more complicated organic compounds from simpler ones.

Chemical reactions generally proceed faster when collision probabilities for reacting molecules are high, as they are in heated, homogeneous solutions. In the past, many reactions were carried out in nonrenewable, petroleum-based solvents such as hydrocarbons, chlorinated hydrocarbons, esters, ketones, and ethers (Sections 1, 3, and 5–7). These solvents are often flammable, toxic, or both and present serious disposal problems. Using the Twelve Principles of Green Chemistry (inside front cover), chemists are now replacing these solvents with greener alternatives—or using no solvent at all. They also are seeking to improve the efficiency of reactions by reducing energy, time, and chemical quantities.

An increasing number of chemical reactions are run successfully in the absence of a solvent but more often in solvents from renewable resources in place of petrochemicals (Principle 5). Aqueous media have become popular because water is an ideal green solvent: cheap, abundant, and safe.

Unfortunately, many organic compounds have little solubility in water. Solutions normally form readily when intermolecular forces in the solvent and solute are of similar strength. Most organic compounds have relatively weak dispersion and dipole–dipole intermolecular forces, whereas water molecules are held together by a strong network of hydrogen bonds. Therefore, water molecules tend to stay associated with one another rather than exchanging some of their hydrogen bonds for weaker attractions to the nonpolar organic solutes.

Homogeneity is not always required, however. K. B. Sharpless (2001 Nobel Laureate) and his colleagues developed procedures in which the reactants are simply floated on water. In these "on water" reactions, rapid stirring produces suspensions of reactants with large surface contact areas that enhance reaction rates. Green benefits include reduced use of organic solvents, faster reaction times, and simplified isolation of hydrophobic products.

Green organic chemistry is also demonstrated in the Pfizer pharmaceutical company's improved route to the antidepressant sertraline (Zoloft®). Four solvents (toluene, tetrahydrofuran, dichloromethane, and hexane) were replaced with ethanol (Section 5). In addition, overall solvent use was reduced from 60,000 gallons to 6,000 gallons per ton of sertra-

line. Pfizer received a Presidential Green Chemistry Challenge Award in 2002 for its improvements.

Another green organic synthesis was developed by Dow Chemical Company to prepare the high-volume commercial chemical epichlorohydrin. Although the compound itself is hazardous, its value in the production of epoxies, paints, and resins has led to a green chemistry focus on improving its synthesis. The traditional synthesis used a petrochemical reactant and only incorporated one-fourth of the Cl atoms used. The Dow process utilizes glycerol, a by-product from the production of biodiesel, to produce epichlorohydrin under solventless reaction conditions. This process prevents the generation of waste and turns a waste material into a valuable product.

Green chemistry can also use microwaves to speed up reactions and reduce energy consumption. Microwaves are a form of electromagnetic radiation and are more energetic than radio waves but less energetic than X-rays. In kitchen microwave ovens, the targets for microwave energy are the water, sugar, and fat molecules in food. Although home microwave ovens must not be used to carry out chemical reactions due to potential dangers, specially designed microwave ovens are available for laboratory use.

Organic chemists today are actively designing ways to use greener solvents, renewable starting materials, and more energy-efficient techniques. These green chemistry innovations will provide sustainable solutions for us and for future generations.

▲ Proper application of green chemistry principles in the synthesis of Sertraline reduced the amount of solvents used by almost 90 percent!

Salicylates: Pain Relievers Based on Salicylic Acid

Salicylic acid is both a carboxylic acid and a phenol. We can use it to illustrate some of the reactions of these two families of compounds.

Salicylic acid

Since ancient times, various peoples around the world have used willow bark to treat fevers. Edward Stone, an English clergyman, reported to the Royal Society in 1763 that an extract of willow bark was useful in reducing fever.

Salicylic acid was first isolated from willow bark in 1838. It was first prepared synthetically in 1860 and soon was used in medicine as an *antipyretic* (fever reducer) and as an *analgesic* (pain reliever). However, it is sour and irritating when taken orally. Chemists sought to use chemical reactions to modify its structure so that these undesirable properties would be reduced while retaining or even enhancing its desirable properties. These reactions are summarized in Figure 13. The first such modification was simply to neutralize the acid (Reaction 1 in Figure 13). The resulting salt, sodium salicylate, was first used in

1875. It was less unpleasant to swallow than the acid but was still highly irritating to the stomach.

By 1886, chemists had produced another derivative (Reaction 2), the phenyl ester of salicylic acid, called *phenyl salicylate*, or *salol*. Salol was less unpleasant to swallow, and it passed largely unchanged through the stomach. In the small intestine, salol was converted to the desired salicylic acid, but phenol was formed as a by-product. A large dose could produce phenol poisoning.

Acetylsalicylic acid, an ester formed when the phenol group of salicylic acid reacts with acetic acid, was first produced in 1853. It is usually made by reacting salicylic acid with acetic anhydride, the acid anhydride of acetic acid (Reaction 3). The German Bayer Company introduced acetylsalicylic acid as a medicine in 1899 under the trade name Aspirin. It soon became the best-selling drug in the world.

Another derivative, methyl salicylate, is made by reacting the carboxyl group of salicylic acid with methanol, producing a different ester (Reaction 4). Methyl salicylate, called *oil of wintergreen*, is used as a flavoring agent and in rub-on analgesics. When applied to the skin, it causes a mild warming sensation, providing some relief for sore muscles.

▲ **Figure 13** Some reactions of salicylic acid. In Reactions 1, 2, and 4, salicylic acid reacts as a carboxylic acid; the reactions occur at the carboxyl group. In Reaction 3, salicylic acid reacts as a phenol; the reaction takes place at the hydroxyl group.

Q: *Can you identify and name the functional groups present in (a) salicylic acid, (b) methyl salicylate, (c) acetylsalicylic acid, and (d) phenyl salicylate?*

Self-Assessment Questions

1. Which of the following formulas represents a carboxylic acid?
   a. $CH_3CH_2CH_2OH$
   b. CH_3CH_2COOH
   c. CH_3COOCH_3
   d. $CH_3CH_2CH_2CHO$

2. Which of the following is the formula for butanoic acid?
   a. CH_3CH_2COOH
   b. $CH_3CH_2CH_2CH_2OH$
   c. $CH_3CH_2CH_2CHO$
   d. $CH_3CH_2CH_2COOH$

3. The carboxylic acid that has a —COOH group attached to a benzene ring is
   a. benzoic acid
   b. benzylic acid
   c. phenol
   d. phenolic acid

4. Alcohols can be oxidized with hot copper oxide to form carboxylic acids. If the alcohol is ethanol, the carboxylic acid will be
   a. CH_3COOH
   b. CH_3CH_2OH
   c. $CH_3CH_2CH_2OH$
   d. CH_3CH_2COOH

5. The general formula for an ester is
   a. ROR'
   b. RCOR'
   c. RCOOR'
   d. RCONHR'

6. A name for the compound with the formula $CH_3CH_2CH_2COOCH_2CH_3$ is
   a. ethyl propanoate
   b. ethyl butanoate
   c. methyl pentanoate
   d. propyl propanoate

7. A name for the compound with the formula $CH_3CH_2COOCH_3$ is
   a. ethyl acetate
   b. ethyl propanoate
   c. methyl pentanoate
   d. methyl propanoate

Answers: 1, b; 2, d; 3, a; 4, a; 5, c; 6, b; 7, d

8 Nitrogen-Containing Compounds: Amines and Amides

Learning Objectives › Name and write formulas for simple amines and amides.
› Recognize a structure as that of a heterocyclic compound.

Many organic substances of interest to us in the chapter that follow contain nitrogen, which is the fourth most common element in organic compounds after carbon, hydrogen, and oxygen. The two nitrogen-containing functional groups that we consider in this section, amines and amides, provide a vital background for the material ahead.

Amines

Amines contain the elements carbon, hydrogen, and nitrogen. An **amine** is derived from ammonia by replacing one, two, or three of the hydrogen atoms by one, two, or three alkyl or aromatic groups:

$$H-\underset{\underset{H}{|}}{N}-H \qquad R-\underset{\underset{H}{|}}{N}-H \qquad R-\underset{\underset{R'}{|}}{N}-H \qquad R-\underset{\underset{R'}{|}}{N}-R''$$

Ammonia   Amines

The simplest amine is methylamine (CH_3NH_2). Amines with two or more carbon atoms can be isomers: Both ethylamine ($CH_3CH_2NH_2$) and dimethylamine (CH_3NHCH_3) have the molecular formula C_2H_7N. With three carbon atoms, there are several possibilities, including trimethylamine $[(CH_3)_3N]$.

CONCEPTUAL Example 10 Amine Isomers: Structures and Names

Write structural formulas and names for the other three-carbon amines.

Solution
Three carbon atoms can be in one alkyl group, and there are two such propyl groups.

$$CH_3CH_2CH_2NH_2 \qquad CH_3CHCH_3$$
$$\underset{NH_2}{|}$$

Propylamine   Isopropylamine

Three carbon atoms can also be split into one methyl group and one ethyl group.

$$CH_3CH_2NHCH_3$$

Ethylmethylamine

■ EXERCISE 10

Write structural formulas for the following amines.
  a. butylamine
  b. diethylamine
  c. methylpropylamine
  d. isopropylmethylamine

The amine with an $-NH_2$ group (called an **amino group**) attached directly to a benzene ring has the special name *aniline*. Like many other aromatic amines, aniline is used in making dyes. Aromatic amines tend to be toxic, and some are strongly carcinogenic.

Simple amines are similar to ammonia in odor, basicity, and other properties. The larger and aromatic amines are more interesting. Figure 14 shows a variety of these.

Aniline

6. Why do dead animals smell so bad? Most amines have unpleasant odors, and many of the compounds formed when animal matter breaks down—such as putrescine and cadaverine—are amines.

Amphetamine

1,6-Hexanediamine

Cadaverine

Pyridoxamine

◄ **Figure 14** Some amines of interest. Amphetamine is a stimulant drug. Cadaverine has the odor of decaying flesh. 1,6-Hexanediamine is used in the synthesis of nylon. Pyridoxamine is a B vitamin.

Q: *1,6-Hexanediamine is the IUPAC name for a compound also known by the common name hexamethylenediamine. Cadaverine is a common name. What is the IUPAC name for cadaverine?*

Among the most important kinds of organic molecules are *amino acids*. As the name implies, these compounds have both amine and carboxylic acid functional groups. Amino acids are the building blocks of proteins. The simplest amino acid, H_2NCH_2COOH, is glycine.

Amides

Another important nitrogen-containing functional group is the **amide group**, which contains a nitrogen atom attached directly to a carbonyl group.

Amide group

Amides

Like those of other compounds that have $C=O$ groups, the formulas of amides are often written on one line.

$$RCONH_2 \quad RCONHR' \quad RCONR'R''$$

Note that urea (H_2NCONH_2), the compound that helped change the understanding of organic chemistry, is an amide.

Complex amides are of much greater interest than the simple ones considered here. Your body contains many kinds of proteins, all held together by amide linkages. Nylon, silk, and wool molecules also contain hundreds of amide functional groups.

Names for simple amides are derived from those of the corresponding carboxylic acids. For example, $HCONH_2$ is formamide (IUPAC name, methanamide), and CH_3CONH_2 is acetamide (IUPAC name, ethanamide). Alternatively, we can also view amide names as based on those of alkanes, with the ending changed from -e to -amide. For example, $CH_3CH_2CH_2CH_2CONH_2$ is pentanamide.

CONCEPTUAL Example 11   Amine or Amide?

Which of the following compounds are amides and which are amines? Identify the functional groups.

    a. $CH_3CH_2CH_2NH_2$ **b.** CH_3CONH_2

    c. $CH_3CH_2NHCH_3$ **d.** $CH_3COCH_2CH_2NH_2$

Solution

    a. An amine: NH_2 is an amine group; there is no $C{=}O$ group.

    b. An amide: $CONH_2$ is the amide functional group.

    c. An amine: NH is an amine functional group.

    d. An amine: NH_2 is an amine functional group; there is a $C{=}O$ group, but the NH_2 is not attached to it.

■ EXERCISE 11

Which of the following compounds are amides and which are amines? Identify the functional groups.

    a. CH_3NHCH_3 **b.** $CH_3CONHCH_3$

    c. $CH_3CH_2N(CH_3)_2$ **d.** $CH_3NHCH_2CONH_2$

Heterocyclic Compounds: Alkaloids and Others

Cyclic hydrocarbons feature rings of carbon atoms. Now let's look at some compounds that have atoms other than carbon within the ring. These **heterocyclic compounds** usually have one or more nitrogen, oxygen, or sulfur atoms.

CONCEPTUAL Example 12   Heterocyclic Compounds

Which of the following structures represent heterocyclic compounds?

       (a)   (b)   (c)   (d)

Solution

Compounds a, b, and d have an oxygen, a sulfur, and a nitrogen atom, respectively, in a ring structure; these are heterocyclic compounds.

■ EXERCISE 12

Which of the following structures represent heterocyclic compounds?

       (a)   (b)   (c)   (d)

Many amines, particularly heterocyclic ones, occur naturally in plants. Like other amines, these compounds are basic. They are called **alkaloids**, which means "like alkalis." Among the familiar alkaloids are morphine, caffeine, nicotine, and cocaine.

Other important heterocyclic amines are pyrimidine, which has two nitrogen atoms in a six-membered ring, and purine, which has four nitrogen atoms in two rings that share a common side. Compounds related to pyrimidine and purine are constituents of nucleic acids.

Pyrimidine   Purine

Self-Assessment Questions

1. A name for $CH_3CH_2CH_2CH_2NH_2$ is
   a. butanamide   **b.** butylamine   **c.** propanamide   **d.** propylamide

2. A name for $CH_3CH_2NHCH_3$ is
   a. butylamine   **b.** ethylmethylamine   **c.** propanamide   **d.** propylamine

3. A name for CH_3CONH_2 is
   a. acetamide   **b.** ethylamine   **c.** propanamide   **d.** propylamine

4. The amide functional group has a carbonyl group attached to
   a. an H atom.   **b.** an N atom   **c.** an OH group   **d.** two other C atoms

5. A cyclic organic compound that contains at least one atom that is not a carbon atom is called a(n)
   a. aromatic compound   **b.** cyclic amide
   c. heterocyclic compound   **d.** saturated compound

6. A basic organic heterocyclic compound that contains at least one nitrogen atom and is found in plants is called a(n)
   a. alkaloid   **b.** amide   **c.** cyclic ester   **d.** phenol

Answers: 1, b; 2, b; 3, a; 4, b; 5, c; 6, a

CRITICAL THINKING EXERCISES

Apply knowledge that you have gained in this chapter and one or more of the FLaReS principles to evaluate the following statements or claims.

1 A television advertisement claims that gasoline with added ethanol burns more cleanly than gasoline without added ethanol.

2 A news feature states that scientists have found that the odor of a certain ester improves workplace performance.

3 An environmental activist states that all toxic chemicals should be banned from the home.

4 An advertisement claims that calcium carbonate from oyster shells is superior to other forms of calcium carbonate because it contains a life force.

5 A Web page claims that acetylsalicylic acid (aspirin), polyester plastics, and polystyrene plastics are all carcinogens (cancer-causing agents). The reason given is that all three contain benzene rings in their structures, and benzene is a carcinogen.

6 A television program suggests that life on a distant planet could be based on silicon instead of carbon, because silicon (like carbon) tends to form four bonds. The narrator of the program proposes that long protein molecules and DNA molecules could be based on silicon chains.

SUMMARY

Section 1—Organic chemistry is the chemistry of carbon-containg compounds. More than 95% of all known compounds contain carbon. Carbon is unique in its ability to form long chains, rings, and branches. Hydrocarbons contain only carbon and hydrogen. One main class of hydrocarbons is aliphatic compounds. Alkanes are hydrocarbons that contain only single bonds; they have names ending in -ane. Alkanes are saturated hydrocarbons because each of their carbon atoms is bonded to the maximum number of hydrogen atoms. A structural formula shows which

atoms are bonded to one another. A condensed structural formula omits the C—H bond lines and is easier to write. A larger straight-chain alkane can be generated by inserting a CH_2 unit into a given straight-chain alkane. A homologous series of such compounds has properties that vary in a regular and predictable manner. A member of a homologous series is called a *homolog*.

Alkanes with more than three carbon atoms have isomers, compounds with the same molecular formula but different structures. Alkanes are nonpolar and insoluble in water. They undergo few chemical reactions and are used mainly as fuels.

Cyclic hydrocarbons have one or more closed rings. Geometric figures often are used to represent such cyclic compounds: for example, a triangle for cyclopropane and a hexagon for cyclohexane.

An alkene is a hydrocarbon with at least one carbon-carbon double bond. Ethylene ($CH_2=CH_2$) is the simplest alkene and the most important one commercially. It is used to make polyethylene plastic and ethylene glycol. An alkyne is a hydrocarbon with at least one carbon-to-carbon triple bond. Acetylene ($HC\equiv CH$), the simplest alkyne, is used in welding torches and as a starting material for other chemical products. Alkenes and alkynes are unsaturated hydrocarbons, to which more hydrogen atoms can be added. They undergo addition reactions in which hydrogen or another small molecule adds to the double or triple bond. They can also add to one another to form polymers.

Section 2—Benzene (C_6H_6) can be drawn as though it has three double bonds, but its ring of carbon atoms has six pairs of bonding electrons between the carbon atoms, plus six unassigned electrons spread over the ring. Benzene and similar compounds with this type of stable ring structure are called aromatic compounds. Substituted benzenes have one or more H atoms replaced by another atom or group called a substituent. Aromatic hydrocarbons are used as solvents and fuels and to make other aromatic compounds.

Section 3—Chlorinated hydrocarbons are derived from hydrocarbons by replacing one or more hydrogen atoms with chlorine atom(s). Chlorofluorocarbons (CFCs) contain both chlorine and fluorine. They are used as aerosol propellants and as refrigerants, but their use has been restricted because of their role in the depletion of the ozone layer. Perfluorinated compounds, in which all hydrogens have been replaced with fluorine, have important uses in plastics manufacture and in medicine.

Section 4—A functional group is an atom or group of atoms that confers characteristic properties to a family of organic compounds. Compounds with the same functional group undergo similar reactions and have similar properties. A functional group is often attached to an alkyl group (R—), an alkane with a hydrogen atom removed.

Section 5—A hydroxyl group (—OH) joined to an alkyl group produces an alcohol (ROH). Methanol (CH_3OH), ethanol (CH_3CH_2OH), and 2-propanol $[(CH_3)_2CHOH]$ are well-known and widely used alcohols. Alcohols with more than one —OH group include ethylene glycol, used in antifreeze, and glycerol, used in skin lotions and as a food additive.

A phenol is a compound with an —OH group attached to a benzene ring. Phenols are slightly acidic, and some are used as antiseptics.

An ether has two alkyl or aromatic groups attached to the same oxygen atom (ROR'). Ethers are used as solvents, and they can react slowly with oxygen to form explosive peroxides. Diethyl ether ($CH_3CH_2OCH_2CH_3$) is a commonly used solvent. Ethylene oxide is a cyclic ether used to make ethylene glycol and to sterilize instruments.

Section 6—An aldehyde contains a carbonyl group ($C=O$) with a hydrogen atom attached to the carbonyl carbon. A ketone has two carbon atoms attached to the carbonyl carbon. Formaldehyde is used in making plastics and as a preservative and a disinfectant. Benzaldehyde is a flavoring ingredient. Acetone, the simplest ketone, is a widely used solvent.

Section 7—A carboxylic acid has a carboxyl group (—COOH) as its functional group. Formic acid (HCOOH) is the acid in ant, bee, and wasp stings. Acetic acid (CH_3COOH) is the acid in vinegar. Butyric acid is the substance that gives rancid butter its odor. Carboxylic acid salts are used as food additives to prevent mold.

The structure of an ester (RCOOR') is similar to that of a carboxylic acid, with an alkyl group replacing the hydrogen atom of the carboxyl group. Esters are made by reaction of a carboxylic acid with an alcohol or phenol. They often have fruity or flowery odors and are used as flavorings and in perfumes.

Section 8—An amine is an organic derivative of ammonia in which one or more hydrogen atoms are replaced by alkyl or aromatic groups. Many amines consist of an alkyl group joined to an amino group (—NH_2). Like ammonia, amines are basic and often have strong odors. Amino acids, the building blocks of proteins, contain both amine and carboxylic acid functional groups. An amide group consists of a carbonyl group whose carbon atom is attached to a nitrogen atom. Proteins, nylon, silk, and wool contain amide groups.

A heterocyclic compound has one or more rings containing one or more nitrogen, sulfur, or oxygen atoms. Alkaloids are (usually heterocyclic) amines that occur naturally in plants and include morphine, caffeine, nicotine, and cocaine. Heterocyclic structures are constituents of DNA and RNA.

Green chemistry Organic chemistry plays an important role in enhancing the quality of human life, such as in the preparation of new life-saving drugs. Organic chemists are designing ways to use greener solvents, renewable starting materials, and more energy-efficient techniques.

Learning Objectives

> Define *hydrocarbon*, and recognize structural features of alkanes, alkenes, and alkynes.   Problems 17, 18, 20, 21, 53, 54

> Identify hydrocarbon molecules as alkanes, alkenes, or alkynes, and name them.   Problems 2, 17–26, 45, 46

> Define *aromatic compound*, and recognize the structural feature such compounds share.   Problems 5, 6

> Name simple aromatic hydrocarbons.   Problem 22

> Name a halogenated hydrocarbon given its formula, and write the formula for such a compound given its name.   Problem 52

> Classify an organic compound according to its functional group(s), and explain why the concept of a functional group is useful in the study of organic chemistry.   Problems 47–51, 62

Organic Chemistry

> Recognize and write the formulas of simple alkyl groups.   Problems 25, 26

> Recognize the general structure for an alcohol, a phenol, and an ether.   Problems 30, 48, 56, 61, 63

> Name simple alcohols, phenols, and ethers.   Problems 9, 27–32

> Name simple aldehydes and ketones, and list their important properties.   Problems 33, 34

> Name simple carboxylic acids and esters, and list their important properties.   Problems 12, 35–38

> Name and write the formulas of simple amines and amides.   Problems 39, 40

> Recognize a structure as that of a heterocyclic compound.   Problems 49, 50

> Identify greener solvents that can replace those from nonrenewable fossil fuels,   Problems 66–71
methods for incorporating renewable resources into organic synthesis, and efficient
energy sources for enhancing chemical reactions.

 REVIEW QUESTIONS

1. List three characteristics of the carbon atom that make possible the existence of millions of organic compounds.

2. Define or give an example for each of the following terms.
   a. hydrocarbon   b. alkyne
   c. alkane   d. alkene

3. What are isomers? How can you tell whether or not two compounds are isomers?

4. What is an unsaturated hydrocarbon? Give examples of two types of unsaturated hydrocarbons.

5. What is the meaning of the circle inside the hexagon in the modern representation of the structure of benzene?

6. What is an aromatic hydrocarbon? How can you recognize an aromatic compound from its structure?

7. Which alkanes are gases at room temperature? Which are liquids? Which are solids? State your answers in terms of the number of carbon atoms per molecule.

8. Compare the densities of liquid alkanes with that of water. If you added hexane to water in a beaker, what would you expect to observe?

9. What are the systematic names for the alcohols known by the following familiar names?
   a. grain alcohol   b. rubbing alcohol
   c. wood alcohol

10. What are some of the long-term effects of excessive ethanol consumption?

11. State an important historical use of diethyl ether. What is its main use today?

12. How do carboxylic acids and esters differ in odor? In chemical structure?

13. For what family is each of the following the general formula?
    a. ROH   b. RCOR′   c. RCOOR′
    d. ROR′   e. RCOOH   f. RCHO

14. What is an alkaloid? Name three common alkaloids.

 PROBLEMS

Organic and Inorganic Compounds

15. Which of the following compounds are organic?
    a. $CH_3CH_2SCH_2CH_3$ b. $F_3CCH_2CH_3$
    c. $HONH_2$ d. H_2SiCl_2

16. Which of the following compounds are organic?
    a. $C_8H_{18}O$ b. H_2CS
    c. OsO_4 d. $Co(NH_3)_6Cl_2$

Names and Formulas of Hydrocarbons

17. How many carbon atoms are there in a molecule of each of the following?
    a. hexane   b. decane
    c. cyclopentane d. 2-pentene

18. How many carbon atoms are there in a molecule of each of the following?
    a. ethane   b. 1-butyne
    c. propene   d. cyclooctane

19. The general formula for an alkane has been provided. Give the molecular formulas for the alkanes with (a) 9 carbon atoms and (b) 13 carbon atoms.

20. A particular alkyne has one triple bond and five carbon atoms. How many hydrogen atoms does it have?

21. Name the following hydrocarbons.
    a. $CH_3CH_2CH_2CH_3$ b. $H_2C{=}CH_2$
    c. $HC{\equiv}CH$

22. Name the following hydrocarbons.

    $CH_2{-}CH_2$
    $CH_2{-}CH_2$

    a.   b.   c.

23. Write the molecular formulas and condensed structural formulas for (a) pentane and (b) nonane.

24. Write the structural formulas for the four-carbon alkanes (C_4H_{10}). Identify butane and isobutane.

25. Name the following alkyl groups.
  a. CH_3-
  b. CH_3CH_2CH-
       $\quad\quad\quad\ \ |$
       $\quad\quad\quad\ CH_3$

26. Name the following alkyl groups.
  a. CH_3-CH-
       $\quad\quad\quad\ \ |$
       $\quad\quad\quad CH_3$
  b. CH_3-C-
       $\quad\quad CH_3$
       above: CH_3, below: CH_3

Names and Formulas: Alcohols and Phenols

27. Give a structure to match the name or a name to match the structure for each of the following compounds.
  a. CH_3OH
  b. $CH_3CH_2CH_2OH$
  c. ethanol
  d. 1-heptanol

28. Give a structure to match the name or a name to match the structure for each of the following compounds.
  a. $CH_3CH_2CHCH_3$
       $\quad\quad\quad\quad\ |$
       $\quad\quad\quad\quad OH$
  b. $CH_3CH_2CH_2CH_2CH_2CH_2OH$
  c. *sec*-butyl alcohol
  d. isobutyl alcohol

29. Phenols and other aromatic compounds are often named by numbering the carbon atoms of the benzene ring, starting with the carbon atom bounded to the major functional group. (In a phenol, this group is the $-OH$ group.) To illustrate, the structure in Exercise 6d is named 3-bromophenol. With this information, write the structures for **(a)** 2-methylphenol and **(b)** 4-iodophenol.

30. How do phenols differ from alcohols? How are they similar?

Names and Formulas: Ethers

31. Write the structure for each of the following.
  a. dipropyl ether
  b. butyl ethyl ether

32. Write the structure for **(a)** methyl propyl ether, an anesthetic known as Neothyl, and **(b)** dimethyl ether, used as a compressed gas to "freeze" warts from the skin. What alcohol is an isomer of dimethyl ether?

Names and Formulas: Aldehydes and Ketones

33. Give a structure to match the name or a name to match the formula of each of the following compounds.
  a. acetone
  b. formaldehyde
  c.
       $\quad\quad\quad\quad\quad O$
       $\quad\quad\quad\quad\quad \|$
       $CH_3CH_2CH_2C-H$
  d.
       $\quad\quad\quad\quad O$
       $\quad\quad\quad\quad \|$
       $CH_3CH_2-C-CH_2CH_2CH_2CH_3$

34. Give a structure to match the name or a name to match the formula of each of the following compounds.
  a. ethyl methyl ketone
  b. propionaldehyde
  c.
       $\quad\quad\quad\quad\quad O$
       $\quad\quad\quad\quad\quad \|$
       $CH_3CH_2-C-CH_2CH_3$
  d.
       $\quad\quad\quad O$
       $\quad\quad\quad \|$
       benzene ring $-C-H$

Names and Formulas: Carboxylic Acids

35. Give a structure to match the name or a name to match the structure for each of the following compounds.
  a. CH_3COOH
  b. $CH_3CH_2CH_2CH_2COOH$
  c. formic acid
  d. octanoic acid

36. Give a structure to match the name or a name to match the structure for each of the following compounds.
  a. CH_3CH_2COOH
  b. $CH_3CH_2CH_2CH_2CH_2COOH$
  c. butanoic acid
  d. chloroacetic acid [*Hint*: To what atom must the chlorine atom (chloro group) be attached?]

Names and Formulas: Esters

37. Give a structure to match the name or a name to match the structure for each of the following.
  a. ethyl acetate
  b. methyl butyrate
  c.
       $\quad\quad\quad\quad\quad O$
       $\quad\quad\quad\quad\quad \|$
       $CH_3CH_2COCH_2CH_3$

38. Give a structure to match the name or a name to match the structure for each of the following.
  a. ethyl butyrate
  b. methyl acetate
  c.
       $\quad\quad\quad O$
       $\quad\quad\quad \|$
       $H-C-OCH_2CH_2CH_2CH_3$

Names and Formulas: Nitrogen-Containing Compounds

39. Give a structural formula to match the name or a name to match the structure for each of the following.
  a. methylamine
  b. ethylmethylamine
  c. $CH_3CH_2CH_2NH_2$
  d. $CH_3CH_2NHCH_3$

40. Give a structural formula to match the name or a name to match the structure for each of the following.
  a. ethylamine
  b. isopropylamine
  c. $CH_3CH_2NHCH_2CH_3$
  d. benzene ring $-NH_2$

Organic Chemistry

Isomers and Homologs

41. Indicate whether the structures in each pair represent the same compound or isomers.

    a. CH_3CH_3 and $\underset{\displaystyle |}{\overset{\displaystyle CH_3}{}}CH_3$

    b. $\underset{\displaystyle |}{\overset{\displaystyle CH_3CH_2}{}}CH_3$ and $CH_3CH_2CH_3$

    c. $\underset{\displaystyle |}{\overset{\displaystyle CH_3CHCH_2CH_2CH_3}{}}CH_3$ and $\underset{\displaystyle |}{\overset{\displaystyle CH_3CH_2CHCH_2CH_3}{}}CH_3$

42. Indicate whether the structures in each pair represent the same compound or isomers.

    a. $\underset{\displaystyle |}{\overset{\displaystyle CH_3CHCH_2OH}{}}CH_3$ and $\underset{\displaystyle |}{\overset{\displaystyle CH_3CHCH_2CH_3}{}}OH$

    b. $\underset{\displaystyle |}{\overset{\displaystyle CH_3CHCH_2CH_3}{}}NH_2$ and $\underset{\displaystyle |}{\overset{\displaystyle CH_3CH_2CHNH_2}{}}CH_3$

43. Classify the following pairs as homologs, the same compound, isomers, or none of these.

    a. $CH_3CH_2CH_3$ and $CH_3CH_2CH_2CH_3$

    b. $\begin{array}{c} CH_2\!-\!CH_2 \\ \diagup \qquad \diagdown \\ CH_2 \qquad CH_2 \\ \diagdown \quad \diagup \\ CH_2 \end{array}$ and $CH_3CH_2CH_2CH_2CH_3$

44. Classify the following pairs as homologs, the same compound, isomers, or none of these.

    a. $\underset{\displaystyle |}{\overset{\displaystyle CH_3CHCH_2CH_2CH_3}{}}CH_3$ and $\underset{\displaystyle |}{\overset{\displaystyle CH_3CH_2CH_2CHCH_3}{\overset{\displaystyle CH_3}{}}}$

    b. $\underset{\displaystyle |}{\overset{\displaystyle CH_3CHCH=CH_2}{}}CH_3$ and $\begin{array}{c} CH_2\!-\!CH\!-\!CH_3 \\ |\qquad\quad | \\ CH_2\!-\!CH_2 \end{array}$

Classification of Hydrocarbons

45. Indicate whether each of the following compounds is saturated or unsaturated. Classify each as an alkane, alkene, or alkyne.

    a. $\underset{\displaystyle |}{\overset{\displaystyle CH_3C=CH_2}{}}CH_3$

    b. $CH_3-\underset{\displaystyle |}{\overset{\displaystyle CH_3}{\underset{\displaystyle CH_3}{C}}}-CH_3$

46. Indicate whether each of the following compounds is saturated or unsaturated. Classify each as an alkane, alkene, or alkyne.

    a. $CH_3-C\equiv C-CH_3$ **b.** ⬡

Functional Groups

47. Classify each of the following as an alcohol, amine, amide, ketone, aldehyde, ester, carboxylic acid, or ether. Identify the functional group in each.

    a. $CH_3CH_2\overset{\displaystyle O}{\overset{\displaystyle \|}{C}}OCH_3$

    b. $CH_3CH_2\overset{\displaystyle O}{\overset{\displaystyle \|}{C}}H$

    c. $CH_3CH_2CH_2NH_2$

    d. $CH_3CH_2OCH_3$

    e. $CH_3CH_2\overset{\displaystyle O}{\overset{\displaystyle \|}{C}}CH_2CH_3$

    f. $CH_3CH_2\overset{\displaystyle O}{\overset{\displaystyle \|}{C}}OH$

48. Classify each of the following as an alcohol, amine, amide, ketone, aldehyde, ester, carboxylic acid, or ether. Identify the functional group in each.

    a. $HCOOH$
    b. $CH_3CH_2COOCH_3$
    c. $CH_3CH_2CH_2CH_2OH$
    d. $CH_3CH_2CONHCH_2CH_2CH_3$
    e. $CH_3CH_2CH_2COOH$
    f. $HCOOCH_2CH_2CH_3$

49. Which of the following represents a heterocyclic compound? Classify each compound as an amine, ether, or cycloalkane.

50. Which of the following represents a heterocyclic compound? Classify each compound as an amine, ether, or cycloalkane.

    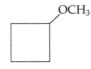

ADDITIONAL PROBLEMS

51. A molecular model of capsaicin, the compound primarily responsible for the "hotness" of jalapenos and other hot peppers, is shown on the chapter opener. The color code for the atoms is carbon (black), hydrogen (white), nitrogen (blue), and oxygen (red). What is the molecular formula of capsaicin? Name three functional groups of capsaicin.

52. Noting the following color code for atoms—carbon (black), hydrogen (white), oxygen (red), nitrogen (blue), and chlorine (green)—write the structural and molecular formulas for the compounds whose models are shown here.

a.

b.

c.

d.

e.

53. As noted, alkenes and alkynes can add hydrogen to form alkanes. These addition reactions, called *hydrogenations*, are carried out using H_2 gas and a catalyst such as nickel or platinum. Write equations, using condensed structural formulas, for the complete hydrogenation of each of the following.

a. $CH_3CH_2C \equiv CCH_3$

b. $$CH_3CH = CCH_2CH_2CH_2CH_3$$
$$|$$
$$CH_3$$

54. As exemplified by the reaction of ethylene, alkenes can add water to form alcohols. These addition reactions, called *hydrations*, are carried out using H_2O and an acid (H^+) as catalyst. Write an equation, using structural formulas, for the hydration of each of the following.

a.

b. $CH_3CH = CHCH_3$

55. As shown, alcohols can be oxidized to aldehydes and ketones. Write the structure of the alcohol that can be oxidized to each of the following.
a. $CH_3CH_2CH_2CHO$ b. $CH_3CH_2COCH_2CH_3$
c. $CH_3COCH(CH_3)_2$ d. C_6H_5CHO

56. Consider the following set of compounds. What concept does the set illustrate?
CH_3OH $\quad\quad\quad\quad$ CH_3CH_2OH
$CH_3CH_2CH_2OH$ $\quad$ $CH_3CH_2CH_2CH_2OH$

57. Consider the following set of compounds. What concept does the set illustrate?
$CH_3CH_2CH_2CH_2OH$ $\quad$ $CH_3CH_2OCH_2CH_3$
CH_3CHCH_2OH $\quad\quad\quad$ CH_3CHOCH_3
$|$ $\quad\quad\quad\quad\quad\quad\quad$ $|$
CH_3 $\quad\quad\quad\quad\quad\quad$ CH_3

58. Methanol is a possible replacement for gasoline. The complete combustion of methanol forms carbon dioxide and water.

$$CH_3OH + O_2 \longrightarrow CO_2 + H_2O$$

Balance the equation. What mass of carbon dioxide is formed by the complete combustion of 775 g of methanol?

59. Water adds to ethylene to form ethyl alcohol.

$$CH_2 = CH_2 + H_2O \xrightarrow{H^+} CH_3CH_2OH$$

Balance the equation. What mass of ethyl alcohol is formed by the addition reaction of water and 445 g of ethylene?

60. Referring to Table 7, give the name and condensed structural formula of (a) the alcohol and the carboxylic acid that would be needed to make pineapple flavoring and (b) the alcohol and the carboxylic acid that would be needed to make apricot flavoring.

61. Describe the type of intermolecular forces that exist (a) between dimethyl ether molecules and (b) between ethanol molecules. Use this information to explain why ethanol is a liquid at room temperature but dimethyl ether is a gas.

62. Diacetyl ($CH_3COCOCH_3$) is an additive used to impart buttery flavor to popcorn. Popcorn-factory workers exposed to high levels of diacetyl may develop a characteristic lung disease. What functional group is present in diacetyl?

63. Hydroquinone ($HO—C_6H_4—OH$), a phenol with two hydroxyl groups in the 1 and 4 (or *para*) positions on the ring, is commonly used as a developer in black and white photography. (a) Write the structural formula for hydroquinone. (*Hint:* See Figure 9.) (b) In the developing process, hydroquinone is oxidized to *para*-benzoquinone ($C_6H_4O_2$), a compound that is not aromatic and has two ketone functions. Write the structural formula for *para*-benzoquinone.

64. Using data from Table 3, a printed reference such as the *CRC Handbook* or the *Merck Index*, or an online source such as the Web site of the National Institutes for Standards and

Technology (NIST), state which of each pair of isomers boils at a lower temperature.

a. hexane or 2,3-dimethylbutane
b. pentane or neopentane (2,2-dimethylpropane)
c. heptane or 2,4-dimethylpentane
d. octane or 2,2,4-trimethylpentane

Use this information to form a generalization about the boiling points of branched-chain versus straight-chain alkanes.

65. Use the ideal gas law to determine the densities in grams per milliliter of the first four alkanes in Table 3 at 1.00 atm and 20.0 °C. (*Hint*: Begin with one mole of each gas.) Suggest a more appropriate unit for expressing these densities.

66. Give three reasons why water is often considered to be a green solvent for organic synthesis.

67. Which of the following is a potential drawback to using water as a solvent for organic synthesis?
a. Water is derived from fossil fuels.
b. Many organic molecules have limited solubility in water.

c. The intermolecular forces in water are similar to those in most organic solvents.
d. Reaction rates are always slower in water.

68. In an "on water" reaction:
a. Reactants are floated on water.
b. Rapid stirring leads to large surface contact areas.
c. Reactions often occur faster than if the reactants were dissolved in an organic solvent.
d. Insoluble products can be separated easily.
e. All of the above are true.

69. Identify two aspects of the new synthesis of sertraline that make it greener than the traditional process.

70. Give two examples of ways in which the improved synthesis of epichlorohydrin is more environmentally benign.

71. What advantage does microwave heating provide in carrying out chemical reactions? Why does it have this advantage?

COLLABORATIVE GROUP PROJECTS

Prepare a PowerPoint, poster, or other presentation (as directed by your instructor) to share with the class.

1. The theory that organic chemistry was the chemistry of living organisms, which was overturned by Wöhler's discovery in 1828, was known as *vitalism*. Search the Internet for information about this theory. What was the effect of this philosophy on areas outside chemistry?

2. Many organic molecules contain more than one functional group. Look up the structural formula for each of the following in this text (use the index), by searching online, or in a reference work such as the *Merck Index*. Identify and name the functional groups in each.
a. butesin   b. estrone   c. tyrosine
d. morphine   e. eugenol   f. methyl anthranilate

3. Prepare a brief report on one of the alcohols with three or more carbon atoms per molecule. List sources and commercial uses.

4. Prepare a brief report on one of the carboxylic acids with three or more carbon atoms per molecule. List sources and commercial uses.

5. Consider the series of compounds methane (CH_4), chloromethane (CH_3Cl), dichloromethane (CH_2Cl_2), trichloromethane ($CHCl_3$), and tetrachloromethane (CCl_4). Repeat parts (a) through (e) of Problem 49 for these compounds. Boiling points may be found in a printed reference such as the *CRC Handbook* or the *Merck Index* or on a Web site such as that of the National Institutes for Standards and Technology (NIST). Use intermolecular forces to explain any deviation in the relationship between molar mass and boiling point.

6. Referring to the graph from Problem 49, use the molar mass to estimate boiling points for (a) acetic acid (CH_3COOH), (b) acetone (CH_3COCH_3), (c) ethanol (CH_3CH_2OH), (d) hexane ($CH_3CH_2CH_2CH_2CH_2CH_3$), and (e) methyl acetate (CH_3COOCH_3). Compare the values obtained from the graph with the actual boiling points. Is molar mass alone a good predictor of boiling point? Explain.

BRIEF ANSWERS TO SELECTED PROBLEMS

Answers are provided for *all in-chapter exercises*. Brief answers are given for *odd-numbered Review Questions*; more complete answers can be obtained by reviewing the text. Answers are provided for *all odd-numbered Problems and Additional Problems*.

NOTE: For numerical problems, your answer may differ slightly from ours because of rounding and the use of significant figures.

1 **a.** molecular: C_6H_{14}; complete structural:

    condensed structural: $CH_3CH_2CH_2CH_2CH_2CH_3$

  b. molecular: C_8H_{18}; complete structural:

    condensed structural: $CH_3CH_2CH_2CH_2CH_2CH_2CH_2CH_3$

2 **A.**

    CH_2
   CH_2 CH_2
   CH_2 — CH_2

  B. C_nH_{2n}

3 **a.** C_6H_{12} **b.** C_7H_{12}

4 **a.** $CHCl_3$ **b.** CCl_4

5 **a.** $CH_3CH_2CH_2CH_2OH$

  b.

    H H H H
    | | | |
  H—C—C—C—C—H
    | | | |
    H H   H
          O—H

6 **a.** alcohol   **b.** ether
  c. ether   **d.** phenol
  e. ether

7 **A.** $CH_3OCH_2CH_2CH_3$ **B.** $CH_3CH_2OC(CH_3)_3$

8 **a.** ketone   **b.** aldehyde   **c.** aldehyde

9 **a.** $CH_3CH_2CH_2COOH$
  b. CH_3CHO
  c. $CH_3CH_2COCH_2CH_3$
  d. $CH_3CH_2COCH_2CH_2CH_2CH_2CH_3$
  e. $CH_3CH_2CH_2CH_2CH_2CH_2CHO$
  f. $CH_3CH_2CH_2CH_2CH_2COOH$

10 **a.** $CH_3CH_2CH_2CH_2NH_2$
  b. $CH_3CH_2NHCH_2CH_3$
  c. $CH_3NHCH_2CH_2CH_3$
  d. $(CH_3)_2CHNHCH_3$

11 **a.** amine (NH)   **b.** amide (CONH)
  c. amine (N)   **d.** both (NH and $CONH_2$)

12 heterocyclic compounds: (a) and (d)

1. Carbon atoms can bond strongly to each other; can bond strongly to other elements; can form chains, rings, and other kinds of structures.

3. Isomers have the same molecular formula but different structural formulas.

5. A set of six delocalized electrons

7. 1–4 C, gases; 5–16 C, liquids; >18 C, solids

9. **a.** ethanol   **b.** 2-propanol   **c.** methanol

11. Historical use: anesthetic; modern use: solvent

13. **a.** alcohol   **b.** ketone   **c.** ester
     d. ether   **e.** carboxylic acid   **f.** aldehyde

15. organic: a, b; inorganic: c, d

17. **a.** 6   **b.** 10   **c.** 5   **d.** 5

19. **a.** C_9H_{20} **b.** $C_{13}H_{28}$

21. **a.** butane   **b.** ethylene (ethene)   **c.** acetylene (ethyne)

23. **a.** C_5H_{12}; $CH_3CH_2CH_2CH_2CH_3$
     b. C_9H_{20}; $CH_3CH_2CH_2CH_2CH_2CH_2CH_2CH_2CH_3$

25. **a.** methyl   **b.** *sec*-butyl

27. **a.** methanol   **b.** propyl alcohol (1-propanol)
     c. CH_3CH_2OH
     d. $CH_3CH_2CH_2CH_2CH_2CH_2CH_2OH$

29.

    OH
    |
  (benzene ring)
    |
    CH_3 I—(benzene ring)—OH

31. **a.** $CH_3CH_2CH_2OCH_2CH_2CH_3$
     b. $CH_3CHOCH_2CH_2OCH_2CH_3$

33. **a.**
         O
         ‖
    CH_3—C—CH_3 **b.** HCHO
     c. butyraldehyde (butanal)
     d. butyl ethyl ketone (3-heptanone)

35. **a.** acetic acid (ethanoic acid)
     b. pentanoic acid
     c. HCOOH
     d. $CH_3CH_2CH_2CH_2CH_2CH_2CH_2COOH$

37. **a.** $CH_3COOCH_2CH_3$
     b. $CH_3CH_2CH_2COOCH_3$
     c. ethyl propionate (ethyl propanoate)

39. **a.** CH_3NH_2 **b.** $CH_3CH_2NHCH_3$
     c. propylamine   **d.** ethylmethylamine

41. same: a, b; isomers, c

43. **a.** homologs   **b.** none of these

45. **a.** unsaturated; alkene   **b.** saturated; alkane

47. **a.** ester   **b.** aldehyde   **c.** amine
     d. ether   **e.** ketone   **f.** carboxylic acid

49. **a.** heterocyclic, amine   **b.** not heterocyclic, amine

51. $C_{18}H_{27}NO_3$; ether, phenol, amide

53. **a.** $CH_3CH_2C{\equiv}CCH_3 + 2\,H_2 \xrightarrow{Ni} CH_3CH_2CH_2CH_2CH_3$
     b. $CH_3CH{=}C(CH_3)CH_2CH_2CH_2CH_3 + H_2 \xrightarrow{Ni}$
             $CH_3CH_2CH(CH_3)CH_2CH_2CH_2CH_3$

55. **a.** $CH_3CH_2CH_2CH_2OH$ **b.** $CH_3CH_2CH(OH)CH_2CH_3$
     c. $(CH_3)_2CHCH(OH)CH_3$ **d.** $C_6H_5CH_2OH$

57. isomerism

59. Equation is balanced as is. 731 g

61. **a.** dispersion and (weak) dipole-dipole
     b. hydrogen bonds. The stronger hydrogen bonds cause ethanol to remain a liquid at room temperature.

63.
  a. HO—(benzene ring)—OH   **b.** O=(ring)=O

65. **a.** 0.000655 g/mL
     b. 0.001250 g/mL
     c. 0.001830 g/mL
     d. 0.002410 g/mL. Grams per liter would be more appropriate.

67. b

69. Solvent is renewable and less toxic, and less solvent is used.

71. Less energy is used; molecules absorb energy directly so less energy is lost to the surroundings.

Polymers

From Chapter 10 of *Chemistry for Changing Times*, Thirteenth Edition. John W. Hill, Terry W. McCreary, Doris K. Kolb.

Learning Objectives

> Define *polymer* and *monomer*. (1)

> List several natural polymers including a chemically modified one. (1)

> Describe the structure and properties of the two main types of polyethylene. (2)

> Use the terms *thermoplastic* and *thermosetting* to explain how polymer structure determines properties. (2)

> Identify the monomer(s) of an addition polymer, and write the structural formula for a polymer from its monomer structure(s). (3)

> Define *cross-linking*, and explain how it changes the properties of a polymer. (4)

> Differentiate between addition and condensation polymerization. (5)

> Write the structures of the monomers that form polyesters and polyamides. (5)

> Understand the concept of the glass transition temperature. (6)

> Explain how crystallinity affects the physical properties of polymers. (6)

> Describe the environmental problems associated with plastics and plasticizers. (7)

> Name two types of sustainable, non-petroleum-derived polymers and give their sources. (7)

> Describe plastic recycling, biodegradation, and production from renewable resources.

Polymers

Have You Ever Wondered?

1. **Are all polymers synthetic?**

2. **Why is it important to recycle plastics?**

3. **Is it really dangerous to burn plastic plumbing pipe?**

4. **Is silicone the same thing as silicon?**

5. **How are permanent-press fabrics made?**

Giants Among Molecules

Look around you. Polymers are everywhere. Carpets, curtains, upholstery, towels, sheets, floor tile, books, furniture, most toys and containers (not to mention such things as telephones, toothbrushes, and piano keys), and even your clothes are made of polymers. Your car's dashboard, seats, tires, steering wheel, floor mats, and many parts that you cannot see are made of polymers. Much of the food you eat contains polymers, and many vital molecules in your body are polymers. You couldn't live without them. Some of the polymers that permeate our lives come from nature, but many are synthetic, made in chemical plants in an attempt to improve on nature in some way.

Plastics—synthetic polymers—are used in most consumer items, including bottles, telephones, calculators, computers, cooking utensils, wire insulation, sunglasses, pens, and most types of packaging. The source of most of these polymers is crude oil, of which there is a limited supply. This means that it is important to recycle these polymers when possible. The bales of plastics shown above are ready to go to the recycling center, where they may be used directly to make toys, pipes, or building materials. Or the recycled material may be converted to shreds or beads of plastic (left) that can be used by molding machines. In this chapter, we examine how polymers are made, review their useful properties, and explain why they have those properties.

1 Polymerization: Making Big Ones Out of Little Ones

Learning Objectives ❯ Define *polymer* and *monomer*. ❯ List several natural polymers including a chemically modified one.

Polymers are composed of *macromolecules* (from the Greek *makros*, meaning "large" or "long"). Macromolecules are not actually very large (in fact, most such "giant" molecules are invisible to the human eye), but compared to other molecules, they are enormous.

A **polymer** (from the Greek *poly*, meaning "many," and *meros*, meaning "part") is made from much smaller molecules called *monomers* (from the Greek *monos*, meaning "one"). Hundreds, even thousands, of monomer units combine to make one polymer molecule. A **monomer** is a small-molecule building block from which a polymer is made. The process by which monomers are converted to polymers is called *polymerization*. A polymer is as different from its monomer as a long strand of spaghetti is from tiny specks of flour. For example, polyethylene, the familiar waxy material used to make plastic bags, is made from the monomer ethylene, a gas.

Natural Polymers

Polymers have served humanity for centuries in the starches and proteins in our food, in the wood we use for shelter, and in the wool, cotton, and silk we make into clothing. Starch is a polymer made up of glucose ($C_6H_{12}O_6$, a simple sugar) units. Cotton is made of cellulose, also a glucose polymer; and wood is largely cellulose as well. Proteins are polymers made up of amino acid monomers. Wool and silk are two of the thousands of different kinds of proteins found in nature.

Living things could not exist without polymers. Each plant and animal requires many different specific types of polymers. Probably the most amazing natural polymers are nucleic acids, which carry the coded genetic information that makes each individual unique. In this chapter, we focus mainly on macromolecules made in the laboratory.

Celluloid: Billiard Balls and Collars

The oldest attempt to improve on natural polymers involved chemical modification of a common macromolecule. The semisynthetic material **celluloid**, as its name implies, was derived from natural cellulose (from cotton and wood, for example). When cellulose is treated with nitric acid, a derivative called *cellulose nitrate* is formed.

In response to a contest to find a substitute for ivory to use in billiard balls, American inventor John Wesley Hyatt (1837–1920) found a way to soften cellulose nitrate by treating it with ethyl alcohol and camphor. The softened material could be molded into smooth, hard balls. Thus, Hyatt brought the game of billiards within the economic reach of more people—and saved a number of elephants.

Celluloid was also used in movie film and for stiff shirt collars (which didn't require laundering and repeated starching). Because of its dangerous flammability (cellulose nitrate is also used as smokeless gunpowder), celluloid was removed from the market when safer substitutes became available. Today, movie film is made mainly from polyethylene terephthalate, a polyester (Section 5). And high, stiff collars on men's shirts are out of fashion.

It didn't take long for the chemical industry to recognize the potential of synthetics. Scientists found ways to make macromolecules from small molecules rather than simply modifying large ones. The first such truly synthetic polymers were phenol–formaldehyde resins (such as Bakelite), first made in 1909. These complex polymers are discussed in Section 5. We'll look at some simpler ones next.

Shutterstock

▲ Cotton is nearly pure cellulose, a natural polymer of the simple sugar glucose.

1. Are all polymers synthetic? The total weight of natural polymers on Earth's surface far exceeds the weight of synthetic polymers. Starches, proteins, cellulose, latex, DNA, and RNA all are natural polymers.

A century ago, celluloid was widely used as a substitute for more expensive substances such as ivory, amber, and tortoiseshell. The movie industry was once known as the "celluloid industry." The 1988 Oscar-winning Italian movie *Cinema Paradiso* shows the evolution of film technology and includes a tragic scene in which the heat from a bulb in the movie projector ignites a fire in a film that failed to wind properly through the machine.

Self-Assessment Questions

1. A long-chain protein molecule is an example of a(n)
   a. fat   **b.** isomer   **c.** monomer   **d.** polymer

2. Which is *not* a polymer?
   a. cellulose   **b.** glucose   **c.** silk   **d.** wool

3. The first semisynthetic polymer was actually made from a natural polymer. It was
   a. Bakelite, based on bacon grease
   b. celluloid, based on cellulose from cotton
   c. polypropylene, based on isopropyl alcohol
   d. polypantene, based on human hair

4. The first truly synthetic polymer was
   a. Bakelite, made from phenol and formaldehyde
   b. cellulose, made from glucose
   c. polyethylene, made from ethanol
   d. rubber, made from isoprene

Answers: 1, d; 2, b; 3, b; 4, a

2 Polyethylene: From the Battle of Britain to Bread Bags

Learning Objectives ❯ Describe the structure and properties of the two main types of polyethylene. ❯ Use the terms *thermoplastic* and *thermosetting* to explain how polymer structure determines properties.

The prevalent plastic *polyethylene* is the simplest and least expensive synthetic polymer. It is familiar to us in the form of plastic bags used for packaging fruit and vegetables, garment bags for dry-cleaned clothing, garbage-can liners, and many other items. Polyethylene is made from ethylene ($CH_2=CH_2$), an unsaturated hydrocarbon. Ethylene is produced in large quantities from the cracking of petroleum, a process by which large hydrocarbon molecules are broken down into simpler hydrocarbons.

With pressure and heat and in the presence of a catalyst, ethylene monomers join together in long chains.

The ellipses (···) and tildes (~) serve as *et ceteras*; they indicate, respectively, that the number of monomers is greater than the four shown and that the polymer structure extends for many more units in each direction.

$$\cdots+\overset{\displaystyle H \quad H}{\underset{\displaystyle H \quad H}{C=C}} + \overset{\displaystyle H \quad H}{\underset{\displaystyle H \quad H}{C=C}} + \overset{\displaystyle H \quad H}{\underset{\displaystyle H \quad H}{C=C}} + \overset{\displaystyle H \quad H}{\underset{\displaystyle H \quad H}{C=C}} + \cdots \longrightarrow {\sim}\overset{\displaystyle H \, H \, H \, H \, H \, H \, H \, H}{\underset{\displaystyle H \, H \, H \, H \, H \, H \, H \, H}{C-C-C-C-C-C-C-C}}{\sim}$$

Using condensed formulas, this becomes

$$\cdots + CH_2=CH_2 + CH_2=CH_2 + CH_2=CH_2 + CH_2=CH_2 + \cdots \longrightarrow {\sim}CH_2CH_2CH_2CH_2CH_2CH_2CH_2CH_2{\sim}$$

Such equations can be tedious to draw, so we often use abbreviated forms like these:

$$n\,\overset{\displaystyle H \quad H}{\underset{\displaystyle H \quad H}{C=C}} \longrightarrow \left[\overset{\displaystyle H \quad H}{\underset{\displaystyle H \quad H}{C-C}}\right]_n \quad \text{or} \quad n\,CH_2=CH_2 \longrightarrow {\Large[}CH_2CH_2{\Large]}_n$$

The molecular fragment within square brackets is called the *repeat unit* of the polymer. In the formula for the polymeric product, the repeat unit is placed within brackets with bonds extending to both sides. The subscript n indicates that this unit is repeated many times (n in the equation above) in the full polymer structure.

The simplicity of the abbreviated formulas facilitates certain comparisons between the monomer and the polymer. Note that the monomer ethylene contains a double bond and polyethylene does not. The double bond of the reactant consists of two shared pairs of electrons. One of these pairs is used to connect one monomer unit to the next in the polymer (indicated by the lines sticking out to the sides in the repeat unit). This leaves only a single pair of electrons—a single bond—between the two carbon atoms of the repeat unit. Note also that each repeat unit in the polymer has the same composition (C_2H_4) as the monomer.

Molecular models provide three-dimensional representations. Figure 1 presents models of a tiny part of a very long polyethylene molecule, whose number of carbon atoms can vary from a few hundred to several thousand.

(a)

◀ **Figure 1** Ball-and-stick (a) and space-filling (b) models of a short segment of a polyethylene molecule.

(b)

Richard Megna/Fundamental Photographs

2. Why is it important to recycle plastics?
Polyethylene and most other polymers are made of petroleum. Since our supply of petroleum is limited, we can make the best use of that resource by reusing those polymers. Most plastic items are imprinted with a code number so that they can be sorted for recycling.

Polyethylene was invented shortly before the start of World War II. It proved to be tough and flexible, excellent as an electric insulator, and able to withstand both high and low temperatures. Before long, it was used for insulating cables in radar equipment, a top-secret invention that helped British pilots detect enemy aircraft before the aircraft could be spotted visually. Without polyethylene, the British could not have had effective radar, and without radar, the Battle of Britain might have been lost. The invention of this simple plastic helped change the course of history.

Types of Polyethylene

Today, there are three main kinds of polyethylene. *High-density polyethylene* (*HDPE*) has mostly linear molecules that pack closely together and can assume a fairly well-ordered, crystalline structure. HDPEs therefore are rather rigid and have good tensile strength. As the name implies, the densities of HDPEs (0.94–0.96 g/cm^3) are high compared to those of other polyethylenes. HDPEs are used for such items as threaded bottle caps, toys, bottles, and milk jugs.

Low-density polyethylene (*LDPE*), on the other hand, has many side chains branching off the polymer molecules. The branches prevent the molecules from packing closely together and assuming a crystalline structure. LDPEs are waxy,

The Many Forms of Carbon

In many of the smaller molecules and the macromolecules that we encounter here, carbon atoms are bonded to other atoms, especially hydrogen. Carbon atoms alone can form a variety of interesting structures, however, some of which have been known since ancient times. Diamond is pure crystalline carbon, in which each atom is bonded to four other atoms. In graphite, the black material of pencil lead, each carbon atom is bonded to three others. But the most intriguing forms of carbon were discovered only in the last few decades.

Andre Geim and Konstantin Novoselov of the University of Manchester, United Kingdom, used adhesive tape to lift one-atom-thick planar sheets of carbon atoms from graphite. The material, called *graphene*, is like molecular-scale chicken wire made of carbon atoms. Graphene has properties that make it suitable for applications in electronics, sensing devices, and touch screens and for fundamental studies of electron flow in two-dimensional materials. Geim and Novoselov were awarded the 2010 Nobel Prize in Physics for their work on graphene.

Graphite is composed of many stacked graphene layers. A stack of three million graphene sheets would be only a millimeter thick. Graphene can also be thought of as an extremely large aromatic molecule, a system of fused benzene rings.

Many other structures are formed exclusively of carbon atoms. The tube-shaped carbon molecule called a *nanotube* can be visualized as a sheet of graphene rolled into a hollow cylinder. Nanotubes have unusual mechanical and electrical properties. They are good conductors of heat, and they are among the strongest and stiffest materials known.

Yet another structure consisting only of carbon is a roughly spherical collection of hexagons and pentagons like the pattern on a soccer ball. This carbon molecule has the formula C_{60}. Because it resembles the geodesic-dome structures pioneered by architect R. Buckminster Fuller, the molecule is called *buckminsterfullerene*. The general name *fullerenes* is used for C_{60} and similar molecules with formulas such as C_{70}, C_{74}, and C_{82}, which are often colloquially referred to as "buckyballs." These materials have enormous potential in basic studies as well as in applied research.

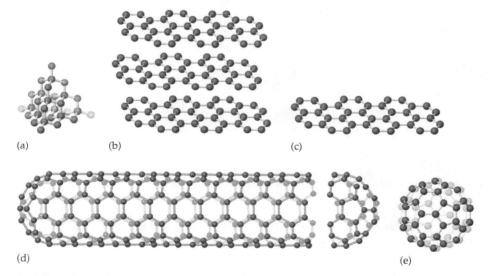

(a) (b) (c)

(d) (e)

▲ Different forms of carbon have dramatically different properties. (a) Diamond is hard and transparent. (b) Graphite is soft, gray, and conducts electricity. (c) Graphene is a single layer of graphite. (d) Rolling a sheet of graphene into a cylinder makes a carbon nanotube, the strongest material known. (e) Buckminsterfullerene, a C_{60} molecule, resembles a soccer ball.

Scientists estimate that plastic bags and other plastic trash thrown into the ocean kill as many as a million sea creatures each year.

bendable plastics that have lower densities ($0.91–0.94 \, \text{g/cm}^3$) and are lower melting than high-density polyethylenes. Objects made of HDPE hold their shape in boiling water, whereas those made of LDPE are severely deformed (Figure 2). LDPEs are used to make plastic bags, plastic film, squeeze bottles, electric wire insulation, and many common household products for which flexibility is important.

The third type of polyethylene, called *linear low-density polyethylene* (LLDPE), is actually a **copolymer**, a polymer formed from two (or more) different monomers. LLDPEs are made by polymerizing ethylene with a branched-chain alkene such as 4-methyl-1-pentene.

$$n\ CH_2{=}CH_2 + m\ CH_2{=}CH \longrightarrow \left[\!\!\!{-}CH_2{-}CH_2{-}\!\!\right]_{\!n}\!\left[\!CH_2{-}CH\!\right]_{\!m}$$

CH₂ ... CH₂
CH₃—CH—CH₃ ... CH₃—CH—CH₃

Ethylene   4-Methyl-1-pentene   An LLDPE

LLDPEs are used to make such things as plastic films for use as landfill liners, trash cans, tubing, and automotive parts.

Thermoplastic and Thermosetting Polymers

Polyethylene is one of a variety of thermoplastic polymers. Because its molecules can slide past one another when heat and pressure are applied, a **thermoplastic polymer** can be softened and then reshaped. It can be repeatedly melted down and remolded. Total annual production of thermoplastic polymers in the United States is about 40 billion kg, of which 17 billion kg is polyethylene.

Not all polymers can be readily melted. About 12% of U.S. production of polymers consists of *thermosetting polymers*, which harden permanently when formed. They cannot be softened by heat and remolded. Instead, strong heating causes them to discolor and decompose. The permanent hardness of thermosetting plastics is due to cross-linking (side-to-side connection) of the polymer chains, which we'll discuss later in this chapter.

Self-Assessment Questions

1. When addition polymers form, the monomer units are joined by
   a. delocalized electrons that flow along the polymer chain
   b. dispersion forces
   c. double bonds
   d. new bonds formed by electrons from the double bonds in the monomers

2. Compared to HDPE, LDPE has a lower melting point because it
   a. is made from less polar monomers
   b. is composed of molecules with a much lower molecular mass
   c. has fewer cross-links
   d. has more branches in its molecules, preventing them from packing closely

3. Which of the following is *not* made of polyethylene?
   a. electric wire insulation
   b. foamed coffee cups
   c. plastic grocery bags
   d. squeeze bottles

4. A copolymer is made
   a. by blending two simple polymers
   b. from cobalt and an alkene
   c. from two identical monomers
   d. from two different monomers

5. A polymer that cannot be melted and reshaped is said to be
   a. highly crystalline
   b. rubbery
   c. thermoplastic
   d. thermosetting

▲ **It DOES Matter!**
Polyethylene with a molecular mass from two to six million, called *ultra-high-molecular-weight polyethylene (UHMWPE)*, is used to make fibers 10 times stronger than steel and around 40% stronger than Kevlar (see Problem 30) for use in body armor. Most modern skis are coated with UHMWPE on the bottom surface.

About 180 billion kg of various plastics and 22 billion kg of rubber are manufactured globally each year.

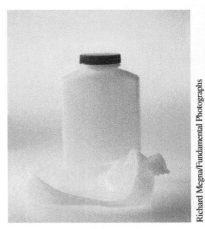

▲ **Figure 2** Two bottles, both made of polyethylene, were heated in the same oven for the same length of time.

Q: *Which of these bottles is made of HDPE and which of LDPE? Explain.*

3 Addition Polymerization: One + One + One + ··· Gives One!

Learning Objectives > Identify the monomer(s) of an addition polymer, and write the structural formula for a polymer from its monomer structure(s).

There are two general types of polymerization reactions: addition polymerization and condensation polymerization. In **addition polymerization** (also called *chain-reaction polymerization*), the monomer molecules add to one another in such a way that the polymeric product contains all the atoms of the starting monomers. The polymerization of ethylene to form polyethylene is an example. In polyethylene, as we noted in Section 2, the two carbon atoms and the four hydrogen atoms of each monomer molecule are incorporated into the polymer structure. In *condensation polymerization* (Section 5), some part of each monomer molecule is not incorporated in the final polymer.

Polypropylene

Most of the many familiar addition polymers are made from derivatives of ethylene in which one or more of the hydrogen atoms are replaced by another atom or group. Replacing one of the hydrogen atoms with a methyl group gives the monomer propylene (propene). Polypropylene molecules look much like polyethylene's molecules, except that there is a methyl group ($-CH_3$) attached to every other carbon atom.

$$\sim CH_2-\underset{\underset{CH_3}{|}}{CH}-CH_2-\underset{\underset{CH_3}{|}}{CH}-CH_2-\underset{\underset{CH_3}{|}}{CH}-CH_2-\underset{\underset{CH_3}{|}}{CH}\sim \quad \text{or} \quad \left[CH_2-\underset{\underset{CH_3}{|}}{CH}\right]_n$$

Polypropylene

The chain of carbon atoms is called the polymer *backbone*. Groups attached to the backbone, such as the CH_3 groups of polypropylene, are called *pendant groups*.

Polypropylene is a tough plastic material that resists moisture, oils, and solvents. It is molded into hard-shell luggage, battery cases, and various kinds of appliance parts. It is also used to make packaging material, fibers for textiles such as upholstery fabrics and carpets, and ropes that float. Because of polypropylene's high melting point (121 °C), objects made of it can be sterilized with steam.

Polystyrene

Replacing one of the hydrogen atoms in ethylene with a benzene ring gives a monomer called *styrene*, which has the formula $C_6H_5CH=CH_2$, where C_6H_5 represents the benzene ring. Polymerization of styrene produces polystyrene, which has benzene rings as pendant groups.

Styrene   Polystyrene

Polystyrene is the plastic used to make transparent disposable drinking cups. With color and filler added, it is the material of thousands of inexpensive toys and household items. When a gas is blown into polystyrene liquid, it foams and hardens into the familiar material (called Styrofoam®) of ice chests and disposable coffee cups. The polymer can easily be formed into shapes as packing material for shipping instruments and appliances, and it is widely used for home insulation.

Vinyl Polymers

Would you like a tough synthetic material that looks like leather at a fraction of the cost? Perhaps a clear, rigid material from which unbreakable bottles could be made? Do you need an attractive, long-lasting floor covering? Or lightweight, rust-proof, easy-to-connect plumbing? Polyvinyl chloride (PVC) has all these properties—and more.

Replacing one of the hydrogen atoms of ethylene with a chlorine atom gives vinyl chloride (CH_2=$CHCl$), a compound that is a gas at room temperature. Polymerization of vinyl chloride yields the tough thermoplastic material PVC. A segment of the PVC molecule is shown below.

$$\sim CH_2CH-CH_2CH-CH_2CH-CH_2CH\sim$$
$$\quad\ \ |\qquad\quad |\qquad\quad |\qquad\quad |$$
$$\quad\ \ Cl\qquad\ \ Cl\qquad\ \ Cl\qquad\ \ Cl$$

Polyvinyl chloride (PVC)

PVC is readily formed into various shapes. The clear, transparent polymer is used in plastic wrap and clear plastic bottles. Adding color and other ingredients to a vinyl plastic yields artificial leather. Most floor tile and shower curtains are made from vinyl plastics, which are also widely used to simulate wood in home siding panels and window frames. About 40% of the PVC produced is molded into pipes.

Shutterstock

James Edward Bates/Biloxi Sun-Herald/MCT/Newscom

Inara Prusakova/Shutterstock

Vinyl chloride, the monomer from which vinyl plastics are made, is a carcinogen. Several people who worked closely with this gas later developed a kind of cancer called *angiosarcoma*.

PTFE: The Nonstick Coating

In 1938, young Roy Plunkett, a chemist at DuPont, was working with the gas tetrafluoroethylene (CF_2=CF_2). He opened the valve on a tank of the gas—and nothing came out. Rather than discarding the tank, he decided to investigate. The tank was found to be filled with a waxy, white solid. He attempted to analyze the solid but ran into a problem: It simply wouldn't dissolve, even in hot concentrated acids. Plunkett had discovered polytetrafluoroethylene (PTFE), the polymer of tetrafluoroethylene, best known by its trade name, Teflon®.

$$\sim CF_2-CF_2-CF_2-CF_2-CF_2-CF_2-CF_2-CF_2\sim$$

Teflon

Because its C—F bonds are exceptionally strong and resistant to heat and chemicals, PTFE is a tough, unreactive, nonflammable material. It is used to make electric insulation, bearings, and gaskets, as well as to coat surfaces of cookware to eliminate sticking of food.

Dennis McDonald/PhotoEdit

▲ Styrofoam insulation saves energy by reducing the transfer of heat from the warm interior of a house to the outside in winter and from the hot outside to the cooled interior in summer.

◀ Some furniture, window sashes, house trim, and waterproof clothing are made from PVC. PVC can also be coated onto copper wire for insulation, made into colorful resilient flooring, or formed into many other familiar consumer products.

3. Is it really dangerous to burn plastic plumbing pipe? Most plastic plumbing pipe is made of PVC. When PVC is burned, its carcinogenic monomer, vinyl chloride, can be released. PVC may be safely burned in specially constructed incinerators that reach temperatures that decompose the monomer.

Shutterstock

▲ Frying pans, baking pans, and other cookware often take advantage of the inert, non-stick nature of PTFE.

CONCEPTUAL Example 1   Repeat Units in Polymers

What is the repeat unit in polyvinylidene chloride? A segment of the polymer is represented as

$$
\begin{array}{cccccc}
\text{H} & \text{Cl} & \text{H} & \text{Cl} & \text{H} & \text{Cl} \\
| & | & | & | & | & | \\
\sim\!\text{C} & \!\!-\!\!\text{C} & \!\!-\!\!\text{C} & \!\!-\!\!\text{C} & \!\!-\!\!\text{C} & \!\!-\!\!\text{C}\!\sim \\
| & | & | & | & | & | \\
\text{H} & \text{Cl} & \text{H} & \text{Cl} & \text{H} & \text{Cl}
\end{array}
$$

Solution
Inspection of the segment above reveals that it consists of three repeat units, each with two carbon atoms, two hydrogen atoms, and two chlorine atoms. Placing a double bond between the carbon atoms of one unit, we get

$$
\begin{array}{cc}
\text{H} & \text{Cl} \\
| & | \\
\text{C} & \!\!=\!\!\text{C} \\
| & | \\
\text{H} & \text{Cl}
\end{array}
$$

Joining hundreds of these units would yield a molecule of the polymer.

■ EXERCISE 1
What is the repeat unit in polyacrylonitrile? A segment of the polymer is represented as

$$
\sim\!\underset{\overset{|}{\text{CN}}}{\text{CH}_2\text{CH}}\text{CH}_2\underset{\overset{|}{\text{CN}}}{\text{CH}}\text{CH}_2\underset{\overset{|}{\text{CN}}}{\text{CH}}\text{CH}_2\underset{\overset{|}{\text{CN}}}{\text{CH}}\text{CH}_2\underset{\overset{|}{\text{CN}}}{\text{CH}}\text{CH}_2\underset{\overset{|}{\text{CN}}}{\text{CH}}\!\sim
$$

▲ Granular polymeric resins are the basic stock for many molded plastic goods.

Example 2   Structure of Polymers

Write the structure of the polymer made from vinyl fluoride ($CH_2\!=\!CHF$). Show at least four repeat units.

Solution
The carbon atoms bond to form a chain with only single bonds between carbon atoms. The fluorine atom is a pendant group on the chain. (Two of the electrons in the double bond of the monomer form the bond joining units.) The polymer is

$$
\sim\!\text{CH}_2\underset{\overset{|}{\text{F}}}{\text{CH}}\text{CH}_2\underset{\overset{|}{\text{F}}}{\text{CH}}\text{CH}_2\underset{\overset{|}{\text{F}}}{\text{CH}}\text{CH}_2\underset{\overset{|}{\text{F}}}{\text{CH}}\!\sim
$$

■ EXERCISE 2
Write the structures of the polymers made from **(a)** methyl vinyl ketone ($CH_2\!=\!CHCOCH_3$) and **(b)** vinyl acetate ($CH_2\!=\!CHOCOCH_3$). Show at least four repeat units of each polymer.

▲ Large plastic items with thin walls, such as the polyethylene terephthalate containers shown here, are often blow-molded. Blow molding is very similar to blowing a soap bubble, except that the bubble is blown inside a mold.

Processing Polymers

In everyday life, many polymers are called plastics. In chemistry, a *plastic* material is one that can be made to flow under heat and pressure. The material can then be shaped in a mold or in other ways. Plastic products are often made from granular polymeric material. In *compression molding*, heat and pressure are applied directly to such grains in the mold cavity. In *transfer molding*, the polymer is softened by heating before being poured into molds to harden.

There also are several methods of molding molten polymers. In *injection molding,* the plastic is melted in a heating chamber and then forced by a plunger into cold molds to set. In *extrusion molding,* the melted polymer is extruded through a die in continuous form to be cut into lengths or coiled. Bottles and similar hollow objects often are *blow-molded*; a "bubble" of molten polymer is blown up like a balloon inside a hollow mold.

Table 1 lists some of the more important addition polymers, along with a few of their uses.

Table 1   Some Addition Polymers

Monomer	Polymer	Polymer Name	Some Uses
$CH_2{=}CH_2$	(see figure)	Polyethylene	Bags, bottles, toys, electrical insulation
$CH_2{=}CH{-}CH_3$	(see figure)	Polypropylene	Carpeting, bottles, luggage
$CH_2{=}CH{-}$⬡	(see figure)	Polystyrene	Simulated wood furniture, insulation, cups, toys, packing materials
$CH_2{=}CH{-}Cl$	(see figure)	Polyvinyl chloride (PVC)	Food wrap, simulated leather, plumbing, garden hoses, floor tile
$CH_2{=}CCl_2$	(see figure)	Polyvinylidene chloride (Saran®)	Food wrap, seat covers
$CF_2{=}CF_2$	(see figure)	Polytetrafluoroethylene (Teflon)	Nonstick coating for cooking utensils, electrical insulation
$CH_2{=}CH{-}C{\equiv}N$	(see figure)	Polyacrylonitrile (Acrilan, Creslan, Dynel)	Yarns, wigs, paints
$CH_2{=}CH{-}OCOCH_3$	(see figure)	Polyvinyl acetate	Adhesives, textile coatings, chewing gum resin, paints
$CH_2{=}C(CH_3)COOCH_3$	(see figure)	Polymethyl methacrylate (Lucite, Plexiglas)	Glass substitute, bowling balls

Conducting Polymers: Polyacetylene

Acetylene (H—C≡C—H) has a triple bond rather than a double bond, but it can still undergo addition polymerization, forming polyacetylene (Figure 3). Notice that, unlike polyethylene, which has a carbon chain containing only single bonds, every other carbon to carbon bond in polyacetylene is a double bond.

$$\sim CH=CH—CH=CH—CH=CH—CH=CH—CH=CH—CH=CH\sim$$

Figure 3 A ball-and-stick model of polyacetylene.

Q: *Write an equation for the formation of polyacetylene similar to that for polyethylene, in which the repeat polymer unit is placed within brackets.*

The alternating double and single bonds form a *conjugated* system. Such a system makes it easy for electrons to travel along the chain, so polyacetylene is able to conduct electricity. Most other plastics are electrical insulators. Polyacetylene and similar conjugated polymers can be used as lightweight substitutes for metal. In fact, the plastic even has a silvery luster like metal.

Polyacetylene, the first conducting polymer, was discovered in 1970. Since then, a number of other polymers that conduct electricity have been made.

Geoff Tompkinson/
Photo Researchers, Inc.

▲ Conducting polymers have conjugated systems, as seen in Figure 3, and they are used to make electronic sensors, such as the ones shown here. The conductivity of the polymer is affected by impurities on the surface. The change in conductivity varies with the concentration of that impurity.

Self-Assessment Questions

1. Starting materials for many polymers are
   a. alkanes   **b.** alkenes   **c.** carboxylic acids   **d.** esters   **e.** ethers

2. The monomer styrene ($C_6H_5CH=CH_2$, where C_6H_5 represents a benzene ring) forms a polymer that has chains with repeating
   a. eight-carbon units in the backbone
   b. six-carbon units in the backbone and two-carbon groups as pendants
   c. CH_2CH units in the backbone and C_6H_5 groups as pendants
   d. $CH_2=CH$ units in the backbone and C_6H_5 groups as pendants

3. Which of the following could *not* serve as the monomer to make an addition polymer?
   a. $C_2H_2F_2$ **b.** C_2F_4 **c.** C_2H_5Cl **d.** $C_2H_3C_6H_5$

4. A buckyball is a
   a. large carbon molecule (C_{60})
   b. carbon nanotube wound up like a ball of string
   c. long polymer molecule wound up like a ball of string
   d. circular ring of carbon atoms

Answers: 1, b; 2, c; 3, c; 4, a

4 Rubber and Other Elastomers

Learning Objectives   ❯ Define *cross-linking*, and explain how it changes the properties of a polymer.

Although rubber is a natural polymer, it was the basis for much of the development of the synthetic polymer industry. During World War II, Japanese occupation of Southeast Asia cut off most of the Allies' supply of natural rubber. The search for synthetic substitutes resulted in much more than just a replacement for natural rubber. The plastics industry, to a large extent, developed out of the search for synthetic rubber.

Natural rubber can be broken down into a simple hydrocarbon called *isoprene*. Isoprene is a volatile liquid, whereas rubber is a semisolid, elastic material. Chemists can make polyisoprene, a substance identical to natural rubber, except that the isoprene comes from petroleum refineries rather than from the cells of rubber trees.

$$n\, CH_2{=}C{-}CH{=}CH_2 \longrightarrow \left[CH_2{-}C{=}CH{-}CH_2 \right]_n$$
$$\qquad\qquad | \qquad\qquad\qquad\qquad |$$
$$\qquad\qquad CH_3 \qquad\qquad\qquad\qquad CH_3$$

Isoprene   Polyisoprene (rubber)

Chemists have also developed several synthetic rubbers and devised ways to modify these polymers to change their properties.

Vulcanization: Cross-Linking

The long-chain molecules that make up rubber are coiled and twisted and intertwined with one another. When rubber is stretched, its coiled molecules are straightened. Natural rubber is soft and tacky when hot. It can be made harder by reaction with sulfur. In this process, called **vulcanization**, sulfur atoms *cross-link* the hydrocarbon chains side-to-side (Figure 4). Charles Goodyear discovered vulcanization and was issued U.S. Patent 3633 in 1844 for the process.

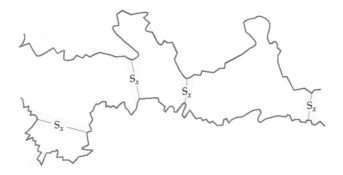

◄ **Figure 4** Vulcanized rubber has long hydrocarbon chains (represented here by red lines) cross-linked by short chains of sulfur atoms. The subscript x indicates a small, indefinite number of S atoms, usually not more than four.

Its cross-linked structure makes vulcanized rubber a harder, stronger substance that is suitable for automobile tires. Surprisingly, cross-linking also improves the elasticity of rubber. With just the right degree of cross-linking, the individual chains are still free to uncoil and stretch somewhat. When stretched vulcanized rubber is released, the cross-links pull the chains back to their original arrangement (Figure 5). Rubber bands owe their snap to this sort of molecular structure. Materials that can be extended and will return to their original size are called **elastomers**.

(a)   (b)   (c)

= Carbon

= Sulfur

▲ **Figure 5** Vulcanization of rubber cross-links the hydrocarbon chains. (a) In unvulcanized rubber, the chains slip past one another when the rubber is stretched. (b) Vulcanization involves the addition of sulfur cross-links between the chains. (c) When vulcanized rubber is stretched, the sulfur cross-links prevent the chains from slipping past one another. Vulcanized rubber is stronger than unvulcanized rubber.

Synthetic Rubber

Natural rubber is a polymer of isoprene, and some synthetic elastomers are closely related to natural rubber. For example, polybutadiene is made from the monomer butadiene (CH_2＝CH—CH＝CH_2), which differs from isoprene only in that it lacks a methyl group on the second carbon atom. Polybutadiene is made rather easily from this monomer.

$$n\ CH_2\text{＝}CH\text{—}CH\text{＝}CH_2 \longrightarrow \text{+}CH_2\text{—}CH\text{＝}CH\text{—}CH_2\text{+}_n$$

However, this polymer has only fair tensile strength and poor resistance to gasoline and oils. These properties limit its value for automobile tires, the main use of elastomers.

Another synthetic elastomer, polychloroprene (Neoprene), is made from a monomer similar to isoprene, but with a chlorine in place of the methyl group on isoprene.

Neoprene is more resistant to oil and gasoline than other elastomers are. It is used to make gasoline pump hoses and similar items used at automobile service stations.

Styrene–butadiene rubber (SBR) is a copolymer of styrene (about 25%) and butadiene (about 75%). A segment of an SBR molecule might look something like this.

$$\sim CH_2CH\text{＝}CHCH_2\text{—}CH_2CH\text{—}CH_2CH\text{＝}CHCH_2\text{—}CH_2CH\text{＝}CHCH_2\sim$$

| Butadiene unit | Styrene unit | Butadiene unit | Butadiene unit |

SBR is more resistant to oxidation and abrasion than natural rubber, but its mechanical properties are less satisfactory.

Like those of natural rubber, SBR molecules contain double bonds and can be cross-linked by vulcanization. SBR accounts for about a third of the total U.S. production of elastomers and is used mainly for making tires.

Polymers in Paints

A surprising use for elastomers is in paints and other coatings. The substance in a paint that hardens to form a continuous surface coating, often called the *binder*, or resin, is a polymer, usually an elastomer. Paint made with elastomers is resistant to cracking. Various kinds of polymers can be used as binders, depending on the specific qualities desired in the paint. Latex paints, which have polymer particles dispersed in water, and thus avoiding the use of organic solvents, are most common. Brushes and rollers are easily cleaned in soap and water. This replacement of the hazardous organic solvents historically used in paints with water is a good example of green chemistry.

Self-Assessment Questions

1. Natural rubber is a polymer of
   a. butadiene   **b.** isobutylene   **c.** isoprene   **d.** propylene

2. Which of the following is the structure of isoprene?
   a. CH_2＝CH—C≡N **b.** CH_2＝$C(CH_3)$—CH_3
   c. CH_2＝CCl—CH—CH_2 **d.** CH_2＝$C(CH_3)$—CH＝CH_2

3. Vulcanization of natural rubber
   a. cross-links the rubber, making it harder and tougher
   b. makes the rubber more crystalline and thus more glassy
   c. makes the rubber totally amorphous
   d. makes the rubber tacky, forming rubber cement

4. Charles Goodyear discovered that natural rubber could be cross-linked by heating it with
   a. a binder   **b.** carbon   **c.** isoprene   **d.** sulfur

▲ It DOES Matter!

A polymer related to SBR is poly(styrene-butadiene-styrene), or SBS. Called a *block copolymer*, SBS has molecules made up of three segments: one end is a chain of polystyrene repeat units; the middle is a long chain of polybutadiene repeat units; and the other end is another chain of polystyrene repeat units. SBS is a hard rubber used in items where durability is important, such as shoe soles and tire treads.

▲ Synthetic polymers serve as binders in paints. Pigments provide color and opacity to the paint. Titanium dioxide (TiO_2), a white solid, is the most widely used pigment.

5. Styrene–butadiene rubber is an example of a
   a. copolymer
   b. natural elastomer
   c. natural cross-linked polymer
   d. polyamide

6. Polymers, usually elastomers, are used in paints as the
   a. binder   **b.** initiator   **c.** pigment   **d.** solvent

5 Condensation Polymers

Learning Objectives ❯ Differentiate between addition and condensation polymerization. ❯ Write the structures of the monomers that form polyesters and polyamides.

The polymers considered so far are all addition polymers. All the atoms of the monomer molecules are incorporated into the polymer molecules. In a *condensation polymer*, part of the monomer molecule is not incorporated in the final polymer. During **condensation polymerization**, also called *step-reaction polymerization*, a small molecule, usually water but sometimes methanol, ammonia or HCl, is formed as a by-product.

Nylon and Other Polyamides

As an example, let's consider the formation of nylon. The monomer in one type of nylon, called *nylon 6*, is a six-carbon carboxylic acid with an amino group on the sixth carbon atom: 6-aminohexanoic acid ($HOOCCH_2CH_2CH_2CH_2CH_2NH_2$). (There are several different nylons, each prepared from a different monomer or set of monomers, but all share certain common structural features.)

In the polymerization reaction, a carboxyl group of one monomer molecule forms an amide bond with the amine group of another.

$$n\ HO-\overset{\overset{\displaystyle O}{\|}}{C}CH_2(CH_2)_3CH_2\overset{\overset{\displaystyle H}{|}}{N}-H\ +\ n\ HO-\overset{\overset{\displaystyle O}{\|}}{C}CH_2(CH_2)_3CH_2\overset{\overset{\displaystyle H}{|}}{N}-H\ \longrightarrow$$

$$\sim\overset{\overset{\displaystyle O}{\|}}{C}CH_2(CH_2)_3CH_2\overset{\overset{\displaystyle H}{|}}{N}-\overset{\overset{\displaystyle O}{\|}}{C}CH_2(CH_2)_3\overset{\overset{\displaystyle H}{|}}{N}\sim\ +\ 2n\ H_2O$$

Amide linkage

Water molecules are formed as a by-product. This formation of a nonpolymeric by-product distinguishes condensation polymerization from addition polymerization. Note that the formula of a repeat unit of a condensation polymer is not the same as that of the monomer.

Because the linkages holding the polymer together are amide bonds, nylon 6 is a **polyamide**. Another nylon is made by the condensation of two different monomers: 1,6-hexanediamine ($H_2NCH_2CH_2CH_2CH_2CH_2CH_2NH_2$) and adipic acid ($HOOCCH_2CH_2CH_2CH_2COOH$). Each monomer has six carbon atoms; the polymer is called *nylon 66*.

$$n\ H-\overset{\overset{\displaystyle H}{|}}{N}CH_2CH_2CH_2CH_2CH_2CH_2\overset{\overset{\displaystyle H}{|}}{N}-H\ +\ n\ HO-\overset{\overset{\displaystyle O}{\|}}{C}(CH_2)_4\overset{\overset{\displaystyle O}{\|}}{C}-OH\ \longrightarrow$$

1,6-Hexanediamine   Adipic acid

$$\text{+}\overset{\overset{\displaystyle H}{|}}{N}CH_2CH_2CH_2CH_2CH_2CH_2\overset{\overset{\displaystyle H}{|}}{N}-\overset{\overset{\displaystyle O}{\|}}{C}CH_2CH_2CH_2CH_2\overset{\overset{\displaystyle O}{\|}}{C}\text{+}_n\ +\ 2n\ H_2O$$

Amide linkage

This was the original nylon polymer discovered in 1937 by DuPont chemist Wallace Carothers. Note that one monomer has two amino groups and the other has two carboxyl groups, but the product is still a polyamide, quite similar to nylon 6. Silk and wool, which are protein fibers, are natural polyamides.

Although nylon can be molded into various shapes, most nylon is made into fibers. Some is spun into fine thread to be woven into silklike fabrics, and some is made into yarn that is much like wool. Carpeting, which was once made primarily from wool, is now made largely from nylon.

Polyethylene Terephthalate and Other Polyesters

A **polyester** is a condensation polymer made from molecules with alcohol and carboxylic acid functional groups. The most common polyester is made from ethylene glycol and terephthalic acid. It is called *polyethylene terephthalate (PET)*.

Polyethylene terephthalate

The hydroxyl groups in ethylene glycol react with the carboxylic acid groups in terephthalic acid to produce long chains held together by many ester linkages.

PET can be molded into bottles for beverages and other liquids. It can also be formed into a film, which is used to laminate documents and to make tough packaging tape. Polyester finishes are used on premium wood products such as guitars, pianos, and the interiors of vehicles and boats. Polyester fibers are strong, quick-drying, and resistant to mildew, wrinkling, stretching, and shrinking. They are used in home furnishings such as carpets, curtains, sheets and pillow cases, and upholstery. Because polyester fibers do not absorb water, they are ideal for outdoor clothing to be worn in wet and damp environments and for insulation in boots and sleeping bags. For other clothing, they are often blended with cotton for a more natural feel. A familiar use of polyester film (Mylar®) is in the shiny balloons that are filled with helium to celebrate special occasions.

Phenol–Formaldehyde and Related Resins

Let's go back to Bakelite, the original synthetic polymer. Bakelite, a phenol–formaldehyde resin, was first synthesized by Leo Baekeland, who received U.S. Patent 942,699 for the process in 1909. Phenolic resins are no longer important as industrial polymers, but they are used as a substitute for porcelain and in board and tabletop game pieces such as billiard balls, dominoes, and checkers.

Phenol–formaldehyde resins are formed in a condensation reaction that also yields water molecules, the hydrogen atoms coming from the benzene ring of phenol and the oxygen atoms from the aldehyde. The reaction proceeds stepwise, with formaldehyde first adding to the 2 or 4 position of the phenol molecule.

Phenol   Formaldehyde

The substituted phenol molecules then link up as water molecules are formed. (Remember that there are hydrogen atoms at all the unsubstituted corners of a benzene ring.) The hookup of molecules continues until an extensive network is achieved.

Phenol–formaldehyde resin

Water is driven off by heat as the polymer sets. The structure of the polymer is extremely complex, a three-dimensional network somewhat like the framework of a giant building. Note that the phenolic rings are joined together by CH_2 units from the formaldehyde. These network polymers are **thermosetting resins**; they cannot be melted and remolded. Instead, they decompose when heated to high temperatures.

Formaldehyde is also condensed with urea [$H_2N(C{=}O)NH_2$] to make urea–formaldehyde resins and with melamine to form melamine–formaldehyde resins. (Melamine is formed by condensation of three molecules of urea.)

These resins, like phenolic resins, are thermosetting. The polymers are complex three-dimensional networks formed by the condensation reaction of formaldehyde ($H_2C{=}O$) molecules and amino ($-NH_2$) groups. Urea–formaldehyde resins are used to bind wood chips together in panels of particle board. Melamine–formaldehyde resins are used in plastic (Melmac) dinnerware and laminate countertops.

Melamine

Other Condensation Polymers

There are many other kinds of condensation polymers, but we will look at only a few.

Polycarbonates are "clear as glass" polymers tough enough to be used in bulletproof windows. They are also used in protective helmets, safety glasses, clear plastic water bottles, baby bottles, and even dental crowns. One polycarbonate is made from bisphenol-A (BPA) and phosgene ($COCl_2$).

A polycarbonate

▲ Composite construction using carbon fiber and epoxies makes bicycle frames incredibly strong and light (about 1 kg!). The direction of the carbon fiber allows the maker to tailor the material for maximum strength where needed.

Silicon is in the same group (4A) as carbon and, like carbon, is tetravalent and able to form chains. However, carbon can form chains consisting only of carbon atoms (as in polyethylene), whereas the chains of silicone polymers have alternating silicon and oxygen atoms.

4. Is silicon the same thing as silicone? Although the names are very similar, the materials are quite different. *Silicon* is a hard, brittle element. A *silicone* is a polymer that contains silicon as well as carbon, hydrogen, and oxygen. Most silicones are flexible.

Polyurethanes are similar to nylon polymers in structure. The repeat unit in one common polyurethane is

$$\sim\!\overset{\overset{\displaystyle O}{\|}}{C}\!-\!NH\!-\!CH_2CH_2CH_2CH_2CH_2CH_2\!-\!NH\!-\!\overset{\overset{\displaystyle O}{\|}}{C}\!-\!O\!-\!CH_2CH_2CH_2CH_2\!-\!O\!\sim$$

Polyurethanes may be elastomeric or tough and rigid, depending on the monomers used. They are common in foamed padding (foam rubber) in cushions, mattresses, and padded furniture. They are also used for skate wheels, in running shoes, and in protective gear for sports activities.

Epoxies make excellent surface paints and coatings. They are used to protect steel pipes and fittings from corrosion. The insides of metal cans are often coated with an epoxy to prevent rusting, especially in cans for acidic foods like tomatoes. A common epoxy is made from epichlorohydrin and BPA.

An epoxy

Epoxies also make powerful adhesives. These adhesives usually have two components that are mixed just before use. The polymer chains become cross-linked, and the bonding is extremely strong.

Composite Materials

Composite materials are made up of high-strength fibers (of glass, graphite, synthetic polymers, or ceramics) held together by a polymeric matrix, usually a thermosetting condensation polymer. The fiber reinforcement provides the support, and the surrounding plastic keeps the fibers from breaking.

Among the most commonly used composite materials are polyester resins reinforced with glass fibers. These are widely used in boat hulls, molded chairs, automobile panels, and sports gear such as tennis rackets. Some composite materials have the strength and rigidity of steel but with a fraction of the weight of steel.

Silicones

Not all polymers are based on chains of carbon atoms. A good example of a different type of polymer is **silicone** (polysiloxane), whose chains have a series of alternating silicon and oxygen atoms.

(In simple silicones, R represents a hydrocarbon group, such as methyl, ethyl, or butyl.)

Silicones can be linear, cyclic, or cross-linked networks. They are heat-stable and resistant to most chemicals and are excellent waterproofing materials. Depending on chain length and amount of cross-linking, silicones can be oils or greases, rubbery compounds, or solid resins. Silicone oils are used as hydraulic fluids and lubricants; other silicones are used in such products as sealants, auto polish, shoe polish, and waterproof sheeting. Fabrics for raincoats and umbrellas are frequently treated with silicone.

An interesting silicone product is Silly Putty. It can be molded like clay or rolled up and bounced like a ball. But it is actually a liquid and flows very slowly on standing.

Perhaps the most remarkable silicones are the ones used for synthetic human body parts, ranging from finger joints to eye sockets. Artificial ears and noses are also made from silicone polymers. These can even be specially colored to match the surrounding skin.

Cookware made of silicone is colorful, flexible, and nonstick.

Example 3 — Condensed Structural Formulas for Polymers

Write the condensed structural formula for the polymer formed from dimethylsilanol, $(CH_3)_2Si(OH)_2$.

Solution

Let's start by writing the structural formula of the monomer.

$$\begin{array}{c} CH_3 \\ | \\ HO-Si-OH \\ | \\ CH_3 \end{array}$$

Because there are no double bonds in this molecule, we do not expect it to undergo addition polymerization. Rather, we expect a condensation reaction, in which an OH group of one molecule and an H atom of another combine to form a molecule of water. Moreover, because there are two OH groups per molecule, each monomer can form bonds with two others, on both sides. This is a key requirement for polymerization. We can represent the reaction as follows.

$$\begin{array}{c}CH_3\\|\\HO-Si-OH\\|\\CH_3\end{array} + \begin{array}{c}CH_3\\|\\HO-Si-OH\\|\\CH_3\end{array} + \begin{array}{c}CH_3\\|\\HO-Si-OH\\|\\CH_3\end{array} + \cdots \longrightarrow \left[\begin{array}{c}CH_3\\|\\Si-O\\|\\CH_3\end{array}\right]_n + n\,H_2O$$

■ **EXERCISE 3**
a. Write the structural formula for the polymer formed from glycolic acid (hydroxyacetic acid, $HOCH_2COOH$), showing at least four repeat units.
b. Write a condensed structural formula in which the repeat unit in part (a) is shown in brackets.

Silicone is an excellent material for some replacement body parts. It is very flexible and chemically inert; the body does not often reject silicone.

Self-Assessment Questions

1. In a condensation polymerization, the two products formed are a polymer and (usually)
   a. an acid
   b. a base
   c. carbon dioxide
   d. water

2. Which of the following pairs of molecules can form a polyester?
   a. $HOCH_2CH_2OH$ and $HOCH_2CH_2CH_2CH_2OH$
   b. $H_2NCH_2CH_2CH_2CH_2CH_2NH_2$ and $HOOCCH_2CH_2CH_2CH_2COOH$
   c. $H_2NCH_2CH_2CH_2CH_2CH_2NH_2$ and $HOCH_2CH_2CH_2CH_2CH_2OH$
   d. $HOOCCH_2CH_2CH_2CH_2COOH$ and $HOCH_2CH_2CH_2CH_2OH$

3. Which of the following molecules can serve as the sole monomer for a polyamide?
   a. $H_2NCH_2CH_2CH_2CH_2OH$
   b. $H_2NCH_2CH_2CH_2CH_2NH_2$
   c. $HOOCCH_2CH_2CH_2CH_2CH_2NH_2$
   d. $HOOCCH_2CH_2CH_2CONH_2$

4. Thermosetting polymers
   a. are easily recycled
   b. are always addition polymers
   c. cannot be melted and remolded
   d. usually melt at a lower temperature than do thermoplastic polymers

5. The backbone of a silicone polymer chain is composed of the repeating unit
   a. $\sim OCH_2CH_2OSi\sim$
   b. $\sim OCH_2CH_2Si\sim$
   c. $\sim SiO\sim$
   d. $\sim OSiSi\sim$

6 Properties of Polymers

Learning Objectives › Understand the concept of the glass transition temperature.
› Explain how crystallinity affects the physical properties of polymers.

Polymers differ from substances consisting of small molecules in three main ways. First, the long chains can be entangled with one another, much like the strands in a dish of spaghetti. It is difficult to untangle the polymer molecules, especially at low temperatures. This property lends strength to many plastics, elastomers, and other materials.

Second, although intermolecular forces affect polymers just as they do small molecules, these forces are greatly multiplied for large molecules. The larger the molecules are, the greater the intermolecular forces between them. Even when ordinarily weak dispersion forces are the only intermolecular forces present, they can strongly bind polymer chains. This property, too, provides strength in polymeric materials. For example, polyethylene is nonpolar, with only dispersion forces between its molecules. Ultra-high-molecular-weight polyethylene forms fibers so strong they can be used in bullet-proof vests.

Third, large polymer molecules move more slowly than small molecules do. A group of small molecules (monomers) can move around more rapidly and more randomly when independent than they can when joined together in a long chain (polymer). The slower molecular speed makes a polymeric material different from one made of small molecules. For example, a polymer dissolved in a solvent will form a solution that is a lot more viscous than the pure solvent.

Crystalline and Amorphous Polymers

Some polymers are highly crystalline; their molecules line up neatly to form long fibers of great strength. Other polymers are largely amorphous, composed of randomly oriented molecules that get tangled up with one another (Figure 6). Crystalline polymers tend to make good synthetic fibers, while amorphous polymers are often elastomers.

▶ **Figure 6** Organization of polymer molecules. (a) Crystalline arrangement. (b) Amorphous arrangement.

(a)   (b)

Sometimes, the same polymer is crystalline in one region and amorphous in another. For example, scientists designed spandex fibers (used in stretch fabrics [Lycra] in ski pants, exercise clothing, and swimsuits) to combine the tensile strength of crystalline fibers with the elasticity of amorphous rubber. Two molecular structures are combined in one polymer chain, with crystalline blocks alternating with amorphous blocks. The amorphous blocks are soft and rubbery, while the crystalline parts are quite rigid. The resulting polymer exhibits both sets of properties—flexibility and rigidity.

The Glass Transition Temperature

An important property of most thermoplastic polymers is the **glass transition temperature** (T_g). Above this temperature, the polymer is rubbery and tough. Below it, the polymer is like glass: hard, stiff, and brittle. Each polymer has a characteristic T_g.

We can apply the glass transition temperature in everyday life. For example, we can remove chewing gum from clothing by applying ice to lower the temperature of the polyvinyl acetate resin that gives the gum its "chewiness" below its T_g. The cold, brittle resin then crumbles readily and can be removed.

We want automobile tires to be tough and elastic, so we make them from polymers with low T_g values. On the other hand, we want plastic substitutes for glass to be glassy. Therefore, these polymers have T_g values well above room temperature.

Fiber Formation

Not all synthetic polymers can be formed into useful fibers, but those that can often yield fibers with properties superior to those of natural fibers. More than half of the 60 billion kg of textile fibers produced each year in the United States are synthetic.

Silk fabrics are beautiful and have a luxurious "feel," but nylon fabrics are also attractive and feel much like silk. Moreover, nylon fabrics wear longer, are easier to care for, and are less expensive than silk.

Polyesters such as PET can substitute for either cotton or silk, but they outperform the natural fibers in many ways. Polyesters are not subject to mildew as cotton is, and many polyester fabrics do not need ironing. Fabrics in which polyester fibers are blended with 35–50% cotton combine the comfort of cotton with the no-iron easy care of polyester.

Acrylic fibers, made from polyacrylonitrile, can be spun into yarns that look like wool. Acrylic sweaters have the beauty and warmth of wool, but they do not shrink in hot water, are not attacked by moths, and do not cause the allergic skin reaction wool causes in some people.

Exceedingly fine fibers—called *microfibers* because they measure less than 10 μm in diameter, half as thick as a silk fibers—can be made from almost any fiber-forming polymer, but most are made of polyesters or polyamides or a combination of the two. Varying the size, shape, and composition of the fibers results in products that are water repellent (for apparel) or absorbent (for a mop). Microfibers can be shaped for efficient trapping of dust or for wicking away liquids. These fibers already have many uses and are likely to have many more.

Self-Assessment Questions

1. The glass transition temperature of a polymer is the temperature
   a. above which the polymer becomes highly crystalline
   b. at which the polymer changes to a thermosetting material
   c. at which the polymer melts to a clear liquid
   d. below which the polymer becomes glassy and brittle

2. Crystalline polymers are
   a. elastic   b. flexible   c. highly cross-linked   d. used in fibers

Answers: 1, d; 2, d

5. How are permanent-press fabrics made? Cotton is largely cellulose, which can engage in hydrogen bonding among its molecules. Moisture causes random hydrogen bonding in cotton fabric, which causes wrinkles. The earliest permanent-press fabrics were designed to allow less hydrogen bonding than in cotton. Newer permanent-press clothing takes advantage of the fabric's low T_g to minimize wrinkles after drying.

▲ Formation of fibers by extrusion through a spinneret. A melted polymer is forced through the tiny holes to make fibers that solidify as they cool.

7 Plastics and the Environment

Learning Objectives > Describe the environmental problems associated with plastics and plasticizers. > Name two types of sustainable, non-petroleum-derived polymers and give their sources.

An advantage of many plastics is that they are durable and resistant to environmental conditions. Perhaps some of them are too resistant: They last almost forever. Once plastic objects are dumped, they do not go away. You see them littering our parks, our sidewalks, and our highways, and if you should go out into the middle of the ocean, you would see them there, too. Many small fish have been found dead with their digestive tracts clogged by bits of plastic foam ingested with their food.

Plastics make up about 12% by mass of solid waste in the United States, but about 25% by volume. Their bulk creates a problem because 55% of all solid waste goes into landfills, and it is increasingly difficult to find suitable landfill space.

Americans use about 60 million plastic bottles each day, with only about 12% being recycled. Recycling one plastic bottle conserves enough energy to burn a 60-W lightbulb for six hours. Recycling plastics reduces our dependency on oil and decreases CO_2 emissions due to the use of fossil fuels.

▲ Recycled plastic can be used for many things. The Adirondack chair and the cafe chair are colorful and strong and made from recycled milk jugs.

Another way to dispose of discarded plastics is to burn them. Most plastics have a high fuel value. For example, a pound of polyethylene has about the same energy content as a pound of fuel oil. Some communities generate electricity with the heat from garbage incinerators. Some utility companies burn powdered coal mixed with a small proportion of ground-up rubber tires, thereby not only obtaining extra energy from the tires but also helping to solve the problem of tire disposal.

On the other hand, the burning of plastics and rubber can create new problems. For example, PVC produces toxic hydrogen chloride and vinyl chloride gases when it burns, and burning automobile tires give off soot and a stinking smoke. Incinerators are corroded by acidic fumes and clogged by materials that are not readily burned.

Degradable Plastics

About half of the waste plastic generated in the United States is from packaging. One approach to the problem of disposal of plastics is to make plastic packages that are biodegradable or photodegradable (broken down in the presence of bacteria or light). Of course, such packages must remain intact and not start to decompose while still being used. And many people still seem reluctant to pay extra for garbage bags that are designed to fall apart. Recently, though, there has been an increase in degradable, more environmentally friendly plastic items, including plastic tableware, cups, bottles, and delicatessen food containers.

Recycling

Recycling is perhaps the best way to handle waste plastics. The plastics must be collected, sorted, chopped, melted, and then remolded. Collection works well when there is strong community cooperation. The separation step is simplified by code numbers stamped on plastic containers. Once the plastics have been separated, they can be chopped into flakes, melted, and remolded or spun into fibers.

Only two kinds of plastics are recycled on a large scale, PET (28% recycled) and HDPE (29%). PET bottles can be made into fibers, mainly for carpets, and HDPE containers can be remolded into detergent bottles. Recycling is green because it keeps plastics out of landfills, and it increases sustainability by lessening the use of petroleum-derived monomers or hazardous chemicals. We have a long way to go: in 2009, only about 7% of the 27 billion kg per year of plastic wastes in the United States are recycled.

Plastics and Fire Hazards

The accidental ignition of fabrics, synthetic or other, has caused untold human misery. The U.S. Department of Health and Human Services estimates that fires involving flammable fabrics kill several thousand people annually and injure between 150,000 and 200,000.

Research has led to a variety of flame-retardant fabrics. Many incorporate chlorine and bromine atoms within the polymeric fibers. In particular, federal regulations require that children's sleepwear be made of such flame-retardant materials.

Another synthetic fabric, meta-aramid, or Nomex (from DuPont), has such high heat resistance that it is used for protective clothing for firefighters and race-car drivers. The fibers don't ignite or melt when exposed to flames or high heat. Nomex is also used in electric insulation and for machine parts exposed to high heat.

Burning plastics often produce toxic gases. Hydrogen cyanide is formed in large quantities when polyacrylonitrile and other nitrogen-containing polymers burn. Lethal amounts of cyanide found in the bodies of victims of plane crashes have been traced to burned plastics. Firefighters often refuse to enter burning buildings without gas masks for fear of being overcome by fumes from burning plastics. Smoldering fires also produce lethal quantities of carbon monoxide. To make plastics safer, green chemists are making new kinds of polymers that don't burn or that don't generate toxic chemicals when burned.

310

Jennifer L. Young, *ACS Green Chemistry Institute®*

Greener Polymers

Many products that we use today are made of plastic. Therefore, it is important to apply the twelve principles of green chemistry to plastics and polymers. You might ask, how can plastics be made sustainably using green chemistry? Two areas where greener processes have had large impacts are the recycling and biodegradation of plastics (Section 7, Principle 10) and the production of plastics from renewable resources (Principle 7).

You probably use polyethylene bags (Section 2), polystyrene cups (Section 3), polyethylene terephthalate (PET) soft drink bottles (Section 5), nylon clothing and carpeting (Section 5), and styrene–butadiene rubber tires (Section 4). These polymers and most others on the market are made from nonrenewable resources and do not biodegrade. After use, the polymers often are discarded into the environment or buried in landfills.

There are other, greener options for plastic materials. Many polymers that you use every day are recyclable. Recycling decreases the amount of plastic that ends up in landfills and also reduces the amount of new plastic that must be made from fossil fuels.

To make recycling easier, most plastic objects are stamped with a triangular recycle symbol and a number code. These numbers, called *resin identification codes*, identify types of plastics as follows: #1, polyethylene terephthalate (PET or PETE); #2, high-density polyethylene (HDPE); #3, polyvinyl chloride (PVC or V); #4, low-density polyethylene (LDPE); #5, polypropylene (PP); #6, polystyrene (PS); and #7, all other kinds of polymers.

PET (#1) and HDPE (#2) are the most commonly recycled plastics. Other types may also be accepted for recycling in some locales. In the recycling process, the plastics are separated by resin identification code. The plastic is then chopped up, softened by raising the temperature above the polymer's glass transition temperature (Section 6), molded into a new shape, and cooled back to room temperature to harden. Because the process uses heat to recycle the polymer, only thermoplastics (not thermosetting polymers; Section 2) can be recycled in this way.

Typically, recycled plastic is used to make different objects than the things recycled because the polymer's properties are changed. For example, park benches and plastic outdoor decking material are made from recycled plastic bottles. Just because

Xinhua/Photoshot/Newscom

▲ Although they may appear to be like any other pens at first glance, these pens from Micro Roller are made from corn and straw. The pens are over 70% degradable within a relatively short period of time.

a polymer falls into the "other" category (#7) does not mean that the polymer cannot be recycled. For instance, nylon-based carpet is commonly recycled.

Some polymers, including PET, can be depolymerized. Chemical reactions can reverse the polymerization and break the polymer into the original monomer units. The monomer can then be polymerized again to make polymer that is as pure as the original material. Since the new polymer has the same properties as the original polymer, it can be used to make the same objects. Some companies that make these types of plastics will accept their plastic products for recycling, then depolymerize and reuse the monomers.

Some types of plastics can be degraded into carbon dioxide and water. Over some period of time, these polymers will biodegrade under the right conditions of temperature and moisture or in the presence of microorganisms. This means biodegradable plastics generally do not degrade readily when thrown at the side of the road or when dumped into trash that ends up in a landfill. Official bodies apply different definitions for biodegradability. For instance, the USA ASTM D6400 Standard requires 60% conversion into carbon dioxide in 180 days, and the European Standard EN13432 requires 90% conversion over the same span of time.

New kinds of polymers are being made from renewable resources, such as corn, soy, grass, and other types of biomass. One example is polylactic acid (PLA), made from corn. PLA is used to make plastic bottles, salad containers, coffee mugs, and even fibers for clothing. PLA can be depolymerized to monomers and can also degrade by composting. Cargill Dow LLC (now NatureWorks LLC) received a Presidential Green Chemistry Challenge Award for developing PLA from renewable resources. Polyhydroxyalkanoates (PHAs) are made from plant sugars and oils, are biodegradable, and can even be made using bacteria. Metabolix, Inc. was awarded a Presidential Green Chemistry Challenge Award for producing PHAs with microorganisms. For many plastics, the most sustainable approach is using renewable resources—especially nonfood crops—as the source of the monomer.

Plasticizers and Pollution

Chemicals used in plastics manufacture can also present problems. Plasticizers are an important example. Some plastics, particularly vinyl polymers, are hard and brittle and thus difficult to process. A **plasticizer** can make such a plastic more flexible and less brittle by lowering its glass transition temperature. Unplasticized PVC is rigid and is used for water pipes. Thin sheets of pure PVC crack and break easily, but plasticizers make them soft and pliable. Plastic raincoats, garden hoses, and seat covers for automobiles can be made from plasticized PVC. Plasticizers are liquids of low volatility, but they are generally lost by diffusion and evaporation as a plastic article ages. The plastic becomes brittle and then cracks and breaks.

Once used widely as plasticizers but now banned, polychlorinated biphenyls (PCBs) are derived from biphenyl ($C_{12}H_{10}$), a hydrocarbon that has two benzene rings joined at a corner. In PCBs, some of the hydrogen atoms of biphenyl are replaced with chlorine atoms (Figure 7). Note that PCBs are structurally similar to the insecticide DDT.

Figure 7 Biphenyl and some of the PCBs derived from it (only a few of the hundreds of possible PCBs). DDT is also shown for comparison.

PCBs were also widely used as insulating materials in electric transformers because their stability and low polarity gave them high electrical resistance and the ability to absorb heat. The same properties that made PCBs so desirable as industrial chemicals cause them to be an environmental hazard. They degrade slowly in nature, and their solubility in nonpolar media—animal fat as well as vinyl plastics—leads to their becoming concentrated in the food chain, PCB residues have been found in fish, birds, water, and sediments. The physiological effect of PCBs is similar to that of DDT. Monsanto Corporation, the only company in the United States that produced PCBs, discontinued production in 1977, but the compounds still remain in the environment.

Today, the most widely used plasticizers for vinyl plastics are phthalate esters, a group of diesters derived from phthalic acid (1,2-benzenedicarboxylic acid). Phthalate plasticizers (Figure 8) have low acute toxicity and, although some studies have suggested possible harm to young children, the FDA has recognized these plasticizers as being generally safe. They pose little threat to the environment because they degrade fairly rapidly. Another approach of green chemists is to make plastics that have the right amount of flexibility and thus do not require any plasticizers when they are manufactured.

Plastics and the Future

Widely used today, synthetic polymers are the materials of the future. New kinds and new uses will be discovered. We already have polymers that conduct electricity, amazing adhesives, and synthetic materials that are stronger than steel but much lighter in weight. Plastics present problems, but they have become such an important part of our daily lives that we would find it difficult to live without them.

◀ **Figure 8** Phthalic acid and some esters derived from it. Dioctyl phthalate is also called di-2-ethylhexyl phthalate.

Phthalic acid

Dibutyl phthalate (DBP)

Dimethoxyethyl phthalate (DMEP)

Dioctyl phthalate (DOP)

In medicine, body replacement parts made from polymers have become common. There are about 200,000 total hip replacements in the United States each year. Artificial lungs and artificial hearts are available, but they are enormously expensive and used for the most part only during recovery from injury or illness or until donor organs are available for transplantation. The cost of these replacements is likely to drop, and their efficacy will probably improve, in the future.

PVC water pipes, siding, and window frames, plastic foam insulation, and polymeric surface coatings are used in home construction today. Some homes also contain lumber and wall panels of artificial wood, made from recycled plastics.

Synthetic polymers are used extensively in airplane interiors, and the bodies and wings of some planes are made of lightweight composite materials. Many automobiles have bodies made from plastic composites. Electrically conducting polymers will aid in making lightweight batteries for electric automobiles. The electronics industry will use increasing amounts of electrically conducting thermoplastics in miniaturized circuits.

But here is something to think about: Most synthetic polymers are made from petroleum or natural gas. Both of these natural resources are nonrenewable, and our supplies are limited. We are likely to run out of petroleum during this century. You might suppose that we would be actively conserving this valuable resource, but unfortunately this is not the case. We are taking petroleum out of the ground at a rapid rate, converting most of it to gasoline and other fuels, and then simply burning it. There are other sources of energy, but is there anything that can replace petroleum as the raw material for making plastics? Yes! Several new types of plastics, such as polylactic acid and polyhydroxybutyrates, are made from renewable resources such as corn, soybeans, and sugarcane. Polymers are an active area of green chemistry research.

Self-Assessment Questions

1. In general, the best way to dispose of plastics is
   a. composting
   b. incineration
   c. in landfills
   d. recycling

2. Many plastics are fire hazards because they burn and produce
   a. CFCs
   b. nitrogen oxides
   c. solid wastes
   d. toxic gases

3. A plasticizer acts by
   a. initiating addition polymerization
   b. lowering the glass transition temperature
   c. participating in condensation polymerization
   d. wetting polymer powders

4. Many flame-retardant fabrics incorporate
   a. Br and Cl atoms   **b.** CFCs
   c. PCBs   **d.** phthalate plasticizers

5. Most synthetic polymers are made from
   a. coal   **b.** cotton
   c. petroleum and natural gas   **d.** sustainable sources

6. A polymer made from a renewable resource is
   a. LDPE   **b.** polyacrylonitrile
   c. polylactic acid   **d.** styrene–butadiene rubber

Answers: 1, d; 2, d; 3, b; 4, a; 5, c; 6, c

CRITICAL THINKING EXERCISES

Apply knowledge that you have gained in this chapter and one or more of the FLaReS principles to evaluate the following statements or claims.

1 An environmental activist states that all synthetic plastics should be banned and replaced by those derived from natural materials.

2 A news report states that incinerators that burn plastics are a major source of chlorine-containing toxic compounds called *dioxins*.

3 Vinyl chloride is a carcinogen. Some people warn that children will get cancer from playing with toys made of PVC.

4 The Plastics Division of the American Chemistry Council says that, in comparison to paper bags, "plastic bags are . . . an environmentally responsible choice."

SUMMARY

Section 1—A polymer is a giant molecule made from smaller molecules. The small molecules that are the building blocks used to make polymers are called monomers. There are many natural polymers, including starch, cellulose, nucleic acids, and proteins.

Celluloid was the first semisynthetic polymer, made from natural cellulose treated with nitric acid.

Section 2—The simplest, least expensive, and highest-volume synthetic polymer is polyethylene, made from the monomer ethylene. High-density polyethylene molecules can pack closely together to yield a rigid, strong structure. Low-density polyethylene molecules have many side chains, resulting in more flexible plastics. Linear low-density polyethylene is a copolymer, formed from two (or more) different monomers.

Polyethylene is one of many thermoplastic polymers that can be softened and reshaped with heat and pressure. *Thermosetting* polymers decompose, rather than soften, when heated. They cannot be reshaped.

Section 3—In addition polymerization, the monomer molecules add to one another; the polymer contains all the atoms of the monomers. Addition polymers, such as polyethylene, polypropylene, polystyrene, and PVC, are made from monomers containing carbon-to-carbon double bonds. Polypropylene is tough and resists moisture, oils, and solvents. Polystyrene is used mainly to make Styrofoam. PVC or polyvinyl chloride is used for plumbing, artificial leather,

and flexible tubing. PTFE, or Teflon, is chemically inert and nonflammable; it is widely used in nonstick coatings. Thermoplastic polymers can be molded in many different ways.

Section 4—Natural rubber is an elastomer, a material that returns to its original shape after being stretched. The monomer of natural rubber, isoprene, can be made artificially and polymerized. Polyisoprene is soft and tacky when hot. In a process called vulcanization, polyisoprene is reacted with sulfur. The sulfur atoms cross-link the hydrocarbon chains, making the rubber harder, stronger, and more elastic.

Other elastomers that are similar in structure to polyisoprene include polybutadiene, polychloroprene, and styrene–butadiene rubber (SBR). All of these have molecules that can coil and uncoil. Elastomers are used as binders in paints.

Section 5—In condensation polymerization, parts of the monomer molecules are not incorporated in the product. Small molecules such as water are formed as by-products. Nylon is a condensation polymer that is a polyamide, with amide [—(CO)NH—] linkages joining the monomers.

A polyester is a condensation polymer made from monomers with alcohol and carboxylic acid functional groups. Polyethylene terephthalate (PET) is the most common polyester.

Various thermosetting resins can be prepared by condensing formaldehyde with urea, melamine, or phenol. Other condensation polymers include polycarbonates (bulletproof windows), polyurethanes (foam rubber), and epoxies (coatings and adhesives). Combining a polymer with high-strength fibers gives a composite material that exploits the best properties of both materials. Silicones, which have chains consisting of silicon and oxygen atoms instead of carbon atoms, have varied structures and many uses.

Section 6—Properties of polymers differ greatly from those of their monomers. A polymer's strength arises partly because the molecules entangle with one another and partly because the large molecules have strong dispersion forces. Polymers may be crystalline or amorphous. Above the glass transition temperature (T_g) a polymer is rubbery and tough; below it, the polymer is brittle. Strong synthetic fibers are made from crystalline polymers because their long molecules align neatly with one another.

Section 7—The durability of plastics means that they make up a large fraction of the content of landfills. Proper incineration is one way of disposing of discarded plastics, but it can produce toxic gases. Some polymers are engineered to be degradable. Recycling of plastics requires that they be collected and sorted according to the code numbers. Recycled plastics are being used more and more. Flame-retardant fabrics for clothing are made of polymers that often incorporate chlorine or bromine atoms.

The chemicals used in manufacturing plastics, especially plasticizers, can present problems. A plasticizer makes a polymer more flexible. Polychlorinated biphenyls (PCBs) were once used as plasticizers but are now banned. Phthalate esters are the most widely used plasticizers today.

Synthetic polymers will be used even more in the future. However, most synthetic polymers come from petroleum, a limited and nonrenewable resource. This is another important reason for recycling plastics.

Green chemistry Many products we use today are made of plastic. Green chemistry applies to the recycling and biodegradation of plastics and to the production of plastics from renewable resources.

Learning Objectives

❭ Define *polymer* and *monomer*.	Problems 3, 5, 7
❭ List several natural polymers including a chemically modified one.	Problems 9, 43, 55
❭ Describe the structure and properties of the two main types of polyethylene.	Problems 13, 14
❭ Use the terms *thermoplastic* and *thermosetting* to explain how polymer structure determines properties.	Problem 8
❭ Identify the monomer(s) of an addition polymer, and write the structural formula for a polymer from its monomer structure(s).	Problems 15–20 , 21, 37–39, 41–45, 52, 53
❭ Define *cross-linking*, and explain how it changes the properties of a polymer.	Problem 22
❭ Differentiate between addition and condensation polymerization.	Problems 3, 35, 36
❭ Write the structures of the monomers that form polyesters and polyamides.	Problem 46
❭ Understand the concept of the glass transition temperature.	Problems 33, 40
❭ Explain how crystallinity affects the physical properties of polymers.	Problems 13, 14, 33, 34
❭ Describe the environmental problems associated with plastics and plasticizers.	Problems 11, 12
❭ Name two types of sustainable, non-petroleum-derived polymers and give their sources.	Problems 54, 55, 57
❭ Describe plastic recycling, biodegradation, and production from renewable resources.	Problems 55–58

REVIEW QUESTIONS

1. How does the structure of PVC differ from that of polyethylene? List several uses of PVC.

2. Define the following terms.
   a. macromolecule   **b.** elastomer
   c. copolymer   **d.** plasticizer

3. What is addition polymerization? What structural feature usually characterizes molecules used as monomers in addition polymerization?

4. What is Teflon? What special property does it have? What are some of its uses?

5. From what monomer are disposable foamed plastic coffee cups made?

6. What plastic is used to make **(a)** gallon milk jugs and **(b)** 2-L soft drink bottles?

7. What is Bakelite? From what monomers is it made?

8. What is a thermosetting polymer? Give an example.

9. Which type of fibers, natural or synthetic, is used most in the United States? Why?

10. What are PCBs? Why are they no longer used as plasticizers?

11. What steps must be taken to recycle plastics?

12. What problems arise when plastics are **(a)** discarded into the environment, **(b)** disposed of in landfills, and **(c)** disposed of by incineration?

Polymers

PROBLEMS

Polyethylene

13. Describe the structure of low-density polyethylene (LDPE). How does this structure explain the properties of this polymer?

14. Describe the structure of high-density polyethylene (HDPE). How does this structure explain the properties of this polymer?

Addition Polymerization

15. Write the structure of the monomer from which each of the following polymers is made.
   a. polyethylene
   b. polyacrylonitrile

16. Write the structure of the monomer from which each of the following polymers is made.
   a. polypropylene
   b. polytetrafluoroethylene

17. Write the structure of a chain segment that is at least eight carbon atoms long for the polymer made from each of the following.
   a. polyvinyl chloride
   b. vinylidene fluoride (H_2C=CF_2)

18. Write the structure of a chain segment that is at least four repeat units long for the polymer formed from each of the following monomers.
   a. styrene
   b. methyl methacrylate

$$CH_2=\overset{\overset{\displaystyle CH_3}{|}}{C}COOCH_3$$

19. Write the structure of the polymer made from each of the following. Show at least four repeat units.
   a. 1-pentene (CH_2=$CHCH_2CH_2CH_3$)
   b. methyl cyanoacrylate

$$CH_2=\overset{\overset{\displaystyle C\equiv N}{|}}{C}COOCH_3$$

20. Write the structure of the polymer made from each of the following. Show at least four repeat units.
   a. vinyl acetate [H_2C=CH—$O(C$=$O)CH_3$]
   b. methyl acrylate [H_2C=CH—$(C$=$O)OCH_3$]

Rubber and Other Elastomers

21. Draw the structure of the monomer from which polybutadiene is made.

22. Describe the process of vulcanization. How does vulcanization change the properties of rubber?

23. Explain why rubber is elastic, while many other polymers are rigid.

24. How does polybutadiene differ from natural rubber in properties? In structure?

25. How is SBR made? From what monomer(s) is it made?

26. Name three synthetic elastomers and the monomer(s) from which they are made.

Condensation Polymers

27. Nylon 88 is made from the monomers $H_2N(CH_2)_8NH_2$ and $HOOC(CH_2)_6COOH$. Draw the structure of nylon 88, showing at least two repeat units from each monomer.

28. Kodel is a polyester fiber. The monomers used to make it are terephthalic acid and 1,4-cyclohexanedimethanol (shown below). Write a condensed structural formula for the repeat unit of Kodel molecule.

$$HOCH_2-\!\!\!\bigcirc\!\!\!-CH_2OH$$

1,4-Cyclohexanedimethanol

29. Draw the structure of a polymer made from glycolic acid (hydroxyacetic acid, $HOCH_2COOH$). Show at least four repeat units. (*Hint:* Compare with nylon 6 in Section 5.)

30. Kevlar, a polyamide used to make bulletproof vests, is made from terephthalic acid and *para*-phenylenediamine (shown below). Write a condensed structural formula for the repeat unit of the Kevlar molecule.

$$H_2N-\!\!\!\bigcirc\!\!\!-NH_2$$

para-Phenylenediamine

Properties of Polymers

31. What three factors give polymers properties that are different from those of materials made up of small molecules?

32. What does the word *plastic* mean **(a)** in everyday life and **(b)** in chemistry?

33. What is the glass transition temperature (T_g) of a polymer? For what uses do we want polymers with a low T_g? With a high T_g?

34. How do plasticizers make polymers less brittle?

Additional Problems

35. In the following equation, identify the parts labeled a, b, and c as monomer, polymer, and repeat unit. What type of polymerization (addition or condensation) is represented?

$$n\,\overset{a}{\overbrace{CH_2=CHF}} \longrightarrow$$

$$\underbrace{\sim CH_2-CHF-\overbrace{CH_2-CHF}^{b}-CH_2-CHF-CH_2-CHF\sim}_{c}$$

36. Is nylon 88 (Problem 27) an addition polymer or a condensation polymer? Explain.

37. One type of Saran has the structure shown below. Write the structures of the two monomers from which it is made.

$$\sim CH_2CCl_2-CH_2CHCl-CH_2CCl_2-CH_2CHCl\sim$$

38. From what monomers could the following copolymer, called poly(styrene-co-acrylonitrile) (SAN), be made?

$$\sim CH_2CH-CH_2CH-CH_2CH\sim$$

with substituents $C\equiv N$, phenyl ring, $C\equiv N$

39. Cyanoacrylates, such as those made from methyl cyanoacrylate (Problem 19b), are used in instant-setting "superglues." However, poly(methyl cyanoacrylate) can irritate tissues. Cyanoacrylates with longer alkyl ester groups are less harsh and can be used in surgery in place of sutures. A good example is poly(octyl cyanoacrylate). Write a polymerization reaction for the formation of poly(octyl cyanoacrylate) from octyl cyanoacrylate, using a condensed structural formula to show the repeat unit of the polymer.

40. Polyethylene terephthalate has a high T_g. How can its T_g be lowered so that a manufacturer can permanently crease a pair of polyethylene terephthalate slacks?

41. Isobutylene $[CH_2{=}C(CH_3)_2]$ polymerizes to form polyisobutylene, a sticky polymer used as an adhesive. Draw the structure of polyisobutylene. Show at least four repeat units.

42. Copolymerization of isoprene and isobutylene (Problem 41) forms butyl rubber. Write the structure of butyl rubber. Show at least three isobutylene repeat units and one isoprene repeat unit.

43. The bacteria *Alcaligenes eutrophus* produce a polymer called polyhydroxybutyrate whose structure is shown below. Write the structure of the hydroxy acid from which this polymer is made.

$$\left[O-\underset{\underset{CH_3}{|}}{CH}-CH_2-\underset{\underset{O}{\|}}{C} \right]_n$$

44. DSM Engineering Plastics makes two specialty polymers: Stanyl® nylon 46 and polytetramethylene terephthalamide (PA$_4$T). (A methylene group is CH_2; tetramethylene consists of four methylene groups: $CH_2CH_2CH_2CH_2$.) Both polymers are made using 1,4-diaminobutane as the diamine. **(a)** What diacid is used for each? Write a condensed structural formula showing the repeat unit of **(b)** Stanyl® nylon 46 and **(c)** PA$_4$T.

45. A student writes the formula for polypropylene as shown below. Identify the error(s) in the formula.

$$\left[CH_2-CH-CH_3 \right]_n$$

46. Based on the condensed structural formula of the repeat unit of poly(ethylene naphthalate) (PEN) shown below, **(a)** write the structure(s) of the monomer(s) and **(b)** state whether the polymer is a polyester or a polyamide.

$$\left[O-\underset{\underset{O}{\|}}{C}-\text{(naphthalene)}-\underset{\underset{O}{\|}}{C}-O-CH_2-CH_2 \right]_n$$

47. A rubber ball dropped from 100 cm will bounce back up to about 60 cm. Balls made from polybutadiene, called SuperBalls, bounce back up to about 85 cm. Golf balls, made from cross-linked polybutadiene, bounce back up to 89 cm. What type of polymer are all three balls made of? Which kind of ball exhibits the property of this type of polymer to the greatest degree?

48. Draw a structure of a likely product if 1,3-propanediol ($HOCH_2CH_2CH_2OH$) is substituted for ethylene glycol in the reaction with terephthalic acid.

49. A student is asked to synthesize a polyester from terephthalic acid and 1,4-butanediol ($HOCH_2CH_2CH_2CH_2OH$). By mistake, the student uses 1-butanol rather than 1,4-butanediol. What is the likely result of this substitution?

50. A student is asked to synthesize a polyester from terephthalic acid and 1,4-butanediol ($HOCH_2CH_2CH_2CH_2OH$). By mistake, the student uses isophthalic acid (shown below) rather than terephthalic acid. What is the likely result of this substitution?

(structure: benzene ring with two COOH groups) COOH ... COOH

51. Draw the structure of the silicone polymer formed from the compound shown below, showing four repeating units.

$$(CH_3)_2CH-\underset{\underset{OH}{|}}{\overset{\overset{OH}{|}}{Si}}-CH_2CH_3$$

52. The two alkenes shown below are different compounds, but when each undergoes addition polymerization, the same polymer is formed. Explain.

$$CH_3-\underset{\underset{Cl}{|}}{C}{=}\underset{\underset{Br}{|}}{C}-CH_2CH_3 \qquad CH_3-\underset{\underset{Cl}{|}}{C}{=}\underset{\underset{CH_2CH_3}{|}}{C}-Br$$

53. The structures of epoxies contain heterocyclic rings, similar to those shown. Some heterocyclic rings are polymerized by breaking one of the bonds between a carbon atom and the oxygen, nitrogen, or sulfur atom and then undergoing an addition reaction. Draw the structures of the polymers that could result from polymerization of the molecules in parts (a) and (b). Show four repeat units for each polymer.

54. Each *amino acid* has an amino group ($-NH_3^+$) and a carboxylic acid group ($-COO^-$). (In each case, a proton has been donated from the carboxylic group to the amino group.) Proteins are polymers of amino acids. Draw the structure of the protein formed by polymerization of glycine, showing four repeat units.

55. Which polymer can be made from renewable resources such as corn?
a. polystyrene (PS)
b. polylactic acid (PLA)
c. polyethylene terephthalate (PET)
d. polyvinyl chloride (PVC)

56. Will a biodegradable polymer degrade in a landfill?

57. Which two polymers are most commonly recycled?
a. polystyrene (PS) and polyvinyl chloride (PVC)
b. low-density polyethylene (LDPE) and polypropylene (PP)
c. polyethylene terephthalate (PET) and high-density polyethylene (HDPE)
d. polylactic acid (PLA) and polyhydroxyalkanoate (PHA)

58. Which type of polymer can be recycled using heat?

COLLABORATIVE GROUP PROJECTS

Prepare a PowerPoint, poster, or other presentation (as directed by your instructor) to share with the class.

1. Prepare a brief report on possible sources of plastics when Earth's supplies of coal and petroleum become scarce.

2. Prepare a brief report on biobased polymers such as bioHDPE, nylon 11 (polyundecylamide), biobased PET, and biobased polytrimethylene terephthalate (PTT). Identify the natural source from which each is derived, and describe intermediate steps from source to final product.

3. Evaluate fully the competition between Pepsi and Coca-Cola as to which company is doing more to reduce its environmental impact by using biobased plastic bottles.

4. Do a risk–benefit analysis of the use of synthetic polymers for one or more of the following.
   - **a.** grocery bags
   - **b.** building materials
   - **c.** clothing
   - **d.** carpets
   - **e.** food packaging
   - **f.** picnic coolers
   - **g.** automobile tires
   - **h.** artificial hip sockets

5. To what extent is plastic litter a problem in your community? Survey one city block (or other area as directed by your instructor), and inventory the litter found. (You might as well pick it up while you are at it.) What proportion of the litter is plastics? What proportion of it is fast-food containers? To what extent are plastics recycled in your community? What factors limit further recycling?

6. Prepare a brief report on one of the following polymers. List sources and commercial uses.
   - **a.** polybutadiene
   - **b.** ethylene–propylene rubber
   - **c.** polyurethanes
   - **d.** epoxy resins

7. Do some research on Kevlar, which is used in body armor. Report on its other uses, and explain why it is so strong. Describe the Kevlar Survivors' Club, jointly sponsored by the International Chiefs of Police and DuPont.

8. Compare the treatment of the topic of the environmental impact of plastics and other polymers at several Web sites, such as those of the American Plastics Council, an industry group, and an environmental group such as Greenpeace or the Sierra Club.

BRIEF ANSWERS TO SELECTED PROBLEMS

Answers are provided for *all in-chapter exercises*. Brief answers are given for *odd-numbered Review Questions*; more complete answers can be obtained by reviewing the text. Answers are provided for *all odd-numbered Problems and Additional Problems*.

NOTE: For numerical problems, your answer may differ slightly from ours because of rounding and the use of significant figures.

1. $-CH_2CH(C\equiv N)-$

2. A. $+CH_2CH(COCH_3)CH_2CH(COCH_3)CH_2CH(COCH_3)$
   $CH_2CH(COCH_3)+$
   B. $+CH_2CH(OCOCH_3)CH_2CH(OCOCH_3)$
   $CH_2CH(OCOCH_3)CH_2CH(OCOCH_3)+$

3. a. $+OCH_2COOCH_2COOCH_2COOCH_2CO+$
   b. $+OCH_2C(=O)+_n$

1. PVC has a Cl atom on alternate C atoms.

3. Polymerization in which all the monomer atoms are incorporated in the polymer; a double bond

5. styrene

7. The first synthetic polymer; phenol and formaldehyde

9. Synthetic fibers; they are cheaper and have a wider range of properties.

11. For many applications, plastics must be separated by type, melted, and formed into new objects.

13. LDPE has highly branched molecules—a loosely packed, amorphous structure that makes it soft and flexible compared with HDPE.

15. a. $CH_2=CH_2$ b. $CH_2=CH-C\equiv N$

17. a. $+CH_2CHClCH_2CHClCH_2CHClCH_2CHCl+$
    b. $+CH_2CF_2CH_2CF_2CH_2CF_2CH_2CF_2+$

19. a. $+CH_2CH(CH_2CH_2CH_3)CH_2CH(CH_2CH_2CH_3)$
    $CH_2CH(CH_2CH_2CH_3)+$
    b. $+CH_2CH(CN)(COOCH_3)CH_2CH(CN)(COOCH_3)$
    $CH_2CH(CN)(COOCH_3)CH_2CH(CN)(COOCH_3)+$

21. $CH_2=CH-CH=CH_2$

23. When stretched, rubber's coiled molecules are straightened. When released, the molecules coil again.

25. SBR is made by copolymerization of styrene and butadiene.

27. $+CO(CH_2)_6CONH(CH_2)_8NHCO(CH_2)_6CONH(CH_2)_8NH+$

29. $+OCH_2COOCH_2COOCH_2COOCH_2CO+$

31. The long chains can entangle with one another; intermolecular forces are greatly multiplied in large molecules; large polymer molecules move more slowly than do small molecules.

33. The temperature at which the properties of the polymer change from hard, stiff, and brittle to rubbery and tough; rubbery materials such as automobile tires should have a low T_g; glass substitutes, a high T_g.

35. Monomer: a; repeating unit: b; polymer: c. addition polymerization

37. $CH_2=CHCl$ and $CH_2=CCl_2$

39.

41. $\sim CH_2C(CH_3)_2CH_2C(CH_3)_2CH_2C(CH_3)_2CH_2C(CH_3)_2\sim$

43. $CH_3CH(OH)CH_2COOH$

45. There are only two C atoms in a backbone segment of polypropylene; the CH_3 is a pendant group.

47. Elastomer; the golf ball

49. A simple diester, dibutylterephthalate, rather than a polymer

51.

53. a. $+CH_2CH_2OCH_2CH_2OCH_2CH_2OCH_2CH_2O+$
    b. $+CH_2CH_2SCH_2CH_2SCH_2CH_2SCH_2CH_2S+$

55. b

57. c

Biochemistry

From Chapter 16 of *Chemistry for Changing Times*, Thirteenth Edition. John W. Hill, Terry W. McCreary, Doris K. Kolb.

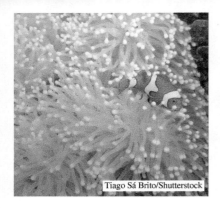

Tiago Sá Brito/Shutterstock

Learning Objectives

> List the major parts of a cell, and describe the function of each part. (1)

> Name the primary source of energy for plants and three classes of substances that are the sources of energy for animals. (1)

> Compare and contrast starch, glycogen, and cellulose. (2)

> Describe the fundamental structure of a fatty acid and of a fat. (3)

> Classify fats as saturated, monounsaturated, or polyunsaturated. (3)

> Draw the fundamental structure of an amino acid, and show how amino acids combine to make proteins. (4)

> Describe the four levels of protein structure, and give an example of each. (5)

> Describe how enzymes work as catalysts. (5)

> Name the two types of nucleic acids, and describe the function of each type. (6)

> Explain complementary base pairing, and describe how a copy of DNA is synthesized. (6)

> Explain how mRNA is synthesized from DNA and how a protein is synthesized from mRNA. (7)

> List important characteristics of the genetic code. (7)

> Describe recombinant DNA technology, and explain how it is used. (8)

> Name some advantages of using biochemistry to create useful molecules.

> Give examples of the use of biochemistry for energy production and other applications.

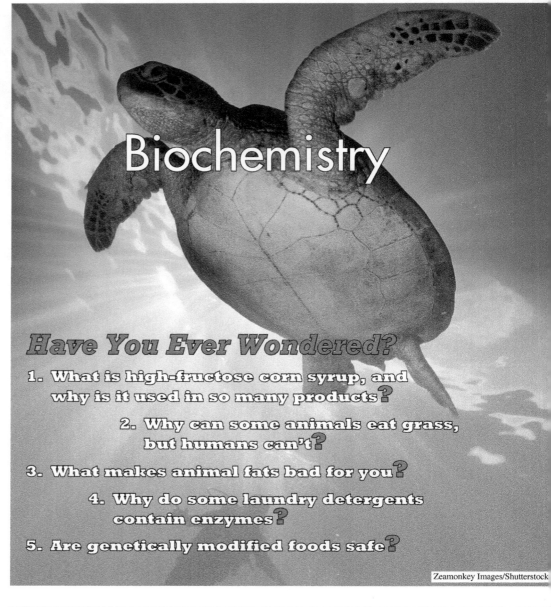

Biochemistry

Have You Ever Wondered?

1. **What is high-fructose corn syrup, and why is it used in so many products?**

2. **Why can some animals eat grass, but humans can't?**

3. **What makes animal fats bad for you?**

4. **Why do some laundry detergents contain enzymes?**

5. **Are genetically modified foods safe?**

Zeamonkey Images/Shutterstock

A Molecular View of Life

The human body is an incredible chemical factory, far more complex than any industrial plant. To stay in good condition and perform its varied tasks, it needs many specific chemical compounds—most of which it manufactures in an exquisitely organized network of chemical production lines.

Every minute of every day, thousands of chemical reactions take place within each of the 100 trillion tiny cells in your body. The study of these reactions and the chemicals they produce is called *biochemistry*.

picturepartners/Shutterstock

Every form of life is chemical in nature. The substances and reactions that occur in living organisms are often more complex than the ones we have already studied. Nonetheless, basic chemical concepts such as acid-base reactions, intermolecular forces, and the reactivity of organic functional groups all apply to living organisms. In this chapter, we will examine acid-base reactions that govern the behavior of proteins in our bodies. We will look at intermolecular forces that influence the properties and behavior of DNA and RNA. And we will see that the functional groups on fats are the same as those on other organic compounds we have studied.

1 Energy and the Living Cell

Learning Objectives > List the major parts of a cell, and describe the function of each part. > Name the primary source of energy for plants and three classes of substances that are the sources of energy for animals.

Biochemistry is the chemistry of living things and life processes. The structural unit of all living things is the *cell*. Every cell is enclosed in a *cell membrane*, through which it gains nutrients and gets rid of wastes. Plant cells (Figure 1) also have walls made of cellulose. Animal cells (see Figure 2) do not have cell walls. Cells have a variety of interior structures that serve a multiplicity of functions. We can consider only a few of them here.

The largest interior structure of a cell is usually the *nucleus*, which contains the material that controls heredity. Protein synthesis takes place in the *ribosomes*. The *mitochondria* are the cell's "batteries," where energy is produced. Plant cells (but not animal cells) also contain *chloroplasts*, in which energy from the Sun is converted to chemical energy, which is stored in the plant in the form of carbohydrates.

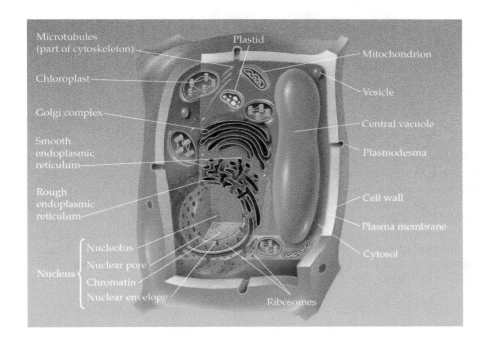

◀ **Figure 1** The general form of a plant cell. Not all the structures shown here occur in every type of plant cell.

Energy in Biological Systems

Life requires energy. Living cells are inherently unstable, and only a continued input of energy keeps them from falling apart. Living organisms are restricted to using certain forms of energy. Supplying a plant with heat energy by holding it in a flame will do little to prolong its life. On the other hand, a green plant is uniquely able to use sunlight, the richest source of energy on Earth. Chloroplasts in green plant cells capture the radiant energy of the Sun and convert it to chemical energy, which is then stored in carbohydrate molecules. The photosynthesis of glucose is represented by the equation

$$6\,CO_2 + 6\,H_2O \longrightarrow C_6H_{12}O_6 + 6\,O_2$$

Plant cells can also convert the carbohydrate molecules to fat molecules and, given the proper inorganic nutrients, to protein molecules.

▶ **Figure 2** An animal cell. The entire range of structures shown here seldom occurs in a single cell, and only a few of them are discussed in this text. Each kind of plant or animal tissue has cells specific to the function of that tissue. Muscle cells differ from nerve cells, nerve cells differ from red blood cells, and so on.

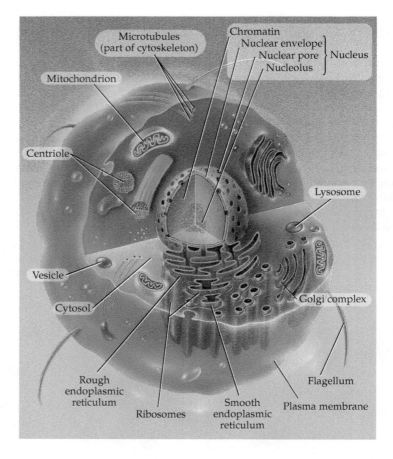

This chapter, deals mainly with the synthesis and structure of carbohydrates, fats, and protiens.

Animals cannot directly use the energy of sunlight. They must get their energy by eating plants or by eating other animals that eat plants. Animals obtain energy from three major types of substances: carbohydrates, fats, and proteins.

Once digested and transported to a cell, a food molecule can be used as a building block to make new cell parts or to repair old ones, or it can be "burned" for energy. The entire series of coordinated chemical reactions that keep cells alive is called **metabolism**. In general, metabolic reactions are divided into two classes: The degrading of molecules to provide energy is called **catabolism**, and the process of building up, or synthesizing, the molecules of living systems is termed **anabolism**.

Self-Assessment Questions

1. The three major types of substances from which we obtain energy are
   a. amino acids, proteins, and carbohydrates
   b. burgers, pizza, and soft drinks
   c. carbohydrates, fats, and proteins
   d. proteins, nucleic acids, and oils

2. The process of degrading molecules to provide energy within a living cell is called
   a. anabolism
   b. catabolism
   c. depolymerization
   d. transcription

3. The overall set of chemical reactions that keep cells alive is called
   a. anabolism
   b. enzymology
   c. metabolism
   d. proteolysis

Answers: 1, c; 2, b; 3, c

2 Carbohydrates: A Storehouse of Energy

Learning Objectives › Compare and contrast starch, glycogen, and cellulose.

It is difficult to give a simple formal definition of *carbohydrates*. Chemically, **carbohydrates** are polyhydroxy aldehydes or ketones or compounds that can be hydrolyzed (split by water) to form such aldehydes and ketones. Composed of the elements carbon, hydrogen, and oxygen, carbohydrates include sugars, starches, and cellulose. Usually, the atoms of these elements are present in a ratio expressed by the formula $C_x(H_2O)_y$. Glucose, a simple sugar, has the formula $C_6H_{12}O_6$, which we can write as $C_6(H_2O)_6$. The term *carbohydrate* is derived from formulas written in this way, but keep in mind that carbohydrates are not actually hydrates of carbon.

Some Simple Sugars

Sugars are sweet-tasting carbohydrates. The simplest sugars are **monosaccharides**, carbohydrates that cannot be further hydrolyzed. Three familiar dietary monosaccharides are shown in Figure 3. They are *glucose* (also called *dextrose*), *galactose* (a component of lactose, the sugar in milk), and *fructose* (fruit sugar). Glucose and galactose are **aldoses**, monosaccharides with an aldehyde functional group. Fructose is a **ketose**, a monosaccharide with a ketone functional group. Pure fructose is about 25% sweeter than table sugar (sucrose, shown on the next page); glucose is about 25% less sweet than table sugar.

| CONCEPTUAL **Example 1** | Classification of Monosaccharides |

Shown below are structures of (left to right) erythrulose, used in some sunless tanning lotions; mannose, a sugar found in some fruits, including cranberries; and ribose, a component of ribonucleic acid (RNA; Section 7).

$$
\begin{array}{ccc}
 & \begin{array}{c} \text{CHO} \\ | \\ \text{HO}-\text{C}-\text{H} \\ | \end{array} & \\
\begin{array}{c} \text{CH}_2\text{OH} \\ | \\ \text{C}=\text{O} \\ | \\ \text{HO}-\text{C}-\text{H} \\ | \\ \text{CH}_2\text{OH} \end{array} &
\begin{array}{c} \text{HO}-\text{C}-\text{H} \\ | \\ \text{H}-\text{C}-\text{OH} \\ | \\ \text{H}-\text{C}-\text{OH} \\ | \\ \text{CH}_2\text{OH} \end{array} &
\begin{array}{c} \text{CHO} \\ | \\ \text{H}-\text{C}-\text{OH} \\ | \\ \text{H}-\text{C}-\text{OH} \\ | \\ \text{H}-\text{C}-\text{OH} \\ | \\ \text{CH}_2\text{OH} \end{array} \\
\text{Erythrulose} & \text{Mannose} & \text{Ribose}
\end{array}
$$

Classify erythrulose and ribose as an aldose or a ketose.

Solution

Erythrulose is a ketose. The carbonyl (C=O) group is on the second C atom from the top; it is between two other C atoms, an arrangement that defines a ketone. Ribose is an aldose. The carbonyl group includes a chain-ending carbon atom, as in all aldehydes.

■ EXERCISE 1

How does the structure of mannose (shown above) differ from that of glucose?

The monosaccharides glucose, galactose, and fructose are represented in Figure 3 as open-chain compounds to show the aldehyde or ketone functional groups. However, these sugars exist in solution mainly as cyclic molecules (see Figure 4).

1. What is high-fructose corn syrup, and why is it used in so many products? High-fructose corn syrup (HFCS) has had some of its glucose enzymatically converted to fructose. This makes it significantly sweeter than ordinary corn syrup, because fructose is sweeter than glucose. HFCS is quite cheap in the United States. Unfortunately, like table sugar, it provides little more than empty calories.

Figure 3 Three common monosaccharides. All have hydroxyl groups. Glucose and galactose have aldehyde functional groups, and fructose has a ketone group. Glucose and galactose differ only in the arrangement of the H and OH on the fourth carbon (green) from the top. Living cells use glucose as a source of energy. Fructose is fruit sugar, and galactose is a component of milk sugar.

Q: *What is the molecular formula of each of the three monosaccharides? How are the three compounds related?*

Aldehyde functional group

Ketone functional group

Glucose   Galactose   Fructose

Aldoses   **A ketose**

Figure 4 Cyclic structures for glucose, galactose, and fructose. A corner with no letter represents a carbon atom. Glucose and galactose differ only in the arrangement of the H and OH (green) on the fourth carbon. Some sugars exist in more than one cyclic form, but, for simplicity, only one form of each is shown here.

Glucose   Galactose   Fructose

▲ Although we have represented the cyclic monosaccharides as flat hexagons, they are actually three-dimensional. Most assume a conformation (shape) called a *chair conformation* because it somewhat resembles a reclining chair.

Sucrose and lactose are examples of **disaccharides**, carbohydrates whose molecules can be hydrolyzed to yield two monosaccharide units (Figure 5). Sucrose is split into glucose and fructose. Hydrolysis of lactose yields glucose and galactose.

$$Sucrose + H_2O \longrightarrow Glucose + Fructose$$

$$Lactose + H_2O \longrightarrow Glucose + Galactose$$

Sucrose   Lactose

▲ **Figure 5** Sucrose and lactose are disaccharides. On hydrolysis, sucrose yields glucose and fructose, whereas lactose yields glucose and galactose. Sucrose is cane or beet sugar, and lactose is milk sugar.

Q: *What is the molecular formula of each of these disaccharides? How are the two compounds related? Label the two monosaccharide units in each as fructose, galactose, or glucose.*

Polysaccharides: Starch and Cellulose

Polysaccharides are composed of large molecules that yield many monosaccharide units on hydrolysis. Polysaccharides include starches, which comprise the main energy-storage system of many plants, and cellulose, which is the structural material of plants. Figure 6 shows short segments of starch and cellulose molecules.

Biochemistry

(a) Segment of a starch molecule

(b) Segment of a cellulose molecule

Figure 6 Both starch and cellulose are polymers of glucose. They differ in that the glucose units are joined by alpha linkages (blue) in starch and by beta linkages (red) in cellulose.

Q: *The formulas for most polymers can be written in condensed form. Write a condensed formula for starch. How would the condensed formula for cellulose differ from that of starch?*

Notice that both are polymers of glucose. Starch molecules generally have from 100 to about 6000 glucose units. Cellulose molecules are composed of 1800–3000 or more glucose units.

A crucial structural difference between starch and cellulose is the way the glucose units are hooked together. In starch, with the —CH₂OH group at the top as a reference, the oxygen atom joining the glucose units is pointed *down*. This arrangement is called an *alpha linkage*. In cellulose, again with the —CH₂OH group as the point of reference, the oxygen atom connecting the glucose units is pointed *up*, an arrangement called a *beta linkage*.

This subtle but important difference in linkage determines whether the material can be digested by humans. The different linkages also result in different three-dimensional forms for cellulose and starch. For example, cellulose in the cell walls of plants is arranged in *fibrils*, bundles of parallel chains. As shown in Figure 7(a), these fibrils lie parallel to each other in each layer of the cell wall. In alternate layers, the fibrils are perpendicular, an arrangement that imparts great strength to the cell wall.

There are two kinds of starches found in plants. One, called *amylose*, has glucose units joined in a continuous chain like beads on a string. The other kind, *amylopectin*, has branched chains of glucose units. These starches are perhaps best represented schematically, as in Figure 8, where each glucose unit is represented by filled circles.

2. Why can some animals eat grass, but humans can't? Although both cellulose and starch are glucose polymers, humans do not have the enzyme to break the beta linkages in cellulose. The digestive systems of cows, horses, and deer contain bacteria that can break these linkages, allowing these ruminants to digest the cellulose in grass.

Figure 7 Cellulose molecules form fibers, whereas starch molecules (glycogen) form granules. Electron micrographs of (a) the cell wall of an alga, made up of successive layers of cellulose fibers in parallel arrangement, and (b) glycogen granules in a liver cell of a rat.

(a)

(b)

325

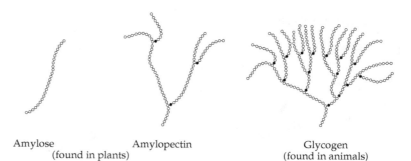

Amylose
(found in plants)

Amylopectin

Glycogen
(found in animals)

▶ **Figure 8** Schematic representations of amylose, amylopectin, and glycogen. Amylose is unbranched. Amylopectin has a branch approximately every 25 glucose units. Glycogen branches about every 10 glucose units.

When cornstarch is heated at about 400 °F for an hour, the starch polymers are broken down into shorter chains to form a product called *dextrin*, which has properties intermediate between those of sugars and starches. Mixed with water, dextrin makes a slightly thick, sticky mixture. Starch and dextrin adhesives account for about 58% of the U.S. packaging market.

Animal starch is called *glycogen*. Like amylopectin, it is composed of branched chains of glucose units. In contrast to cellulose, we see in Figure 7(b) that glycogen in muscle and liver tissue is arranged in granules, clusters of small particles. Plant starch, on the other hand, forms large granules. Granules of plant starch rupture in boiling water to form a paste, which gels when it cools. Potatoes and cereal grains form this type of starchy broth. All forms of starch are hydrolyzed to glucose during digestion.

Self-Assessment Questions

1. A monosaccharide with an aldehyde group is called
   a. an aldol   **b.** an aldose   **c.** aldicarb   **d.** aldosterol

2. A ketose is a monosaccharide
   a. diet aid   **b.** that forms polyhydroxy cellulose
   c. that causes ketosis   **d.** with a ketone group

3. When most monosaccharides dissolve in water, they form
   a. branched polysaccharides   **b.** disaccharides
   c. ring structures   **d.** polysaccharides

4. The two monosaccharide units that make up a lactose molecule are
   a. both glucose   **b.** fructose and galactose
   c. glucose and fructose   **d.** glucose and galactose

5. Which of these polysaccharide molecules consists of branched chains of glucose units?
   a. amylose and amylopectin   **b.** amylose and cellulose
   c. amylose and glycogen   **d.** amylopectin and glycogen

6. Carbohydrates are stored in the liver and muscle tissue as
   a. amylose   **b.** amylopectin   **c.** cellulose   **d.** glycogen

Answers: 1, b; 2, d; 3, c; 4, d; 5, d; 6, d

3 Fats and Other Lipids

Learning Objectives ❯ Describe the fundamental structure of a fatty acid and of a fat.
❯ Classify fats as saturated, monounsaturated, or polyunsaturated.

Fats are the predominant forms of a class of compounds called *lipids*. These substances are not defined by a functional group, as are most other families of organic compounds. Rather, lipids have common solubility properties. A **lipid** is a cellular component that is insoluble in water but soluble in organic solvents of low polarity, such as hexane, diethyl ether, and chloroform. In addition to fats, the lipid family includes **fatty acids** (long-chain carboxylic acids), steroids such as cholesterol and sex hormones, fat-soluble vitamins, and other substances. Figure 9 shows three representations of palmitic acid, a typical fatty acid.

(a)

(b)

(c)

◀ **Figure 9** Three representations of palmitic acid: (a) Condensed structural formula. (b) Line-angle formula, in which the lines denote bonds and each intersection of lines or end of a line represents a carbon atom. (c) Space-filling model.

A **fat** is an ester of fatty acids and the trihydroxy alcohol glycerol (Figure 10). A fat has three fatty acid chains joined to glycerol through ester linkages (which is why fats are often called *triglycerides*, or *triacylglycerols*). Related compounds are also classified according to the number of fatty acid chains they contain: A *monoglyceride* has one fatty acid chain joined to glycerol, and a *diglyceride* has two.

Glycerol   Fatty acids   A triglyceride
(a)

(b)

◀ **Figure 10** Triglycerides (triacylglycerols) are esters in which the trihydroxy (having three OH groups) alcohol glycerol is esterified with three fatty acid groups. (a) The equation for the formation of a triglyceride. (b) Space-filling model of a triglyceride.

Naturally occurring fatty acids nearly always have an even number of carbon atoms. Representative ones are listed in Table 1. Animal fats are generally rich in saturated fatty acids (fatty acids with no carbon-to-carbon double bonds) and have a smaller proportion of unsaturated fatty acids. At room temperature, most animal fats are solids. Liquid fats, called *oils*, are obtained mainly from vegetable sources. Oils typically have a higher proportion of unsaturated fatty acid units than do fats. Fats and oils feel greasy. They are less dense than water and float on it.

Fats are often classified according to the degree of unsaturation of the fatty acids they incorporate. A *saturated fatty acid* contains no carbon-to-carbon double bonds, a *monounsaturated fatty acid* has one carbon-to-carbon double bond per molecule, and a *polyunsaturated fatty acid* has two or more carbon-to-carbon double bonds. A *saturated fat* contains a high proportion of saturated fatty acids; these fat molecules have relatively few carbon-to-carbon double bonds. A *polyunsaturated fat* (oil) incorporates mainly unsaturated fatty acids; these fat molecules have many double bonds.

Table 1 Some Fatty Acids in Natural Fats

Number of Carbon Atoms	Condensed Structural Formula	Name	Source
4	$CH_3CH_2CH_2COOH$	Butyric acid	Butter
6	$CH_3(CH_2)_4COOH$	Caproic acid	Butter
8	$CH_3(CH_2)_6COOH$	Caprylic acid	Coconut oil
10	$CH_3(CH_2)_8COOH$	Capric acid	Coconut oil
12	$CH_3(CH_2)_{10}COOH$	Lauric acid	Palm kernel oil
14	$CH_3(CH_2)_{12}COOH$	Myristic acid	Oil of nutmeg
16	$CH_3(CH_2)_{14}COOH$	Palmitic acid	Palm oil
18	$CH_3(CH_2)_{16}COOH$	Stearic acid	Beef tallow
18	$CH_3(CH_2)_7CH{=}CH(CH_2)_7COOH$	Oleic acid	Olive oil
18	$CH_3(CH_2)_4CH{=}CHCH_2CH{=}CH(CH_2)_7COOH$	Linoleic acid	Soybean oil
18	$CH_3CH_2(CH{=}CHCH_2)_3(CH_2)_6COOH$	Linolenic acid	Fish oils
20	$CH_3(CH_2)_4(CH{=}CHCH_2)_4CH_2CH_2COOH$	Arachidonic acid	Liver

The iodine number is a measure of the degree of unsaturation of a fat or oil. The **iodine number** is the mass in grams of iodine that is consumed by 100 g of fat or oil. Iodine, like other halogens, adds to a carbon-to-carbon double bond.

$$\text{C}{=}\text{C} + I_2 \longrightarrow -\overset{|}{\underset{|}{\text{C}}}-\overset{|}{\underset{|}{\text{C}}}-$$

3. What makes animal fats bad for you? The saturated fats found in most animal fats can pack closely together to form artery-clogging plaque, which contributes to heart disease. The structures of unsaturated fats do not stack neatly and do not form this plaque.

The more double bonds a fat contains, the more iodine is required for the addition reaction. Thus, a high iodine number means a high degree of unsaturation. Representative iodine numbers are listed in Table 2. Note the generally lower values for animal fats (butter, tallow, and lard) compared with those for vegetable oils. Coconut oil, which is highly saturated, and fish oils, which are relatively unsaturated, are notable exceptions to the general rule.

Table 2 Typical Iodine Numbers for Some Fats and Oils[a]

Fat or Oil	Iodine Number	Fat or Oil	Iodine Number
Coconut oil	8–10	Cottonseed oil	100–117
Butter	25–40	Corn oil	115–130
Beef tallow	30–45	Fish oils	120–180
Palm oil	37–54	Canola oil	125–135
Lard	45–70	Soybean oil	125–140
Olive oil	75–95	Safflower oil	130–140
Peanut oil	85–100	Sunflower oil	130–145

[a]Oils shown in blue are from plant sources.

▲ Many salad dressings are made of an oil and vinegar. The one shown here has olive oil floating on balsamic vinegar, an aqueous solution of acetic acid.

Self-Assessment Questions

1. Lipids are defined by their
   a. chemical reactivity
   b. functional group
   c. function in the body
   d. solubility properties

Questions 2–6 refer to the structures S, T, U, and V.

> S: $CH_3(CH_2)_{10}COOH$ T: $CH_3(CH_2)_{16}COOH$
>
> U: $CH_3(CH_2)_7CH{=}CH(CH_2)_7COOH$ V: $CH_3CH_2(CH{=}CHCH_2)_3(CH_2)_6COOH$

2. Which are saturated fatty acids?
   a. S and T   **b.** S and U   **c.** T and U   **d.** U and V

3. Which is a monounsaturated fatty acid?
   a. S   **b.** T   **c.** U   **d.** V

4. Which is a polyunsaturated fatty acid?
   a. S   **b.** T   **c.** U   **d.** V

5. Saturated fats often have a high proportion of
   a. S and T   **b.** S and U   **c.** T and U   **d.** U and V

6. Polyunsaturated fats (oils) often have a high proportion of
   a. S   **b.** T   **c.** U   **d.** V

7. The iodine number of a fat or oil expresses its
   a. calories per gram
   b. degree of acidity
   c. degree of unsaturation
   d. digestibility

8. In general, animal fats differ from vegetable oils in that the fat molecules
   a. are higher in calories
   b. are shorter
   c. have fewer $C{=}C$ bonds
   d. have more $C{=}C$ bonds

Answers: 1, d; 2, a; 3, c; 4, d; 5, a; 6, d; 7, c; 8, c

4 Proteins: Polymers of Amino Acids

Learning Objective ❯ Draw the fundamental structure of an amino acid, and show how amino acids combine to make proteins.

Proteins are vital components of all life. No living part of the human body—or of any other organism, for that matter—is completely without protein. There is protein in blood, muscles, brain, and even tooth enamel. The smallest cellular organisms—bacteria—contain protein. Viruses, so small that they make bacteria look like giants, are little more than proteins and nucleic acids, a combination that is the stuff of life itself.

Each type of cell makes its own kinds of proteins. Proteins serve as the structural materials of animals, much as cellulose does in plants. Muscle tissue is largely protein, and so are skin and hair. Silk, wool, nails, claws, feathers, horns, and hooves are proteins. All proteins contain the elements carbon, hydrogen, oxygen, and nitrogen, and most also contain sulfur. The structure of a short segment of a typical protein molecule is shown in Figure 11.

Like starch and cellulose, *proteins* are polymers. They differ from other polymers that we have studied in that the monomer units are about 20 different amino acids (Table 3). The amino acids differ in their side chains (shown in green). An **amino acid** has two functional groups, an amino group (—NH_2) and a carboxyl group (—COOH), attached to the same carbon atom (called the *alpha carbon*).

$$H_2N{-}\underset{\underset{H}{|}}{\overset{\overset{R}{|}}{C}}{-}COOH$$

▶ **Figure 11** Space-filling model (a) and structural formula (b) of a short segment of a protein molecule. In the structural formula, hydrocarbon side chains (green), an acidic side chain (red), a basic side chain (blue), and a sulfur-containing side chain (amber shading) are highlighted. The dashed lines crossing the formula indicate where two amino-acid units join (see Section 5).

Q: *The formulas for most polymers can be written in condensed form. Those for natural proteins cannot. Explain.*

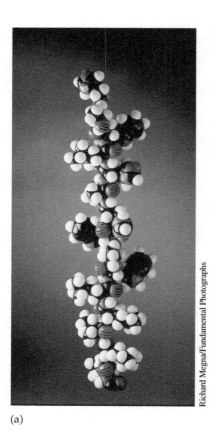

(a)

(b)

In this formula, the R can be a hydrogen atom (as it is in glycine, the simplest amino acid) or any of the groups shown in green in Table 3. The formula shows the proper placement of the groups, but it is not really correct. Acids react with bases to form salts. The carboxyl group is acidic, and the amino group is basic. The two functional groups interact, the acid transferring a proton to the base. The resulting product is an inner salt, or **zwitterion**, a compound in which the negative charge and the positive charge are on different parts of the same molecule.

$$H_3N^+ - \overset{\overset{\displaystyle R}{|}}{\underset{\underset{\displaystyle H}{|}}{C}} - COO^-$$

A zwitterion

Plants can synthesize proteins from carbon dioxide, water, and minerals such as nitrates (NO_3^-) and sulfates (SO_4^{2-}). Animals need to consume proteins in their foods. Humans can synthesize some of the amino acids in Table 3. Others must be part of the proteins consumed in a normal diet. The latter are called *essential amino acids*.

The Peptide Bond: Peptides and Proteins

The human body contains tens of thousands of different proteins. Each of us has a tailor-made set. Proteins are polyamides. The amide linkage is called a **peptide bond** (shaded part of the structure below) when it joins two amino-acid units.

$$H_2N - \overset{\overset{\displaystyle R_1}{|}}{\underset{\underset{\displaystyle H}{|}}{C}} - \overset{}{\underset{\underset{\displaystyle O}{||}}{C}} - \overset{\overset{\displaystyle H}{|}}{N} - \overset{\overset{\displaystyle H}{|}}{\underset{\underset{\displaystyle R_2}{|}}{C}} - COOH$$

Table 3 The 20 Amino Acids Specified by the Human Genetic Code

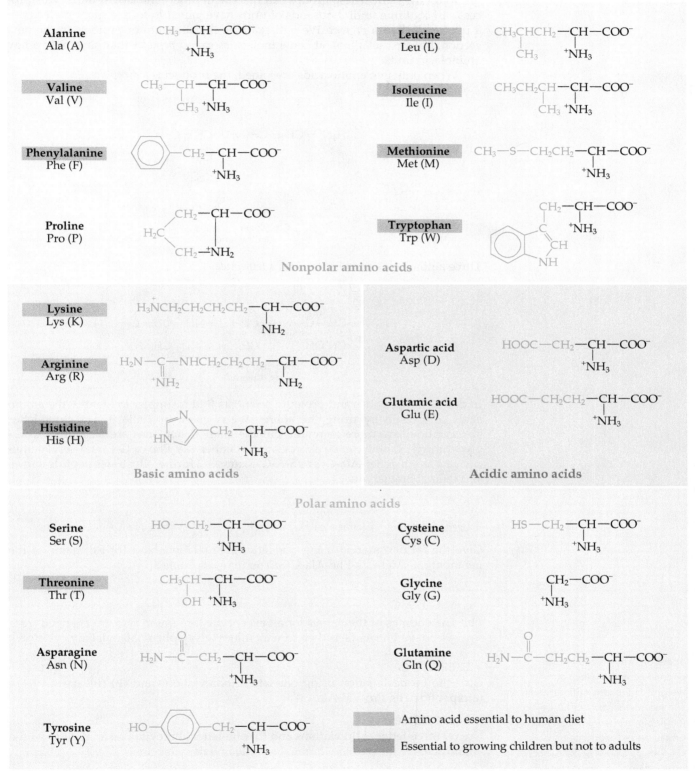

Nonpolar amino acids

Basic amino acids

Acidic amino acids

Polar amino acids

Amino acid essential to human diet

Essential to growing children but not to adults

Note that this molecule still has a reactive amino group on the left and a carboxyl group on the right. These groups can react with other amino-acid units. This process can continue until thousands of units have joined to form a giant molecule—a polymer called a *protein*. We will examine the structure of proteins in the next section, but first let's look at some molecules called *peptides* that have only a few amino-acid units.

When only two amino acids are joined, the product is a *dipeptide*.

$$H_3N^+ - CH_2 - \overset{\overset{\displaystyle O}{\|}}{C} - NH - CH - \overset{\overset{\displaystyle O}{\|}}{C} - O^-$$

Glycylphenylalanine
(a dipeptide)

Three amino acids combine to form a *tripeptide*.

$$H_3N^+ - CH - \overset{\overset{\displaystyle O}{\|}}{C} - NH - CH - \overset{\overset{\displaystyle O}{\|}}{C} - NH - CH - \overset{\overset{\displaystyle O}{\|}}{C} - O^-$$

Serylalanylcysteine
(a tripeptide)

In describing peptides and proteins, scientists find it simpler to identify the amino acids in a chain by using the abbreviations given in Table 3. The three-letter abbreviations are more common, but the single-letter ones are also used. Thus, glycylphenylalanine can be abbreviated as either Gly-Phe or G-F, and serylalanylcysteine as either Ser-Ala-Cys or S-A-C. Example 2 further illustrates peptide names and their abbreviations.

Example 2   Names of Peptides

Give the **(a)** designation using one-letter abbreviations and **(b)** full name of the pentapeptide Met-Gly-Phe-Ala-Cys. You may use Table 3.

Solution

a. M-G-F-A-C
b. The endings of the names for all except the last amino acid are changed from *-ine* to *-yl*. The name is therefore methionylglycylphenylalanylalanylcysteine.

■ EXERCISE 2A
Give the **(a)** designation using one-letter abbreviations and **(b)** full name of the tetrapeptide His-Pro-Val-Ala.

■ EXERCISE 2B
Use **(a)** three-letter abbreviations and **(b)** one-letter abbreviations to identify all the amino acids in the peptide threonylglycylalanylalanylleucine.

Some protein molecules are enormous, with molecular weights in the tens of thousands. The molecular formula for hemoglobin, the oxygen-carrying protein in red blood cells, is $C_{3032}H_{4816}O_{780}N_{780}S_8Fe_4$, corresponding to a molar mass of 64,450 g/mol. Although they are huge compared with ordinary molecules, a billion average-sized protein molecules could still fit on the head of a pin.

A molecule with more than 10 amino-acid units is often simply called a **polypeptide**. When the molecular weight of a polypeptide exceeds about 10,000, it is called a **protein**. These distinctions are arbitrary and not always precisely applied.

GREEN CHEMISTRY

Principles 1, 2, 3, 4, 5, 6, 7, 8, 9, 10, 12

David A. Vosburg, *Harvey Mudd College*

Green Chemistry and Biochemistry

Chemistry has gone on constantly for millions of years in plants, animals, and bacteria. These living systems perform many chemical reactions, and plants have evolved to harness energy from the Sun using photosynthesis. Living things store energy in the form of carbohydrates (like glucose, sucrose, and cellulose, Section 2) and lipids (fats and oils, Section 3). These renewable feedstocks (Principle 7) hold great potential for supplying human energy needs in the future.

Chemists are devising ways of converting these natural energy reservoirs into substitutes for nonrenewable petroleum fuels, and biochemists are engineering existing biochemical pathways in various microorganisms to directly produce usable fuels. In 2009 and 2010, three Presidential Green Chemistry Challenge Awards were given for work in this area to Virent Energy Systems, James Liao, and LS9. Virent's process transforms plant carbohydrates into gasoline, which could reduce U.S. dependence on fossil fuels. Liao and coworkers (UCLA and Easel Biotechnologies) have engineered bacteria to turn carbohydrates and carbon dioxide into alcohols that can be used as fuels. The LS9 company developed microorganisms that directly produce hydrocarbon fuels. All of these achievements use the products or processes of biochemistry to address the energy needs of tomorrow.

Using biochemistry to make molecules has several distinct advantages over traditional chemical synthesis and invokes many of the green chemistry principles. The reactions normally occur in water, a ubiquitous, nontoxic, and nonflammable solvent (Principle 5). When reaction products are nonpolar, they can often be separated easily from the more polar water. In contrast to many current industrial reactions that are performed at very high temperatures and pressures, most biochemical reactions are extremely rapid and occur at mild temperatures and atmospheric pressure. These reactions reduce both energy costs and potential hazards (Principles 6 and 12). The atom economy of biochemical reactions is very high, as protecting groups and auxiliaries are not necessary (Principles 2 and 8), and toxic reagents and products can also be avoided in most cases (Principles 3 and 4). Biological reactions are frequently catalytic, using a single enzyme (Section 5) for thousands or millions of repeated reactions to selectively generate products with very little waste produced (Principles 1 and 9). Furthermore, the products formed (and the biological catalysts themselves) are generally biodegradable and innocuous (Principle 10). Also, when compounds are not themselves biodegradable, other biochemical pathways may be employed to degrade molecules that would otherwise

persist in the environment. This bioremediation of environmental waste by cleaning up toxins and purifying water is a very important advantage of using biochemistry.

A common challenge associated with organic reactions is the production of specific isomers of molecules. Although these processes traditionally have relied on metal compounds as catalysts, new biochemical routes are increasingly preferred. For example, Merck and Codexis received a Presidential Green Chemistry Challenge Award in 2010 for their development of an enzyme catalyst for the production of the diabetes drug Januvia. As an example of the pace of innovation, the new method replaced a high-pressure reaction that used hydrogen gas and an expensive rhodium catalyst, a process that had been recognized with a Presidential Green Chemistry Challenge Award in 2006. The new biochemical pathway increases the yield of the drug and dramatically reduces the amount of waste produced. These innovations benefit the pharmaceutical companies, diabetics, the environment, and society at large.

The self-replicating nature of the cell and its DNA and the self-assembling (folding) properties of proteins (Section 5) make biological systems ideal candidates for the discovery and implementation of novel chemical processes. One of the greatest strengths of biochemical reactions is also the greatest challenge: specificity. Biological catalysts have evolved to have exquisite selectivity for their natural substrate(s), so adapting these catalysts to have more general function for a wider range of (potentially unnatural) substrates is difficult. Yet this is precisely what was done by Merck and Codexis for the synthesis of Januvia, so there is hope that similar approaches could lead to other successes.

UCLA Henry Samueli School of Engineering and Applied Science

▲ Genetic engineering of bacteria may transform natural energy sources into materials that will be energy-rich for human use. *Synechococcus elongatus*, shown here, may be particularly useful because of its small genome and its aptitude for photosynthesis.

333

The Sequence of Amino Acids

For peptides and proteins to function properly, it is not enough that they incorporate certain *amounts* of specific amino acids. The order, or *sequence*, in which the amino acids are connected, is also of critical importance. The sequence is written starting at the free amino group ($-NH_3^+$), called the *N-terminal* end, and continuing to the free carboxyl group ($-COO^-$), called the *C-terminal* end.

$$H_3N^+ \: CHC-NHCHC \left(NHCHC \right)_n NHCHC-NHCHC-O^-$$

N-terminal end   C-terminal end

Glycylalanine (Gly-Ala) is therefore different from alanylglycine (Ala-Gly). Although the difference seems minor, the structures are different, and the two substances behave differently in the body.

$$H_3N^+ \: CH_2CO-NHCHCOO^- \qquad H_3N^+ \: CHCO-NHCH_2COO^-$$

Glycylalanine   Alanylglycine

As the length of a peptide chain increases, the number of possible sequential variations becomes enormous. Just as millions of different words can be made from the 26 letters of the English alphabet, millions of different proteins can be made from the 20 amino acids. And just as we can write gibberish with the English alphabet, nonfunctioning proteins can be formed by putting together the wrong sequence of amino acids.

Example 3   Numbers of Peptides

How many different tripeptides can be made from one unit each of the three amino acids methionine, valine, and phenylalanine? Write the sequences of these tripeptides, using the three-letter abbreviations in Table 3.

Solution

We write the various possibilities. Two begin with Met, two start with Val, and two with Phe:

Met-Val-Phe	Val-Met-Phe	Phe-Val-Met
Met-Phe-Val	Val-Phe-Met	Phe-Met-Val

There are six possible tripeptides.

EXERCISE 3A

How many different tripeptides can be made from two methionine units and one valine unit?

EXERCISE 3B

How many different tetrapeptides can be made from one unit each of the four amino acids methionine, valine, tyrosine, and phenylalanine?

Although the correct sequence is ordinarily of utmost importance, it is not always absolutely required. Just as you can sometimes make sense of incorrectly spelled English words, a protein with a small percentage of "incorrect" amino acids may function, but just not as well. And sometimes a seemingly minor difference can have a disastrous effect. Some people have hemoglobin with one incorrect amino-acid unit out of about 300. That "minor" error is responsible for sickle cell anemia, an inherited condition that often proves fatal.

Self-Assessment Questions

1. Proteins are polymers of
   a. amino acids
   b. fatty acids
   c. monoacylglycerides
   d. monosaccharides

2. The 20 amino acids that make up proteins differ mainly in their
   a. alpha carbon atoms
   b. amino groups
   c. carboxyl groups
   d. side chains

3. Which of the following is *not* an alpha amino acid?
   a. $CH_3C(CH_3)(NH_2)COOH$
   b. $(CH_3)_2CHCH(NH_2)COOH$
   c. H_2NCH_2COOH
   d. $H_2NCH_2CH_2CH_2COOH$

4. Which of the following is a zwitterion?
   a. $H_2NCH_2COO^-$
   b. $^-NHCH_2COO^-$
   c. $H_3N^+CH_2COOH$
   d. $^+H_3NCH_2COO^-$

5. In a dipeptide, two amino acids are joined through a(n)
   a. amide linkage
   b. dipolar interaction
   c. ionic bond
   d. hydrogen bond

6. The N-terminal amino acid and the C-terminal amino acid of the peptide Met-Ile-Val-Glu-Cys-Tyr-Gln-Trp-Asp are, respectively,
   a. Asp and Met
   b. Met and Asp
   c. Met and Ile
   d. Trp and Asp

7. How many different tripeptides can be formed from alanine, valine, and lysine, when each appears only once in each product?
   a. 1   **b.** 3   **c.** 6   **d.** 9

8. The tripeptides represented as Ala-Val-Lys and Lys-Val-Ala are
   a. different only in name
   b. different in molar mass
   c. exactly the same
   d. two different peptides

Answers: 1, a; 2, d; 3, d; 4, d; 5, a; 6, b; 7, c; 8, d

5 Structure and Function of Proteins

Learning Objectives ❯ Describe the four levels of protein structure, and give an example of each. ❯ Describe how enzymes work as catalysts.

The structures of proteins have four organizational levels:

- **Primary structure.** Amino acids are linked by peptide bonds to form polypeptide chains. The primary structure of a protein molecule is simply the order of its amino acids. By convention, this order is written from the amino (N-terminal end) to the carboxyl (C-terminal end).
- **Secondary structure.** Polypeptide chains can fold into regular structures such as the alpha helix and the beta pleated sheet (described in this section).
- **Tertiary structure.** Protein folding creates spatial relationships between amino-acid units that are relatively far apart in the protein chain.
- **Quaternary structure.** Two or more polypeptide chains can assemble into multiunit structures.

To specify the primary structure, we write out the sequence of amino acids. For even a small protein molecule, this sequence can be quite long. For example, it takes about two pages, using the one-letter abbreviations, to give the sequence of the 1927 amino-acid units in lactase, the enzyme that catalyzes the hydrolysis of the disaccharide lactose into galactose and glucose. The primary structure of angiotensin II, a peptide that causes powerful constriction of blood vessels and is produced in the kidneys, is

Asp-Arg-Val-Tyr-Ile-His-Pro-Phe

Figure 12 Beta pleated sheet structure consisting of protein chains. (a) Ball-and-stick model. (b) Model emphasizing the pleats. The side chains extend above or below the sheet and alternate along the chain. The protein chains are held together by interchain hydrogen bonds.

(a)

(b)

Intermolecular hydrogen bonds

▲ The protein strands in an alpha helix are often represented as coiled ribbons.

▲ The protein strands in a pleated sheet are often represented as ribbons.

Figure 13 Two representations of the α-helical conformation of a protein chain. (a) Intrachain hydrogen bonding between turns of the helix is shown in the ball-and-stick model. (b) The skeletal representation better shows the helix.

This sequence specifies an octapeptide with aspartic acid at the N-terminal end, followed by arginine, valine, tyrosine, isoleucine, histidine, proline, and then phenylalanine at the C-terminal end.

The secondary structure of a protein refers to the arrangement of chains about an axis. The two main types of secondary structure are a *pleated sheet*, as in silk, and a *helix*, as in wool.

In the pleated-sheet conformation (Figure 12), protein chains are arranged in an extended zigzag arrangement, with hydrogen bonds holding adjacent chains together. The appearance gives this type of secondary structure its name, the **beta (β) pleated sheet**. This structure, with its multitude of hydrogen bonds, makes silk strong and flexible.

The protein molecules in wool, hair, and muscle contain large segments arranged in the form of a right-handed helix, or **alpha (α) helix** (Figure 13). Each turn of the helix requires 3.6 amino-acid units. The N—H group at one turn forms a hydrogen bond to a carbonyl (C=O) group at another turn. These helices wrap around one another in threes or sevens like strands of a rope. Unlike

(a)

(b)

Intramolecular hydrogen bond

Intramolecular hydrogen bond

Protein chain   Heme group

◀ **Figure 14** The tertiary structure of myoglobin. The protein chain is folded to form a globular structure, much as a string can be wound into a ball. The disk shape represents the heme group, which binds the oxygen carried by myoglobin (or hemoglobin).

silk, wool can be stretched, much like stretching a spring by pulling the coils apart.

The tertiary structure of a protein refers to folding that affects the spatial relationships between amino-acid units that are relatively far apart in the chain. An example is the protein chain in a **globular protein**. Figure 14 shows the tertiary structure of myoglobin, which is folded into a compact, spherical shape.

Quaternary structure exists only if there are two or more polypeptide chains, which can form an aggregate of subunits. Hemoglobin is the most familiar example. A single hemoglobin molecule contains four polypeptide units, and each unit is roughly comparable to a myoglobin molecule. The four units are arranged in a specific pattern (Figure 15). The quaternary structure of hemoglobin is this arrangement of the four units.

Protein chain   Protein chain

◀ **Figure 15** The quaternary structure of hemoglobin has four coiled protein chains, each analogous to myoglobin (Figure 14), grouped in a nearly tetrahedral arrangement.

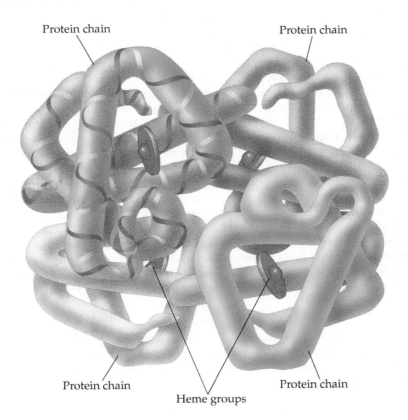

Protein chain   Heme groups   Protein chain

Four Ways to Link Protein Chains

As we noted earlier, the primary structure of a protein is the order of the amino acids, which are held together by peptide bonds. What forces determine the secondary, tertiary, and quaternary structures? Four kinds of forces operate between protein chains: hydrogen bonds, ionic bonds, disulfide linkages, and dispersion forces. These forces are illustrated in Figure 16.

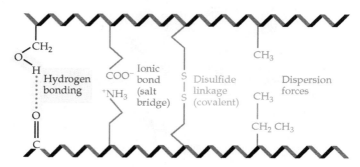

Figure 16 The tertiary structure of proteins is maintained by four different types of forces.

Hydrogen bonds and dispersion forces, introduced as intermolecular forces, can also be intramolecular, as occurs in proteins.

The most important hydrogen bonding in a protein involves an interaction between the atoms of one peptide bond and those of another. The amide hydrogen (N—H) of one peptide bond can form a hydrogen bond to a carbonyl (C=O) oxygen located (a) some distance away on the same chain, an arrangement that occurs in the secondary structure of wool (alpha helix), or (b) on an entirely different chain, as in the secondary structure of silk (beta pleated sheet). In either case, there is usually a pattern of such interactions. Because peptide bonds are regularly spaced along the chain, the hydrogen bonds also occur in a regular pattern, both intramolecularly (in wool) and intermolecularly (in silk). Other types of hydrogen bonding can occur (between side chains of amino acids, for example) but are less important.

Ionic bonds, sometimes called *salt bridges*, occur when an amino acid with a basic side chain is located near one with an acidic side chain. Proton transfer results in opposite charges, which then attract one another. These interactions can occur between groups that ordinarily are relatively distant that happen to come in contact because of folding or coiling of a single chain. They also occur between groups on adjacent chains.

A **disulfide linkage** is formed when two cysteine units (whether on the same chain or on two different chains) are oxidized. A disulfide linkage is a covalent bond, and thus much stronger than a hydrogen bond. Although far less numerous than hydrogen bonds, disulfide linkages are critically important in determining the shape of some proteins (for example, many of the proteins that act as enzymes) and the strength of others (such as the fibrous proteins in connective tissue and hair).

Dispersion forces are the only kind of forces that exist between nonpolar side chains. Recall that dispersion forces are relatively weak. These interactions can be important, however, when other types of forces are missing or are minimized. Dispersion forces are increased by the cohesiveness of the water molecules surrounding the protein. Nonpolar side chains minimize their exposure to water by clustering together on the inside folds of the protein in close contact with one another (Figure 17). Dispersion forces become fairly significant in structures such as that of silk, in which a high proportion of amino acids in the protein have nonpolar side chains.

Figure 17 A protein chain often folds with its nonpolar groups on the inside, where they are held together by dispersion forces. The outside has polar groups, visible in this space-filling model of a myoglobin molecule as oxygen atoms (red) and nitrogen atoms (blue). The carbon atoms (black) are mainly on the inside.

Enzymes: Exquisite Precision Machines

A highly specialized class of proteins, **enzymes**, are biological catalysts produced by cells. They have enormous catalytic power and are ordinarily highly specific, catalyzing only one reaction or a closely related group of reactions. Nearly all known enzymes are proteins.

Biochemistry

Infectious Prions: Deadly Protein

In the early years of the twenty-first century, a malady called *mad cow disease* cast a shadow over the beef industry, causing concern over the safety of beef. Two cows in the United States were found to have the disease, properly called *bovine spongiform encephalopathy (BSE)*.

BSE is not a bacterial disease like anthrax or cholera, nor is it a viral disease like influenza and AIDS. Rather, BSE seems to be caused by an infectious *prion*, an abnormal form of a protein. Because they are simple proteins rather than living organisms, prions can remain unchanged when subjected to considerable heat, disinfectants, or antibiotics, conditions that are used to destroy bacteria and viruses.

Much of the fear over BSE is unfounded, because it is not contagious like bacterial and viral diseases. It is generally spread by consumption of contaminated feed. The U.S. Department of Agriculture has imposed restrictions on the materials that may be used in cattle feed, which have been quite effective. The incidence of prion-caused diseases is extremely low among people. The best-known example is *kuru*, or laughing sickness, which seems to arise from cannibalistic practices in certain societies. Nonetheless, the U.S. government continues to be vigilant in avoiding any potential spread of BSE because it is impossible to treat the disease once it is contracted.

Enzymes enable reactions to occur at much more rapid rates and lower temperatures than they otherwise would. They do this by changing the reaction path. The reacting substance, called the **substrate**, attaches to an area on the enzyme called the **active site**, to form an enzyme–substrate complex. Biochemists often use the model pictured in Figure 18, called the *induced-fit model*, to explain enzyme action. In this model, the shapes of the substrate and the active site are not perfectly complementary, but the active site adapts to fit the substrate, much as a glove molds to fit the hand that is inserted into it. The enzyme–substrate complex decomposes to form products, and the enzyme is regenerated. We can represent the process as follows.

Enzyme + Substrate $\longrightarrow$ Enzyme–substrate complex $\rightleftharpoons$ Enzyme + Products

An enzyme–substrate complex is also usually held together by electrical attraction. Certain charged groups on the enzyme complement certain charged or partially charged groups on the substrate. The formation of new bonds between enzyme and substrate weakens bonds within the substrate, and these weakened bonds can then be more easily broken to form products.

Portions of the enzyme molecule other than the active site may be involved in the catalytic process. Some interaction at a position remote from the active site can change the shape of the enzyme and thus change its effectiveness as a catalyst. In this way, it is possible to slow or stop the catalytic action. Figure 19 illustrates a model for the inhibition of enzyme catalysis. An inhibitor molecule attaches to the enzyme at a position (called the *allosteric site*) away from the active site where the substrate is bound. The enzyme changes shape as it accommodates the inhibitor, and the substrate is no longer able to bind to the enzyme. This is one of the mechanisms by which cells "turn off" enzymes when their work is done.

Some enzymes consist entirely of protein chains. In others, another chemical component, called a **cofactor**, is necessary for proper function of the enzyme. This cofactor may be a metal ion such as zinc (Zn^{2+}), manganese (Mn^{2+}), magnesium (Mg^{2+}), iron(II) (Fe^{2+}), or copper(II) (Cu^{2+}). An organic cofactor is called a **coenzyme**. By definition, coenzymes are nonprotein. The pure protein part of an enzyme is called the **apoenzyme**. Both the coenzyme and the apoenzyme must be present for enzymatic activity to take place.

$$\underset{\substack{\text{Nonprotein} \\ \text{(inactive)}}}{\text{Coenzyme}} + \underset{\substack{\text{Protein} \\ \text{(inactive)}}}{\text{Apoenzyme}} \longrightarrow \underset{\text{(active)}}{\text{Enzyme}}$$

Many coenzymes are vitamins or are derived from vitamin molecules. Enzymes are essential to the function of every living cell.

▲ **Figure 18** The induced-fit model of enzyme action. In this case, a single substrate molecule is broken into two product molecules.

Enzymes as Green Catalysts

Scientists are hard at work trying to find enzymes to carry out all kinds of chemical conversions. Enzymes are often more efficient than the usual chemical catalysts, and they are more specific in that they produce more of the desired product and fewer by-products that have to be disposed of. Further, processes involving enzymes do not require toxic solvents and thus produce less waste.

Companies have spent hundreds of millions of dollars studying the special characteristics of the enzymes inside *extremophiles*, microorganisms that live in harsh environments that would kill other creatures. Scientists hope to replace ordinary enzymes with enzymes from extremophiles. They are already finding uses for these enzymes in specialty chemicals and new drugs. Many industrial processes can only be carried out at high temperatures and pressures. Enzymes make it possible to carry out some of these processes at fairly low temperatures and atmospheric pressure, thus reducing the energy used and the need for expensive equipment.

Another area of enzyme use is in cleaning up pollution. For example, polychlorinated biphenyls (PCBs), notoriously persistent pollutants, are usually destroyed by incineration at 1200 °C. Microorganisms have been isolated that can degrade PCBs and thus have the potential to destroy these toxic pollutants. However, much research is still needed to make them cost-effective.

(a)

(b)

▲ **Figure 19** A model for the inhibition of an enzyme. (a) The enzyme and its substrate fit exactly. (The allosteric site is where the inhibitor binds.) (b) With the inhibitor bound to the enzyme, the active site of the enzyme is distorted, and the enzyme cannot bind to its substrate.

Applications of Enzymes

Enzymes find many uses in medicine, industry, and everyday life. One widespread use is in the test strips used by diabetics. Each strip contains *glucose oxidase*, an enzyme that catalyzes the oxidation of glucose at an electrode. The reaction generates an electrical current that is proportional to the amount of glucose in the blood that has reacted with the enzyme. The result is displayed directly on an external meter.

Clinical analysis for enzymes in body fluids or tissues is a common diagnostic technique in medicine. For example, enzymes normally found only in the liver may leak into the bloodstream from a diseased or damaged liver. The presence of these enzymes in blood confirms liver damage.

Enzymes are used to break up blood clots after a heart attack. If these medicines are given immediately after an attack, the patients' survival rate increases significantly. Other enzymes are used to do just the opposite: Blood-clotting factors are used to treat hemophilia, a disease in which the blood fails to clot normally.

Enzymes are widely used in a variety of industries, from baby foods to beer. Enzymes in intact microorganisms have long been used to make bread, beer, wine, yogurt, and cheese. Now the use of enzymes has been broadened to include such things as the following:

- Enzymes that act on proteins (called *proteases*) are used in the manufacture of baby foods to predigest complex proteins and make them easier for infants to digest.

- Enzymes that act on starches (*carbohydrases*) are used to convert corn starch to corn syrup (mainly glucose) for use as a sweetener.

- Enzymes called *isomerases* are used to convert the glucose in corn syrup into fructose, which is sweeter than glucose and can be used in smaller amounts to give the same sweetness. (Glucose and fructose are isomers, both having the molecular formula $C_6H_{12}O_6$.)

- Protease enzymes are used to make beer and fruit juices clear by breaking down the proteins that cause cloudiness.

- Enzymes that degrade cellulose (*cellulases*) are used in stonewashing blue jeans. These enzymes break down the cellulose polymers of cotton fibers. By carefully controlling their activity, manufacturers can get the desired effect without destroying the cotton material. Varying the cellulase enzymes creates different effects to make true "designer jeans."

- Proteases and carbohydrases are added to animal feed to make nutrients more easily absorbed and improve the animals' digestion.

Biochemistry

Enzymes are important components in some detergents. Enzymes called *lipases* attack the fats and grease that make up many stains. Proteases attack the proteins in certain types of stains, such as those from blood, meat juice, and dairy products, breaking them down into smaller, water-soluble molecules. Total worldwide production of enzymes is worth more than $1 billion per year.

Self-Assessment Questions

1. Hydrogen bonds form between the N—H group of one amino acid and the C═O group of another, giving a protein molecule the form of an alpha helix or a beta pleated sheet. What level of protein structure do those forms represent?
   a. primary   **b.** quaternary   **c.** secondary   **d.** tertiary

2. The folding of a protein chain into a globular form is an example of
   a. primary structure
   c. secondary structure
   b. quaternary structure
   d. tertiary structure

3. The arrangement of several protein subunits into a specific pattern, as in hemoglobin, is an example of
   a. primary structure
   c. secondary structure
   b. quaternary structure
   d. tertiary structure

4. The cross-links between cysteine units in protein chains of fibrous proteins such as those in hair are
   a. dispersion linkages
   c. hydrogen bonds
   b. disulfide linkages
   d. salt bridges

5. An acidic side chain of an amino-acid unit on a protein chain reacts with the basic side chain of an amino-acid unit on another chain or at some distance away on the same chain to form a
   a. dispersion linkage
   c. hydrogen bond
   b. disulfide linkage
   d. salt bridge

6. When nonpolar side chains of amino-acid units in a protein chain interact with other nonpolar side chains of amino-acid units on another chain or at some distance away on the same chain, the interactions are
   a. dispersion forces
   b. a disulfide linkage
   c. a hydrogen bond
   d. a salt bridge

7. The molecule on which an enzyme acts is called the enzyme's
   a. catalyst   **b.** coenzyme   **c.** cofactor   **d.** substrate

8. According to the induced fit model of enzyme action, the
   a. action of an enzyme is enhanced by an inhibitor
   b. active site is the same as the allosteric site
   c. shapes of active sites are rigid and only fit substrates with exact complementary shapes
   d. shape of the active site can change somewhat to fit a substrate

9. An organic, nonprotein component of an enzyme molecule is called a(n)
   a. accessory enzyme
   b. allosteric group
   c. coenzyme
   d. stimulator

10. Enzyme cofactors are
    a. always ions such as Ca^{2+}, Mg^{2+}, and K^+
    b. always nonprotein organic molecules
    c. either ions such as Zn^{2+}, Mg^{2+}, and Mn^{2+} or nonprotein organic molecules
    d. small protein molecules

11. The pure protein part of an enzyme is called a(n)
    a. apoenzyme
    c. holoenzyme
    b. coenzyme
    d. ribozyme

Klaudia Steiner/iStockphoto

▲ It DOES Matter!

You can demonstrate protein hydrolysis. Mix a gelatin-dessert powder according to directions. Divide into two parts. Add fresh pineapple, kiwi, or papaya to one portion. Add cooked fruit or none at all to the other. The portion with the fresh fruit will not gel! These fruits contain a protease enzyme that breaks down proteins (gelatin is a protein). The enzyme is inactivated by cooking, so canned pineapple is perfectly fine in gelatin. (Why do you think cooking ham with pineapple tenderizes the ham, and eating too much raw pineapple can "burn" the lips?)

4. Why do some laundry detergents contain enzymes?

Enzymes in laundry detergents catalytically break down proteins that used to be difficult for detergents and bleaches to remove. Years ago, grass stains in children's clothing were almost impossible to remove, because the proteins of grass have a strong attraction for cotton and other cloth. Enzymes have alleviated that problem.

Answers: 1, c; 2, d; 3, b; 4, b; 5, d; 6, a; 7 d; 8, d; 9, c; 10, c; 11, a

6 Nucleic Acids: Parts, Structure, and Function

Learning Objectives ❯ Name the two types of nucleic acids, and describe the function of each type. ❯ Explain complementary base pairing, and describe how a copy of DNA is synthesized.

Life on Earth has a fantastic range of forms, but all life arises from the same molecular ingredients: five nucleotides that serve as the building blocks for nucleic acids, and 20 amino acids (Section 4) that are the building blocks for proteins. These components limit the chemical reactions that can occur in cells and thus determine what Earth's living things are like.

▲ **Figure 20** The components of nucleic acids. The sugars are 2-deoxyribose (in DNA) and ribose (in RNA). Note that deoxyribose differs from ribose in that it lacks an oxygen atom on the second carbon atom. *Deoxy* indicates that an oxygen atom is "missing." Phosphate units are often abbreviated as P_i ("inorganic phosphate"). Heterocyclic bases in nucleic acids are adenine, guanine, and cytosine in both DNA and RNA. Thymine occurs only in DNA, and uracil only in RNA. Note that thymine has a methyl group (red) that is lacking in uracil.

Nucleic acids serve as the information and control centers of the cell. There are two kinds of nucleic acids: *Deoxyribonucleic acid (DNA)* provides a mechanism for heredity and serves as the blueprint for all the proteins of an organism. *Ribonucleic acid (RNA)* carries out protein assembly. DNA is a coiled threadlike molecule found primarily in the cell nucleus. RNA is found in all parts of the cell, where different forms do different jobs. Both DNA and RNA are chains of repeating units called **nucleotides**. Each nucleotide in turn consists of three parts (Figure 20): a pentose (five-carbon sugar), a phosphate unit, and a heterocyclic amine base. The sugar is either ribose (in RNA) or deoxyribose (in DNA). Looking at the sugar in the nucleotide, note that the hydroxyl group on the first carbon atom is replaced by one of five bases. The bases with two fused rings, adenine and guanine, are classified as **purines**. The **pyrimidines**, cytosine, thymine, and uracil, have only one ring.

The hydroxyl group on the fifth carbon of the sugar unit is converted to a phosphate ester group. Adenosine monophosphate (AMP) is a representative nucleotide. In AMP, the base (blue) is adenine and the sugar (black) is ribose.

Biochemistry

Nucleotides can be represented schematically as in the following, where P_i is biochemists' designation for "inorganic phosphate." A general representation is shown on the left, and a specific schematic for AMP on the right.

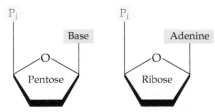

Nucleotides are joined to one another through the phosphate group to form nucleic acid chains. The phosphate unit on one nucleotide forms an ester linkage with the hydroxyl group on the third carbon atom of the sugar unit in a second nucleotide. This unit is in turn joined to another nucleotide, and the process is repeated to build up a long nucleic acid chain (Figure 21). The backbone of the chain consists of alternating phosphate and sugar units, and the heterocyclic bases are branches off this backbone.

~sugar-P_i-sugar-P_i-sugar-P_i-sugar-P_i-sugar-P_i-sugar-P_i~

base base base base base base

The numbers in Figure 21 refer to positions on the pentose sugar ring (look again at Figure 20). The 3′ end has a hydroxyl group and the 5′ end has a phosphate group. If the above diagram represents DNA, the sugar is deoxyribose and the bases are adenine, guanine, cytosine, and thymine. In RNA, the sugar is ribose and the bases are adenine, guanine, cytosine, and uracil.

▲ **Figure 21** A DNA molecule. Each repeating unit is composed of a sugar, a phosphate unit, and a base. The sugar and phosphate units form backbones on the outside. The bases are attached to the sugar units. Pairs of bases make "steps" on the inside of the spiral staircase.

Example 4   Nucleotides

Consider the following nucleotide. Identify the sugar and the base. State whether it is found in DNA or RNA.

Solution
The sugar has two H atoms on the second C atom and therefore is deoxyribose, found in DNA. The base is a pyrimidine (one ring). The amino group ($-NH_2$) helps identify it as cytosine.

■ EXERCISE 4A
Consider the following nucleotide. Identify the sugar and the base. State whether it is found in DNA or RNA.

(continued)

A. Barrington Brown/Photo Researchers, Inc.

▲ Francis H. C. Crick (1916–2004) (seated) and James D. Watson (b. 1928) used data obtained by British chemist Rosalind Franklin (1920–1958) to propose a double helix model of DNA in 1953. Franklin used a technique called X-ray diffraction, which showed DNA's helical structure. Without her permission, Franklin's colleague Maurice Wilkins shared her work with Watson and Crick. The data helped Watson and Crick decipher DNA's structure. Wilkins, Watson, and Crick were awarded the Nobel Prize for this discovery in 1962, a prize Franklin might have shared had she lived.

Base pair

Sugar–phosphate backbone

▲ **Figure 22** A model of a portion of a DNA double helix is shown in Figure 21. This schematic representation of the double helix shows the sugar–phosphate backbones as ribbons and the complementary base pairs as steps on the spiral staircase.

■ EXERCISE 4B
A nucleotide is composed of a phosphate unit, ribose, and thymine. Is it found in DNA, RNA, or neither? Explain.

The vast amount of genetic information needed to build living organisms is stored in a primary structure, the *sequence* of the four bases along the nucleic acid strand. Not surprisingly, these molecules are huge, with molecular masses ranging into the billions for mammalian DNA. Along these chains, the four bases can be arranged in almost infinite variations. We will examine this aspect of nucleic acid chemistry shortly, after considering another important feature of nucleic acid structure.

The Double Helix

The three-dimensional, or secondary, structure of DNA was the subject of an intensive research effort in the late 1940s and early 1950s. Experiments showed that the molar amount of adenine (A) in DNA corresponds to the molar amount of thymine (T). Similarly, the molar amount of guanine (G) is the same as that of cytosine (C). To maintain this balance, researchers concluded the bases in DNA must be paired, A to T and G to C. But how?

At the midpoint of the twentieth century, it was clear that whoever answered this question would win a Nobel Prize. Many illustrious scientists worked on the problem, but two who were relatively unknown announced in 1953 that they had worked out the structure of DNA. Using data that involved quite sophisticated chemistry, physics, and mathematics, and working with models not unlike a child's construction set, James D. Watson and Francis H. C. Crick determined that DNA must be composed of two helices wound about one another. The two strands are antiparallel; they run in opposite directions. The phosphate and sugar backbones of the polymer chains form the outside of the structure, which is rather like a spiral staircase. The heterocyclic amines are paired on the inside—with guanine always opposite cytosine and adenine always opposite thymine. In the spiral staircase analogy, these base pairs are the steps (Figure 22).

Why do the bases pair in this precise pattern, always A to T and T to A and always G to C and C to G? The answers: hydrogen bonding, and a truly elegant molecular arrangement. Figure 23 shows the two sets of base pairs. You should notice two things. First, a pyrimidine is paired with a purine in each case, and the long dimensions of both pairs are identical (1.085 nm).

Second, notice the hydrogen bonding between the bases in each pair. When guanine is paired with cytosine, three hydrogen bonds can be formed between the bases. No other pyrimidine–purine pairing permits such extensive interaction. Indeed, in the combinations shown in the figure, each pair of bases fits like a lock and a key.

Other scientists around the world quickly accepted the Watson–Crick structure because it answered so many crucial questions: how cells are able to divide and go on functioning, how genetic data are passed on to new generations, and even how proteins are built to required specifications. All of these processes depend on the base pairing.

Structure of RNA

Most RNA molecules consist of a single strand of nucleic acids. Some internal (intramolecular) base pairing can occur in sections where the molecule folds back on itself. Portions of some RNA molecules exist in double-helical form (Figure 24).

DNA: Self-Replication

Dogs have puppies that grow up to be dogs. Chickens lay eggs that hatch and grow up to be chickens. How is it that each species reproduces its own kind?

CH₃ ... (chemical structure diagram)

Thymine

To chain

1.085 nm

Adenine

H   H

Cytosine

To chain

1.085 nm

Guanine

H

To chain

To chain

(a)

(b)

▲ **Figure 23** Pairing of the complementary bases thymine and adenine (a) and cytosine and guanine (b). The pairing involves hydrogen bonding.

How does a fertilized egg "know" that it should develop into a kangaroo and not a koala?

The physical basis of heredity has been known for a long time. Most higher organisms reproduce sexually. A sperm cell from the male unites with an egg cell from the female. The fertilized egg that results must carry all the information needed to make the various cells, tissues, and organs necessary for the functioning of a new individual. Further, if the species is to survive, information must be passed along in the germ cells—both sperm and egg—for the production of new individuals.

The hereditary material is found in the nuclei of all cells, concentrated in elongated, threadlike bodies called *chromosomes*. Chromosomes form compressed X-shaped structures when strands of DNA coil up tightly just before a cell divides. The number of chromosomes varies with the species. In sexual reproduction, chromosomes come in pairs, with one member of each pair provided by each parent. Each human inherits 23 pairs and so has 46 chromosomes in his or her body's cells. Thus, the entire complement of chromosomes is achieved only when the egg's 23 chromosomes combine with a like number from the sperm.

Chromosomes are made of DNA and proteins. Arranged along the chromosomes are the basic units of heredity, the genes. Structurally, a **gene** is a section of the DNA molecule, although some viral genes contain only RNA. Genes control the synthesis of proteins, which tell cells, organs, and organisms how to function in their surroundings. The environment helps determine which genes become active at a particular time. The complete set of genes of an organism is called its *genome*. When cell division occurs, each chromosome produces an exact duplicate of itself. Transmission of genetic information therefore requires the **replication** (copying or duplication) of DNA molecules.

The double helix provides a precise model for replication. If the two chains of the double helix are pulled apart, each chain can direct the synthesis of a new DNA chain using nucleotides from the cellular fluid surrounding the DNA. Each of the separating chains serves as a template, or pattern, for the formation of a new complementary chain. The two DNA strands are *antiparallel*. One chain runs in the direction labeled $3' \rightarrow 5'$, and the other runs in the appropriate direction labeled $5' \rightarrow 3'$. Synthesis begins with a base on a nucleotide pairing with its complementary base on the DNA strand—adenine with thymine and guanine with cytosine (Figure 25). Each base unit in the separated strand can only pick up a base unit identical to the one with which it was paired before. For example, if a 12-base-pair strand

James D. Watson gave a personal account of the discovery of the structure of DNA in his book *The Double Helix* (New York: New American Library, 1968).

▲ **Figure 24** RNA occurs as single strands that can form double-helical portions through internal pairing of bases.

▲ Human chromosomes before cell division have a distinctive X-shape.

Genes have functional regions called *exons* interspersed with inactive portions called *introns*. During protein synthesis, introns are snipped out and not translated. Some genes, called *house-keeping genes*, are expressed in all cells at all times and are essential for the most basic cellular functions. Other genes are expressed only in specific types of cells or at certain stages of development. For example, the genes that encode brain nerve cells are expressed only in brain cells, not in the liver.

running in the 5′ → 3′ direction has guanine as the third base, the guanine will pick up base cytosine as the tenth base of the complementary 12-base-pair strand running in the opposite direction.

$$3'\text{-ATGGGTCTATAT-}5'$$

$$5'\text{-TACCCAGATATA-}3'$$

As the nucleotides align, enzymes connect them to form the new chain. In this way, each strand of the original DNA molecule forms a duplicate of its former partner. Whatever information was encoded in the original DNA double helix is now contained in each of the replications. When the cell divides, each daughter cell gets one of the DNA molecules and thus has all the information that was available to the parent cell.

How is information stored in DNA? The code for the directions for building all the proteins that comprise an organism and enable it to function resides in the *sequence* of bases along the DNA chain. Just as *cat* means one thing in English and *act* means another, the sequence of bases CGT means one amino acid and GCT means another. Although there are only four "letters"—the four bases—in the genetic code of DNA, their sequence along the long strands can vary so widely that unlimited information storage is available. Each cell carries in its DNA all the information that determines its hereditary characteristics.

▶ Figure 25 A simplified schematic diagram of DNA replication. The original double helix is "unzipped," and new nucleotides (as triphosphate derivatives) are brought into position by the enzyme DNA polymerase. Phosphate bridges are formed, restoring the original double-helix configuration. Each newly formed double helix consists of one old strand and one new strand.

Self-Assessment Questions

1. The monomer units of nucleic acids are
   a. amino acids
   b. monosaccharides
   c. nucleosomes
   d. nucleotides

2. A DNA nucleotide could contain
   a. A, P_i, and ribose
   b. G, P_i, and glucose
   c. T, P_i, and deoxyribose
   d. U, P_i, and deoxyribose

3. A possible base pair in DNA is
   a. A-G
   b. A-T
   c. A-U
   d. T-G

4. A possible base pair in RNA is
   a. A-G
   b. A-T
   c. A-U
   d. T-G

5. Nucleic acid base pairs are joined by
   a. amide bonds
   b. ester bonds
   c. glucosidic bonds
   d. hydrogen bonds

6. Replication of a DNA molecule involves breaking bonds between the
   a. base pairs
   b. pentose sugars
   c. phosphate units
   d. bases and pentoses

7. The first step of DNA replication involves
   a. bonding of free nucleotides in the correct sequence
   b. formation of a single-stranded RNA molecule
   c. linking of a phosphate group to an amino acid
   d. unzipping of the DNA molecule when the hydrogen bonds break

8. If an original DNA strand has the base sequence 3'-TAGC-5', the complementary strand will have the base sequence
   a. 5'-ATCG-3'
   b. 5'-GCAT-3'
   c. 5'-TACG-3'
   d. 5'-UACG-3'

9. If a portion of a gene has the base sequence 3'-TCGAAT-5', what base sequence appears in the complementary DNA strand when the gene is replicated?
   a. 5'-ACGTTA-3'
   b. 5'-AGCTTA-3'
   c. 5'-TCGAAT-3'
   d. 5'-UGCAAU-3'

Answers: 1, d; 2, c; 3, b; 4, c; 5, d; 6, a; 7, d; 8, a; 9, b

7 RNA: Protein Synthesis and the Genetic Code

Learning Objectives ⟩ Explain how mRNA is synthesized from DNA and how a protein is synthesized from mRNA. ⟩ List important characteristics of the genetic code.

DNA carries a message that must somehow be transmitted and then acted on in a cell. Because DNA does not leave the cell nucleus, its information, or "blueprint," must be transported by something else, and it is. In the first step, called **transcription**, a segment of DNA called the *template strand* transfers its information to a special RNA molecule called *messenger RNA (mRNA)*. The base sequence of DNA specifies the base sequence of mRNA. Thymine in DNA calls for adenine in mRNA, cytosine specifies guanine, guanine calls for cytosine, and adenine requires uracil (Table 4). Remember that in RNA molecules, uracil appears in place of DNA's thymine. Notice the similarity in the structure of these two bases (revisit Figure 20). When transcription is completed, the RNA is released, and the DNA helix reforms.

Table 4   DNA Bases and Their Complementary RNA Bases

DNA Base	Complementary RNA Base
Adenine (A)	Uracil (U)
Thymine (T)	Adenine (A)
Cytosine (C)	Guanine (G)
Guanine (G)	Cytosine (C)

The next step in creating a protein involves deciphering the code copied by mRNA followed by **translation** of that code into a specific protein structure. The decoding occurs when the mRNA travels from the nucleus and attaches itself to a ribosome in the cytoplasm of the cell. Ribosomes are constructed of about 65% RNA and 35% proteins.

Another type of RNA molecule, called *transfer RNA (tRNA)*, carries amino acids from the cell fluid to the ribosomes. A tRNA molecule has the looped structure shown in Figure 26. At the head of the molecule is a set of three base units, a *base triplet* called the *anticodon*, that pairs with a set of three complementary bases on mRNA, called the **codon**. The codon triplet determines which amino acid is car-

▲ **Figure 26** A transfer RNA (tRNA) molecule doubles back on itself, forming three loops with intermolecular hydrogen bonding between complementary bases. The anticodon triplet at the head of the molecule joins with a complementary codon triplet on mRNA. Here the base triplet CAU in the anticodon specifies the amino acid valine.

Why is a code that must specify 20 different amino acids based on a triplet of bases? Four "letters" can be arranged in $4 \times 4 \times 4 = 64$ possible three-letter "words." A "doublet" code of four letters would have only $4 \times 4 = 16$ different words, and a "quadruplet" code of four letters can be arranged in $4 \times 4 \times 4 \times 4 = 256$ different ways. A triplet code specifies 20 different amino acids with some redundancy, a doublet code is inadequate, and a quadruplet code would provide too much redundancy.

Errors can occur at each step in the replication–transcription–translation process. In replication alone, each time a human cell divides, 4 billion bases are copied to make a new strand of DNA, and there may be up to 2000 errors. Most such errors are corrected, and others are unimportant, but some have terrible consequences: genetic disease or even death may result.

Angela Waye/Shutterstock

▲ **It DOES Matter!**

Blue eyes result from a genetic mutation that involved the change of a single base in the code, from A to G. This change is thought to have occurred between 6000 and 10,000 years ago; before that time, no humans had blue eyes. The mutation turned off a gene involved in the production of melanin, the pigment that gives color to hair, eyes, and skin. Only people who inherit this gene from both parents have blue eyes.

ried at the tail of the tRNA. In Figure 26, for example, the codon GUA on the segment of mRNA pairs with the anticodon base triplet CAU on the tRNA molecule. All tRNA molecules with the base triplet CAU always carry the amino acid valine. Once the tRNA has paired with the base triplet of mRNA, it releases its amino acid and returns to the cell fluid to pick up another amino acid molecule.

Each of the 61 different tRNA molecules carries a specific amino acid into place on a growing peptide chain. The protein chain gradually built up in this way is released from the tRNA as it is formed. A complete dictionary of the genetic code has been compiled (Table 5). It shows which amino acids are specified by all the possible mRNA base triplets. There are 64 possible triplets and only 20 amino acids, so there is some redundancy in the code. Three amino acids (serine, arginine, and leucine) are each specified by six different codons. Two others (tryptophan and methionine) have only one codon each. Three base triplets on mRNA are "stop" signals that call for termination of the protein chain. The codon AUG signals "start" as well as specifying methionine in the chain. Figure 27 provides an overall summary of protein synthesis.

Table 5 The Genetic Code

FIRST BASE		SECOND BASE				THIRD BASE
		U	C	A	G	
U	U	UUU=Phe UUC=Phe UUA=Leu UUG=Leu	UCU=Ser UCC=Ser UCA=Ser UCG=Ser	UAU=Tyr UAC=Tyr UAA=Termination UAG=Termination	UGU=Cys UGC=Cys UGA=Termination UGG=Trp	U C A G
	C	CUU=Leu CUC=Leu CUA=Leu CUG=Leu	CCU=Pro CCC=Pro CCA=Pro CCG=Pro	CAU=His CAC=His CAA=Gln CAG=Gln	CGU=Arg CGC=Arg CGA=Arg CGG=Arg	U C A G
	A	AUU=Ile AUC=Ile AUA=Ile AUG=Met	ACU=Thr ACC=Thr ACA=Thr ACG=Thr	AAU=Asn AAC=Asn AAA=Lys AAG=Lys	AGU=Ser AGC=Ser AGA=Arg AGG=Arg	U C A G
	G	GUU=Val GUC=Val GUA=Val GUG=Val	GCU=Ala GCC=Ala GCA=Ala GCG=Ala	GAU=Asp GAC=Asp GAA=Glu GAG=Glu	GGU=Gly GGC=Gly GGA=Gly GGG=Gly	U C A G

▲ **Figure 27** Protein synthesis occurs by transcription from DNA to mRNA, translation by tRNA, and building of a protein.

Self-Assessment Questions

1. The synthesis of mRNA from a strand of DNA is called
   a. transaction   **b.** transcription   **c.** transition   **d.** translation

2. The base sequence of a strand of mRNA that is transcribed from a segment of DNA that has the base sequence 5'-TACG-3' is
   a. 3'-AUGC-5'   **b.** 3'-CGAU-5'   **c.** 3'-TAGC-5'   **d.** 3'-UAGC-5'

3. The anticodon base triplet is found on the
   a. original DNA   **b.** ribosome   **c.** mRNA   **d.** tRNA

4. How many amino acids and how many codons are involved in the genetic code
   a. 20 amino acids, 20 codons   **b.** 20 amino acids, 64 codons
   c. 64 amino acids, 20 codons   **d.** 64 amino acids, 64 codons

5. Each amino acid except tryptophan and methionine is coded for by more than one codon, indicating that the genetic code has
   a. evolved   **b.** redundancy
   c. sequence assurance   **d.** translation equability

6. Refer to Table 5; the codon UUA
   a. codes for Leu and signals "start"   **b.** codes for Leu and signals "stop"
   c. codes for Leu only   **d.** signals "stop" only

Answers: 1, b; 2, a; 3, d; 4, b; 5, b; 6, c

8 The Human Genome

Learning Objective ⟩ Describe recombinant DNA technology, and explain how it is used.

In 1990, scientists set out to determine the sequence of all 3 billion base pairs in the human genome. The Human Genome Project was completed in 2003 at a cost of about $2.7 billion. We can now read the complete genetic blueprint for a human. This project has driven a worldwide revolution in biotechnology—and today a genome can be sequenced in a few days at a cost of a few hundred dollars.

Many human diseases have clear genetic components. Some are directly caused by one defective gene, and others arise through involvement of several genes. The Human Genome Project has already led to the discovery of 2000 or more genes related to disease, allowing the development of more than 2000 genetic tests for human disorders. These tests enable patients to learn their genetic risk for certain diseases and also help health-care professionals to diagnose these diseases.

A gene suspected of causing an inherited disease can be located on the human genome map in a few days, instead of the years it took before the genome sequence was known. Once the genes are identified, the ability to use this information to diagnose and cure genetic diseases will revolutionize medicine.

DNA is sequenced by using enzymes to cleave it into segments of a few to several hundred nucleotides each. These fragments differ in length from each other by a single base that is identified in a later step. The pieces are duplicated and amplified by a technique called the *polymerase chain reaction (PCR)*. PCR employs enzymes called *DNA polymerases* to amplify the small amount of DNA by making millions of copies of each fragment. This builds a minuscule sample into a far larger quantity, which is needed for DNA sequencing. An electric current is used to sort the DNA segments by length, and the base at the end of each fragment is identified. Computers are then used to compile the short sequences into longer segments that recreate the original sequence of bases for the short pieces generated in the first step.

Humans were long thought to have 80,000 or more active genes. When scientists completed the Human Genome Project in 2003, they had found only about 20,000 to 25,000 genes in the human genome.

DNA Profiling

About 99.9% of DNA sequences are the same in every human, yet the 0.1% difference is enough to distinguish one person from another (except for identical twins). DNA profiling does not require sequencing of an entire genome. Rather, it uses *short tandem repeats*, or *STRs*, at 13 particular locations on the human genome. An STR is typically from two to five base units long and is repeated several times. An example is ACGT-ACGT-ACGT. The number of such repeats at the key points differs from one person to another. This is the key to a DNA fingerprint. When all 13 points are considered, each person has a different profile.

DNA fingerprinting is used to screen newborn babies for inherited disorders such as cystic fibrosis, sickle cell anemia, Huntington's disease, hemophilia, and many others. Early detection of such disorders enables doctors and parents to choose and initiate proper treatment of the child.

Because children inherit half their DNA from each parent, DNA fingerprinting is also used to establish parentage when there is a question about paternity.

The odds of identifying the father through DNA fingerprinting are at least 99.99%, and they are 100% for excluding a man as a possible father.

British scientist Alec Jeffreys invented DNA fingerprinting in 1985 and gave it its name. Like fingerprints, each person's DNA is unique. Any cells—skin, blood, semen, saliva, and so on—can supply the necessary DNA sample.

DNA fingerprinting was a major advance in criminal investigation, allowing thousands of criminal cases to be solved. DNA samples from evidence found at a crime scene are amplified by PCR and compared with DNA obtained from suspects and other people known to have been at the scene.

This technique has led to many criminal convictions, but perhaps more important, it can readily prove someone innocent. If the DNA does not match, the suspect could not have left the biological sample. Nearly 300 people have been shown to be innocent and freed, some after spending years in prison, including 17 who had been condemned to death. The technique is a major advance in the search for justice.

▲ This DNA test included samples from the mother (top), the child (middle), and the alleged father (bottom). The maternal marker 6 has been passed to the child. This means that marker 7 of the child must have come from the father, and the alleged father does indeed have a marker 7.

Recombinant DNA: Using Organisms as Chemical Factories

All living organisms (except some viruses) have DNA as their hereditary material. *Recombinant DNA* is DNA that has been created artificially. DNA from two different sources is incorporated into a single recombinant DNA molecule. The first step is to cut the DNA to extract a fragment of it, which scientists accomplish with an enzyme obtained from bacteria called an *endonuclease*. Endonuclease is a type of *restriction enzyme*, so called because its ability to cleave DNA is restricted to certain short sequences of DNA called *restriction sites*. This enzyme cuts two DNA molecules at the same site. There are three different methods by which recombinant DNA is made. We will consider just one of them here.

After scientists determine the base sequence of the gene that codes for a particular protein, they can isolate it and amplify it by PCR. The gene can then be spliced into a special kind of bacterial DNA called a *plasmid*. The recombined plasmid is then inserted into the host organism, the bacteria from which the plasmids came (Figure 28). Once inside the host bacteria, the plasmids replicate, making multiple exact copies of themselves, a process called *cloning*. As the engineered bacteria multiply, they become effective factories for producing the desired protein.

What kinds of proteins might scientists wish to produce using biotechnology? Insulin, a protein coded by DNA, is required for the proper use of glucose by cells. People with diabetes, an insulin-deficiency disease, formerly had to use insulin from pigs or cattle. Now human insulin is made using recombinant DNA technology. Scientists take the human gene for insulin production and paste it into the DNA of *Escherichia coli*, a bacterium commonly found in the human digestive tract. Expression factors, signals that provide instructions for transcription and translation of the gene by the cell, are also added. The bacterial cells multiply rapidly, making billions of copies of themselves, and each new *E. coli* cell carries in its DNA a replica of the gene for human insulin. The hope for the future is that a functioning gene for insulin can be incorporated directly into the cells of insulin-dependent diabetics.

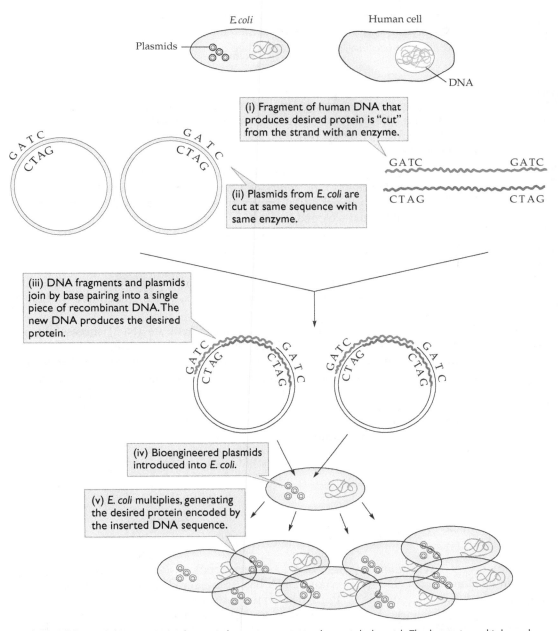

▲ **Figure 28** Recombinant DNA: cloning a human gene into a bacterial plasmid. The bacteria multiply and, in doing so, make multiple copies of the recombinant gene. The gene can be one that codes for insulin, human growth hormone, or another valuable protein. Potentially, a gene from any organism—microbe, plant, or animal—can be incorporated into any other organism.

In addition to insulin, many other valuable materials that are used in human therapy and are difficult to obtain in any other way can now be made using recombinant DNA technology. Some examples are

- *human growth hormone* (HGH), which replaced cadaver-harvested HGH for treating children who fail to grow properly;
- *erythropoietin* (EPO) for treating anemia resulting from chronic kidney disease and from treatment for cancer;
- *factor VIII* (formerly harvested from blood), a clotting agent for treating males with hemophilia;
- *tissue plasminogen activator* (TPA) for dissolving blood clots associated with diseases such as heart attack and stroke;

- *interferons*, which assist the immune response and induce the resistance of host cells to viral infection and are promising anticancer agents; and
- *recombinant vaccines*, such as that for hepatitis B.

Gene Therapy

In gene therapy, a functioning gene is introduced into a person's cells to correct the action of a defective gene. Viruses are commonly used to carry DNA into cells. Current gene therapy is experimental, and human gene transplants so far have had only modest success.

- In 1999, ten children with severe combined immunodeficiency disease (SCID) were injected with working copies of a gene that helps the immune system develop. Almost all the children improved and most are healthy today, but in 2002, two of them developed leukemia.
- Four severely blind young adults had a curative gene injected into their eyes. They can now see more light and have enough vision to walk without help. Two of them can read several lines of an eye chart.
- Genetically altered cells injected into the brain of patients with Alzheimer's disease appear to nourish ailing neurons and may slow cognitive decline in these people.
- In 2006, researchers at the National Cancer Institute (NCI) successfully re-engineered immune cells to attack cancer cells in patients with advanced melanoma, the first successful use of gene therapy to treat cancer in humans.
- Researchers have genetically engineered the formation of new beta cells in the liver of mice. They also added a gene that inhibits activity of the T cells around the new beta cells in the liver and not in the rest of the body. (The T cells would otherwise destroy the new beta cells.) If this works in humans, diabetics could produce their own insulin.

▲ It DOES Matter!

GM rice ("golden rice"), developed in 1999, has new genes implanted from daffodils and a bacterium. Golden rice was developed as a fortified food containing high amounts of β-carotene, a precursor of vitamin A. It was to be used in areas where children face a shortage of dietary vitamin A to help them overcome vitamin A deficiency. An estimated 124 million people in Africa and Southeast Asia are affected by vitamin A deficiency, which has caused 1–2 million deaths and 500,000 cases of blindness. Opposition to and complex regulation of transgenic crops have prevented golden rice from being grown on farms; it is still in field trials.

Genetically Modified Organisms: Controversy and Promise

Genes can be transferred from nearly any organism to any other. New animals can be cloned from cells in adult animals. Genetically modified (GM) organisms are in widespread—and often controversial—use. For example, by 2010 in the United States, 93% of the soybeans, 93% of the cotton, and 86% of the maize (corn) planted were GM varieties.

- Genes for herbicide resistance are now incorporated into soybeans so that herbicide application will kill weeds without killing the soybean plants. People worry that these genes will escape into wild plants (weeds), making them resistant to herbicides.
- Genes from the bacteria *Bacillus thuringiensis* (Bt) are incorporated into corn and cotton plants. The genes cause the plants to produce a protein toxin that kills caterpillars that would otherwise feed on the plants. People worry that insects will quickly become resistant to the toxin and that butterflies and other desirable insects will also be killed by it.

GM foods are foods made from GM organisms whose DNA has been altered. GM foods first entered the market in the early 1990s. The most common modified foods—soybeans, corn, canola oil, and cottonseed oil—are derived from GM plants. People worry that GM foods will have proteins that will cause allergic reactions in some people. To protect against such developments, strict guidelines for recombinant DNA research have been instituted. Some people think that these are not strict enough.

Molecular genetics has already resulted in some impressive achievements. Its possibilities are mind-boggling—elimination of genetic defects, a cure for cancer, and who knows what else? Knowledge gives power, but it does not necessarily give wisdom. Who will decide what sort of creature the human species should be? The greatest problem we are likely to face in our use of bioengineering is choosing who is to play God with the new "secret of life."

Many problems remain, including getting the gene in the right place and targeting it so that it inserts itself only into the cells where it is needed. The stakes in gene therapy are huge. We all carry some defective genes. About one in ten people either has or will develop an inherited genetic disorder. Gene therapy could become an efficient way of curing many diseases.

Self-Assessment Questions

1. Recombinant DNA cloning involves
   a. combining DNA from two different organisms to make a single new organism
   b. creating a genetically identical organism from a skin cell
   c. isolation of a genetically pure colony of cells
   d. splitting of a fertilized egg into two cells to generate identical twins

2. In producing recombinant DNA, the DNA from the two sources is cut with
   a. DNA ligase
   b. phages
   c. restriction enzymes
   d. vectors

3. Recombinant DNA is currently used in the biotechnology industry to
   a. create new species of animals
   b. eliminate all infectious diseases in domestic animals
   c. increase the frequency of mutations
   d. synthesize insulin, interferon, and human growth hormone

4. Some geneticists suggest transferring some genes that direct photosynthesis from an efficient crop plant to a less efficient one, thus producing a more productive plant variety. This project would most likely involve
   a. genetic profiling
   b. genetic engineering
   c. genetic screening
   d. transcription

Answers: 1, a; 2, c; 3, d; 4, b

5. Are genetically modified foods safe? There are potential problems with today's genetically modified foods, but in practice we have been using genetically modified foods for over a century—ever since Mendel discovered the concept of genetics. Most of today's foods are hybrids, the result of genetic modification by cross-breeding. Of course, sometimes a hybrid tomato isn't tasty or is too small. Likewise, some genetically modified plants aren't exactly what we'd like.

CRITICAL THINKING EXERCISES

Apply knowledge that you have gained in this chapter and one or more of the FLaReS principles to evaluate the following statements or claims.

1   The wrapper of an energy bar claims, in large print, "21,000 mg of amino acids in each bar!"

2   DNA is an essential component of every living cell. An advertisement claims that DNA is a useful diet supplement.

3   A restaurant menu states, "Other restaurants use saturated beef fat for frying. We use only pure vegetable oil to fry our fish and french fries, for healthier eating."

4   The label on a bag of sugar says, "NOW CERTIFIED CARBON FREE."

5   A dietician states that a recommendation of 60 g of protein per day for an adult is somewhat misleading. She claims that the right kinds of proteins, with the proper amino acids in them, must be consumed; otherwise, even a much larger amount of protein per day may be insufficient to maintain health.

6   A man convicted of rape claims that he is innocent because DNA fingerprinting of a semen sample taken from the rape victim showed that it contains DNA from another man.

 SUMMARY

Section 1—Biochemistry is the chemistry of life processes. Life requires chemical energy. Metabolism is the set of chemical reactions that keep cells alive. Metabolism includes many processes of both anabolism (building up of molecules) and catabolism (breaking down of molecules). Substances that provide animals with energy are carbohydrates, fats, and proteins.

Section 2—A carbohydrate is a compound whose formula can be written as a hydrate of carbon. Sugars, starches, and cellulose are carbohydrates. The simplest sugars are monosaccharides, carbohydrates that cannot be further hydrolyzed. A monosaccharide is either an aldose (having an aldehyde functional group) or a ketose (having a ketone functional group). Glucose and fructose are monosaccharides. A disaccharide can be hydrolyzed to yield two monosaccharide units. Sucrose and lactose are disaccharides. Polysaccharides contain many monosaccharide units linked together. Starches and cellulose are polysaccharides. Starches are polymers of glucose units held together by alpha linkages; cellulose is a glucose polymer held together by beta linkages. There are two kinds of plant starches, amylose and amylopectin. Animal starch is called glycogen.

Section 3—A lipid is a cellular component that is insoluble in water and soluble in solvents of low polarity. Lipids include solid fats and liquid oils; both are triglycerides (esters of fatty acids with glycerol). Lipids also include steroids, hormones, and fatty acids (long-chain carboxylic acids). A fat is an ester of fatty acids and glycerol. Fats may be saturated (all carbon-to-carbon bonds in the fatty acid are single bonds), monounsaturated (one C=C), or polyunsaturated (more than one C=C). The iodine number of a fat or oil is the mass in grams of iodine that reacts with 100 g of the fat or oil. Oils tend to have higher iodine numbers than fats because there are more double bonds in oils.

Section 4—An amino acid contains an amino ($-NH_2$) group and a carboxyl ($-COOH$) group. An amino acid exists as a zwitterion, in which a proton from the carboxyl group has been transferred to the amino group. Proteins are polymers of amino acids, with 20 amino acids forming millions of different proteins. Plants can synthesize proteins from CO_2, water, and minerals, but animals require proteins in their diets.

The bond that joins two amino-acid units in a protein is called a peptide bond. Two amino acids form a dipeptide, three forms a tripeptide, and more than 10 forms a polypeptide. When the molecular weight of a polypeptide exceeds about 10,000, it is called a protein. The sequence of the amino acids in a protein is of great importance to its function. Three-letter or single-letter abbreviations are used to designate amino acids.

Section 5—Protein structure has four levels. The primary structure of a protein is simply the sequence of its amino acids. The secondary structure is the arrangement of polypeptide chains about an axis. Two such arrangements are the beta pleated sheet, in which the arrays of chains form zigzag sheets, and the alpha helix, in which protein chains coil around one another. The tertiary structure of a protein is its folding pattern; globular proteins such as myoglobin are folded into compact shapes. Some proteins have a quaternary structure consisting of an aggregate of subunits arranged in a specific pattern.

There are four types of forces that determine the secondary, tertiary, and quaternary structures of proteins: (a) hydrogen bonds; (b) ionic bonds formed between acidic and basic side chains; (c) disulfide linkages, which are S—S bonds formed between cysteine groups; and (d) dispersion forces arising between nonpolar side chains.

Enzymes are biological catalysts. In operation, the reacting substance, or substrate, attaches to the active site of the enzyme to form a complex, which then decomposes to the products. An enzyme is often made up of an apoenzyme (a protein) and a cofactor that is necessary for proper function and that may be a metal ion. An organic cofactor (such as a vitamin) is called a coenzyme.

Section 6—Nucleic acids are the information and control centers of a cell. DNA (deoxyribonucleic acid) and RNA (ribonucleic acid) are polymers of nucleotides. Each nucleotide contains a pentose sugar unit, a phosphate unit, and one of four amine bases. Bases with one ring are called pyrimidines, and those with two fused rings are purines. In DNA, the sugar is deoxyribose and the bases are adenine, thymine, guanine, and cytosine. In RNA, the sugar is ribose and the bases are the same as those in DNA, except that uracil replaces thymine. Nucleotides are joined through their phosphate groups to form nucleic acid chains. In DNA, the bases thymine and adenine are always paired, as are the bases cytosine and guanine. Pairing occurs via hydrogen bonding between the bases and gives rise to the double-helix structure of DNA. RNA consists of single strands of nucleic acids, some parts of which may hydrogen bond to form double helixes. Chromosomes are made of DNA and proteins. A gene is a section of DNA. Genetic information is stored in the base sequence; a three-base sequence code for a particular amino acid. Transmission of genetic information requires replication, or copying, of the DNA molecules. When the chains of DNA are pulled apart, each half can replicate using nucleotides in the cellular fluid. Each base unit picks up a unit identical to that with which it was paired before. Enzymes connect the paired nucleotides to form the new chain. When a cell divides, one DNA molecule goes to each daughter cell, providing all the necessary genetic information.

Section 7—In transcription, a segment of DNA transfers its information to messenger RNA (mRNA). The next step is the translation of the code into a specific protein structure. Transfer RNA (tRNA) delivers amino acids to the growing protein chain. Each base triplet on a tRNA pairs with a set of three complementary bases on mRNA, called the codon, which codes for a specific amino acid.

Section 8—Many diseases have genetic components. In genetic testing, DNA is cleaved and duplicated. The patterns of DNA fragments are examined and compared to those of individuals with genetic diseases, to identify and predict the occurrence of such diseases. A similar technique is used to compare DNA from different sources in DNA fingerprinting. In recombinant DNA technology, the base sequence for the gene that codes for a desired protein is determined and amplified; the gene is then spliced into a plasmid. The recombined plasmid is inserted into a host organism, which generates the protein as it reproduces. Gene therapy—replacement of defective genes—could be used to cure diseases. Genetic engineering holds great promise and carries with it great responsibility.

Green chemistry Biochemistry has important applications in renewable energy and offers several advantages over traditional chemical synthesis, including the use of water as the solvent and the low levels of waste and energy use. Drugs and fuels are examples of products that may be made using biochemical methods.

Learning Objectives

> List the major parts of a cell, and describe the function of each part.   Problem 2

> Name the primary source of energy for plants and three classes of substances that   Problems 1, 4, 8
  are the sources of energy for animals.

> Compare and contrast starch, glycogen, and cellulose.   Problems 19, 20

> Describe the fundamental structure of a fatty acid and of a fat.   Problems 31, 32, 35, 36

> Classify fats as saturated, monounsaturated, or polyunsaturated.   Problems 33, 34

> Draw the fundamental structure of an amino acid, and show how amino acids   Problems 39, 40, 42–48, 70
  combine to make proteins.

> Describe the four levels of protein structure, and give an example of each.   Problem 69

> Describe how enzymes work as catalysts.   Problem 50

> Name the two types of nucleic acids, and describe the function of each type.   Problems 51, 52

> Explain complementary base pairing, and describe how a copy of DNA is synthesized.   Problems 55, 56–58, 74

> Explain how mRNA is synthesized from DNA and how a protein is synthesized   Problems 59–68, 77
  from mRNA.

> List important characteristics of the genetic code.   Problems 14, 59

> Describe recombinant DNA technology, and explain how it is used.   Problem 15

> Name some advantages of using biochemistry to create useful molecules.   Problems 79, 82

> Give examples of the use of biochemistry for energy production and other applications.   Problems 80, 81

REVIEW QUESTIONS

1. What is the importance of photosynthesis to plants and animals?

2. Briefly identify and state a function of each of the following parts of a cell.
   a. cell membrane   b. cell nucleus
   c. chloroplasts   d. mitochondria
   e. ribosomes

3. In what parts of the body are proteins found? What tissues are largely proteins?

4. How does the elemental composition of proteins differ from those of carbohydrates and fats?

5. What is the chemical nature of proteins?

6. Amino-acid units in a protein are linked by peptide bonds. What is another name for this kind of bond?

7. What is the difference between a polypeptide and a protein?

8. What provides most of the energy for plants? Write the equation for the reaction that is driven by that energy.

9. What kind of intermolecular force is involved in base pairing?

10. Describe how replication and transcription are similar and how they differ.

11. How do DNA and RNA differ in structure?

12. What is the relationship among the cell parts called chromosomes, the units of heredity called genes, and the nucleic acid DNA?

13. What is the polymerase chain reaction (PCR)?

14. Explain what is meant by redundancy in the genetic code. Does redundancy exist for every amino acid?

15. List the steps in recombinant DNA technology.

How can a virus be used to replace a defective gene in a human being?

PROBLEMS

Carbohydrates

17. What is a monosaccharide? Name three common ones.

18. What is a disaccharide? Name three common ones.

19. What is glycogen? How does it differ from amylose? From amylopectin?

20. In what way are amylose and cellulose similar? What is the main structural difference between starch and cellulose?

21. Which of the following are monosaccharides?
    a. amylose   b. cellulose
    c. mannose   d. glucose

22. Which of the following are monosaccharides?
    a. sucrose   **b.** galactose
    c. fructose   **d.** lactose

23. Which of the carbohydrates in Problems 21 and 22 are disaccharides?

24. Which of the carbohydrates in Problems 21 and 22 are polysaccharides?

25. What are the hydrolysis products of each of the following?
    a. amylose   **b.** glycogen

26. What are the hydrolysis products of each of the following?
    a. amylopectin   **b.** cellulose

27. What functional groups are present in the formula for the open-chain form of fructose?

28. Write the formula for the open-chain form of glucose. What functional groups are present?

29. What functional groups are present in the formula for the open-chain form of galactose? How does the structure of galactose differ from that of glucose?

30. Mannose differs from glucose only in having the positions of the H and OH on the second carbon atom reversed. Write the formula for the open-chain form of mannose. What functional groups are present?

Lipids: Fats and Oils

31. How do fats and oils differ in structure? In properties?

32. Define *monoglyceride*, *diglyceride*, and *triglyceride*.

33. Which of the following fatty acids are saturated? Which are unsaturated?
    a. palmitic acid   **b.** linoleic acid
    c. oleic acid   **d.** stearic acid

34. Which of the fatty acids in Problem 33 are monounsaturated? Which are polyunsaturated?

35. How many carbon atoms are in a molecule of each of the following fatty acids?
    a. linoleic acid   **b.** palmitic acid
    c. stearic acid

36. How many carbon atoms are in a molecule of each of the following fatty acids?
    a. linoleic acid   **b.** oleic acid
    c. butyric acid

37. Which of the two foodstuffs shown below would you expect to have a higher iodine number? Explain your reasoning.

38. Which of the two fats shown below is likely to have a lower iodine number? Explain your reasoning.

Proteins

39. What functional groups does amino acid have? What is a zwitterion?

40. What is a dipeptide? A tripeptide? A polypeptide?

41. Of the amino acids glutamic acid, lysine, serine, leucine, and glycine, which are essential to the human diet?

42. Examine Table 3, and write the condensed structural formula for the part of each structure that is identical for 19 of the 20 amino acids. Which amino acid does not have this particular structural feature?

43. Write structural formulas for the following amino acids.
    a. alanine   **b.** cysteine

44. Identify the following amino acids.

$$HOOC-CH_2CH_2-\underset{\overset{|}{^+NH_3}}{CH}-COO^-$$

(a)

$$HS-CH_2-\underset{\overset{|}{^+NH_3}}{CH}-COO^-$$

(b)

45. Write structural formulas for the following dipeptides.
    a. glycylalanine   **b.** alanylserine

46. Identify the following dipeptides.

$$\overset{OH-CH_2}{\underset{^+NH_3-CH}{|}}-CONH-\overset{CH_2CH(CH_3)_2}{\underset{CH}{|}}-COO^-$$

(a)

$$^+NH_3-CH_2-CONH-\overset{HS-CH_2}{\underset{CH}{|}}-COO^-$$

(b)

47. The sweetener *aspartame* has the structure shown below, in which a CH_3O- group (at right) is attached to a dipeptide. Identify the dipeptide.

$$H_2N-\underset{\overset{|}{\underset{COOH}{CH_2}}}{CH}-\overset{O}{\overset{||}{C}}-NH-\underset{\overset{|}{CH_2}}{CH}-\overset{O}{\overset{||}{C}}-OCH_3$$

48. Refer to Problem 47, and draw the structure of the other dipeptide that contains the same amino acids as aspartame.

49. List the four different forces that link protein chains.

50. Describe (a) the induced-fit model of enzyme action and (b) how an inhibitor deactivates an enzyme.

Nucleic Acids: Parts and Structure

51. Which of the following nucleotides can be found in DNA, which in RNA, and which in neither?

a.
thymine
|
deoxyribose—P_i

b.
adenine
|
ribose—P_i

c.
cytosine
|
ribose—P_i

52. Which of the following nucleotides can be found in DNA, which in RNA, and which in neither?

a.
uracil
|
ribose—P_i

b.
adenine
|
deoxyribose—P_i

c.
cytosine
|
deoxyribose—P_i

53. Identify the sugar and the base in the following nucleotide.

54. Identify the sugar and the base in the following nucleotide.

55. In DNA, which base would be paired with the base listed?
a. cytosine
b. adenine
c. guanine
d. thymine

56. In RNA, which base would be paired with the base listed?
a. adenine
b. guanine
c. uracil
d. cytosine

DNA: Self-Replication

57. In replication, a DNA molecule produces two daughter molecules. What is the fate of each strand of the original double helix?

58. DNA controls protein synthesis, yet most DNA resides within the cell nucleus and protein synthesis occurs outside the nucleus. How does DNA exercise its control?

RNA: Protein Synthesis and the Genetic Code

59. Which nucleic acid(s) is(are) involved in (a) the process referred to as transcription and (b) the process referred to as translation?

60. Explain the role of (a) mRNA and (b) tRNA in protein synthesis.

61. A portion of the code for a certain gene has the base sequence 5'-ATGAGCGACTTTGCGGGATTA-3'. What is the base sequence of the complementary strand of DNA?

62. What is the sequence of the mRNA that would be produced during transcription from the segment of DNA shown in Problem 61?

63. If the sequence of bases in an mRNA molecule is 3'-UCCGAU-5', what was the sequence of the DNA template?

64. What anticodon on tRNA would pair with each of the following mRNA codons?
a. 5'-UUU-3'
b. 5'-CAU-3'
c. 5'-AGC-3'
d. 5'-CCG-3'

65. What codon on mRNA would pair with each of the following tRNA anticodons?
a. 5'-UUG-3'
b. 5'-GAA-3'
c. 5'-UCC-3'

66. What codon on mRNA would pair with each of the following tRNA anticodons?
a. UCC
b. CAC
c. 5'-CAC-3'

67. Use Table 5 to identify the amino acids carried by each tRNA molecule in Problem 65.

68. Use Table 5 to determine the amino-acid sequence produced from the mRNA sequence 5'-AUGAGCGACUUUGCGGGAUUA-3'.

ADDITIONAL PROBLEMS

69. Human insulin molecules are made up of two chains with the following sequences.

Chain A: G-I-V-E-Q-C-C-T-S-I-C-S-L-Y-Q-L-E-N-Y-C-N

Chain B: F-V-N-Q-H-L-C-G-D-H-L-V-E-A-L-Y-L-V-C-G-E-R-G-F-F-Y-T-P-K-T

Chain A has a loop formed by a disulfide linkage between the sixth and eleventh amino acids (designated A-6 to A-11) and is joined to chain B by two disulfide linkages (A-7 to B-7 and A-20 to B-19). What level of protein structure is described by (a) the chain sequence of one-letter abbreviations and (b) the description of the loop and chain linkages?

70. Synthetic polymers can be formed from amino-acid units of a single kind. Write the formula for a segment of **(a)** polyglycine and **(b)** polyserine. Show at least four repeating units of each.

71. Identify the base in the structure in **(a)** Problem 53 and **(b)** Problem 54 as a purine or a pyrimidine.

72. Answer the following questions for the molecule shown.

a. Is the base a purine or a pyrimidine?
b. Would the compound be incorporated in DNA or in RNA?

73. Answer the questions posed in Problem 72 for the following compound.

74. Use Table 5 to determine the amino acid specified by the DNA triplet 5'-CTC-3'. What amino acid is specified if a mutation changes the DNA triplet to 5'-CTT-3'? To 5'-CTA-3'? to 5'-CAC-3'?

75. Many laundry detergents have enzymes to aid removal of stains of biological origin, such as those from food or blood. The enzyme subtilisin, produced by *Bacillus subtilis*, is one of these. The natural enzyme was not very effective because it was largely deactivated by the harsh detergent environment. A genetically modified form, in which the base sequence 5'-ACCAGCAUGGCG-3' is replaced by 5'-ACCAGCGCGGCG-3', is much more effective because it is more stable. What is the amino-acid sequence specified by the bases in this segment in **(a)** the original enzyme and **(b)** the genetically modified enzyme? You may consult Table 5.

76. In the novel *Jurassic Park* by Michael Crichton, the cloned dinosaurs were genetically engineered so as to be unable to survive outside the island park because they were unable to synthesize the amino acid lysine.

This was supposed to make the dinosaurs dependent on their makers to feed them a source of lysine. Examine Table 3, and suggest a reason why this genetic engineering would not keep the dinosaurs from surviving elsewhere.

77. With what mRNA codon would the tRNA in the diagram form a codon–anticodon pair?

78. Write the abbreviated versions of the following structural formula using **(a)** the three-letter abbreviations and **(b)** the one-letter abbreviations.

79. What solvent is typically used for biochemical reactions?

80. What types of molecules are used to store energy in biological systems?
a. hydrocarbons
b. carbohydrates and lipids
c. water and carbon dioxide

81. Which is an example of a way to produce a renewable fuel using biochemical processes or products?
a. turn carbohydrates into fuels
b. use bacteria to convert carbohydrates or CO_2 into biofuels
c. engineer microbes to make gasoline
d. all of the above

82. Which of the following is NOT an advantage of using biochemical methods compared to traditional chemical synthesis?
a. Water is often used as a solvent.
b. Separation of products is difficult.
c. Reaction conditions are mild.
d. Reactions are usually catalytic.

COLLABORATIVE GROUP PROJECTS

Prepare a PowerPoint, poster, or other presentation (as directed by your instructor) to share with the class.

1. Prepare a brief report on (**a**) a carbohydrate such as fructose, glycogen, lactose, maltose, sucrose, or starch or (**b**) a lipid such as beef tallow, corn oil, lard, oleic acid, or palmitic acid. List principal sources and uses of the material.

2. Prepare a brief report on enzyme action, including a comparision of the induced-fit model of action with the older lock-and-key model.

3. Prepare a brief report on one of the following products of genetic engineering. List some advantages and disadvantages of the product.
   a. golden rice
   b. herbicide-resistant transgenic soybeans
   c. transgenic cotton that produces Bt toxin
   d. transgenic tobacco that produces human serum albumin
   e. transgenic tomatoes that have improved resistance to viruses
   f. transgenic E. coli that produce human interleukin-2, a protein that stimulates the production of T-lymphocytes that play a role in fighting selected cancers

4. Genetic testing carries both promise and peril, and its use is an important topic in bioethics today. After some online research, write a brief essay on one of the following—or on a similar question assigned by your instructor.
   a. In what cases might a person not want to be tested for a disease his or her parent had?
   b. When is genetic testing most valuable? What privacy issues must be addressed in this area?
   c. Does testing negative for the breast cancer genes mean that a woman doesn't have to have mammograms?

BRIEF ANSWERS TO SELECTED PROBLEMS

Answers are provided for *all in-chapter exercises*. Brief answers are given for *odd-numbered Review Questions*; more complete answers can be obtained by reviewing the text. Answers are provided for *all odd-numbered Problems and Additional Problems.*

NOTE: For numerical problems, your answer may differ slightly from ours because of rounding and the use of significant figures.

1 Mannose differs from glucose in configuration about C-2 only.
2 A. a. H-P-V-A   b. histidylprolylvalylalanine
   B. a. Thr-Gly-Ala-Ala-Leu   b. T-G-A-A-L
3 A. 3   B. 24
4 A. Sugar: ribose; base: uracil; RNA
   B. Neither; thymine occurs only in DNA, ribose only in RNA.
1. Photosynthesis converts solar energy to carbohydrates, which provide energy to plants and to organisms that eat plants.
3. In every cell; muscles, skin, hair, nails
5. Polyamides
7. If the molar mass of a polypeptide exceeds about 10,000 g, it is called a protein.
9. Hydrogen bonds
11. DNA is a double helix; RNA is a single helix with some loops.
13. A process that produces millions of copies of a specific DNA sequence
15. Step 1: isolation and amplification
    Step 2: gene is spliced into a plasmid
    Step 3: plasmid is inserted into a host cell
    Step 4: plasmid replicates, making copies of itself
17. A carbohydrate that cannot be further hydrolyzed; glucose, fructose, and galactose
19. Glycogen is animal starch. Amylose is a plant starch with glucose units joined in a continuous chain. Amylopectin is a plant starch with branched chains of glucose units.
21. c, d
23. Sucrose and lactose
25. a. glucose   b. glucose
27. Ketone and alcohol (hydroxyl)
29. Aldehyde and alcohol (hydroxyl); in configuration about C-4
31. Structurally, oils have more C-to-C double bonds than fats have. At room temperature, fats are solids, and oils are liquid.
33. saturated: a, d; unsaturated: b, c
35. a. 18   b. 16
    c. 18

37. Liquid oil (right); it is unsaturated.
39. An amino group and a carboxyl group; a zwitterion is a molecule that carries both a positive and a negative charge.
41. lysine and leucine
43. a.

$$H_3N^+-CH-C\overset{O}{\underset{O^-}{\big\langle}} \qquad \text{b.} \qquad H_3N^+-CH-C\overset{O}{\underset{O^-}{\big\langle}}$$
$$\underset{CH_3}{\big|} \qquad\qquad\qquad \underset{CH_2SH}{\big|}$$

45. a. $H_3N^+\ CH_2CO-NH\ C\ HCOO^-$
$$\underset{CH_3}{\big|}$$
    b. $H_3N^+\ CH_2CO-NH\ C\ HCOO^-$
$$\underset{CH_3}{\big|}\qquad\underset{CH_2OH}{\big|}$$

47. Aspartylphenylalanine
49. Hydrogen bonds, ionic bonds, disulfide linkages, and dispersion forces
51. DNA: a; RNA: b, c
53. Ribose; uracil
55. a. guanine   b. thymine
    c. cytosine   d. adenine
57. Each strand of the parent DNA double helix remains associated with the newly synthesized DNA strand.
59. a. DNA and mRNA   b. mRNA and tRNA
61. 3'-TACTCGCTGAAACGCCCTAAT-5'
63. 5'-AGGCTA-3'
65. a. 3'-AAC-5'   b. 3'-CUU-5'   c. 3'-AGG-5'
67. a. glutamine   b. phenylalanine   c. glycine
69. a. primary   b. secondary
71. a. pyrimidine   b. pyrimidine
73. a. purine   b. RNA
75. a. ~Thr-Ser-Met-Ala~
    b. ~Thr-Ser-Ala-Ala~
77. 3'-AUG-5' (The sequences must be antiparallel.)
79. Water
81. d

Index

Page references followed by "f" indicate illustrated figures or photographs; followed by "t" indicates a table.